Astronomy and Space Science

interactive SCIENCE

PEARSON

Boston, Massachusetts
Chandler, Arizona
Glenview, Illinois
Upper Saddle River, New Jersey

Teacher's Edition and Resource

AUTHORS

You're an author!

As you write in this science book, your answers and personal discoveries will be recorded for you to keep, making this book unique to you. That is why you are one of the primary authors of this book.

✎ **In the space below, print your name, school, town, and state. Then write a short autobiography that includes your interests and accomplishments.**

YOUR NAME

SCHOOL

TOWN, STATE

AUTOBIOGRAPHY

Your Photo

Acknowledgments appear on pages 177–178, which constitute an extension of this copyright page.

Astronomy and Space Science

interactive SCIENCE

ON THE COVER
A Big Repair Job
How do you repair a telescope that's floating in space? Send an astronaut! This astronaut helped repair the Hubble Space Telescope, or HST, in May 2009. He's shown here outside the space shuttle *Atlantis,* which brought the repair crew to the HST. The astronauts repaired, replaced, and adjusted the HST's instruments.

Program Authors

DON BUCKLEY, M.Sc.
Information and Communications Technology Director,
The School at Columbia University, New York, New York
Mr. Buckley has been at the forefront of K–12 educational technology for nearly two decades. A founder of New York City Independent School Technologists (NYCIST) and long-time chair of New York Association of Independent Schools' annual IT conference, he has taught students on two continents and created multimedia and Internet-based instructional systems for schools worldwide.

ZIPPORAH MILLER, M.A.Ed.
Associate Executive Director for Professional Programs
and Conferences, National Science Teachers Association,
Arlington, Virginia
Associate executive director for professional programs and conferences at NSTA, Ms. Zipporah Miller is a former K–12 science supervisor and STEM coordinator for the Prince George's County Public School District in Maryland. She is a science education consultant who has overseen curriculum development and staff training for more than 150 district science coordinators.

MICHAEL J. PADILLA, Ph.D.
Associate Dean and Director, Eugene P. Moore School of
Education, Clemson University, Clemson, South Carolina
A former middle school teacher and a leader in middle school science education, Dr. Michael Padilla has served as president of the National Science Teachers Association and as a writer of the National Science Education Standards. He is professor of science education at Clemson University. As lead author of the *Science Explorer* series, Dr. Padilla has inspired the team in developing a program that promotes student inquiry and meets the needs of today's students.

KATHRYN THORNTON, Ph.D.
Professor and Associate Dean, School of Engineering
and Applied Science, University of Virginia,
Charlottesville, Virginia
Selected by NASA in May 1984, Dr. Kathryn Thornton is a veteran of four space flights. She has logged over 975 hours in space, including more than 21 hours of extravehicular activity. As an author on the *Scott Foresman Science* series, Dr. Thornton's enthusiasm for science has inspired teachers around the globe.

MICHAEL E. WYSESSION, Ph.D.
Associate Professor of Earth and Planetary Science,
Washington University, St. Louis, Missouri
An author on more than 50 scientific publications, Dr. Wysession was awarded the prestigious Packard Foundation Fellowship and Presidential Faculty Fellowship for his research in geophysics. Dr. Wysession is an expert on Earth's inner structure and has mapped various regions of Earth using seismic tomography. He is known internationally for his work in geoscience education and outreach.

Instructional Design Author

GRANT WIGGINS, Ed.D.
President, Authentic Education,
Hopewell, New Jersey
Dr. Wiggins is a co-author with Jay McTighe of *Understanding by Design, 2nd Edition* (ASCD 2005). His approach to instructional design provides teachers with a disciplined way of thinking about curriculum design, assessment, and instruction that moves teaching from covering content to ensuring understanding.
UNDERSTANDING BY DESIGN® and UbD™ are trademarks of ASCD, and are used under license.

Planet Diary Author

JACK HANKIN
Science/Mathematics Teacher,
The Hilldale School, Daly City, California
Founder, Planet Diary Web site
Mr. Hankin is the creator and writer of Planet Diary, a science current events Web site. He is passionate about bringing science news and environmental awareness into classrooms and offers numerous Planet Diary workshops at NSTA and other events to train middle and high school teachers.

ELL Consultant

JIM CUMMINS, Ph.D.
Professor and Canada Research Chair,
Curriculum, Teaching and Learning
department at the University of Toronto
Dr. Cummins focuses on literacy development in multilingual schools and the role of technology in promoting student learning across the curriculum. *Interactive Science* incorporates essential research-based principles for integrating language with the teaching of academic content based on his instructional framework.

Reading Consultant

HARVEY DANIELS, Ph.D.
Professor of Secondary Education,
University of New Mexico,
Albuquerque, New Mexico
Dr. Daniels is an international consultant to schools, districts, and educational agencies. He has authored or coauthored 13 books on language, literacy, and education. His most recent works are *Comprehension and Collaboration: Inquiry Circles in Action* and *Subjects Matter: Every Teacher's Guide to Content-Area Reading.*

REVIEWERS

Contributing Writers

Edward Aguado, Ph.D.
Professor, Department of Geography
San Diego State University
San Diego, California

Elizabeth Coolidge-Stolz, M.D.
Medical Writer
North Reading, Massachusetts

Donald L. Cronkite, Ph.D.
Professor of Biology
Hope College
Holland, Michigan

Jan Jenner, Ph.D.
Science Writer
Talladega, Alabama

Linda Cronin Jones, Ph.D.
Associate Professor of Science and Environmental Education
University of Florida
Gainesville, Florida

T. Griffith Jones, Ph.D.
Clinical Associate Professor of Science Education
College of Education
University of Florida
Gainesville, Florida

Andrew C. Kemp, Ph.D.
Teacher
Jefferson County Public Schools
Louisville, Kentucky

Matthew Stoneking, Ph.D.
Associate Professor of Physics
Lawrence University
Appleton, Wisconsin

R. Bruce Ward, Ed.D.
Senior Research Associate
Science Education Department
Harvard-Smithsonian Center for Astrophysics
Cambridge, Massachusetts

Content Reviewers

Paul D. Beale, Ph.D.
Department of Physics
University of Colorado at Boulder
Boulder, Colorado

Jeff R. Bodart, Ph.D.
Professor of Physical Sciences
Chipola College
Marianna, Florida

Joy Branlund, Ph.D.
Department of Earth Science
Southwestern Illinois College
Granite City, Illinois

Marguerite Brickman, Ph.D.
Division of Biological Sciences
University of Georgia
Athens, Georgia

Bonnie J. Brunkhorst, Ph.D.
Science Education and Geological Sciences
California State University
San Bernardino, California

Michael Castellani, Ph.D.
Department of Chemistry
Marshall University
Huntington, West Virginia

Charles C. Curtis, Ph.D.
Research Associate Professor of Physics
University of Arizona
Tucson, Arizona

Diane I. Doser, Ph.D.
Department of Geological Sciences
University of Texas
El Paso, Texas

Rick Duhrkopf, Ph.D.
Department of Biology
Baylor University
Waco, Texas

Alice K. Hankla, Ph.D.
The Galloway School
Atlanta, Georgia

Mark Henriksen, Ph.D.
Physics Department
University of Maryland
Baltimore, Maryland

Chad Hershock, Ph.D.
Center for Research on Learning and Teaching
University of Michigan
Ann Arbor, Michigan

Jeremiah N. Jarrett, Ph.D.
Department of Biology
Central Connecticut State University
New Britain, Connecticut

Scott L. Kight, Ph.D.
Department of Biology
Montclair State University
Montclair, New Jersey

Jennifer O. Liang, Ph.D.
Department of Biology
University of Minnesota–Duluth
Duluth, Minnesota

Candace Lutzow-Felling, Ph.D.
Director of Education
The State Arboretum of Virginia
University of Virginia
Boyce, Virginia

Cortney V. Martin, Ph.D.
Virginia Polytechnic Institute
Blacksburg, Virginia

Joseph F. McCullough, Ph.D.
Physics Program Chair
Cabrillo College
Aptos, California

Heather Mernitz, Ph.D.
Department of Physical Science
Alverno College
Milwaukee, Wisconsin

Sadredin C. Moosavi, Ph.D.
Department of Earth and Environmental Sciences
Tulane University
New Orleans, Louisiana

David L. Reid, Ph.D.
Department of Biology
Blackburn College
Carlinville, Illinois

Scott M. Rochette, Ph.D.
Department of the Earth Sciences
SUNY College at Brockport
Brockport, New York

Karyn L. Rogers, Ph.D.
Department of Geological Sciences
University of Missouri
Columbia, Missouri

Laurence Rosenhein, Ph.D.
Department of Chemistry
Indiana State University
Terre Haute, Indiana

Sara Seager, Ph.D.
Department of Planetary Sciences and Physics
Massachusetts Institute of Technology
Cambridge, Massachusetts

Tom Shoberg, Ph.D.
Missouri University of Science and Technology
Rolla, Missouri

Patricia Simmons, Ph.D.
North Carolina State University
Raleigh, North Carolina

William H. Steinecker, Ph.D.
Research Scholar
Miami University
Oxford, Ohio

Paul R. Stoddard, Ph.D.
Department of Geology and Environmental Geosciences
Northern Illinois University
DeKalb, Illinois

John R. Villarreal, Ph.D.
Department of Chemistry
The University of Texas–Pan American
Edinburg, Texas

John R. Wagner, Ph.D.
Department of Geology
Clemson University
Clemson, South Carolina

Jerry Waldvogel, Ph.D.
Department of Biological Sciences
Clemson University
Clemson, South Carolina

Donna L. Witter, Ph.D.
Department of Geology
Kent State University
Kent, Ohio

Edward J. Zalisko, Ph.D.
Department of Biology
Blackburn College
Carlinville, Illinois

Museum of Science.

Special thanks to the Museum of Science, Boston, Massachusetts, and Ioannis Miaoulis, the Museum's president and director, for serving as content advisors for the technology and design strand in this program.

Teacher Reviewers

Herb Bergamini
The Northwest School
Seattle, Washington

David R. Blakely
Arlington High School
Arlington, Massachusetts

Jane E. Callery
Capital Region Education Council (CREC)
Hartford, Connecticut

Jeffrey C. Callister
Former Earth Science Instructor
Newburgh Free Academy
Newburgh, New York

Colleen Campos
Cherry Creek Schools
Aurora, Colorado

Scott Cordell
Amarillo Independent School District
Amarillo, Texas

Dan Gabel
Consulting Teacher, Science
Montgomery County Public Schools
Montgomery County, Maryland

Wayne Goates
Kansas Polymer Ambassador
Intersociety Polymer Education Council (IPEC)
Wichita, Kansas

Katherine Bobay Graser
Mint Hill Middle School
Charlotte, North Carolina

Darcy Hampton
Science Department Chair
Deal Middle School
Washington, D.C.

Sean S. Houseknecht
Elizabethtown Area Middle School
Elizabethtown, Pennsylvania

Tanisha L. Johnson
Prince George's County Public Schools
Lanham, Maryland

Karen E. Kelly
Pierce Middle School
Waterford, Michigan

Dave J. Kelso
Manchester Central High School
Manchester, New Hampshire

Beverly Crouch Lyons
Career Center High School
Winston-Salem, North Carolina

Angie L. Matamoros, Ed.D.
ALM Consulting
Weston, Florida

Corey Mayle
Durham Public Schools
Durham, North Carolina

Keith W. McCarthy
George Washington Middle School
Wayne, New Jersey

Timothy McCollum
Charleston Middle School
Charleston, Illinois

Bruce A. Mellin
Cambridge College
Cambridge, Massachusetts

John Thomas Miller
Thornapple Kellogg High School
Middleville, Michigan

Randy Mousley
Dean Ray Stucky Middle School
Wichita, Kansas

Yolanda O. Peña
John F. Kennedy Junior High School
West Valley, Utah

Kathleen M. Poe
Fletcher Middle School
Jacksonville Beach, Florida

Judy Pouncey
Thomasville Middle School
Thomasville, North Carolina

Vickki Lynne Reese
Mad River Middle School
Dayton, Ohio

Bronwyn W. Robinson
Director of Curriculum
Algiers Charter Schools Association
New Orleans, Louisiana

Sandra G. Robinson
Matoaca Middle School
Chesterfield, Virginia

Shirley Rose
Lewis and Clark Middle School
Tulsa, Oklahoma

Linda Sandersen
Sally Ride Academy
Whitefish Bay, Wisconsin

Roxanne Scala
Schuyler-Colfax Middle School
Wayne, New Jersey

Patricia M. Shane, Ph.D.
Associate Director
Center for Mathematics & Science Education
University of North Carolina at Chapel Hill
Chapel Hill, North Carolina

Bradd A. Smithson
Science Curriculum Coordinator
John Glenn Middle School
Bedford, Massachusetts

Sharon Stroud
Consultant
Colorado Springs, Colorado

Master Teacher Board

Emily Compton
Park Forest Middle School
Baton Rouge, Louisiana

Georgi Delgadillo
East Valley School District
Spokane Valley, Washington

Treva Jeffries
Toledo Public Schools
Toledo, Ohio

James W. Kuhl
Central Square Middle School
Central Square, New York

Bonnie Mizell
Howard Middle School
Orlando, Florida

Joel Palmer, Ed.D.
Mesquite Independent School District
Mesquite, Texas

Leslie Pohley
Largo Middle School
Largo, Florida

Susan M. Pritchard, Ph.D.
Washington Middle School
La Habra, California

Anne Rice
Woodland Middle School
Gurnee, Illinois

Richard Towle
Noblesville Middle School
Noblesville, Indiana

CONTENTS

 Enter the Lab zone for hands-on inquiry.

Chapter Lab Investigation:
• Directed Inquiry: Reasons for the Seasons
• Open Inquiry: Reasons for the Seasons

Inquiry Warm-Ups: • Earth's Sky • What Causes Day and Night? • What Factors Affect Gravity? • How Does the Moon Move? • When Is High Tide? • Why Do Craters Look Different From Each Other?

Quick Labs: • Observing the Night Sky • Watching the Sky • Sun Shadows • What's Doing the Pulling? • Around and Around We Go • Moon Phases • Eclipses • Modeling the Moon's Pull of Gravity • Moonwatching

MY SCIENCE ONLINE.com

Go to MyScienceOnline.com to interact with this chapter's content. Keyword: Earth, Moon, and Sun

UNTAMED SCIENCE
• Phased by the Moon!

PLANET DIARY
• Earth, Moon, and Sun

INTERACTIVE ART
•Constellations •Seasons and Earth's Revolution •Solar and Lunar Eclipses

ART IN MOTION
• Cause of Tides

VIRTUAL LAB
• What Affects Gravity?

 Enter the Lab zone for hands-on inquiry.

△ **Chapter Lab Investigation:**
• Directed Inquiry: Space Spinoffs
• Open Inquiry: Space Spinoffs

△ **Inquiry Warm-Ups:** • What Force Moves a Balloon? • Where on the Moon Did the Astronauts Land? • Using Space Science

△ **Quick Labs:** • History of Rockets • Be a Rocket Scientist • Modeling Multistage Rockets • Humans in Space • Which Tool Would You Use in Space? • Remote Control • What Do You Need to Survive in Space? • Useful Satellites

my science online

Go to MyScienceOnline.com to interact with this chapter's content.
Keyword: Exploring Space

▷ **UNTAMED SCIENCE**
• A Little Outer Space Here on Earth

▷ **PLANET DIARY**
• Exploring Space

▷ **INTERACTIVE ART**
• Multistage Rocket • Build an Orbiter • Space Spinoffs

▷ **VIRTUAL LAB**
• Get a Rocket Into Orbit

CONTENTS

 Enter the Lab zone for hands-on inquiry.

Chapter Lab Investigation:
• Directed Inquiry: Speeding Around the Sun
• Open Inquiry: Speeding Around the Sun

Inquiry Warm-Ups: • What Is at the Center? • How Big Is Earth? • How Can You Safely Observe the Sun? • Ring Around the Sun • How Big Are the Planets? • Collecting Micrometeorites

Quick Labs: • Going Around in Circles • A Loopy Ellipse • Clumping Planets • Layers of the Sun • Viewing Sunspots • Characteristics of the Inner Planets • Greenhouse Effect • Density Mystery • Make a Model of Saturn • Changing Orbits

my science online

Go to MyScienceOnline.com to interact with this chapter's content. Keyword: The Solar System

UNTAMED SCIENCE
• 100 Meters to Neptune

PLANET DIARY
• The Solar System

INTERACTIVE ART
• Objects of the Solar System • Anatomy of the Sun

ART IN MOTION
• Formation of the Solar System

VIRTUAL LAB
• Why Isn't Pluto a Planet?

CHAPTER 4

Stars, Galaxies, and the Universe

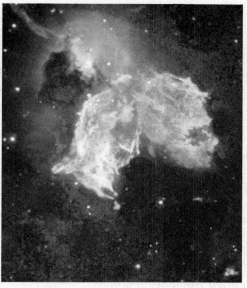

Lab zone® Enter the Lab zone for hands-on inquiry.

△ **Chapter Lab Investigation:**
• Directed Inquiry: Design and Build a Telescope
• Open Inquiry: Design and Build a Telescope

△ **Inquiry Warm-Ups:** • How Does Distance Affect an Image? • Stringing Along • How Stars Differ • What Determines How Long Stars Live? • Why Does the Milky Way Look Hazy? • How Does the Universe Expand?

△ **Quick Labs:** • Observing a Continuous Spectrum • How Far Is That Star? • Measuring the Universe • Star Bright • Interpreting the H-R Diagram • Life Cycle of Stars • Death of a Star • Planets Around Other Stars • A Spiral Galaxy • Future of the Universe

my science online.com

Go to MyScienceOnline.com to interact with this chapter's content.
Keyword: Stars, Galaxies, and the Universe

> PLANET DIARY
• Stars, Galaxies, and the Universe

> INTERACTIVE ART
• Universe at Different Scales • Lives of Stars
• Refracting and Reflecting Telescopes

> ART IN MOTION
• Expanding Universe

> REAL-WORLD INQUIRY
• How Can Light Help You Find Life?

INQUIRY IN THE SCIENCE CLASSROOM

Program Author of
Interactive Science

Associate Dean and Director of
*Eugena P. Moore School of Education
Clemson University
Clemson, South Carolina*

Michael J. Padilla, Ph.D.

"If students are busy doing lots of hands-on-activities, are they using inquiry skills? What is inquiry, anyway? If you are confused, you're not alone. Inquiry is the heart and soul of science education, with most of us in continuous pursuit of achieving it with our students."

What Is Inquiry?

Simply put, inquiry is thinking like a scientist —being inquisitive, asking why, and searching for answers. It's the process of taking a close examination of something in the quest for information.

Minds-on Inquiry

Students are naturally inquisitive; they want to learn, and they are always asking "Why?" They need practice and support to find answers for themselves. That's why they need experiences that are carefully scaffolded to guide them. We built that scaffolding right into this program.

Scaffolded Learning

The framework below illustrates a series of skill levels developed by educational psychologist Benjamin Bloom in the 1950s, later modified in the 1990s to reflect relevance to 21st century work. Look for the skills questions and tasks throughout the student book, scaffolded just right to provide students with the guidance and intellectual challenge they need.

Bloom's Taxonomy (adapted)

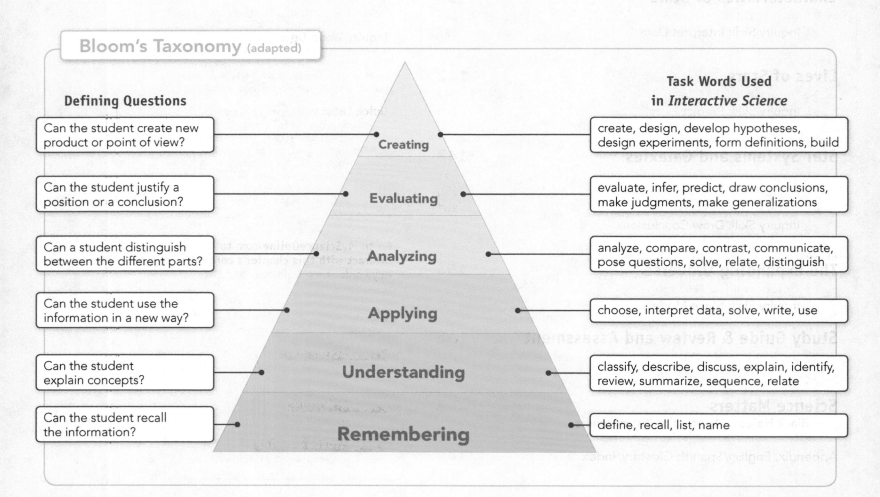

Defining Questions

Can the student create new product or point of view?

Can the student justify a position or a conclusion?

Can a student distinguish between the different parts?

Can the student use the information in a new way?

Can the student explain concepts?

Can the student recall the information?

Creating

Evaluating

Analyzing

Applying

Understanding

Remembering

Task Words Used in *Interactive Science*

create, design, develop hypotheses, design experiments, form definitions, build

evaluate, infer, predict, draw conclusions, make judgments, make generalizations

analyze, compare, contrast, communicate, pose questions, solve, relate, distinguish

choose, interpret data, solve, write, use

classify, describe, discuss, explain, identify, review, summarize, sequence, relate

define, recall, list, name

Student Interactivity

We know that students learn better when they are totally engaged in their work. That's why *Interactive Science* gets students involved in their learning every day, on every page. Because the student book is consumable, it provides students with unique opportunities to become totally engaged, whether it's marking the text, completing an illustration or a chart, summarizing relationships using Venn diagrams or other graphic devices, or recording ideas and findings about scientific concepts.

Apply It! *Students combine new content understandings with their knowledge of scientific process and experimentation.*

Students demonstrate critical connections between text and illustration.

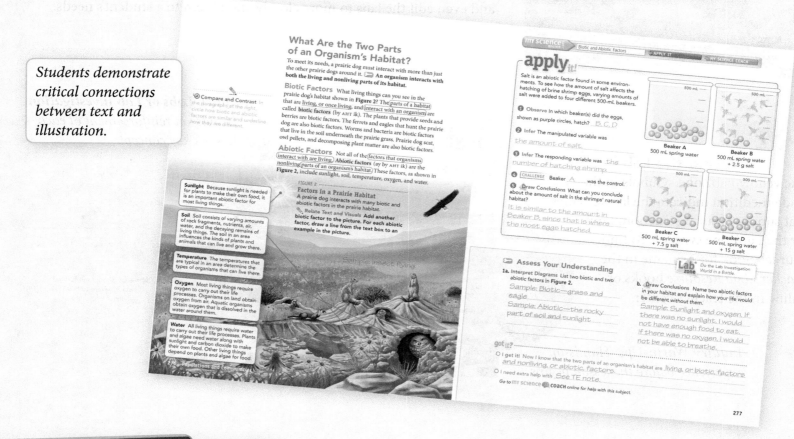

Online Labs and Simulations

For lab experiences without materials, you'll love the Online Virtual Labs. They're realistic, time efficient, and great when meeting in a laboratory is not possible. Have students use them individually, with a partner, or as a class activity to stimulate discussion or shared learning.

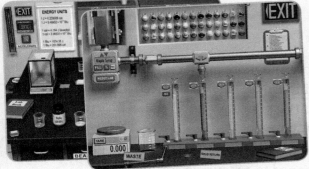

Hands-on Inquiry

We know that it is through student engagement and discovery that students really learn to think like scientists. Hands-on inquiry lab activities are built into the program; there are multiple activities per lesson.

Teacher's Lab Resource

Because there are so many labs, you will want to select which ones are best for your students and your class time. That is why the labs are organized in print as blackline masters in the *Teacher's Lab Resource*. Or access them in your teacher center at MyScienceOnline.com. There you can download and even edit the labs to more closely align them to a student's needs.

Using the Labs

The yellow LabZone symbols in the student edition indicate the lab activities that support your instruction. Look for the LabZone symbol. To find your lab, look for its name in the *Teacher's Lab Resource* books or online in the teacher center.

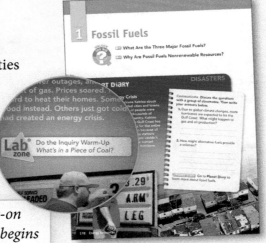

Inquiry Warm-Ups Hands-on experience before the lesson begins

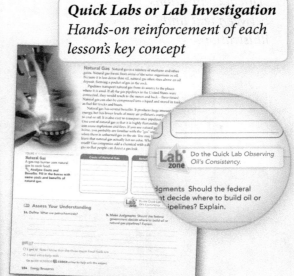

Quick Labs or Lab Investigation *Hands-on reinforcement of each lesson's key concept*

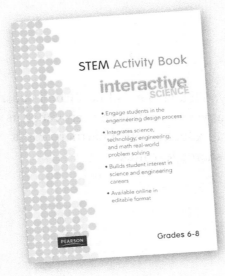

STEM Activity Book

Each day, our lives are filled with more and more products and services that are the result of technology and engineering. The interconnectivity of science, technology, engineering, and mathematics is known as STEM, with each field connected to the others in important ways.

The activities in this book emphasize the interconnectivity of those fields, and use an eight-step design process designed to encourage creativity and imagination in solving design problems.

Inquiry Skill-Building Outside the Student Books

There are many forms of inquiry learning in *Interactive Science*, with lots of options to enrich your students' experiences. All components are in print or online for easy downloading.

Allow students to demonstrate their understanding of chapter concepts in longer term projects.

Provide students with opportunities to apply the science they have learned to other subject areas.

Stretch students with real-life problem solving—perfect for challenging the advanced students.

Offer students minds-on activities that incorporate the scientific method, each targeting specific science process skills.

Interactive Science—Inquiry Learning at Its Best

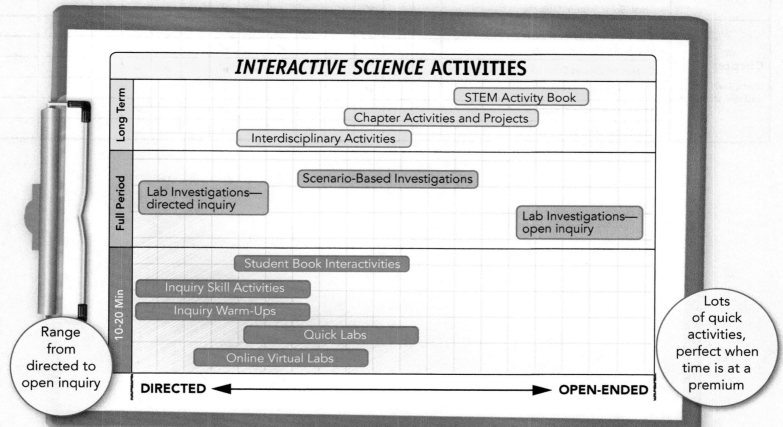

MODULE 5		Inquiry Skills								Integrated Skills					
	Lesson	Observe	Infer	Predict	Classify	Make Models	Calculate	Create Data Tables	Communicate	Develop Hypotheses	Interpret Data	Draw Conclusions	Pose Questions	Critique Scientific Explanations and Models	Demonstrate Consumer Literacy
Chapter 1 Earth, Moon, and Sun	1. The Sky from Earth	✔		✔					✔						
	2. Earth in Space		✔	✔			✔				✔				
	3. Gravity in Motion			✔							✔	✔			
	4. Phases and Eclipses		✔			✔									
	5. Tides	✔	✔								✔				
	6. Earth's Moon							✔	✔	✔					
Chapter 2 Exploring Space	1. The Science of Rockets										✔				
	2. The History of Space Exploration					✔			✔			✔			
	3. Using Space Science on Earth		✔						✔			✔			✔
Chapter 3 The Solar System	1. Models of the Solar System					✔								✔	
	2. Introducing the Solar System						✔				✔				
	3. The Sun				✔				✔		✔				
	4. The Inner Planets		✔						✔		✔				
	5. The Outer Planets						✔		✔	✔			✔		
	6. Small Solar System Objects			✔	✔				✔						
Chapter 4 Stars, Galaxies, and the Universe	1. Telescopes		✔						✔						
	2. The Scale of the Universe						✔		✔						
	3. Characteristics of Stars							✔	✔		✔	✔			
	4. Lives of Stars			✔					✔						
	5. Star Systems and Galaxies								✔			✔			
	6. The Expanding Universe					✔			✔						

CRITICAL THINKING SKILLS

Critical Thinking Skills

Define	Identify	Name	Review	List	Describe	Explain	Sequence	Interpret Diagrams, Photos, Maps, Tables	Read Graphs	Relate Diagrams and Photos	Apply Concepts	Solve Problems	Make Generalizations	Make Judgments	Relate Text and Visuals	Summarize	Relate Cause and Effect	Compare and Contrast	Estimate	Relate Evidence and Explanation	Design a Solution	Evaluate the Design	Identify Faulty Reasoning
						✔		✔					✔										
✔	✔					✔		✔			✔		✔				✔						
	✔								✔				✔					✔					
						✔		✔															
			✔					✔															
				✔						✔		✔											
					✔	✔		✔			✔						✔						
	✔				✔			✔					✔	✔	✔	✔	✔						
✔			✔														✔	✔					
			✔																	✔			
						✔	✔				✔		✔										
✔			✔			✔					✔		✔		✔		✔						
		✔									✔	✔	✔			✔	✔				✔		
					✔			✔					✔	✔	✔	✔		✔	✔				
			✔								✔		✔	✔		✔	✔	✔					
							✔											✔				✔	✔
					✔	✔																	
					✔	✔	✔																
					✔	✔									✔	✔							
✔	✔										✔						✔						
✔								✔									✔			✔			

Writing in the book is helpful because I can take notes near where the information is being presented in the text, and my notes act like a study guide.

—Middle grades student
Winston-Salem, NC

The best part about Interactive Science is that we actually get to apply what we learned.

—Middle grades student
Federal Way, WA

READING, VOCABULARY, MATH SKILLS

MODULE 5	Lesson	Compare, Contrast	Relate Cause, Effect	Relate Text Visuals	Sequence	Outline	Ask Questions	Identify the Main Idea	Identify Supporting Evidence	Summarize	Greek Word Origins	Suffixes	Related Word Forms	Identify Multiple Meanings	Interpret Line Graph	Calculate	Interpret Data	Use Formulas / Solve
								Reading Skills				Vocabulary				Math Skills		
Chapter 1 Earth, Moon, and Sun	1. The Sky from Earth							✔										
	2. Earth in Space				✔											✔	✔	✔
	3. Gravity in Motion						✔								✔		✔	
	4. Phases and Eclipses			✔										✔				
	5. Tides		✔											✔			✔	
	6. Earth's Moon	✔																
Chapter 2 Exploring Space	1. The Science of Rockets			✔											✔		✔	
	2. The History of Space Exploration						✔							✔				
	3. Using Space Science on Earth								✔									
Chapter 3 The Solar System	1. Models of the Solar System				✔													
	2. Introducing the Solar System								✔							✔	✔	✔
	3. The Sun		✔								✔						✔	
	4. The Inner Planets	✔															✔	
	5. The Outer Planets				✔												✔	
	6. Small Solar System Objects									✔	✔							
Chapter 4 Stars, Galaxies, and the Universe	1. Telescopes						✔					✔						
	2. The Scale of the Universe									✔							✔	✔
	3. Characteristics of Stars						✔											
	4. Lives of Stars	✔																
	5. Star Systems and Galaxies		✔															
	6. The Expanding Universe								✔									

PACING GUIDE

CHAPTER	Lesson	Periods (days)	Blocks
Chapter 1 Earth, Moon, and Sun	1. The Sky from Earth	1–2	½–1
	2. Earth in Space	2–3	1–1½
	3. Gravity and Motion	1–2	½–1
	4. Phases and Eclipses	3–4	1½–2
	5. Tides	1–2	½–1
	6. Earth's Moon	1–2	½–1
	Chapter Review and Assessment	1	½
	Chapter 1 Total	10–16	5–8
Chapter 2 Exploring Space	1. The Science of Rockets	2–3	1–1½
	2. The History of Space Exploration	3–4	1½–2
	3. Using Space Science on Earth	2–3	1–1½
	Chapter Review and Assessment	1	½
	Chapter 2 Total	8–10	4–5
Chapter 3 The Solar System	1. Models of the Solar System	1–2	½–1
	2. Introducing the Solar System	2–3	1–1½
	3. The Sun	1–2	½–1
	4. The Inner Planets	3–4	1½–2
	5. The Outer Planets	3–4	1½–2
	6. Small Solar System Objects	2–3	1–1½
	Chapter Review and Assessment	1	½
	Chapter 3 Total	13–18	6½–9
Chapter 4 Stars, Galaxies, and the Universe	1. Telescopes	2–3	1–1½
	2. The Scale of the Universe	1–2	½–1
	3. Characteristics of Stars	2–3	1–1½
	4. Lives of Stars	2–3	1–1½
	5. Star Systems and Galaxies	2–3	1–1½
	6. The Expanding Universe	1–2	½–1
	Chapter Review and Assessment	1	½
	Chapter 4 Total	11–17	5½–8½
	Module 5 Total	42–61	21–30½

Teacher Notes:

interactive SCIENCE

Dear Family Member,

As your child's science teacher, I am looking forward to helping your child learn about science. Because I know that you want your child to be successful, I offer these suggestions so that you can help your child gain proficiency in science.

- Your child's textbook is very different from most—it's meant for students to write in it. Therefore, it is a record of learning. Look through lessons your child has completed recently, and be sure to ask lots of questions. One of the best ways for students to check on their learning is to explain it to someone else.
- Ask your child about homework assignments and check that he or she has completed them.
- Help your child collect materials and information for school activities.
- Encourage computer literacy. Advise your child to use computers in school or at the library. If you have a home computer, help your child do research online.

In this unit of study, your child will be introduced to Earth as part of the solar system, how science, technology, and society affect each other, and the fact that the universe is very old, very large, and constantly changing. Your child will also learn how Earth, the moon, and the sun interact, how exploring space benefits people, and how astronomers learn about the universe. In the following weeks of study, the unit will provide your child with a deepening of understanding about astronomy and space science.

I encourage you to stay involved in your child's learning. By all means, visit the classroom during open house or make an appointment with me if you have questions.

Cordially,

_____

Science Teacher

To learn more about *Interactive Science* and to see how your student is progressing through the program, go to **www.interactivescience.com**.

Estimados familiares:

Como maestro de ciencias de su hijo, me es un placer ayudarlo a descubrir las ciencias. Como sé que ustedes quieren que su hijo tenga un buen desempeño académico, les ofrezco estas sugerencias para que ayuden a su hijo a dominar las ciencias.

- El libro de texto de su hijo es muy diferente de los demás: tiene como objetivo que su hijo escriba en el libro. Por esa razón, es un registro de aprendizaje. Fíjense en las lecciones que su hijo ha terminado recientemente y asegúrense de hacerle muchas preguntas. Para los estudiantes, una de las mejores formas de repasar lo que han aprendido es explicándoselo a otras personas.

- Pregúntenle a su hijo sobre la tarea que se le asigna y asegúrense de que la complete.

- Ayúdenlo a reunir materiales e información relacionados con las actividades escolares.

- Anímenlo a adquirir destrezas con la computadora, y a usar computadoras en la escuela o en la biblioteca. Si tienen una computadora en casa, ayúdenlo a hacer investigaciones en Internet.

En esta unidad del curso, su hijo explorará la Tierra como parte del sistema solar; cómo se interrelacionan la ciencia, la tecnología y la sociedad; y el hecho de que el universo es muy antiguo, muy grande y está en cambio constante. Su hijo también aprenderá cómo interactúan la Tierra, la Luna y el Sol; los beneficios de la exploración espacial y cómo los astrónomos estudian el universo. En las semanas que siguen, la unidad ayudará a su hijo a comprender mejor la astronomía y la ciencia del espacio.

Los animo a que participen en el proceso de aprendizaje de su hijo. Los invito a visitar el salón de clases durante las horas de visita o a que hagan una cita para reunirse conmigo si tienen dudas.

Cordialmente,

_____

Maestro de Ciencias

Para más información sobre *Ciencias interactivas* y para ver cómo está progresando en el programa su hijo, visiten **www.interactivescience.com**.

Big Ideas of Science

According to the Understanding by Design® framework, students reveal their understanding most effectively when provided with complex, authentic opportunities to explain, interpret, apply, shift perspective, empathize, and self-assess. Each chapter in the student edition uses a Big Question to focus students' attention on the content of the chapter. Related Big Questions are organized under one or more Big Ideas. A Big Idea is a concept, theory, principle, or theme that helps learners make sense of a subject.

Students will explore the Big Idea before they read a chapter, writing about what they already know and what they want to know about the topic. After completing the chapter, students will return to these pages in order to record what they have learned and how their thoughts have changed during that learning process.

UNDERSTANDING BY DESIGN® and UbD™ are trademarks of ASCD, and are used under license.

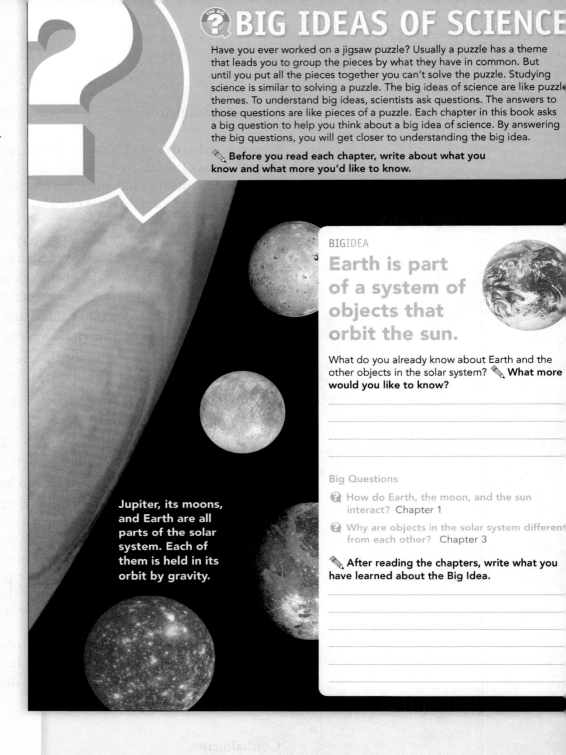

? BIG IDEAS OF SCIENCE

Have you ever worked on a jigsaw puzzle? Usually a puzzle has a theme that leads you to group the pieces by what they have in common. But until you put all the pieces together you can't solve the puzzle. Studying science is similar to solving a puzzle. The big ideas of science are like puzzle themes. To understand big ideas, scientists ask questions. The answers to those questions are like pieces of a puzzle. Each chapter in this book asks a big question to help you think about a big idea of science. By answering the big questions, you will get closer to understanding the big idea.

✎ **Before you read each chapter, write about what you know and what more you'd like to know.**

Jupiter, its moons, and Earth are all parts of the solar system. Each of them is held in its orbit by gravity.

BIGIDEA

Earth is part of a system of objects that orbit the sun.

What do you already know about Earth and the other objects in the solar system? ✎ **What more would you like to know?**

_____
_____
_____
_____

Big Questions

❓ How do Earth, the moon, and the sun interact? Chapter 1

❓ Why are objects in the solar system different from each other?   Chapter 3

✎ **After reading the chapters, write what you have learned about the Big Idea.**

_____
_____
_____
_____
_____
_____

BIGIDEA
Science, technology, and society affect each other.

Astronauts have developed new tools that can be used in space. Some of these tools also make life easier on Earth.

What do you already know about how society and technology affect each other? **What more would you like to know?**

_____

_____

_____

_____

Big Question

How does exploring space benefit people on Earth? Chapter 2

After reading the chapter, write what you have learned about the Big Idea.

_____

_____

_____

_____

BIGIDEA
The universe is very old, very large, and constantly changing.

This galaxy, visible near the Big Dipper, is so far away that light from it takes 12 million years to reach Earth!

What do you already know about the universe? **What more would you like to know?**

_____

_____

_____

_____

Big Question

How do astronomers learn about distant objects in the universe? Chapter 4

After reading the chapter, write what you have learned about the Big Idea.

_____

_____

_____

_____

Connect to the Big Idea

Have students form a group for each Big Idea and assign a notetaker and reporter for each group. Each group discusses what they already know, then individuals write in their student editions what else they personally would like to like to know. Individuals share their items with their group as the notetaker compiles the responses and eliminates duplicates. Each group should agree on one key item they want to learn about. Finally, each group's reporter shares their group's key item with the class and the teacher compiles these items on the board. Remember to vary the roles of group notetaker and reporter to give students a variety of experiences.

EXTENSION Select one item about which students want to learn more as an extra credit project.

Earth, Moon, and Sun

Introduce the Big Q

Have students look at the image and read the Engaging Question and description. Ask the students to explain what they think happened during the period of time shown in the photograph. Have volunteers read their explanations. Point out that the part of the moon you can see is different in each image. Ask: **Have you ever seen this happen to the moon on one night?** *(Sample: Yes)* **What do you suppose was causing the moon to disappear and then reappear bit by bit?** *(Samples: An eclipse; the Earth's shadow passing over the moon)* **Why do you suppose the moon glows darkly red in the last photo?** *(Sample: The moon is entirely within Earth's shadow.)*

Untamed Science Video

PHASED BY THE MOON! Before viewing, invite students to discuss what they know about the moon's phases. Then play the video. Lead a class discussion and make a list of questions that this video raises. You may wish to have students view the video again after they have completed the chapter to see if their questions have been answered.

To access the online resources for this chapter, search on or navigate to *Earth, Moon, and Sun*.

Untamed Science Video shows the phases of the moon.

The Big Question allows students to answer the Engaging Question about the moon.

my science online.com ▶ Earth, Moon, and Sun

WHAT'S HAPPENING TO THE MOON?

THE BIG ? How do Earth, the moon, and the sun interact?

This photograph shows a series of images of the moon taken over the course of an evening. Why do you think the moon looks different in each image? **Develop Hypotheses** **Explain what you think happened during the period of time shown in the photograph.**

Sample: I hypothesize that the moon passed through Earth's shadow.

▶ UNTAMED SCIENCE Watch the **Untamed Science** video to learn more about the moon.

Professional Development Note From the Author

Some topics go in and out of vogue. Centuries ago, when science was making the transition from a geocentric to heliocentric view of the solar system, the relative elliptical orbits of the Earth, Moon, and sun were pretty hot topics. Then planetary orbits were figured out, and the topics became novelties, describing esoteric things like the differences between total and annular solar eclipses. But planetary orbits are once again important subjects. Slight fluctuations in Earth's orbital parameters turn out to be the driving factors for intermediate time-scale climate change, turning Ice Ages on and off. Understanding global climate change requires an understanding of tiny wobbles in the revolutions and rotations of Earth's motions.

✎ *Michael Wysession*

Earth, Moon, and Sun

Chapter at a Glance

CHAPTER PACING: 10–16 periods or 5–8 blocks

INTRODUCE THE CHAPTER: Use the Engaging Question and the opening image to get students thinking about Earth, the moon, and the sun. Activate prior knowledge and preteach vocabulary using the Getting Started pages.

Lesson 1: The Sky From Earth

Lesson 2: Earth in Space

Lesson 3: Gravity and Motion

Lesson 4: Phases and Eclipses

Lesson 5: Tides

Lesson 6: Earth's Moon

ASSESSMENT OPTIONS: Chapter Test, **EXAM**VIEW® Assessment Suite, Performance Assessment, Progress Monitoring Assessments, SuccessTracker™

Preference Navigator, in the online Planning tools, allows you to customize *Interactive Science* to your own teaching style. You can also edit lesson plans by selecting the Lesson Planner option.

Digital Teacher's Edition allows you to access your Teacher's Edition and Resource online.

my science online.com

Differentiated Instruction

L1 Moon Observations Have students do research to find two or three images of the moon. Encourage students to photocopy or scan and print the images they find. Invite students to share their images and discuss their similarities and differences.

L3 History and Lunar Eclipses Have students research traditional beliefs about the causes and consequences of lunar eclipses—beliefs and superstitions that people in various civilizations held before astronomers understood the motions of the moon, sun, and Earth. Invite students to write reports or create posters to share highlights of their research.

1

Getting Started

Check Your Understanding

This activity assesses students' understanding of Earth's axis and equator. After students have shared their answers, point out that the axis and equator are both imaginary lines. They do not exist in reality.

Preteach Vocabulary Skills

Explain to students that a word may have meanings in several areas. For example, *court* has one meaning in social studies, a second meaning in everyday life, and a third meaning in sports. Learning to identify words with multiple meanings can make it easier to learn new vocabulary words. Also point out that when you learn one new word with multiple meanings, you learn multiple new words!

---

1 Getting Started

Check Your Understanding

1. **Background** Read the paragraph below and then answer the question.

Santiago is studying a globe. He sees that Earth has North and South poles. The globe **rotates** around a line through its center between the two poles. Another line called the **equator** divides Earth into two halves, the **Northern Hemisphere** and the **Southern Hemisphere**.

> To **rotate** is to spin in place around a central line, or axis.
>
> The **equator** is the imaginary line that divides Earth into two halves, the **Northern Hemisphere** and the **Southern Hemisphere**.

• Where is the equator found?

Between the Northern and Southern hemispheres

> **MY READING WEB** If you had trouble answering the question above, visit **My Reading Web** and type in *Earth, Moon, and Sun.*

Vocabulary Skill

Identify Multiple Meanings Words you use every day may have different meanings in science. Look at the different meanings of the words below.

Word	Everyday Meaning	Scientific Meaning
weight	*n.* a heavy object used for exercise **Example:** The athlete lifted *weights* to build strength.	*n.* a measure of the force of gravity on an object **Example:** The object's *weight* was 10 newtons.
force	*v.* to use power to make someone do something **Example:** She had to *force* herself to get up early.	*n.* a push or pull exerted on an object **Example:** You exert *force* when you open and close a door.

2. **Quick Check** Circle the sentence below that uses the scientific meaning of *force*.
   • The *force* of gravity holds objects in their orbits.
   • Her parents are trying to *force* her to get a job.

My Reading Web offers leveled readings that offer a foundation for the chapter content.

Vocab Flash Cards offer extra practice with the chapter vocabulary words.

Digital Lesson
• Assign the *Check Your Understanding* activity online and have students submit their work to you.
• Assign the *Vocabulary Skill* activity online and have students submit their work to you.

my science online.com   Earth, Moon, and Sun

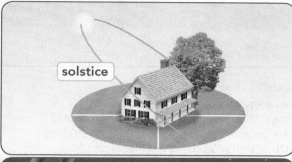
solstice

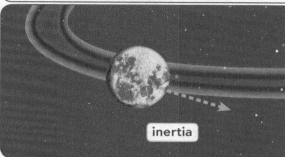
inertia

phase

solar eclipse

Chapter Preview

> VOCAB FLASH CARDS For extra help with vocabulary, visit **Vocab Flash Cards** and type in **Earth, Moon, and Sun.**

3

Preview Vocabulary Terms

Have students create a three-column chart to rate their knowledge of the vocabulary terms before they read the chapter. In the first column of the chart, students should list the terms for the chapter. In the second column, students should identify whether they can define and use the word, whether they have heard or seen the word before, or whether they do not know the word. As the class progresses through the chapter, have students write definitions for each term in the last column of the chart. A list of Academic Vocabulary for each lesson can be found in the Support All Readers box at the start of the lesson.

L1 Have students look at the images on this page as you pronounce the vocabulary word. Have students repeat the word after you. Then read the definition. Use the sample sentence in italics to clarify the meaning of the term.

solstice *(SOHL stis)* Day when the sun appears farthest north or south of the equator. *The Northern Hemisphere receives the most sunlight of the year around June 21, on the summer solstice.*

inertia *(in UR shuh)* The tendency of an object to resist a change in motion. *The moon's inertia keeps it moving ahead.*

phase *(fayz)* Shape of the moon you see from Earth. *The phase of the moon you see depends on how much of the sunlit side of the moon faces Earth.*

solar eclipse *(SOH lur ih KLIPS)* When the moon passes directly between Earth and the sun, blocking sunlight from Earth. *The moon's shadow hits earth during a solar eclipse.*

CHAPTER 1

E L L Support

Have students work in small groups to complete their charts cooperatively for the Preview Vocabulary Terms activity. Read aloud and review the vocabulary terms before students begin their charts.

Beginning
LOW Complete the chart using the vocabulary terms in the native language.

HIGH Write a definition for each known vocabulary term in the native language.

Intermediate
LOW/HIGH Discuss the definitions for known vocabulary terms in cooperative groups.

Advanced
LOW/HIGH Write a sentence using each of the vocabulary terms that is already known.

The Sky from Earth

How do Earth, the moon, and the sun interact?

Lesson Pacing: 1–2 periods or $\frac{1}{2}$–1 block

🕐 **SHORT ON TIME?** To do this lesson in approximately half the time, do the Activate Prior Knowledge activity on page 4. A discussion of the Key Concepts on pages 5, 6, and 8 will familiarize students with the lesson content. Have students do the Quick Labs. The rest of the lesson can be completed by students independently.

> **Preference Navigator,** in the online Planning tools, allows you to customize *Interactive Science* to your own teaching style. You can also edit lesson plans by selecting the Lesson Planner option.
>
> **Digital Teacher's Edition** allows you to access your Teacher's Edition and Resource materials online.

Lesson Vocabulary

- satellite
- planet
- meteor
- comet
- star
- constellation

Content Refresher

Professional Development Note

Constellation Histories Forty-eight constellations described in Ptolemy's *The Almagest* (150 AD) make up the foundation of our constellation system. Historians believe that these 48 constellations originated in ancient Sumer and Babylon and passed from those civilizations to ancient Egypt and Greece. Some areas of the sky eluded ancient constellation namers. The regions of the sky that ancient astronomers could observe depended on the latitude at which they lived. Over the centuries, astronomers have added constellations in these uncharted regions.

Major constellation namers included navigators on trading expeditions to the East Indies (early 1600s) and astronomers Johannes Hevelius (1690) and Nicolas Louis de Lacaille (1750s). Some astronomers named constellations after themselves or dubious animals, such as leeches. Few of these names have survived. The list of 88 constellations in use today was adopted by the International Astronomical Union (IAU) in 1922. In 1930, definitive boundaries between constellations were established, locating each star, nebula, or galaxy within the limits of a single constellation. Contemporary astronomers use the term "constellation" not so much in reference to a figure, animal, or object made of stars but to a precisely defined area of the sky.

LESSON OBJECTIVES

▭ Identify objects and constellations visible without a telescope in the night sky.

▭ Describe the apparent motions of stars and planets throughout the year.

Blended Path
Active learning using Student Edition, Inquiry Path, and Digital Path

ENGAGE AND EXPLORE

Teach this lesson using a variety of resources. Begin by reading **My Planet Diary** as a class. Have students share what they already know about important astronomers from history. Then have students do the **Inquiry Warm-Up activity.** Students will investigate how Earth's location in the universe affects the positions of the stars and constellations as we see them in the night sky. The **After the Inquiry Warm-Up worksheet** sets up a discussion comparing Earth's night sky with another planet's night sky. Have volunteers share their answers to question 4 about the location of the stars in the Big Dipper as seen from Earth.

EXPLAIN AND ELABORATE

Teach Key Concepts by listing the objects in the night sky that can be seen with just your eyes. **Support the Big Q** by explaining that a satellite can be any body that orbits a planet. Continue to **Teach Key Concepts** by discussing the origins of names of constellations. Have students practice the inquiry skill in the **Apply It activity.**

Teach Key Concepts by explaining that the apparent motion of objects in the sky depends on the motions of Earth. **Lead a Discussion** exploring the meaning of the term *apparent motion*.

Hand out the **Key Concept Summaries** as a review of each part of the lesson. Students can also use the online **Vocab Flash Cards** to review key terms.

EVALUATE

Have students take the **Lesson Quiz.** For an alternate assessment, see the **EXAM**VIEW® Assessment Suite, Progress Monitoring Assessments, or SuccessTracker™.

ⓔⓛⓛ Support

1 Content and Language

Have students copy the vocabulary terms into a journal or personal glossary. Then ask them to find the first time the words are used in the chapter. Have them copy the definition of each vocabulary term into their journal or personal glossary.

Lab zone Inquiry Path
Hands-on learning in the Lab zone

Digital Path
Online learning at **my science online**.com

ENGAGE AND EXPLORE

To teach this lesson with an emphasis on inquiry, begin with the **Inquiry Warm-Up activity.** Students will investigate how Earth's location in the universe affects the positions of the stars and constellations as we see them in the night sky. The **After the Inquiry Warm-Up worksheet** sets up a discussion comparing Earth's night sky with another planet's night sky. Have volunteers share their answers to question 4 about the location of the stars in the Big Dipper as seen from Earth.

EXPLAIN AND ELABORATE

Focus on the **Inquiry Skill** for the lesson. Remind students that the skill of predicting involves making an inference about a future event based on current evidence or past experience. What prediction could be made in question 2 of the **Inquiry Warm-Up activity?** *(The same constellations we see in Earth's night sky cannot be seen from another planet.)* **Support the Big Q** by explaining that a satellite can be any body that orbits a planet. Before beginning the **Apply It activity,** copy on the board the figure for Leo shown in the star chart. Help students identify that constellation. Call on a volunteer to explain how students can use the diagram and star chart to find the constellation name for the first image (Cygnus). Assign the activity and have students share their findings about what various constellations represent. Have students do the **Quick Lab** observing the night sky and share their results.

Have students do the **Quick Lab** watching the skies and share their results. Students can use the online **Vocab Flash Cards** to review key terms.

EVALUATE

Have students take the **Lesson Quiz.** For an alternate assessment, see the **EXAM**VIEW® Assessment Suite, Progress Monitoring Assessments, or SuccessTracker™.

ENGAGE AND EXPLORE

Teach this lesson using digital resources. Begin by having students learn more about the night sky and explore real-world connections to the night sky at **My Planet Diary** online. Have them access the Chapter Resources to find the **Unlock the Big Question activity.** There they can answer the questions and refine their responses as they continue through the lesson. You can re-assign the activity and have students submit their work so you can track their progress.

EXPLAIN AND ELABORATE

Students reading above, at, or below the lexile measure of this lesson can access basic content readings at their level at **My Reading Web.** Encourage students to use the online **Vocab Flash Cards** to preview key terms. **Support the Big Q** by explaining that a satellite can be any body that orbits a planet. Use the **Interactive Art activity** online to allow students to explore the constellations. Assign the **Apply It activity** online and have students submit their results to you. Have students do the **Quick Lab** observing the night sky and share their results.

Have students do the **Quick Lab** watching the skies and share their results. The **Key Concept Summaries** online allow students to read a summary and see an image associated with each part of the lesson. Online remediation is available at **My Science Coach.**

EVALUATE

Have students take the **Lesson Quiz.** For an alternate assessment, see the **EXAM**VIEW® Assessment Suite, Progress Monitoring Assessments, or SuccessTracker™.

2 Frontload the Lesson

Have students study **Figure 3.** Discuss the purpose of the insets. Ask students to identify how the drawings in the storyboard show elapsed time. *(Changes in the table setting)* Read the caption for the visual aloud.

3 Comprehensible Input

Have students write sentences that compare and contrast planets and stars. Repeat the activity with meteors and comets.

4 Language Production

Pair or group students with varied language abilities to complete labs collaboratively for language practice. Have each student copy the completed written lab for personal reference.

5 Assess Understanding

Make true or false statements using lesson content and have students indicate agreement with a thumbs up or thumbs down gesture.

The Sky From Earth

Establish Learning Objectives

After this lesson, students will be able to:

🔑 Identify objects and constellations visible without a telescope in the night sky.

🔑 Describe the apparent motions of stars and planets throughout the year.

Engage ————————

Activate Prior Knowledge

MY PLANET DIARY Read *Watching the Stars* with the class. Then direct students' attention to the image. Inform them that a statue of Aryabhata is located at the Inter-University Center for Astronomy and Astrophysics in Pune, India. The sculptor of the statue and the artist of the illustration had to imagine what Aryabhata looked like; no portraits made during his lifetime have survived. Ask: **Who some other important astronomers in world history?** *(Sample: Edwin Hubble)*

BIG IDEAS OF SCIENCE REFERENCE LIBRARY 📖 Have students look up the following topic: Constellations.

Explore ————————

Lab Resource: Inquiry Warm-Up

L1 EARTH'S SKY Students will create and study a model of the Big Dipper.

---

1 The Sky From Earth

🔑 **What Can You See in the Night Sky?**

🔑 **How Do Objects in the Sky Appear to Move?**

my planet diary

BIOGRAPHY

Watching the Stars

When you look up at the night sky, what questions do you ask yourself? Do you wonder why the stars seem to move, or why the moon shines? Aryabhata (ar yah BAH tah) was an early Indian astronomer who thought about these questions. He was born in India in A.D. 476.

Many historians think that Aryabhata realized that the stars appear to move from east to west because Earth rotates from west to east. He also wrote that the moon and the planets shine because they reflect light from the sun. And he made all these inferences using just his eyes and his mind. The first telescopes wouldn't come along for more than a thousand years!

Communicate Discuss Aryabhata's discoveries with a partner. Then answer the questions below.

1. What did Aryabhata infer about the motion of Earth?

   He inferred that Earth turned from west to east.

2. What questions do you think about when you look at stars, the moon, or the planets?

   Sample: I wonder if life exists anywhere else.

> **PLANET DIARY** Go to Planet Diary to learn more about the night sky.

Lab zone Do the Inquiry Warm-Up *Earth's Sky.*

SUPPORT ALL READERS

Lexile Measure = 830L   Lexile Word Count = 1289

Prior Exposure to Content: Most students have encountered this topic in earlier grades

Academic Vocabulary: *main idea, predict, observe, interpret*

Science Vocabulary: *satellite, planet, meteor, comet, star*

Concept Level: Generally appropriate for most students in this grade

Preteach With: My Planet Diary "Watching the Stars" and Figure 1 activity

Go to **My Reading Web** to access leveled readings that provide a foundation for the content.

Vocabulary
- satellite
- planet
- meteor
- comet
- star
- constellation

Skills
- 🔁 Reading: Identify the Main Idea
- △ Inquiry: Predict

What Can You See in the Night Sky?

Depending on how dark the sky is where you are, you might see 2,000 or 3,000 stars using just your eyes. 🔑 On a clear night, you may see stars, the moon, planets, meteors, and comets.

Moon About half of every month, Earth's moon outshines everything else in the night sky. The moon is Earth's only natural satellite. A **satellite** is a body that orbits a planet.

Planets You may see objects that move from night to night against the background stars. These are planets. A **planet** is an object that orbits the sun, is large enough to have become rounded by its own gravity, and has cleared the area of its orbit. There are eight planets in the solar system. Five are visible from Earth without a telescope: Mercury, Venus, Mars, Jupiter, and Saturn.

Meteors and Comets Have you ever seen a "shooting star"? These sudden bright streaks are called **meteors**. A meteor is the streak of light produced when a small object burns up entering Earth's atmosphere. You can see a meteor on almost any night. Comets are rarer. A **comet** is a cold mixture of dust and ice that gives up a long trail of light as it approaches the sun.

Stars Stars appear as tiny points of light. However, scientists infer that a **star** is a giant ball of hot gas, mainly composed of hydrogen and helium. As seen from Earth, the positions of stars relative to each other do not seem to change.

FIGURE 1 ·····
These photos show examples of stars, planets, and other objects.

✏️ **Observe** What can you observe about the objects shown on this page? Include at least two different objects.

Sample: The moon has some dark and some light areas. The comet appears fuzzy. The planet has bright streaks.

5

Explain

Introduce Vocabulary

Read aloud the definitions for *meteor* and *comet*. Contrast the terms for students: Meteors are commonly sighted, whereas comets are rare; meteors are burning, whereas comets are cold.

Teach Key Concepts

Explain to students that you may be able to see many objects, using only your eyes, on a clear night sky. Ask: **What objects might you be able to see with your bare eyes?** *(Stars, the moon, planets, meteors, and comets)* **Which of these objects are you most likely to see?** *(Stars and the moon)* **What type of object is Earth?** *(A planet)* **Which of the planets in the solar system can be seen from Earth without a telescope?** *(Mercury, Venus, Mars, Jupiter, and Saturn)* **What type of object orbits a planet?** *(A satellite)*

Support the Big Q ❓

SATELLITES Students may think of satellites only as objects launched into space from Earth. However, any body that orbits a planet is a satellite. Ask: **How does the moon movie in relation to Earth?** *(The moon orbits Earth.)* **What kind of object is the moon?** *(It is a satellite.)* Point out that the moon is a natural satellite. Weather satellites and GPS satellites are classified as artificial satellites.

My Planet Diary provides an opportunity for students to explore real-world connections to the night sky.

my science online.com ▷ | The Night Sky

ⓔⓛⓛ Support

1 Content and Language
Explain that *constellation* contains the Latin prefix *con-* ("together"), the word *stella* ("star"), and the suffix *-tion* ("condition"). A group of stars seen together in a certain pattern form a *constellation*.

2 Frontload the Lesson
Invite students to recall occasions when they observed the sky at night. Encourage students to share their thoughts and feelings about seeing the moon, stars, and planets.

3 Comprehensible Input
Have pairs of students make two cause-and-effect diagrams. In one diagram, they can write *Earth turns from west to east* as the cause; in the other diagram, they can write the cause *Earth orbits around the sun*. Ask students to find two effects for the first cause and one effect for the second cause.

Explain

Teach Key Concepts 🔑

Explain to students that a constellation is a pattern or group of stars in which people see a figure, animal, or object. Ask: **What constellation names do you know?** *(Sample: Big Dipper, Taurus, Gemini)* **Where do most constellation names come from?** *(From the ancient Greeks, many of the constellations are named after characters from Greek myth.)* **What other group gave constellations many names that we use today?** *(Sample: The ancient Romans, who gave constellations Latin names, such as Leo)*

Teach With Visuals

Tell students to look at **Figure 2.** Have a volunteer come to the front of the classroom and show how to use the chart to identify constellations in the night sky. Then ask: **Why is it helpful to know which direction you are facing to interpret a star chart correctly?** *(Sample: If you know which direction you are facing, you can orient the star chart in the same direction. That way, you will be looking at the constellations and the chart from the same perspective.)* Students may have trouble identifying the stars of the Big Dipper. Tell them to hold the star chart with the label *Western Horizon* at the bottom. In that orientation, the legs, head, and tail of the bear are identifiable. Explain that the Big Dipper is shaped like a ladle, and the handle of the ladle is the tail of the bear. Then have students place a straightedge along the line that connects the two stars at the outer edge of the bowl of the dipper to see that it does lead to the North Star.

Elaborate

Apply It!

L1 Before beginning the activity, copy on the board the figure for Leo shown in the star chart. Help students identify that constellation. Call on a volunteer to explain how students can use the diagram and star chart to find the constellation name for the first image. *(Cygnus)*

Constellations For thousands of years humans have seen patterns in groups of stars and given names to them. 🔑 **A constellation is a pattern or group of stars that people imagined to represent a figure, animal, or object.** Astronomers also use the word *constellation* for an area of the sky and all the objects in that area.

Different cultures have identified different constellations. In Western culture, there are 88 constellations. Most constellation names used today come from the ancient Greeks, who probably took them from the Egyptians and Mesopotamians.

Some constellations' names come from Latin. The constellation Leo, for example, is named from the Latin word meaning "lion." Some constellations are named for people or animals in Greek myths. You may have read some of these myths in school. Do the names *Pegasus* or *Perseus* sound familiar? They are mythological characters and also constellations.

FIGURE 2 ············

▶ **INTERACTIVE ART** **How to Use a Star Chart**
To use a star chart at night, follow these steps.

1. Choose the chart that fits your location and season. This is a summer chart for the Northern Hemisphere. (There are charts for the other seasons in the Appendix.)
2. Hold the chart upright in front of you. Turn the chart so the label at the bottom matches the direction you face. (*Hint:* If you are looking at the Big Dipper, you are looking north.)
3. Hold the chart at eye level. Compare the figures on the bottom half of the chart to the sky in front of you.

Southern Horizon

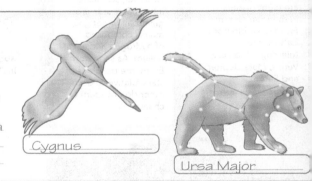

apply it!

❶ **Interpret Diagrams** Find these constellations in **Figure 2.** Then write each constellation's name by its picture.

❷ **CHALLENGE** Choose another constellation from **Figure 2.** What does it represent? Do research to find out.

Sample: Libra represents a set of scales.

Cygnus

Ursa Major

Interactive Art allows students to explore the constellations.

Digital Lesson: Assign the *Apply It* activity online and have students submit their work to you.

my science online.com **The Night Sky**

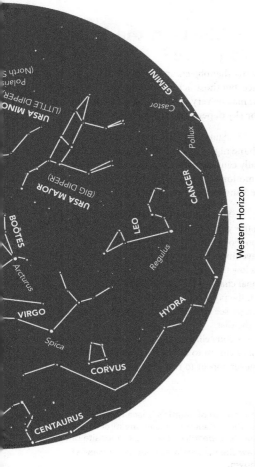

Western Horizon

Finding Constellations A star chart, like the one shown in **Figure 2,** can help you find constellations in the night sky. Read the instructions for how to use the chart. It may seem a little strange at first, but with some practice, these charts are easy to use. Here is one tip to help you get started.

You can probably recognize the Big Dipper. This group of stars is actually not a constellation itself. It is part of the constellation Ursa Major, or the Great Bear. The two stars at the end of the dipper's "bowl" are called the Pointers.

Picture an imaginary line between those two stars. If you continue it away from the "bowl," the first fairly bright star you'll reach is called Polaris (po LA ris). Polaris is commonly called the North Star. It is located close to the sky's North Pole.

In the Appendix, you can find star charts for all four seasons. Take one outside on a clear night and see what you can find!

Cassiopeia

Scorpius

Lab zone Do the Quick Lab *Observing the Night Sky.*

🗨 **Assess Your Understanding**

got it? ....

○ I get it! Now I know that objects visible in the night sky include stars, constellations, the moon, planets, meteors, and comets.

○ I need extra help with *See TE note.*

Go to **my science coach** *online for help with this subject.*

7

21st Century Learning

CREATIVITY Students may know from studying history that the North Star has long been used as a navigation aid. Runaway slaves knew to use the Big Dipper to find the North Star and find their way northward to free states. The song "Follow the Drinking Gourd" is believed to have been a way to pass along this information. The "Drinking Gourd" is the Big Dipper. Challenge students to choose another constellation on the chart and write a poem, song, or short story that could tell someone how to use that constellation to find a direction.

Lab Resource: Quick Lab

L1 **OBSERVING THE NIGHT SKY** Students will examine photos of the night sky and identify constellations.

Evaluate

Assess Your Understanding

After students answer the questions, have them evaluate their understanding by completing the appropriate sentence.

RTI **Response to Intervention**

If have trouble identifying objects visible in the night sky, **then** have them find and reread the Key Concept statements for this section.

my science s coach Have students go online for help in understanding the night sky.

Differentiated Instruction

L1 **Constellation Names** Assign student pairs a constellation not discussed in the text. Have students research to find out how the constellation got its name. Call on partners to share their findings.

L3 **How People Use Constellations** Have students research to identify and find out about one way in which people have used constellations. Have students share their findings with the class. *(Samples: Navigation, religion, agriculture, naming stars)*

LESSON 1.1

Explain

Teach Key Concepts 🔑

Explain to students that the apparent motion of objects in the sky depends on the motions of Earth. Ask: **Why do stars appear to move from east to west throughout the night?** *(Because Earth rotates on its axis from west to east)* **What is the apparent motion of the sun during the day?** *(The sun also seems to move from east to west.)* **Why do the constellations seem to move as the seasons change?** *(Because Earth moves as it revolves around the sun)* **Why do all the planets appear to move through the zodiac from night to night?** *(Because all the planets orbit the sun in about the same plane)*

🔄 **Identify the Main Idea** Explain to students that the main idea is the most important—or biggest—idea in every paragraph or section. If students have difficulty finding the main idea, suggest that they list all of the ideas in the paragraph and then choose the idea that is big enough to include all the others.

21st Century Learning

CRITICAL THINKING Review with students the five planets that can be seen in Earth's night sky without the aid of a telescope. Ask: **Which of these planets do you think is sometimes called the Evening Star or the Morning Star? Explain.** *(Sample: Venus; it is only visible in the evening or morning.)* Ask students if they ever made a wish on the Evening Star, with "Star light, star bright, first star I see tonight…" Then ask why Venus is often the first "star" that is seen. *(It is brighter than the stars, so it would be visible before the sky was completely dark.)*

Make Analogies

L1 **APPARENT MOTION** Draw students' attention to **Figures 3** and **4**. Explain that observing Seattle's Mount Rainier from the restaurant on top of the Space Needle is like observing Mars over several weeks. Ask: **How are these two things alike?** *(Mount Rainier and Mars appear to move because the restaurant and Earth move.)* Invite students to generate additional examples of apparent motion. *(Sample: When you're running clockwise around a track, people in the bleachers appear to move in a counterclockwise direction.)*

⚠️ **Predict** Tell students that the skill of predicting involves making an inference about a future event based on current evidence or past experience.

How Do Objects in the Sky Appear to Move?

Stars, planets, and other objects appear to move over time. They do move in space, but those actual motions and their apparent, or visible, motions may be very different. 🔑 **The apparent motion of objects in the sky depends on the motions of Earth.**

Star Motions Stars generally appear to move from east to west through the night. As Aryabhata thought, this apparent motion is actually caused by Earth turning from west to east. The sun's apparent motion during the day is also caused by Earth's motion. **Figure 3** shows how this kind of apparent motion occurs.

Seasonal Changes Constellations and star patterns remain the same year after year, but which ones you can see varies from season to season. For example, you can find Orion in the eastern sky on winter evenings. But by spring, you'll see Orion in the west, disappearing below the horizon shortly after sunset.

These seasonal changes are caused by Earth's orbit around the sun. Each night, the position of most stars shifts slightly to the west. Soon you no longer see stars once visible in the west, and other stars appear in the east.

There are a few constellations that you can see all year long. These are the ones closest to the North Star. As Earth rotates, these constellations never appear to rise or set.

✏️ **Identify the Main Idea**
Underline the main idea in the paragraph called Star Motions.

FIGURE 3
Opposite Motions
The restaurant on top of Seattle's Space Needle rotates much as Earth does. The restaurant turns in one direction, which makes objects outside appear to move in the opposite direction.

△ **Predict** Draw the mountain as it would appear at each time shown.

Motion of restaurant
6:00 P.M.   6:35 P.M.   7:20 P.M.

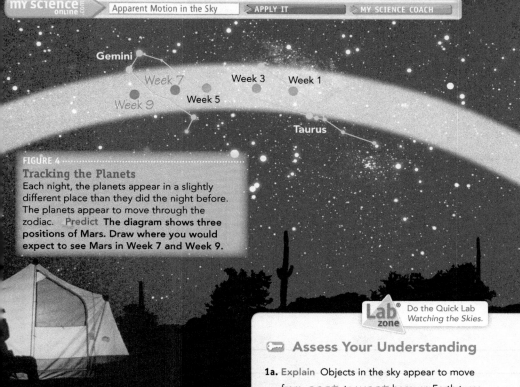

FIGURE 4
Tracking the Planets
Each night, the planets appear in a slightly different place than they did the night before. The planets appear to move through the zodiac. **Predict** The diagram shows three positions of Mars. Draw where you would expect to see Mars in Week 7 and Week 9.

 Do the Quick Lab
Watching the Skies.

Planets Planets appear to move against the background of stars, as shown in **Figure 4.** Because the planets all orbit the sun in about the same plane, they appear to move through a narrow band in the sky. This band is called the zodiac. It includes constellations such as Taurus, Leo, and Virgo.

Some planets, when they are visible, can be seen all night long. Mars, Jupiter, and Saturn are all farther from the sun than Earth is. Sometimes, Earth passes between them and the sun. When this occurs, the planets are visible after sunset, once the sun's bright light no longer blocks the view.

You can see Venus and Mercury only in the evening or morning. They are closer to the sun than Earth, and so they always appear close to the sun. Venus is the brightest object in the night sky, other than the moon. Mercury appears low in the sky and is visible for a limited time around sunrise or sunset.

Assess Your Understanding

1a. Explain Objects in the sky appear to move from _east_ to _west_ because Earth turns from _west_ to _east._

b. Make Generalizations What determines whether a planet is visible all night long?

The planets that are farther from the sun than Earth are visible all night long. Those that are closer to the sun are not.

got it?

○ I get it! Now I know that objects in the sky appear to move _due to Earth's rotation on its axis and orbit around the sun._

○ I need extra help with _See TE note._

Go to **my science coach** *online for help with this subject.*

9

Lead a Discussion

APPARENT MOTION Discuss with students the meaning of the word *apparent* in the term *apparent motion.* The stars, sun, and planets only appear to move in the sky. This motion seems to be real, but it is due to the fact that we, as observers, are moving as Earth rotates on its axis. Display time-lapse photos of the night sky, which show the constellations circling the North Star. Ask students to explain how the photo reveals the apparent motion of the stars in the sky.

Elaborate

Lab Resource: Quick Lab

L2 WATCHING THE SKIES Students will model the apparent movement of constellations.

Evaluate

Assess Your Understanding

After students answer the questions, have them evaluate their understanding by completing the appropriate sentence.

RTI Response to Intervention

1a. If students need help explaining the apparent motion of objects in the sky, **then** have them find and reread the subsection on star motions.

b. If students have trouble identifying what determines whether a planet is visible all night long, **then** tell them to consider where the planets are in relation to Earth's orbit.

my science coach Have students go online for help in understanding apparent motion in the sky.

Differentiated Instruction

L1 Write a Paragraph Have students paraphrase the Key Concept statement and use their paraphrase as the topic sentence in a paragraph explaining the apparent motion of objects in the sky. To support their topic sentence, tell students to use information from the text—restated in their own words.

L3 Make an Illustration Have students make an illustration that explains apparent motion. Students can use **Figure 3** to help them design their illustration, but they should portray a different subject than a revolving restaurant.

Lab zone — After the Inquiry Warm-Up

The Sky From Earth

Inquiry Warm-Up, *Earth's Sky*

In the Inquiry Warm-Up, you investigated how Earth's location in the universe affects the positions of the stars and constellations as we see them in the night sky. Using what you learned from that activity, answer the questions below.

1. **INTERPRET DATA TABLES** In the lab, the length of each straw represents that star's distance from Earth. List the stars in the Big Dipper in order from nearest to Earth to farthest away.

   _____

   _____

2. **APPLY CONCEPTS** Imagine you are on a planet far across the universe from Earth. If you look at the planet's night sky, will you see any of the same constellations we see in Earth's night sky? Explain.

   _____

   _____

   _____

3. **CHALLENGE** You are still on a planet far across the universe from Earth. Name one star you may be able to see in the night sky that is not visible in Earth's night sky.

   _____

4. **DRAW CONCLUSIONS** Recall the moment in Step 4 when you observed your model from above. Now imagine the classroom is the universe. It is full of beads on straws pointing from all directions toward your eye, representing Earth. What can you say about the location of the stars in the Big Dipper as seen from Earth?

   _____

   _____

   _____

   _____

Assess Your Understanding

The Sky From Earth

What Can You See in the Night Sky?

got it? ....

○ **I get it!** Now I know that objects visible in the night sky include _____

_____

_____

○ **I need extra help with** _____

_____

How Do Objects in the Sky Appear to Move?

1a. EXPLAIN Objects in the sky appear to move from _____

to _____ because Earth turns from _____

to _____.

b. MAKE GENERALIZATIONS What determines whether a planet is visible all night long?

_____

_____

got it? ....

○ **I get it!** Now I know objects in the sky appear to move _____

_____

○ **I need extra help with** _____

_____

The Sky From Earth

What Can You See in the Night Sky?

On a clear night, you may see stars, the moon, planets, meteors, and comets. The moon is Earth's only natural satellite. A **satellite** is a body that orbits a planet. A **planet** is an object that orbits the sun, is large enough to have become rounded by its own gravity, and has cleared the area of its orbit. Five planets are visible from Earth without a telescope: Mercury, Venus, Mars, Jupiter, and Saturn.

A **meteor** is the streak of light produced when a small object burns up entering Earth's atmosphere.

You can see a meteor on almost any night. Comets are rarer. A **comet** is a cold mixture of dust and ice that gives up a long trail of light as it approaches the sun.

A **star** is a giant ball of hot gas, mainly composed of hydrogen and helium. **A constellation is a pattern or group of stars that people imagine to represent a figure, animal, or object.** A star chart can help you find constellations in the night sky.

How Do Objects in the Sky Appear to Move?

Stars, planets, and other objects move in space, but their actual motions and their apparent, or visible, motions may be very different. **The apparent motion of objects in the sky depends on the motions of Earth.**

Stars generally appear to move from east to west through the night. This apparent motion is caused by Earth's turning from west to east. The sun's apparent motion during the day is also caused by Earth's motion.

Which constellations you can see varies from season to season. These seasonal changes are caused by Earth's orbit around the sun. Each night, the position of most stars shifts slightly to the west.

Because the planets all orbit the sun in about the same plane, they appear to move through a narrow band in the sky. This band is called the zodiac.

On a separate sheet of paper, list five kinds of objects you can see in the night sky. Explain why the objects' actual motion may be different than their apparent motion.

Review and Reinforce

The Sky From Earth

Understanding Main Ideas

Answer the following questions in the spaces provided. Use a separate sheet of paper if you need more room.

1. Where do constellations' names come from?

_____

_____

_____

2. What tool can help you find constellations in the night sky?

_____

3. On what does the apparent motion of objects in the sky depend?

_____

_____

Building Vocabulary

Match each term with its definition by writing the letter of the correct definition in the right column on the line beside the term in the left column.

4. ___ meteor

5. ___ satellite

6. ___ star

7. ___ planet

8. ___ star chart

9. ___ constellation

10. ___ zodiac

a. giant ball of hot gas, mainly hydrogen and helium

b. group of stars that people imagine to represent a figure or object

c. body that orbits a planet

d. narrow band in the sky through which planets appear to move

e. streak of light produced when a small object burns up entering Earth's atmosphere

f. tool that helps you find constellations in your location and season

g. object that orbits the sun, is large enough to have been rounded by its gravity, and has cleared the area of its orbit

Name _____ Date _____ Class _____

The Sky from Earth

> Read the passage and study the figure. Then answer the questions that follow on a separate sheet of paper.

Weightlessness

Think about the last time you rode on a roller coaster. You first climbed a high hill in the track. Then you plummeted down the other side at high speed. As you rode down, you felt as though you were going to leave your seat. During this time, you were almost weightless. The people in orbit around Earth on the International Space Station feel weightless for the same reason. At the altitude of the International Space Station, Earth's gravity is almost as strong as it is on Earth's surface. The astronauts experience weightlessness because they are falling around Earth.

What would happen if the International Space Station were not moving sideways in orbit? Earth's gravity would pull it straight down to Earth's surface. If the space station were moving sideways at a low speed, it would fall to Earth's surface along a curved path. But if the space station moves at just the right speed, it can fall all the way around Earth. These three situations are shown in the diagram below. The reason astronauts experience weightlessness while on the International Space Station is that they are constantly falling around Earth together with the space station. As they fall they feel weightless, just as you did when you last rode a roller coaster.

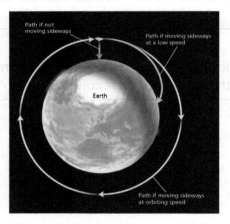

1. Does Earth's gravity pull on the International Space Station? Explain.
2. What would happen to the International Space Station if it were not moving sideways?
3. What do you think would happen to the International Space Station if it were moving sideways faster than orbital speed?
4. How is riding down on a roller coaster similar to being on the International Space Station?
5. Explain why astronauts on the space station experience weightlessness.

The Sky From Earth

Write the letter of the correct answer on the line at the left.

1. ___ The moon is Earth's only natural
   A zodiac
   B meteor
   C comet
   D satellite

2. ___ A planet is large enough to have been rounded by its
   A rotation
   B gravity
   C moon
   D orbit

3. ___ You can match constellations to your location and the season using a
   A GPS receiver
   B star chart
   C horoscope
   D telescope

4. ___ Planets appear to move against the background of
   A other planets
   B other planets' moons
   C the sun
   D stars

If the statement is true, write _true_. If the statement is false, change the underlined word or words to make the statement true.

5. _____ Earth's underline{rotation on its axis} causes seasonal changes in the constellations you can observe.

6. _____ Stars are made up mainly of hydrogen and underline{oxygen}.

7. _____ Different cultures have identified underline{the same} constellations.

8. _____ You can see five planets from Earth without a telescope: Mercury, Venus, Mars, Jupiter, and underline{Uranus}.

9. _____ The underline{actual} motion of objects in the sky depends on the motions of Earth.

10. _____ underline{The North Star} is the brightest object in the night sky.

The Sky From Earth

Answer Key

After the Inquiry Warm-Up

1. Megrez, Merak, Alioth, Mizar, Phecda, Dubhe, Alkaid

2. No, I will not see any of the same constellations we see in Earth's night sky because the apparent arrangement of stars depends on the location from which you view them.

3. the sun

4. The stars in the Big Dipper are all located in the same general direction, as seen from Earth.

Key Concept Summaries

Sample: Stars, planets, comets, meteors, the moon. The objects' actual motion may be different than their visible, or apparent motion, because their apparent motion depends on the motion of Earth. For example, Earth turns from west to east as it rotates, so stars generally appear to move from east to west.

Review and Reinforce

1. Sample: Some constellations' names come from Latin words or Greek myths. Leo comes from the Latin word meaning "lion." Pegasus is the name of a flying horse in a Greek myth.

2. a star chart

3. The apparent motion of objects in the sky depends on the motion of Earth.

4. e   5. c

6. a   7. g

8. f   9. b

10. d

Enrich

1. Yes. Earth's gravity pulls almost as strongly on the International Space Station as it does on Earth's surface.

2. It would fall directly to Earth's surface.

3. It would escape Earth's gravity and fly off into space.

4. In both cases, people are falling and may feel weightless or nearly weightless.

5. The astronauts and the space station are both falling around Earth at the same rate.

Lesson Quiz

1. D   2. B

3. B   4. D

5. orbit around the sun   6. helium

7. different   8. Saturn

9. apparent   10. Venus

Place the outside corner, the corner away from the dotted line, in the corner of your copy machine to copy onto letter-size paper.

Earth in Space

Lesson Pacing: 2–3 periods or 1–1½ blocks

🕐 **SHORT ON TIME?** To do this lesson in approximately half the time, do the Activate Prior Knowledge activity on page 10. A discussion of the Key Concepts on pages 11 and 14 will familiarize students with the lesson content. Have students do the Quick Lab. The rest of the lesson can be completed by students independently.

> **Preference Navigator,** in the online Planning tools, allows you to customize *Interactive Science* to your own teaching style. You can also edit lesson plans by selecting the Lesson Planner option.
>
> **Digital Teacher's Edition** allows you to access your Teacher's Edition and Resource materials online.

Lesson Vocabulary

- axis • rotation • revolution • orbit • calendar • solstice
- equinox

Content Refresher

Earth's Rotation Earth's rotation is gradually slowing through time. This change is a result of the pull of the moon's gravity on Earth's tidal bulges. Earth has tides in the solid planet and in its oceans. However, because Earth's ocean-water bulges are larger and more massive, they have a greater effect on slowing Earth's rotation. Because Earth rotates, the tidal bulges are not on a direct line connecting the moon and Earth. The bulge on the side of Earth facing the moon, for example, is ahead of the line connecting Earth and the moon. The moon pulls on this displaced mass and creates tidal friction, which is gradually slowing Earth's rate of rotation. Most of the friction between the water bulges and Earth occurs through tidal currents and other tidal effects. As Earth's rotation slows, angular momentum is transferred to the moon, which moves farther from Earth.

Consequences of Earth's changing rate of rotation include lengthening days. The length of the day on Earth is increasing at a rate of about 2.3 milliseconds per century. Approximately 500 million years ago, there were only about 22 hours in one day.

LESSON OBJECTIVES

- Demonstrate how Earth moves in space.
- Explain what causes the cycle of seasons on Earth.

Blended Path
Active learning using Student Edition, Inquiry Path, and Digital Path

ENGAGE AND EXPLORE

Teach this lesson using a variety of resources. Begin by reading **My Planet Diary** as a class. Have students discuss why the seasons change. Then have students do the **Inquiry Warm-Up activity.** Students will use a globe and a lamp with a bare bulb to model Earth's rotation. The **After the Inquiry Warm-Up worksheet** sets up a discussion about how the sun and Earth interact to produce night and day on Earth. Have volunteers share their answers to question 4 about whether or not the sun really moves across the sky during the day.

EXPLAIN AND ELABORATE

Teach Key Concepts by explaining that Earth moves through space by rotation and revolution. **Support the Big Q** by reviewing how Earth's rotation affects day and night and how Earth's revolution affects how we mark time.

Teach Key Concepts by explaining that the tilt of Earth's axis and Earth's changing position as it revolves around the sun cause seasons. **Lead a Discussion** using **Figure 5** to explain the conditions that cause the seasons to change in the Northern Hemisphere.

Hand out the **Key Concept Summaries** as a review of each part of the lesson. Students can also use the online **Vocab Flash Cards** to review key terms.

EVALUATE

Have students take the **Lesson Quiz.** For an alternate assessment, see the **EXAM**VIEW® Assessment Suite, Progress Monitoring Assessments, or SuccessTracker™.

ⒺⒽⒽ Support

1 Content and Language
Review the definitions of the vocabulary terms. Then ask small groups to work together to use *axis, rotates, revolves,* and *orbit* to complete this sentence: *The Earth ____ on its ____ as it ____ in its ____ around the Sun.*

Lab zone Inquiry Path
Hands-on learning in the Lab zone

Digital Path
Online learning at **my science online**.com

ENGAGE AND EXPLORE

To teach this lesson with an emphasis on inquiry, begin with the **Inquiry Warm-Up activity.** Students will use a globe and a lamp with a bare bulb to model Earth's rotation. The **After the Inquiry Warm-Up worksheet** sets up a discussion about the how the sun and Earth interact to produce night and day on Earth. Have volunteers share their answers to question 4 about whether or not the sun really moves across the sky during the day.

EXPLAIN AND ELABORATE

Focus on the **Inquiry Skill** for the lesson. Remind students that to make an inference, they use what they already know to interpret an observation. How did students use what they already knew to answer question 3 in the **Inquiry Warm-Up activity?** *(They already knew that the sun comes up in the east and sets in the west.)* Do the **Teacher Demo** modeling how Foucault's pendulum proved that Earth rotates. **Support the Big Q** by reviewing how Earth's rotation affects day and night and how Earth's revolution affects how we mark time. Have students do the **Quick Lab** to test their predictions about how the sun's shadow changes through the day.

Build Inquiry to allow students to compare and contrast angles of sunlight as they hit Earth's surface. Have students do the **Lab Investigation** to explore how the tilt of Earth's axis affects the light that Earth receives as it orbits the sun. Students can use the online **Vocab Flash Cards** to review key terms.

EVALUATE

Have students take the **Lesson Quiz.** For an alternate assessment, see the **EXAM**VIEW® Assessment Suite, Progress Monitoring Assessments, or SuccessTracker™.

ENGAGE AND EXPLORE

Teach this lesson using digital resources. Begin by having students learn more about Earth's motions and explore real-world connections to Earth's motions at **My Planet Diary** online. Have them access the Chapter Resources to find the **Unlock the Big Question activity.** There they can answer the questions and refine their responses as they continue through the lesson. You can re-assign the activity and have students submit their work so you can track their progress.

EXPLAIN AND ELABORATE

Students reading above, at, or below the lexile measure of this lesson can access basic content readings at their level at **My Reading Web.** Encourage students to use the online **Vocab Flash Cards** to preview key terms. **Support the Big Q** by reviewing how Earth's rotation affects day and night and how Earth's revolution affects how we mark time. Have students do the **Quick Lab** to test their predictions about how the sun's shadow changes through the day.

Use the **Interactive Art activity** online to show how Earth's movement around the sun causes the four seasons. Assign the **Do the Math activity** online and have students submit their work to you. The **Key Concept Summaries** online allow students to read a summary and see an image associated with each part of the lesson. Online remediation is available at **My Science Coach.**

EVALUATE

Have students take the **Lesson Quiz.** For an alternate assessment, see the **EXAM**VIEW® Assessment Suite, Progress Monitoring Assessments, or SuccessTracker™.

2 Frontload the Lesson
Have students work together to create a word wall to display the vocabulary terms for the chapter. Be sure to discuss and analyze each term before posting it on the wall. As the class progresses through the chapter, the words can be sorted and categorized in different ways.

3 Comprehensible Input
Challenge students to write simple mathematical equations that define *equinox, one rotation of Earth on its axis, one revolution of Earth,* and *one moon cycle. (12 hours = 12 hours; 1 rotation = 1 day; 1 revolution = 1 year; 1 moon cycle = approx. 1 month)*

4 Language Production
Pair or group students with varied language abilities to complete labs collaboratively for language practice. Have each student copy the completed written lab for personal reference.

5 Assess Understanding
Ask students to make notes about Key Concepts from the lesson and use the notes to prepare an oral presentation of the concepts. Encourage students to use the visuals in the lesson to support their presentations.

LESSON 1.2

Earth in Space

Establish Learning Objectives

After this lesson, students will be able to:

🔑 Demonstrate how Earth moves in space.

🔑 Explain what causes the cycle of seasons on Earth.

Engage

Activate Prior Knowledge

MY PLANET DIARY Read *The Seasons* with the class. Point out that the number of hours of daylight changes as the seasons change. Ask: **What are the four seasons?** *(Winter, summer, spring, and fall)* **In which season is there the least daylight?** *(Winter)* **Suppose you lived at the Equator. Would you experience winter and summer?** *(No)* Challenge students to explain why not.

BIG IDEAS OF SCIENCE REFERENCE LIBRARY 📖 Have students look up the following topic: Summer Solstice.

Explore

Lab Resource: Inquiry Warm-Up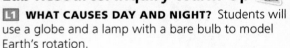

L1 **WHAT CAUSES DAY AND NIGHT?** Students will use a globe and a lamp with a bare bulb to model Earth's rotation.

UNLOCK
THE BIG
?

🔑 **How Does Earth Move?**

🔑 **What Causes Seasons?**

MY PLANET DIARY

MISCONCEPTION

The Seasons

Misconception: The seasons change because Earth's distance from the sun changes.

Fact: Seasons are the result of Earth's tilted axis.

Evidence: Earth's distance from the sun does change, but that's not why Earth has seasons. If that were the cause, people in the Northern and Southern hemispheres would have the same seasons at the same time. Instead, seasons in the Northern and Southern hemispheres are reversed. As Earth moves around the sun, sometimes the Northern Hemisphere is tilted toward the sun. At other times the Southern Hemisphere is tilted toward the sun.

January 21

Where are you and what are you doing today?

Before you read the rest of this lesson, answer the questions below.

1. Why are summers generally warmer than winters?

   During the summer, Earth is tilted toward the sun, bringing more sunlight.

2. Where on Earth is the tilt of Earth least likely to affect seasons? Why?

   At the equator, because the amount of sun there stays about the same

▶ PLANET DIARY Go to Planet Diary to learn more about Earth's motions.

Lab zone Do the Inquiry Warm-Up *What Causes Day and Night?*

10 Earth, Moon, and Sun

SUPPORT ALL READERS

Lexile Measure = 860L   Lexile Word Count = 1503

Prior Exposure to Content: May be the first time students have encountered this topic

Academic Vocabulary: *infer, sequence, identify, explain, define*

Science Vocabulary: *axis, rotation, revolution, orbit*

Concept Level: May be difficult for students who struggle with abstract ideas

Preteach With: My Planet Diary "The Seasons" and Figure 2 activity

Go to **My Reading Web** to access leveled readings that provide a foundation for the content.

MY SCIENCE online.com

Vocabulary
- axis • rotation • revolution • orbit
- calendar • solstice • equinox

Skills
- Reading: Sequence
- Inquiry: Infer

How Does Earth Move?

Until a few hundred years ago, most people thought that Earth stood still and the sun, moon, and stars moved around it. But today, scientists know that Earth itself moves and that objects seem to move across the sky because of Earth's motion. **Earth moves in space in two major ways: rotation and revolution.**

Rotation The imaginary line that passes through Earth's center and the North and South poles is Earth's **axis.** The spinning of Earth on its axis is called **rotation.**

Earth's rotation causes day and night, as you can see in **Figure 1.** As Earth rotates eastward, the sun appears to move west across the sky. As Earth continues to turn to the east, the sun appears to set in the west. Sunlight can't reach the side of Earth facing away from the sun, so it is night there. It takes Earth about 24 hours to rotate once. As you know, each 24-hour cycle of day and night is called a day.

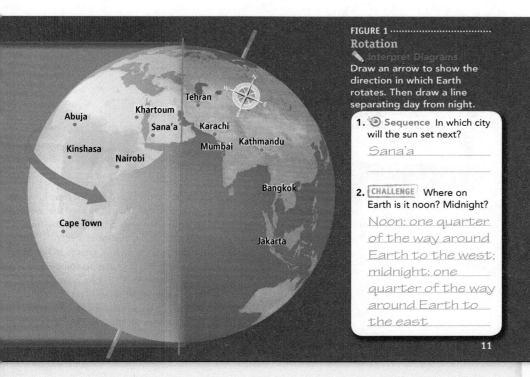

FIGURE 1
Rotation
Interpret Diagrams
Draw an arrow to show the direction in which Earth rotates. Then draw a line separating day from night.

1. Sequence In which city will the sun set next?

   Sana'a

2. CHALLENGE Where on Earth is it noon? Midnight?

   Noon: one quarter of the way around Earth to the west; midnight: one quarter of the way around Earth to the east

11

Explain

Introduce Vocabulary

Draw students' attention to the terms *axis* and *rotation.* Explain to students how the terms are related. *(The spinning of Earth on its axis is Earth's rotation.)*

Sequence Explain that a sequence is the order in which a series of events occurs. Tell students that a cycle diagram or flowchart can help them visualize a sequence.

Teach Key Concepts

Explain to students that Earth moves through space in two major ways. Ask: **What are Earth's two main motions called?** *(Rotation and revolution)* **What is rotation?** *(The spinning of Earth on its axis)* **What is Earth's axis?** *(An imaginary line that passes through its center and the North and South poles)* **How long does it take for Earth to make one rotation?** *(About 24 hours)* **What change do we see as a result of Earth's rotation?** *(Day and night)*

Elaborate

Teacher Demo

L3 MODEL ROTATION

Materials ring stand, string, tape, turntable (such as a lazy Susan), weight

Time 15 minutes

Tell students that in 1851, physicist Jean Foucault used a pendulum to prove that Earth rotates. To model Foucault's pendulum, hang a small weight from the arms of a ring stand. Swing the pendulum.

Ask: **What happens?** *(The weight swings back and forth in one plane.)* Place the pendulum on the center of the turntable. Mark one side of the turntable with a piece of tape. Start the pendulum swinging and then slowly spin the turntable.

Ask: **What does the turntable represent?** *(Earth rotating on its axis)* **What does the tape represent?** *(A location on Earth)* **Suppose this activity models a pendulum at the North Pole. How could such a model prove that Earth rotates?** *(If a pendulum were swinging above the North Pole, the direction of its swing would appear to make one complete rotation every 24 hours.)*

My Planet Diary provides an opportunity for students to explore real-world connections to Earth's motions.

Earth's Movement

ELL Support

1 Content and Language
Write the terms *revolution* and *revolve* on the board. Explain that one meaning of *revolution* is "a complete change of any kind." Point out that in astronomy, *revolution* means "the movement of one object around another." Tell students that the related verb form is *revolve.*

2 Frontload the Lesson
Invite students to think about divisions of time on a calendar. Encourage students to name the time periods *day, week, month,* and *year.* Tell them that they will learn the scientific facts that underlie three of these terms.

3 Comprehensible Input
Have students work in pairs to create cluster diagrams for the terms *season, solstice,* and *equinox.* Tell students to add definitions for each term, as well as details that identify its cause and that describe some of its characteristics.

11

Explain

Support the Big Q

EARTH-SUN INTERACTIONS Review how Earth rotates. Ask: **As Earth rotates, how does the interaction of Earth and the sun affect day and night?** *(Earth's rotation causes day and night as different sides of Earth face toward and away from the sun.)* Point out that both rotation and revolution are interactions of Earth and the sun. Ask: **As Earth revolves, how does the interaction of Earth and the sun affect how we mark time?** *(Sample: The calendar that we use defines a year as the time it takes Earth to complete one revolution of the sun.)*

Make Analogies

ROTATION AND REVOLUTION Pantomime a figure skater first twirling in place and then skating around a rink. Explain what you are doing. Ask: **How were the motions of the skater I pantomimed like those of Earth's rotation and revolution?** *(Sample: When the skater twirled, he moved around his own center in the same way as Earth moves when it rotates on its axis. When the skater skated around an imaginary rink, he moved in the same way as Earth moves when it revolves around the sun.)*

21st Century Learning

L1 INTERPERSONAL SKILLS If students need additional help visualizing rotation and revolution, invite two volunteers to stand up and take the roles of Earth and the sun to show Earth's two movements. To help students better visualize the concepts, have the students in the role of the sun hold a flashlight pointed at the students in the role of Earth. *("The sun" stands still while "Earth" simultaneously spins and moves in a path around "the sun.")*

Sequence Explain that when they sequence a series of events, they show the order in which the events took place.

Revolution In addition to rotating, Earth travels around the sun. **Revolution** is the movement of one object around another. One revolution of Earth around the sun is called a year. Earth's path, or **orbit**, is a slightly elongated circle, or ellipse. Earth's orbit brings the planet closest to the sun in January.

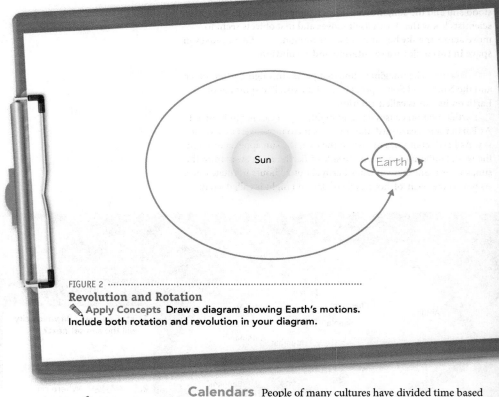

FIGURE 2 ....

Revolution and Rotation

✎ **Apply Concepts** Draw a diagram showing Earth's motions. Include both rotation and revolution in your diagram.

✎ **Sequence** Which calendar discussed in this section was developed most recently?

Gregorian

Calendars People of many cultures have divided time based on the motions of Earth and the moon. They have used the motions to establish calendars. A **calendar** is a system of organizing time that defines the beginning, length, and divisions of a year.

The most common calendar today is divided into years, months, and days. One year equals the time it takes Earth to complete one orbit. One day equals the time it takes Earth to turn once on its axis. People also divide the year into months based on the moon's cycle. The time from one full moon to another is about 29 days, though modern months do not match the moon's cycle exactly.

12 Earth, Moon, and Sun

The History of the Calendar

Egyptian

The ancient Egyptians created one of the first calendars. Based on star motions, they calculated that the year was about 365 days long. They divided the year into 12 months of 30 days each, with an extra 5 days at the end.

Roman

The Romans borrowed the Egyptian calendar. But Earth's orbit actually takes about 365¼ days. The Romans adjusted the Egyptian calendar by adding one day every four years. You know this fourth year as "leap year," when February is given 29 days instead of its usual 28. Using leap years helps to ensure that annual events, such as the beginning of summer, occur on the same date each year.

Gregorian

The Roman calendar was off by a little more than 11 minutes a year. Over the centuries, these minutes added up. By the 1500s, the beginning of spring was about ten days too early. To straighten things out, Pope Gregory XIII dropped ten days from the year 1582. He also made some other minor changes to the Roman system to form the calendar that we use today.

 Do the Quick Lab *Sun Shadows.*

Assess Your Understanding

1a. Identify What are the two major motions of Earth as it travels through space?

Rotation and revolution

b. Explain Which motion causes day and night?

Rotation

c. Infer Why do people use Earth's motions to determine units of time?

Sample: Earth's motions are regular, so people can use them to measure time consistently.

got it?

○ I get it! Now I know that Earth moves by *rotating on its axis and revolving around the sun.*

○ I need extra help with *See TE note.*

Go to **MY SCIENCE COACH** *online for help with this subject.*

13

Differentiated Instruction

L3 Calculate Earth's Movements Tell students that Earth moves at a speed of about 30 km/sec as it travels around the sun. Ask: **How many kilometers does Earth travel in a minute? An hour? A day? A year?** Before they begin their calculations, suggest that students set up the problems on paper to make sure that units cancel out. *(In one minute, 1,800 km; in one hour, 108,000 km; in one day, 2,592,000 km; in one year, about 946,080,000 km)*

L1 Differentiate Key Terms The word pair *rotation* and *revolution* can be confusing. Provide examples such as *rotating* a doorknob (it moves around its center). Give an example, such as "The librarian's life revolved around books," to illustrate the expression of a person's life *revolving* around something. Point out that *books* is the center. Encourage students to think of additional examples.

Elaborate

21st Century Learning

CRITICAL THINKING Display an image of a calendar such as Stonehenge, a monument with giant stones that mark the directions in which the sun rises and sets on the shortest and longest days of the year. Explain that ancient people used Stonehenge to make astronomical observations. Inform students that, on the morning of the summer solstice a person standing in the center of the circle could see the sun rising directly over the 35-ton heel stone erected there. Then ask: **Can only paper tables be used as calendars?** *(No)* **Why not?** *(Sample answer: Anything, such as the giant stones at Stonehenge, that is used to keep track of days, months, and years can be thought of as a calendar.)*

Lab Resource: Quick Lab

L2 SUN SHADOWS Students will predict how the sun's shadow changes through the day and then test their predictions.

Evaluate

Assess Your Understanding

After students answer the questions, have them evaluate their understanding by completing the appropriate sentence.

RTI Response to Intervention

1a. If students have trouble identifying Earth's two major motions, **then** have them review the boldfaced Key Concept statement.

b. If students need help differentiating rotation and revolution, **then** have them find and reread the sections in which these highlighted vocabulary terms appear.

c. If students have trouble inferring why people use Earth's motions to determine units of time, **then** ask them to think about the importance of everyone's being able easily to use the same units to measure time.

MY SCIENCE COACH Have students go online for help in understanding Earth's motions.

Explain

Teach Key Concepts 🔑

Explain to students that the tilt of Earth's axis and Earth's changing position as it revolves around the sun cause seasons. Ask: **At what angle is Earth's axis tilted?** *(23.5° from the vertical)* **What would happen if Earth's axis were straight up and down?** *(Temperatures in a particular area would remain fairly constant all year round.)* **Does the North Pole point in different directions as Earth revolves around the sun?** *(No, the North Pole always points in the same direction.)*

Teach With Visuals

STRONG SUNLIGHT If students have difficulty visualizing the area where sunlight is most concentrated, suggest that they draw a circle or oval at each location where sunlight is shown. After they decide which area has the most direct sunlight, they can add an X to the other areas. Ask: **In which hemisphere is the area of strongest sunlight?** *(Southern Hemisphere)* **What season is it there?** *(Summer)* **Where would the circle be on the first day of spring?** *(Over the equator)*

▲ **Infer** Explain to students that to make an inference, you use what you know already to interpret an observation.

What Causes Seasons?

Many places that are far from Earth's equator and its poles have four distinct seasons: winter, spring, summer, and autumn. But there are differences in temperature from place to place. For instance, it is generally warmer near the equator than near the poles. Why?

How Sunlight Hits Earth **Figure 3** shows how sunlight strikes Earth's surface. Notice that, near the equator, sunlight hits Earth's surface from almost overhead. Near the poles, sunlight arrives at a steep angle. As a result, it is spread out over a greater area. That's why it is warmer near the equator than near the poles.

Earth's Tilted Axis If Earth's axis were straight up and down relative to its orbit, temperatures in an area would remain fairly constant year-round. There would be no seasons. 🔑 **Earth has seasons because its axis is tilted as it revolves around the sun.**

Notice in **Figure 4** that Earth's axis is always tilted at an angle of 23.5° from the vertical. The North Pole always points in the same direction. As Earth revolves around the sun, the north end of its axis is tilted away from the sun for part of the year and toward the sun for part of the year. Summer and winter are caused by Earth's tilt as it revolves around the sun.

FIGURE 3 ·····························
Sunlight on Earth
The diagram shows how Earth's tilted axis affects the strength of sunlight in different places.
△ **Infer** Draw a circle around the area where sunlight is most direct. Mark an X on the places that sunlight reaches, but where it is less direct.

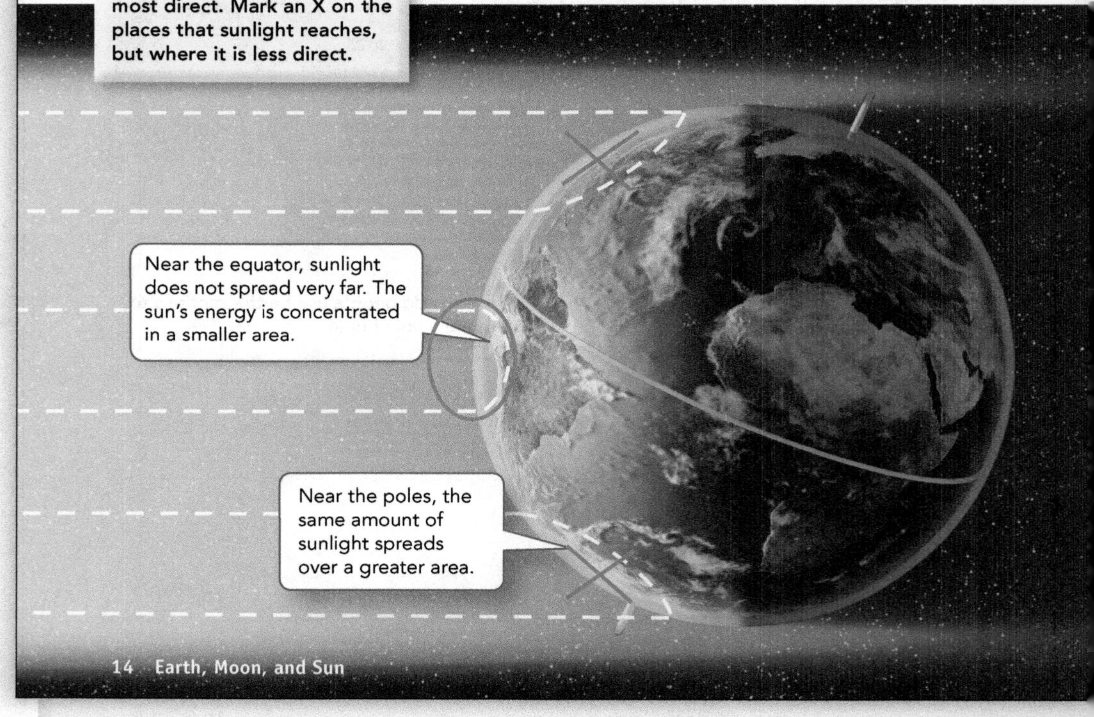

Near the equator, sunlight does not spread very far. The sun's energy is concentrated in a smaller area.

Near the poles, the same amount of sunlight spreads over a greater area.

14   Earth, Moon, and Sun

Interactive Art shows how Earth's movement around the sun causes the four seasons.

my science online.com   **Seasons**

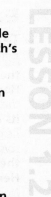

June In June, the north end of Earth's axis is tilted toward the sun. In the Northern Hemisphere, the noon sun is high in the sky and there are more hours of daylight than darkness. The sun's rays are concentrated. It is summer in the Northern Hemisphere.

At the same time south of the equator, the sun's energy is spread over a larger area. The sun is low in the sky and days are shorter than nights. It is winter in the Southern Hemisphere.

December In December, people in the Southern Hemisphere receive the most direct sunlight, so it is summer. At the same time, the sun's rays in the Northern Hemisphere are more slanted and there are fewer hours of daylight. So it is winter in the Northern Hemisphere.

March

June

December

September

FIGURE 4 ·····················
▶ INTERACTIVE ART **Seasons**
The diagram shows how Earth moves during the year. It is not drawn to scale.

✎ **Make Generalizations**
Describe the weather and sunlight in the Northern and Southern hemispheres in March and September.

Sample: In both March and September, the intensity of sunlight is about the same in both hemispheres. Both hemispheres have similar conditions.

15

Teach With Visuals

Tell students to look at **Figure 4.** Ask: **Is the angle of the tilt different at different points in Earth's revolution?** *(No)* **What is different?** *(Whether the north end of the axis is tilted toward or away from the sun)* **What season is it in the Northern Hemisphere when the north end of the axis is pointed the most directly toward the sun?** *(Summer)* **What season is it in the Northern Hemisphere when the south end of the axis is pointed the most directly toward the sun?** *(Winter)* **When it is winter in the Northern Hemisphere, what season is it in the Southern Hemisphere?** *(Summer)*

Elaborate ——————

Build Inquiry [Lab zone]

L1 **COMPARE AND CONTRAST ANGLES OF SUNLIGHT**

Materials flashlight, graph paper

Time 15 minutes

Remind students that sunlight hits Earth's surface at different angles. Have students work in groups to shine a flashlight directly above the graph paper and trace around the lighted area. Next, have students shine the flashlight at an angle and trace around the lighted area.

Ask: **Which area represents sunlight at the equator?** *(The smaller area)* **Which receives more energy, the smaller area or the larger area?** *(Both areas receive the same amount.)* **If this were Earth's surface, why would the larger area be colder? Explain in terms of the graph paper squares.** *(Each square in the larger area, the poles, receives less energy than each square in the smaller area, the equator.)*

Differentiated Instruction

L1 **Model** Place a lamp with a bare bulb on a desk. Tilt a globe so that the Northern Hemisphere is pointed toward the lamp. Ask: **Which season does this represent in the Northern Hemisphere?** *(Summer)* Walk around the lamp in a circle, but keep the tilt of the globe the same relative to the room, not the lamp. Turn the globe so that the United States is facing the sun. As you walk, stop every 90° to represent Earth's position at the equinoxes and the winter solstice. Have students identify each season and describe the conditions in the United States.

Explain

Teach With Visuals

L1 Tell students to look at **Figure 5.** Ask: **When is the sun at its maximum height in the Northern Hemisphere?** *(The sun is at its maximum height in the Northern Hemisphere at the June solstice.)* **At its minimum height?** *(The sun is at its minimum height in the Northern Hemisphere at the December solstice.)* **When is the sun at equal heights in the Northern Hemisphere and Southern Hemisphere?** *(The sun is at equal heights in the Northern and Southern hemispheres at the March and September equinoxes.)*

Lead a Discussion

SOLSTICES Point out the diagram at the left of **Figure 5.** Ask: **What two conditions cause it to be summer in the Northern Hemisphere?** *(In June, the sun shines more directly on the surface. The sun is above the horizon for a longer period each day.)* Have students look at the diagram in the lower right. **What are two conditions that cause it to be winter in the Northern Hemisphere?** *(In December, the sun shines less directly on the surface. The sun is above the horizon for a shorter period each day.)*

21st Century Learning

L3 **INFORMATION LITERACY** Challenge students to learn more about Earth's analemma. An *analemma* is the curve created by the sun's mean position each day in the sky as viewed from Earth. If you were to plot the position of the sun in the sky at the same time each day from the same position on Earth, the resulting curve would look like a figure eight. Have students print out photographs of anelemmas and identify the location of the sun on the two solstices and the two equinoxes. Encourage volunteers to explain to the class how these photographs are created.

Solstices The sun appears farthest north of the equator once each year and farthest south once each year. Each of these days is known as a **solstice** (SOHL stis). The day when the sun appears farthest north is the summer solstice in the Northern Hemisphere and the winter solstice in the Southern Hemisphere. This solstice occurs around June 21 each year. It is the longest day of the year in the Northern Hemisphere and the shortest day in the Southern Hemisphere. As you can see in **Figure 5,** the sun rises to the northeast and sets to the northwest.

Similarly, around December 21, the sun appears farthest south. This is the winter solstice in the Northern Hemisphere and the summer solstice in the Southern Hemisphere. The sun rises to the southeast and sets to the southwest.

Equinoxes Halfway between the solstices, neither hemisphere is tilted toward the sun. The noon sun is directly overhead at the equator, rises due east, and sets due west. Each of these days is known as an **equinox,** which means "equal night." During an equinox, day and night are each about 12 hours long everywhere. The vernal (spring) equinox occurs around March 21 and marks the beginning of spring in the Northern Hemisphere. The fall, or autumnal, equinox occurs around September 22. It marks the beginning of fall in the Northern Hemisphere.

FIGURE 5 ·······················

Solstices and Equinoxes

The diagrams show the apparent path of the sun at the solstices and equinoxes in the Northern Hemisphere. The sun rises and sets farthest north at the June solstice and farthest south at the December solstice.

✎ **Apply Concepts** Draw the sun's path at the equinoxes and the December solstice for the Southern Hemisphere.

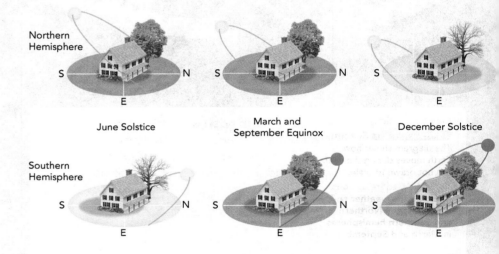

Northern Hemisphere

S   N
E
June Solstice

S   N
E
March and September Equinox

S   N
E
December Solstice

Southern Hemisphere

S   N
E

S   N
E

S   N
E

16   Earth, Moon, and Sun

Digital Lesson: Assign the *Do the Math* activity online and have students submit their work to you.

my science online   **Seasons**

do the math! Sample Problem

Calculating Percents

The table shows the number of hours of sunlight in three cities at different times of year. What percentage of a 24-hour day has sunlight in Guadalajara on January 1?

STEP 1 Divide the number of hours of sunlight by the total number of hours.

$$\frac{\text{Hours of sunlight}}{\text{Total hours}} = \frac{10.90 \text{ hours}}{24 \text{ hours}} = 0.45$$

STEP 2 Multiply by 100 to find the percent.

$$0.45 \times 100 = 45\%$$

In Guadalajara, 45% of a 24-hour day has sunlight on January 1.

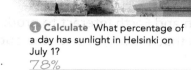

1 **Calculate** What percentage of a day has sunlight in Helsinki on July 1?
78%

2 **Calculate** What is the difference in the percentage of the day that has sunlight in Helsinki and in Philadelphia on January 1?
14%

3 **Infer** What percentage of the day would you expect to have sunlight at the equator in January? In June?
About 50% in both January and June

City	Approximate Latitude	Hours of Daylight			
		January 1	April 1	July 1	October 1
Helsinki, Finland	60°N	5.98	13.33	18.80	11.45
Philadelphia, United States	40°N	9.38	12.68	14.95	11.77
Guadalajara, Mexico	20°N	10.90	12.37	13.37	11.95

Lab zone Do the Lab Investigation *Reasons for the Seasons.*

Assess Your Understanding

2a. Define The noon sun is directly overhead at the equator during (a solstice/~~an equinox~~).

b. Relate Cause and Effect What causes the seasons? *As Earth orbits the sun, changes in the amount of sunlight result from the tilt of Earth's axis.*

c. Predict How would the seasons be different if Earth were not tilted on its axis? Explain.
Temperatures would remain mostly constant year-round. Both hemispheres would receive the same amount of sunlight all year.

got it?

○ I get it! Now I know that Earth's seasons are caused by *yearly changes in temperature resulting from Earth's tilted axis.*

○ I need extra help with *See TE note.*

Go to **my science COACH** *online for help with this subject.*

17

Differentiated Instruction

L1 **Write a Paragraph** Have students write a paragraph describing the changes that take place each season in the region where they live. Challenge students to explain how seasonal changes in temperature and hours of daylight relate to changes in Earth's position as it moves around the sun.

L3 **Write and Model** Ask students to choose a place on the globe that they are not familiar with and write a description of the amount of sunlight received there throughout the year. Call on students to use a lamp with a bare bulb and a globe to model their written descriptions.

Elaborate

Do the Math!

L1 Direct students' attention to Question 2. Ask: **What do you need to do first?** (*Find the percentage of a day that has sunlight in Helsinki and in Philadelphia on January 1*) **What do you need to do next?** (*Subtract the smaller percentage from the larger percentage*) **What word in the question tells you to subtract?** (*Difference*)

 Infer Explain to students that to make an inference, you use what you know already to interpret an observation. Encourage students to use what they already know about how sunlight strikes the equator year-round to answer Question 3.

See *Math Skill and Problem-Solving Activities* for support.

21st Century Learning

CRITICAL THINKING Have students read *Gravity* in the **Big Ideas of Science Reference Library** and write a story about a birthday party held at the International Space Station. Have students describe the effect microgravity has on various party activities. How would it affect the candles on the cake? One of the guests reports being a different height: Is he or she taller or shorter? Why?

Lab Resource: Lab Investigation **Lab zone**

L2 **REASONS FOR THE SEASONS** Students will explore how the tilt of Earth's axis affects the light that Earth receives as it orbits the sun.

Evaluate

Assess Your Understanding

After students answer the questions, have them evaluate their understanding by completing the appropriate sentence.

R T I Response to Intervention

2a. If students need help distinguishing a solstice and an equinox, **then** have them review the explanations of each term.

b. If students have trouble explaining what causes the seasons, **then** have them review Figure 4.

c. If students need help explaining the importance of Earth's tilted axis to changing seasons, **then** review with them the positions of Earth's axis during summer and winter.

my science COACH Have students go online for help in understanding seasons.

Lab zone **After the Inquiry Warm-Up**

Earth in Space

Inquiry Warm-Up, *What Causes Day and Night?*

In the Inquiry Warm-Up, you investigated how the sun and Earth interact to produce night and day on Earth. Using what you learned from that activity, answer the questions below.

1. **COMMUNICATE** Draw three diagrams to show the relationship between the light and the globe in Step 3 of the lab. The first diagram should show the globe before you turned it, the second should show the globe when it was turned 180 degrees, and the third one should show the globe after you stopped turning it. In all three diagrams, be sure to identify your location on the globe and indicate any motion.

2. **PREDICT** Based on your model, what do you think would happen in terms of night and day if Earth stopped rotating?

   _____

   _____

3. **INFER** Think of the directions from which the sun rises in the morning and sets in the evening. If you are looking straight down at Earth's North Pole, which way does Earth rotate, clockwise or counterclockwise?

   _____

4. **DRAW CONCLUSIONS** Does the sun really move across the sky during the day? Explain.

   _____

   _____

Assess Your Understanding

Earth in Space

How Does Earth Move?

1a. **IDENTIFY** What are the two major motions of Earth as it travels through space?

_____

b. **EXPLAIN** Which motion causes day and night?

_____

c. **INFER** Why do people use Earth's motions to determine units of time? _____

_____

got it? ···

○ **I get it!** Now I know that Earth moves by _____

_____

○ **I need extra help with** _____

_____

What Causes Seasons?

2a. **DEFINE** The noon sun is directly overhead at the equator during (a solstice/an equinox).

b. **RELATE CAUSE AND EFFECT** What causes the seasons?

_____

_____

c. **PREDICT** How would the seasons be different if Earth were not tilted on its axis? Explain.

_____

_____

got it? ···

○ **I get it!** Now I know that Earth's seasons are caused by _____

_____

○ **I need extra help with** _____

_____

Earth in Space

How Does Earth Move?

Earth moves in space in two major ways: rotation and revolution. Rotation is the spinning of Earth on its axis. Earth's **axis** is an imaginary line that passes through Earth's center and the North and South poles. The rotation of Earth causes day and night.

Revolution is the movement of one object around another. One revolution of Earth around the sun is one year. Earth's path, or **orbit,** around the sun is an ellipse. The ellipse brings the planet closest to the sun in January.

People of many cultures have used the motions of Earth and the moon to establish calendars. A **calendar** is a system of organizing time that defines the beginning, length, and divisions of a year.

What Causes Seasons?

Near the equator, sunlight hits Earth's surface from almost overhead. Near the poles, sunlight arrives at a steep angle. As a result, near the poles sunlight is spread out over a greater area. That's why it is warmer near the equator than near the poles.

If Earth's axis were straight up and down relative to its orbit, temperatures in an area would remain fairly constant year-round. There would be no seasons. However, Earth's axis is tilted at an angle of 23.5° from the vertical. So as Earth revolves around the sun, the north end of its axis is tilted away from the sun for part of the year and toward the sun for part of the year. **Earth has seasons because its axis is tilted as it revolves around the sun.**

The sun appears farthest north or south of the equator twice each year. Each of these days is called a **solstice.** In the Northern Hemisphere, the summer solstice occurs around June 21. That is the longest day of the year in the Northern Hemisphere and the shortest day in the Southern Hemisphere. Similarly, around December 21, the winter solstice occurs in the Northern Hemisphere, while the summer solstice occurs in the Southern Hemisphere. Halfway between the solstices, neither hemisphere is tilted toward the sun. Each of these days is called an **equinox.** On an equinox, the noon sun is directly overhead at the equator, rises due east, and sets due west.

On a separate sheet of paper, identify the two major ways Earth moves in space. Then, explain how the tilt of Earth's axis affects the seasons.

Name _____ Date _____ Class _____

Earth in Space

Understanding Main Ideas

Use the diagram below to answer Questions 1–3 on a separate sheet of paper.

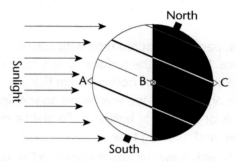

1. In the diagram, what season is it in North America?
2. Would a person at each of the points A, B, and C see the sun? If so, where would the sun be in the sky?
3. Which is a person standing at point B seeing, sunrise or sunset? Explain.

Building Vocabulary

Match each term with its definition by writing the letter of the correct definition in the right column on the line beside the term in the left column.

4. ___ axis

5. ___ rotation

6. ___ revolution

7. ___ orbit

8. ___ calendar

9. ___ equinox

10. ___ solstice

a. path of Earth as it revolves around the sun

b. defines the beginning, length, and divisions of a year

c. line passing through Earth's center and poles

d. when the sun is farthest north or south of the equator

e. movement of Earth around the sun

f. movement of Earth around its axis

g. when the noon sun is directly overhead at the equator

Enrich

Earth in Space

Read the passage, follow the directions for building a simple sundial, and study the figures below. Then use a separate sheet of paper to answer the questions that follow.

Build a Simple Sundial

Long before the invention of clocks, people measured time with *sundials.* A simple sundial is a vertical pointer projecting from a flat surface. Marks on the surface show where the shadow cast by the tip of the pointer falls at different times. You tell time by noting where the pointer's shadow falls on these marks. For the shadow to fall in the right places, the sundial has to stay in one place, so sundials are usually built on permanent pedestals or as parts of buildings. To build a simple sundial, you can start with two pieces of stiff poster board and masking tape.

- On the first piece of poster board, draw the figure shown in Figure 1. Cut it out, and fold it along the dotted lines. This will become your pointer.

- On the second piece of poster board, draw the figure shown in Figure 2, with the point of the angle close to a corner of the poster board. Now, tape the pointer onto the second piece of poster board so that its base aligns with the figure you have drawn. The finished sundial will look like Figure 3.

- Around midday, place the sundial on a stable, flat, sunlit surface, such as an outdoor tabletop, so that the pointer's shadow falls towards the opposite corner of the poster board. Tape down the sundial so it won't move. Every half hour, mark the location of the shadow of the pointer's tip and label it with the time. Continue this process throughout the afternoon and again the next morning to "set your clock."

Figure 1

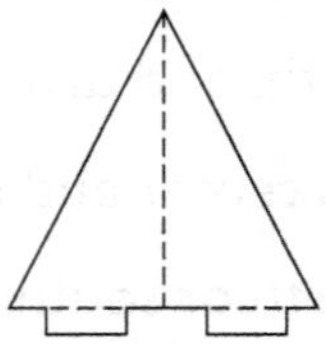

Base: 20 cm
Height: 20 cm

Figure 2

10 cm
10 cm

Figure 3

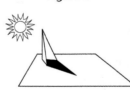

1. At some moment when you don't know what time it is, look at your sundial and read the time. Compare your sundial time with the time on a clock. How accurate is your sundial?

2. Do you think a "moondial" could be made to tell time at night? Explain.

3. Name two practical disadvantages of sundials compared with clocks.

Lesson Quiz

Earth in Space

Write the letter of the correct answer on the line at the left.

1. ___ Earth is closest to the sun when it is summer in the
   A   Southern Hemisphere
   B   Northern Hemisphere
   C   Western Hemisphere
   D   Eastern Hemisphere

2. ___ When it is summer in the Southern Hemisphere, it is winter in the
   A   equator
   B   Northern Hemisphere
   C   Western Hemisphere
   D   Eastern Hemisphere

3. ___ In June, there are fewer hours of daylight and less direct sunlight in the
   A   Southern Hemisphere
   B   Northern Hemisphere
   C   Western Hemisphere
   D   Eastern Hemisphere

4. ___ Each of the two days of the year when neither hemisphere is tilted toward or away from the sun is called a(n)
   A   winter solstice
   B   summer solstice
   C   rotation
   D   equinox

Fill in the blank to complete each statement.

5. Earth has _____ because its axis is tilted as it revolves around the sun.

6. Earth's _____ causes day and night.

7. Earth's orbit is a slightly elongated circle, or _____.

8. One revolution of Earth around the sun is called a(n) _____.

9. The most common _____ in use today is divided into years, months, and days.

10. The _____ occurs around March 21 in the Southern Hemisphere.

Earth in Space

Answer Key

1. Diagrams will vary, depending on which location the students initially had facing the light bulb. The first diagram should show that location, facing the bulb, the second diagram should show it on the opposite side of the globe, and the last one should show it again facing the bulb. Counterclockwise rotation of the globe, as seen from the North Pole, should be indicated in all three parts.

2. One side of Earth would have permanent day, and the other side would have permanent night.

3. counterclockwise

4. No, the sun does not really move across the sky. It appears to move across the sky because Earth is rotating.

Key Concept Summaries

Sample: Rotation and revolution are the two major ways Earth moves in space. The tilt of Earth's axis, at an angle of 23.5° from the vertical, causes the seasons. As Earth revolves around the sun, the north and south ends of its axis are each tilted away from the sun for part of the year and toward the sun for part of the year. This causes winter and summer in the Northern and Southern hemispheres.

Review and Reinforce

1. winter

2. At point A the sun would be directly overhead; at point B it would be on the horizon; at point C it would not be visible because it is night.

3. sunset; Earth rotates from west to east.

4. c   5. f

6. e   7. a

8. b   9. g

10. d

Enrich

1. Answers will vary. Students will probably find that telling time within 15 minutes is difficult with a sundial.

2. Answers will vary. Sample: A "moondial" couldn't be made because the moon's position in the sky from day to day varies much more than the position of the sun.

3. Accept any two responses: Sundials can't easily be moved. They don't work at night, indoors, or in cloudy weather. They are not as accurate as clocks.

Lesson Quiz

1. A   2. B
3. A   4. D
5. seasons   6. rotation
7. ellipse   8. year
9. calendar   10. autumnal (fall) equinox

Place the outside corner, the corner away from the dotted line, in the corner of your copy machine to copy onto letter-size paper.

Gravity and Motion

LESSON

3 **How do Earth, the sun, and the moon interact?**

Lesson Pacing: 1–2 periods or $\frac{1}{2}$–1 block

🕐 **SHORT ON TIME?** To do this lesson in approximately half the time, do the Activate Prior Knowledge activity on page 18. A discussion of the Key Concepts on pages 19 and 20 will familiarize students with the lesson content. Have students do the Quick Labs. The rest of the lesson can be completed by students independently.

> **Preference Navigator,** in the online Planning tools, allows you to customize *Interactive Science* to your own teaching style. You can also edit lesson plans by selecting the Lesson Planner option.
>
> **Digital Teacher's Edition** allows you to access your Teacher's Edition and Resource materials online.

Lesson Vocabulary

- force • gravity • law of universal gravitation • mass • weight
- inertia • Newton's first law of motion

Content Refresher

Perturbation The law of universal gravitation states that every object in the universe exerts a force on every other object. When discussing the effect of the sun's gravitational pull on the orbits of planets, astronomers must take into account perturbation—variances in the expected orbits of planets caused by other bodies in the solar system exerting gravitational force on one another. For example, Jupiter slows down the orbital period of Saturn by one week relative to its expected orbital period based on the sun's gravitational pull. The perturbation of Uranus's orbit led astronomers to predict the existence of an eighth planet, which was eventually sighted in 1846 and named Neptune.

Beyond the confines of the solar system, perturbations in the orbits of stars caused by the gravitational forces of orbiting bodies have led to the discovery of a number of extrasolar planetary systems. Until the last decade of the twentieth century, our solar system was the only known planetary system. Nevertheless, speculation that other planetary systems exist dates back to antiquity. Astronomers have continuously searched for Earthlike planets circling sunlike stars. The breakthrough came in 1992. Astronomers detected three planets orbiting a pulsar. However, because pulsars are not normal stars, this was not considered a true planetary system. The first detection of an extrasolar planet around a normal star was made in 1995. The first discovery of multiple planets orbiting a sunlike star was announced in 1999.

LESSON OBJECTIVES

🔑 Identify what determines the strength of the force of gravity between two objects.

🔑 Describe two factors that keep the moon and Earth in orbit.

Blended Path
Active learning using Student Edition, Inquiry Path, and Digital Path

ENGAGE AND EXPLORE

Teach this lesson using a variety of resources. Begin by reading **My Planet Diary** as a class. Have students discuss their understandings of gravity. Then have students do the **Inquiry Warm-Up activity.** Students will investigate the factors that affect gravity. The **After the Inquiry Warm-Up worksheet** sets up a discussion about the factors that affect gravity. Have volunteers share their answers to question 4 about the force-of-gravity values for each probe.

EXPLAIN AND ELABORATE

Teach Key Concepts by explaining that the strength of a gravitational force between two objects depends on the masses of the objects and the distance between them.

Teach Key Concepts by explaining that inertia and gravity combine to keep objects in orbit. **Lead a Discussion** about how gravity pulls all objects toward each other. **Support the Big Q** by using **Figure 2** to show how Earth and the moon interact through gravitational forces.

Hand out the **Key Concept Summaries** as a review of each part of the lesson. Students can also use the online **Vocab Flash Cards** to review key terms.

EVALUATE

Have students take the **Lesson Quiz.** For an alternate assessment, see the **EXAM**VIEW® Assessment Suite, Progress Monitoring Assessments, or SuccessTracker™.

ⒺⓁⓁ Support

1 Content and Language
Explain to students that the terms *force, gravity,* and *mass* have multiple meanings. Have them find the definitions of the terms in a dictionary and then use the visuals in the chapter to predict which of the meanings fits the way the word will be used in the chapter. Have them check their predictions as they read.

Lab zone Inquiry Path
Hands-on learning in the Lab zone

Digital Path
Online learning at my science online.com

ENGAGE AND EXPLORE

To teach this lesson with an emphasis on inquiry, begin with the **Inquiry Warm-Up activity.** Students will investigate the factors that affect gravity. The **After the Inquiry Warm-Up worksheet** sets up a discussion about the factors that affect gravity. Have volunteers share their answers to question 4 about the force-of-gravity values for each probe.

EXPLAIN AND ELABORATE

Focus on the **Inquiry Skill** for the lesson. Explain to students that a conclusion is a statement that sums up what they have learned. What conclusion could be drawn about the force-of-gravity values for the probes in question 1 in the **Inquiry Warm-Up activity?** *(The force-of-gravity values for Probe 2 are twice as great as those for Probe 1 at every distance value.)* Have students do the **Quick Lab** and share their results.

Do the **Teacher Demo** to demonstrate inertia and relate it to orbital motion. **Support the Big Q** by using **Figure 2** to show how Earth and the moon interact through gravitational forces. Have students do the **Quick Lab** and share their results. Students can use the online **Vocab Flash Cards** to review key terms.

EVALUATE

Have students take the **Lesson Quiz.** For an alternate assessment, see the **EXAM**VIEW® Assessment Suite, Progress Monitoring Assessments, or SuccessTracker™.

ENGAGE AND EXPLORE

Teach this lesson using digital resources. Begin by having students learn more about gravity and explore real-world connections to gravity and motion at **My Planet Diary** online. Have them access the Chapter Resources to find the **Unlock the Big Question activity.** There they can answer the questions and refine their responses as they continue through the lesson. You can re-assign the activity and have students submit their work so you can track their progress.

EXPLAIN AND ELABORATE

Students reading above, at, or below the lexile measure of this lesson can access basic content readings at their level at **My Reading Web.** Encourage students to use the online **Vocab Flash Cards** to preview key terms. Have students do the **Quick Lab** and share their results. Use the **Virtual Lab activity** online to allow students to explore how different masses and distances affect the orbit of planets.

Support the Big Q by using **Figure 2** to show how Earth and the moon interact through gravitational forces. Assign the **Do the Math activity** online and have students submit their work to you. Have students do the **Quick Lab** and share their results. The **Key Concept Summaries** online allow students to read a summary and see an image associated with each part of the lesson. Online remediation is available at **My Science Coach.**

EVALUATE

Have students take the **Lesson Quiz.** For an alternate assessment, see the **EXAM**VIEW® Assessment Suite, Progress Monitoring Assessments, or SuccessTracker™.

2 Frontload the Lesson
Have students create a three-column chart to rate their knowledge of the terms, listing terms in the first column, noting how familiar each term is in the second column, and, as they read, defining each term in the third column.

3 Comprehensible Input
Have students restate Newton's law of universal gravitation and Newton's first law of motion in their own words. Encourage them to use examples to make their definitions clearer.

4 Language Production
Pair or group students with varied language abilities to complete labs collaboratively for language practice. Have each student copy the completed written lab for personal reference.

5 Assess Understanding
Divide the class into small groups. Have each student identify a Key Concept to discuss in his or her group. After the discussions, have students talk about the Key Concepts as a group.

LESSON 1.3

Gravity and Motion

Establish Learning Objectives

After this lesson, students will be able to:

 Identify what determines the strength of the force of gravity between two objects.

 Describe two factors that keep the moon and Earth in orbit.

Engage

Activate Prior Knowledge

MY PLANET DIARY Read *Gravity Assists* with the class. Inform students that several robotic spacecraft, including *Voyagers 1* and *2* and the *Cassini-Huygens* spacecraft, have used gravity assists. Ask: **How did reading the Planet Diary change your understanding of gravity?** *(Sample: Like the Planet Diary says, I never thought of gravity doing anything but bringing objects down. Now I know that gravity can pull objects in directions other than down.)*

BIG IDEAS OF SCIENCE REFERENCE LIBRARY
Have students look up the following topic: Gravity.

Explore

Lab Resource: Inquiry Warm-Up

WHAT FACTORS AFFECT GRAVITY? Students will graph data to explore what factors affect the force of gravity.

LESSON

3 Gravity and Motion

 What Determines Gravity?

 What Keeps Objects in Orbit?

MY PLANET DiARY

Gravity Assists

You might think that gravity only brings objects down. But gravity can also speed things up and send them flying! If a space probe comes close to a planet, the planet's gravity changes the probe's path. Engineers plan space missions to take advantage of these "gravity assists." A gravity assist can shorten the probe's interplanetary trip by many years. The diagram shows how the probe *Voyager 2* used gravity assists to visit all four outer planets!

Path of spacecraft

TECHNOLOGY

Use what you know about gravity to answer this question.
How does a planet's gravity change the path of a space probe?

The planet's gravity pulls the space probe into a new direction.

> **PLANET DIARY** Go to **Planet Diary** to learn more about gravity.

Lab zone Do the Inquiry Warm-Up *What Factors Affect Gravity?*

What **Determines Gravity?**

Earth revolves around the sun in a nearly circular orbit. The moon orbits Earth in the same way. But what keeps Earth and the moon in orbit? Why don't they just fly off into space?

The first person to answer these questions was the English scientist Isaac Newton. In the 1600s, Newton realized that there must be **a force acting between Earth and the moon that** kept the moon in orbit. A **force** is a push or a pull.

18 Earth, Moon, and Sun

SUPPORT ALL READERS

Lexile Measure = 900L   Lexile Word Count = 842

Prior Exposure to Content: May be the first time students have encountered this topic

Academic Vocabulary: *conclusions, questions, compare, contrast*

Science Vocabulary: *force, gravity, mass, weight, inertia*

Concept Level: May be difficult for students who struggle with abstract ideas

Preteach With: My Planet Diary "Gravity Assists" and Figure 2 activity

Go to **My Reading Web** to access leveled readings that provide a foundation for the content.

my science online.com

Vocabulary

- force
- gravity
- law of universal gravitation
- mass
- weight
- inertia
- Newton's first law of motion

Skills

- Reading: Ask Questions
- Inquiry: Draw Conclusions

Gravity Newton hypothesized that the force that pulls an apple to the ground also pulls the moon toward Earth, keeping it in orbit. This force, called **gravity,** attracts all objects toward each other. Newton's **law of universal gravitation** states that every object in the universe attracts every other object. **The strength of the force of gravity between two objects depends on two factors: the masses of the objects and the distance between them.**

Gravity, Mass, and Weight The strength of gravity depends in part on the masses of each of the objects. **Mass** is the amount of matter in an object. Because Earth is so massive, it exerts a much greater force on you than this book does.

The measure of the force of gravity on an object is called **weight.** Mass doesn't change, but an object's weight can change depending on its location. On the moon, you would weigh about one sixth as much as on Earth. This is because the moon has less mass than Earth, so the pull of the moon's gravity on you would also be less.

Gravity and Distance Gravity is also affected by the distance between two objects. The force of gravity decreases rapidly as distance increases. If the distance between two objects doubles, the force of gravity decreases to one fourth of its original value.

did you know?

You could say we owe our **understanding of gravity to disease!** In 1665, Isaac Newton was a student. Then a disease called plague shut down the university for 18 months. Newton had to go home. While he was there, he thought of the ideas that led to his theory. (But it may not be true that he got the idea when an apple fell from a tree.)

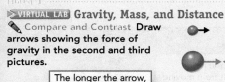

> **VIRTUAL LAB** **Gravity, Mass, and Distance**
> ✏ Compare and Contrast **Draw arrows showing the force of gravity in the second and third pictures.**

The longer the arrow, the greater the force.

Lab zone Do the Quick Lab *What's Doing the Pulling?*

Assess Your Understanding

got it?

○ I get it! Now I know that the force of gravity depends on *the mass of the objects and the distance between them.*

○ I need extra help with *See TE note.*

Go to my science coach *online for help with this subject.*

19

Explain

Introduce Vocabulary
Write the terms *force* and *gravity* on the board, and explain how they are related. Tell students that gravity is a type of force—a force that attracts all objects toward each other.

Teach Key Concepts 🔑
Explain to students that the strength of a gravitational force between two objects depends on two factors. Ask: **What are the two factors that affect the force of gravity?** *(The masses of the objects and the distance between them.)* **What is mass?** *(The amount of matter in an object)* **How does mass affect the force of gravity?** *(The more mass an object has, the greater the force it can exert.)* **How does distance affect the force of gravity?** *(The greater the distance between two objects, the smaller the force of gravity between them.)*
Explain that the moon's mass is about 1% of Earth's, but the force of gravity at the moon's surface is about one-sixth that at Earth's surface. Because the distance from the moon's center to its surface is much less than the distance from Earth's center to its surface, the force of gravity on the moon is greater than it would be if the moon's mass were spread over a volume the same as Earth's.

Elaborate

Lab Resource: Quick Lab 🔬
L1 **WHAT'S DOING THE PULLING?** Students will use magnets to model the force of gravity.

Evaluate

Assess Your Understanding
Have students evaluate their understanding by completing the appropriate sentence.

RTI Response to Intervention
If students have trouble identifying the two factors that determine the force of gravity, **then** have them reread the Key Concept statement.

my science coach Have students go online for help in understanding gravity.

Virtual Lab allows students to explore how different masses and distances affect the orbit of planets.

Explain

Teach Key Concepts 🔑

Explain to students that inertia and gravity combine to keep objects in orbit. Ask: **Who discovered that inertia and gravity combine to keep objects in orbit?** *(Isaac Newton)* **What motion of Earth does this explain?** *(Earth's revolution around the sun)* **What path of the moon does this explain?** *(The moon's orbit around Earth)*

🔄 **Ask Questions** Explain to students that asking themselves questions as they read is an excellent way to focus on and remember information.

Lead a Discussion

INERTIA Remind students that gravity pulls all objects toward each other. Ask: **Why does a baseball continue to move after a pitcher lets go of it and stops applying force?** *(The ball has inertia.)* **Why would the ball eventually hit the ground?** *(Gravity would pull it down.)*

21st Century Learning

CRITICAL THINKING Remind students of the classic trick in which a magician pulls a tablecloth off a table, leaving the dishes that were on top of it in place. Ask: **What role does inertia play in this magic trick?** *(The inertia of the dishes causes them to resist being moved.)*

Elaborate

Teacher Demo 🔬

L1 DEMONSTRATE INERTIA

Materials quarter; clean, dry coffee mug; 3 × 5 index card

Time 10 minutes

Review Newton's first law of motion by reminding students that an object at rest will stay at rest until acted upon by a force. Then, place the index card over the top of the coffee mug. Place a quarter on top of the card, centering it over the mug. Quickly pull the card out from under the quarter. The quarter will fall into the mug.

Ask: **What kept the quarter from moving with the card?** *(Inertia, which made the quarter "remain at rest")* **Why didn't the quarter move with the card it was sitting on?** *(The sideways pulling force was acting only on the card.)* **How is this demonstration related to orbital motion?** *(An object moving in space will resist a change in motion—much as the quarter did—and tend to keep moving in a straight line.)*

What Keeps Objects in Orbit?

If the sun and Earth are constantly pulling on one another because of gravity, why doesn't Earth fall into the sun? Similarly, why doesn't the moon crash into Earth? The fact that such collisions have not occurred shows that there must be another factor at work. That factor is called inertia.

Inertia The tendency of an object to resist a change in motion is **inertia.** You feel the effects of inertia every day. When you are riding in a car and it stops suddenly, you keep moving forward. If you didn't have a seat belt on, your inertia could cause you to bump into the car's windshield or the seat in front of you. The more mass an object has, the greater its inertia. An object with greater inertia is more difficult to start or stop.

Isaac Newton stated his ideas about inertia as a scientific law. **Newton's first law of motion** says that an object at rest will stay at rest and an object in motion will stay in motion with a constant speed and direction unless acted on by a force.

Orbital Motion Why do Earth and the moon remain in orbit? 🔑 **Newton concluded that inertia and gravity combine to keep Earth in orbit around the sun and the moon in orbit around Earth.** You can see how this occurs in **Figure 2.**

🔄 **Ask Questions** Before you read the paragraphs under Inertia, write a question you would like to have answered. Look for the answer as you read.

Sample: What is inertia? Answer: The tendency of an object to resist a change in motion.

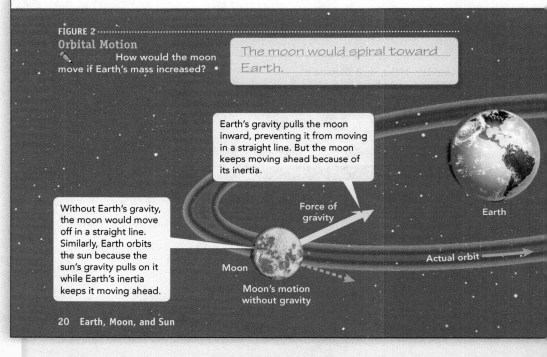

FIGURE 2
Orbital Motion
✏️ How would the moon move if Earth's mass increased? •

The moon would spiral toward Earth.

Earth's gravity pulls the moon inward, preventing it from moving in a straight line. But the moon keeps moving ahead because of its inertia.

Without Earth's gravity, the moon would move off in a straight line. Similarly, Earth orbits the sun because the sun's gravity pulls on it while Earth's inertia keeps it moving ahead.

Force of gravity

Earth

Actual orbit

Moon

Moon's motion without gravity

20 Earth, Moon, and Sun

Digital Lesson: Assign the *Do the Math* activity online and have students submit their work to you.

my science online   **Orbital Motion**

do the math! Analyzing Data

Gravity Versus Distance

As a rocket leaves a planet's surface, the force of gravity between the rocket and the planet changes. Use the graph to answer the questions below.

❶ Read Graphs The variables being graphed are _force of gravity_ and _distance._

❷ Read Graphs What is the force of gravity on the rocket at the planet's surface?

4 million newtons

❸ Read Graphs What is the force of gravity on the rocket at two units (twice the planet's radius from its center)?

1 million newtons

❹ Make Generalizations In general, how does the force of gravity on the rocket change as its distance from the planet increases?

The force decreases.

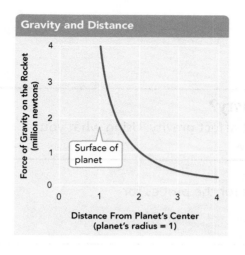

Gravity and Distance

y-axis: Force of Gravity on the Rocket (million newtons)

x-axis: Distance From Planet's Center (planet's radius = 1)

Surface of planet

 Do the Quick Lab *Around and Around We Go.*

Assess Your Understanding

1a. Identify What two factors keep a planet in orbit around the sun?

Gravity and inertia

b. Draw Conclusions What keeps Earth from falling into the sun?

Its inertia

c. [CHALLENGE] How would a planet move if the sun suddenly disappeared? Explain.

The planet would move in a straight line in the direction it had been traveling, because of its inertia.

got it? ....

O **I get it!** Now I know that objects are kept in orbit by _gravity and inertia._

O **I need extra help with** _See TE note._

Go to **my science** **COACH** *online for help with this subject.*

21

Differentiated Instruction

L1 Newton's First Law Have students write a public service announcement urging drivers and passengers to wear seat belts. Tell students to refer to Newton's first law of motion in their posters.

L3 Design an Investigation Have students design an investigation to demonstrate inertia, using simple materials such as a toy car and marbles or a wagon and tennis balls.

Support the Big Q

ORBITAL MOTION Draw students' attention to **Figure 2.** Ask: **How do Earth and the moon interact through gravitational forces?** *(Sample: Earth's gravity pulls on the moon, and the moon's gravity pulls on Earth. Because Earth has greater mass, its gravity pulls the moon with a stronger force. Earth's gravity pulls the moon inward, holding the moon in its orbital path around Earth.)* Explain to students that the moon is very slowly moving away from Earth at a rate of about 4 cm per year.

Elaborate

Do the Math!

L1 Tell students that to overcome gravity, rockets burn a great deal of fuel when they launch.

▲ **Read Graphs** Show students that the force of gravity can be located by moving a finger along the *x*-axis until it reaches the appropriate distance, and then upward until it reaches the curve. From there, moving left will lead students to the *y*-axis where they will find the force of gravity at that distance.

See *Math Skill and Problem-Solving Activities* for support.

Lab Resource: Quick Lab

L2 AROUND AND AROUND WE GO Students will explore factors that affect an object's orbit.

Evaluate

▲ **Draw Conclusions** Explain to students that a conclusion is a statement that sums up what they have learned.

Assess Your Understanding

After students answer the questions, have them evaluate their understanding by completing the appropriate sentence.

R T I Response to Intervention

1a. If students need help identifying the factors that keep a planet in orbit, **then** have them skim the section to find the answer.

b. If students have trouble explaining why Earth doesn't fall into the sun, **then** have them reread the Key Concept statement.

c. If students cannot readily explain how a planet would move if the sun disappeared, **then** review with them the forces shown in **Figure 2.**

my science **COACH** Have students go online for help in understanding orbital motion.

LESSON 1.3

Lab zone **After the Inquiry Warm-Up**

Gravity and Motion

Inquiry Warm-Up, *What Factors Affect Gravity?*

In the Inquiry Warm-Up, you investigated factors that affect gravity. Using what you learned from that activity, answer the questions below.

---

1. **INTERPRET DATA** How are the force-of-gravity values for the probes for each distance value related?

   _____

   _____

2. **INTERPRET DATA** What do you notice about the slope of both lines? What does this tell you about the force of gravity?

   _____

   _____

3. **DRAW CONCLUSIONS** Why is a double line graph a good way to display this data?

   _____

   _____

4. **PREDICT** Based on the values in the table, what would you expect the force-of-gravity values for each probe to be for a distance from Mars value of 6?

   _____

   _____

Assess Your Understanding

Gravity and Motion

> ## What Determines Gravity?

got it? ··

○ **I get it!** Now I know that the force of gravity depends on _____
_____
_____

○ **I need extra help with** _____
_____

> ## What Keeps Objects in Orbit?

1a. IDENTIFY What two factors keep a planet in orbit around the sun?
_____

b. DRAW CONCLUSIONS What keeps Earth from falling into the sun?
_____

c. CHALLENGE How would a planet move if the sun suddenly
disappeared? Explain.
_____
_____

got it? ··

○ **I get it!** Now I know that objects are kept in orbit by _____
_____

○ **I need extra help with** _____
_____

Name _____ Date _____ Class _____

Gravity and Motion

What Determines Gravity?

Objects in space are affected by different forces. A **force** is a push or a pull. A force called **gravity** attracts all objects toward each other. Sir Isaac Newton's **law of universal gravitation** states that every object in the universe attracts every other object. **The strength of the force of gravity between two objects depends on two factors: the masses of the objects and the distance between them.**

Mass is the amount of matter in an object. Because Earth is so massive, it exerts a much greater force on you than this book does. The measure of the force of gravity on an object is called **weight.** An object's weight can change depending on its location. On the moon, you would weigh about one sixth as much as on Earth. That's because the moon has less mass than Earth, so the pull of the moon's gravity on you would also be less.

The force of gravity between two objects decreases rapidly as distance between the objects increases. If the distance doubles, the force of gravity decreases to one fourth of its original value.

What Keeps Objects in Orbit?

Earth and the moon remain in orbit because of inertia. **Inertia** is the tendency of an object to resist a change in motion. You feel the effects of inertia when you are riding in a car and it stops suddenly. You keep moving forward until your seat belt catches you.

The more mass an object has, the greater its inertia. An object with greater inertia is harder to start or stop.

Newton stated his ideas about inertia as a scientific law. **Newton's first law of motion** says that an object at rest will stay at rest and an object in motion will stay in motion with a constant speed and direction unless acted on by a force. **Newton concluded that inertia and gravity combine to keep Earth in orbit around the sun and the moon in orbit around Earth.**

On a separate sheet of paper, explain what determines the force of gravity between two objects and what keeps Earth and the moon in orbit.

Review and Reinforce

Gravity and Motion

Understanding Main Ideas
Answer the following questions in the spaces provided.

1. How are gravity and weight related? _____
_____
_____

2. How does Newton's law of universal gravitation apply to Earth and the moon? _____
_____
_____
_____

3. Use Newton's first law of motion to explain why a basketball rolls across the court. _____
_____
_____

4. How does distance affect the strength of the force of gravity? _____
_____
_____

Building Vocabulary
On a separate sheet of paper, write a definition for each of these terms.

5. force

6. gravity

7. law of universal gravitation

8. mass

9. weight

10. inertia

11. Newton's first law of motion

Enrich

Gravity and Motion

> Read the passage and complete the table below. Then use a separate sheet of paper to answer the questions that follow.

Your Weight in the Solar System

Each object in the solar system has a different mass and diameter. As a result, you would have a different weight on the moon than on Mars or on Earth. Use the table below to calculate a person's weight on the surfaces of some solar system objects. In the case of the sun, you'll have to use your imagination. It's really impossible to stand on the sun's gaseous surface. For your calculations, use the example of an astronaut who weighs 150 pounds on Earth. In your calculations, use newtons instead of pounds. One pound is about equal to 4.5 newtons.

To find your weight on the surface of each object, multiply your weight on Earth by the proportion of Earth's gravity for each object. Enter your weight on each object into the table.

Solar System Object	Proportion of Earth's Gravity	Weight on Surface
Moon	0.165	
Venus	0.905	
Mars	0.379	
Pluto	0.059	
Sun	274	

1. Which object has a much higher gravitational attraction than Earth? Explain.
2. On which object would you weigh the least? Why do you think this is so?
3. Could you jump higher on Venus or on Mars?
4. During the Apollo program, astronauts played golf on the moon. How do you think the moon's low gravity affected their game?
5. Image that the sun contracted to a smaller volume. How would this affect the gravitational force on its surface?

Name _____ Date _____ Class _____

Gravity and Motion

If the statement is true, write *true*. If the statement is false, change the underlined word or words to make the statement true.

1. _____ Newton's first law of <u>inertia</u> says that an object at rest will stay at rest and an object in motion will stay in motion unless acted on by a force.

2. _____ Inertia and <u>distance</u> combine to keep Earth in orbit around the sun and the moon in orbit around Earth.

3. _____ Newton's law of <u>planetary</u> gravitation states that every object in the universe attracts every other object.

4. _____ Gravity decreases to <u>one fourth</u> of its original value if the distance between two objects doubles.

5. _____ Earth's gravity pulls the moon <u>outward</u>.

Fill in the blank to complete each statement.

6. The amount of matter in an object is its _____.

7. _____ attracts all objects toward each other.

8. An object with greater _____ is more difficult to stop or start.

9. The _____ of two objects and their distance from each other determine the gravitational force between them.

10. The measure of the force of gravity on an object is the object's _____.

Gravity and Motion

Answer Key

After the Inquiry Warm-Up

1. The force of gravity values for Probe 2 are twice as great as those for Probe 1 at every distance value.

2. The slopes are the same. This means gravity is constant, regardless of mass.

3. A double line graph shows how data changes as you change the variables in an experiment.

4. Accept all reasonable values. Value for Probe 1 should be smaller than 0.123 and value for Probe 2 should be double the value for Probe 1.

Key Concept Summaries

Sample: The force of gravity between two objects depends on the objects' masses and the distance between them. Inertia and gravity keep Earth and the moon in orbit. Inertia is the tendency of an object to resist a change in motion. Because of inertia, Earth and the moon keep moving ahead. Gravity is a force of attraction between objects. Because of gravity, Earth orbits the sun and the moon orbits Earth.

Review and Reinforce

1. The force of gravity on an object is its weight. The greater the pull of gravity on an object, the greater the weight of that object.

2. Newton's law of universal gravitation states that every object in the universe attracts every other object. The Earth exerts a gravitational force on the moon, pulling the moon toward it. The moon also exerts a gravitational force on Earth.

3. Sample: An object in motion will stay in motion with a constant speed and direction unless acted on by a force. A basketball will roll across the court until friction pulls it to a stop, it runs into another object, or a person stops it.

4. The force of gravity between two objects decreases rapidly as the distance between them increases. Conversely the force of gravity increases rapidly as this distance decreases.

5. push or pull

6. attraction of all objects toward each other

7. every object in the universe attracts every other object.

8. the amount of matter in an object

9. the force of gravity on an object

10. the tendency of an object to resist a change in motion

11. an object at rest will stay at rest and an object in motion will stay in motion with a constant speed and direction unless acted on by a force.

Enrich

1. the sun; It is much more massive than Earth is.

2. Pluto; It has the lowest mass.

3. on Mars; A person weighs less on Mars than on Venus.

4. They were able to drive the ball much farther than they could on Earth.

5. The gravitational force on its surface would increase because the distance between the surface and all of the sun's mass would be reduced.

Lesson Quiz

1. motion	2. gravity
3. universal	4. true
5. inward	6. mass
7. gravity	8. inertia
9. masses	10. weight

Place the outside corner, the corner away from the dotted line, in the corner of your copy machine to copy onto letter-size paper.

Phases and Eclipses

 How do Earth, the moon, and the sun interact?

Lesson Pacing: 3–4 periods or 1½–2 blocks

🕐 **SHORT ON TIME?** To do this lesson in approximately half the time, do the Activate Prior Knowledge activity on page 22. A discussion of the Key Concepts on pages 23, 25, and 26 will familiarize students with the lesson content. Have students do the Quick Labs. The rest of the lesson can be completed by students independently.

> **Preference Navigator,** in the online Planning tools, allows you to customize *Interactive Science* to your own teaching style. You can also edit lesson plans by selecting the Lesson Planner option.
>
> **Digital Teacher's Edition** allows you to access your Teacher's Edition and Resource materials online.

Lesson Vocabulary

- phase
- eclipse
- solar eclipse
- umbra
- penumbra
- lunar eclipse

Content Refresher

Earthshine During certain moon phases, such as a crescent moon, the remaining, unlit portion of the moon can be seen in dim light. This dimly lit portion of the moon is illuminated by Earthshine, which is light reflected from Earth's surface. Because the moon is almost between Earth and the sun at crescent phases, the effects of Earthshine are dramatic. From the moon, Earth would appear almost full. Earthshine does not illuminate a new moon. During the new moon phase, the moon is very close to the sun in the sky; therefore, the sun's bright light blocks out the new moon.

Eclipses Many people have seen total lunar eclipses, but few people have the opportunity to view a total solar eclipse. That's because a total lunar eclipse is visible over at least half of Earth, but a total solar eclipse can be seen only along a narrow path of up to a few hundred miles wide and a few thousand miles long. Astronomers can accurately predict the dates and times of eclipses.

Because solar eclipses occur when the new moon passes near the plane of Earth's orbit, lunar eclipses frequently occur in the two weeks before or the two weeks after a solar eclipse. Six and a half lunar months later, the full moon may be near the plane of Earth's orbit, so more lunar and solar eclipses can occur. Periods when the new moon or full moon is near the plane of Earth's orbit are called *eclipse seasons*.

LESSON OBJECTIVES

- Explain what causes the phases of the moon.
- Describe solar and lunar eclipses.

Blended Path
Active learning using Student Edition, Inquiry Path, and Digital Path

ENGAGE AND EXPLORE

Teach this lesson using a variety of resources. Begin by reading **My Planet Diary** as a class. Have students discuss observations about the moon. Then have students do the **Inquiry Warm-Up activity.** Students will investigate how the moon moves. The **After the Inquiry Warm-Up worksheet** sets up a discussion about the moon's movement around Earth. Have volunteers share their answers to question 4.

EXPLAIN AND ELABORATE

Teach Key Concepts by explaining that the phases of the moon are caused by the changing relative positions of the moon, Earth, and sun. **Lead a Discussion** about what happens to the relative positions of the moon, Earth and sun as the moon revolves. Use **Figure 2** to **Lead a Discussion** about the phases of the moon. Have students practice the inquiry skill in the **Apply It activity.**

Teach Key Concepts by explaining that a solar eclipse occurs when the moon passes directly between the sun and Earth. **Lead a Discussion** about the causes and effects of eclipses. Continue to **Teach Key Concepts** by explaining that a lunar eclipse occurs when Earth blocks sunlight from reaching the moon's surface. **Explore the Big Q** by discussing the arrangement of Earth, the moon, and the sun during a total lunar eclipse in December. **Answer the Big Q** by leading a class discussion about what causes the seasons, the phases of the moon, solar eclipses, and lunar eclipses.

Hand out the **Key Concept Summaries** as a review of each part of the lesson. Students can also use the online **Vocab Flash Cards** to review key terms.

EVALUATE

Have students take the **Lesson Quiz.** For an alternate assessment, see the **EXAM**VIEW® Assessment Suite, Progress Monitoring Assessments, or SuccessTracker™.

ELL Support

1 Content and Language

Pronounce and define aloud vocabulary terms for students. Suggest that they create a personal set of vocabulary flash cards, with each term and its definition on one side of an index card and a visual of the term on the other side.

Lab zone Inquiry Path
Hands-on learning in the Lab zone

Digital Path
Online learning at my science online.com

ENGAGE AND EXPLORE

To teach this lesson with an emphasis on inquiry, begin with the **Inquiry Warm-Up activity.** Students will investigate how the moon moves. The **After the Inquiry Warm-Up worksheet** sets up a discussion about the moon's movement around Earth. Have volunteers share their answers to question 4.

EXPLAIN AND ELABORATE

Focus on the **Inquiry Skill** for the lesson. Remind students that a model is a picture, diagram, computer image, or other representation of a complex object or process. What was modeled in the **Inquiry Warm-Up activity?** *(The movement of the moon around Earth)* Before beginning the **Apply It activity,** review the photographs of the moon, as seen from Earth, in **Figure 2.** Have students do the activity and share their results. Have students do the **Quick Lab.**

Explore the Big Q by discussing the arrangement of Earth, the moon, and the sun during a total lunar eclipse in December. Have students do the **Quick Lab. Answer the Big Q** by leading a class discussion about what causes the seasons, the phases of the moon, solar eclipses, and lunar eclipses. Students can use the online **Vocab Flash Cards** to review key terms.

EVALUATE

Have students take the **Lesson Quiz.** For an alternate assessment, see the **EXAM**VIEW® Assessment Suite, Progress Monitoring Assessments, or SuccessTracker™.

ENGAGE AND EXPLORE

Teach this lesson using digital resources. Begin by having students learn more about eclipses and explore real-world connections to eclipses at **My Planet Diary** online. Have them access the Chapter Resources to find the **Unlock the Big Question activity.** There they can answer the questions and refine their responses as they continue through the lesson. You can re-assign the activity and have students submit their work so you can track their progress.

EXPLAIN AND ELABORATE

Students reading above, at, or below the lexile measure of this lesson can access basic content readings at their level at **My Reading Web.** Encourage students to use the online **Vocab Flash Cards** to preview key terms. Assign the **Apply It activity** online and have students submit their work to you. Have students do the **Quick Lab.**

Explore the Big Q by discussing the arrangement of Earth, the moon, and the sun during a total lunar eclipse in December. Use the **Interactive Art activity** online to allow students to explore solar and lunar eclipses. Have students do the **Quick Lab. Answer the Big Q** by leading a class discussion about what causes the seasons, the phases of the moon, solar eclipses, and lunar eclipses. The **Key Concept Summaries** online allow students to read a summary and see an image associated with each part of the lesson. Online remediation is available at **My Science Coach.**

EVALUATE

Have students take the **Lesson Quiz.** For an alternate assessment, see the **EXAM**VIEW® Assessment Suite, Progress Monitoring Assessments, or SuccessTracker™.

2 Frontload the Lesson
Have students study the diagram of the moon phases in **Figure 2.** Read the labels aloud as students point to them. Then explain the meanings of *waxing, waning, gibbous,* and *crescent.* Discuss what the moon looks like from Earth in each of the phases.

3 Comprehensible Input
Have students draw a diagram of the moon phases viewed from Earth. Have them label the diagram using the appropriate labels from **Figure 2.**

4 Language Production
Pair or group students with varied language abilities to complete labs collaboratively for language practice. Have each student copy the completed written lab for personal reference.

5 Assess Understanding
Have students keep a content area log for this lesson using a two-column format with the headings "What I Understand" and "What I Don't Understand." Follow up so that students can move items from the "Don't Understand" to the "Understand" column.

Phases and Eclipses

Establish Learning Objectives

After this lesson, students will be able to:

🔑 Explain what causes the phases of the moon.

🔑 Describe solar and lunar eclipses.

Engage

Activate Prior Knowledge

MY PLANET DIARY Read *Nicole's Blog* with the class. Tell students that the red color is the result of Earth's atmosphere bending sunlight. As sunlight passes through Earth's atmosphere, red wavelengths are refracted, or bent, into the area of the shadow. Blue and green wavelengths are bent less, and do not enter the shadowed area. If Earth had no atmosphere, the moon would be invisible during an eclipse. Ask: **What observations of the moon have you made?** *(Sample: Its shape changes in the same ways each month.)*

BIG IDEAS OF SCIENCE REFERENCE LIBRARY 📖
Have students look up the following topics: Moon, Solar Eclipse.

Explore

Lab Resource: Inquiry Warm-Up 🔬

L1 **HOW DOES THE MOON MOVE?** Students will explore why observers on Earth always see the same side of the moon.

LESSON 4 **Phases and Eclipses**

 UNLOCK THE BIG ?

🔑 **What Causes the Moon's Phases?**

🔑 **What Are Eclipses?**

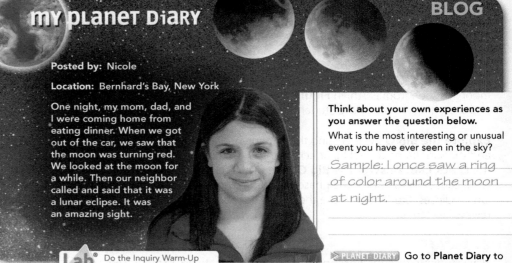

MY PLANET DIARY **BLOG**

Posted by: Nicole

Location: Bernhard's Bay, New York

One night, my mom, dad, and I were coming home from eating dinner. When we got out of the car, we saw that the moon was turning red. We looked at the moon for a while. Then our neighbor called and said that it was a lunar eclipse. It was an amazing sight.

🔬 **Lab zone** Do the Inquiry Warm-Up *How Does the Moon Move?*

Think about your own experiences as you answer the question below.

What is the most interesting or unusual event you have ever seen in the sky?

Sample: I once saw a ring of color around the moon at night.

▶ **PLANET DIARY** Go to **Planet Diary** to learn more about eclipses.

What Causes the Moon's Phases?

Have you ever been kept awake by bright moonlight? The light streaming through your window actually comes from the sun! The moon does not shine with its own light. Instead, it reflects light from the sun. When the moon is full, this light may be bright enough to read by! But at other times, the moon is just a thin crescent in the sky. The different shapes of the moon you see from Earth are called **phases.** Phases are caused by the motions of the moon around Earth.

SUPPORT ALL READERS

Lexile Measure = 890L   Lexile Word Count = 1160

Prior Exposure to Content: May be the first time students have encountered this topic

Academic Vocabulary: *models, relate, identify, infer*

Science Vocabulary: *phase, eclipse, umbra, penumbra*

Concept Level: May be difficult for students who struggle with abstract ideas

Preteach With: My Planet Diary "Nicole's Blog" and Figure 1 activity

Go to **My Reading Web** to access leveled readings that provide a foundation for the content.

my science online.com

Vocabulary
- phase • eclipse • solar eclipse
- umbra • penumbra • lunar eclipse

Skills
- Reading: Relate Text and Visuals
- Inquiry: Make Models

Motions of the Moon When you look up at the moon, you may see what looks like a face. What you are really seeing is a pattern of light-colored and dark-colored areas on the moon's surface that just happens to look like a face. Oddly, this pattern never seems to move. The same side of the moon, the "near side," always faces Earth. The "far side" of the moon always faces away from Earth. Why? The answer has to do with the moon's motions.

Like Earth, the moon moves through space in two ways. The moon revolves around Earth and also rotates on its own axis. The moon rotates once on its axis in the same time that it takes to revolve once around Earth. Thus, a "day" on the moon is the same length as a month on Earth. For this reason, the same side of the moon always faces Earth, as you can see in **Figure 1**.

As the moon orbits Earth, the relative positions of the moon, Earth, and sun change. **The changing relative positions of the moon, Earth, and sun cause the phases of the moon.**

Vocabulary Identify Multiple Meanings Which sentence uses the scientific meaning of *phase*?
- ○ The doctor told the parent that the child was just going through a phase.
- ● The moon goes through a cycle of phases every month.

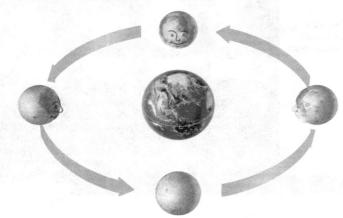

FIGURE 1 ⋯⋯⋯⋯⋯⋯⋯⋯⋯⋯
The Moon's Motion
The diagram shows the moon's rotation and revolution. **Infer** Find the face on the rightmost view of the moon. Draw the face as it would appear on each view.

CHALLENGE How would the moon appear from Earth if the moon did not rotate?

We would be able to see all sides of the moon during the month.

23

1 Content and Language
Write the word *eclipse* on the board. Tell students that *eclipse* comes from a Greek word meaning "fail" or "omit." Point out that during a *solar eclipse* the sun fails to appear, and that during a *lunar eclipse* the moon fails to appear.

2 Frontload the Lesson
Have students brainstorm a list of words and phrases that describe the moon at different points during a month. Tell

students they will learn the names of the shapes of the moon as it makes its 29.5-day orbit around Earth.

3 Comprehensible Input
Explain the Explore the Big Q image and caption, restating information as necessary. Have students draw the diagram of a lunar eclipse in December. Then encourage students to compare their diagrams and the model diagrams.

Explain

Introduce Vocabulary
Point out the three vocabulary terms that contain the word *eclipse*. Tell students that an eclipse occurs when one object in the night sky makes another object less visible, or obscures it.

Teach Key Concepts
Explain to students that the phases of the moon are caused by the changing relative positions of the moon, Earth, and sun. Have students look at the Key Concept statement. Ask: **What is the significance of the word *relative*?** (Sample: The word *relative* signifies that it's the changing positions of the moon, Earth, and sun—not as isolated objects but in relation to each other—that cause the phases of the moon.)

Lead a Discussion
MOON MOVEMENTS Remind students that the moon has the same two basic movements, rotation and revolution, that Earth has. Ask: **As the moon revolves, what happens to the relative positions of the moon, Earth, and the sun?** (The angle between them changes) **How does the moon's orbit affect which phase of the moon you see?** (Sample: You see more or less of the sunlit side of the moon—and, therefore, a different phase—depending on the position of the moon in its orbit of Earth.)

Teach With Visuals
MOON REVOLUTION Help students understand that the moon rotates once in the same amount of time it takes to make a complete revolution around Earth. Check that students have correctly drawn faces on the top and left moon. Ask: **Why can't you draw a face on the moon at the bottom of the diagram?** (Because the face is on the side facing Earth, and the side we can see in the diagram is the "back" of the moon, the side away from the face.) As you work through the visuals in this lesson, remind students that the diagrams are not to scale. The moon is much farther from Earth than the diagrams show.

My Planet Diary provides an opportunity for students to explore real-world connections to eclipses.

my science online.com | The Moon's Phases

LESSON 1.4

Explain

Lead a Discussion

EXPLORING PHASES OF THE MOON Have students examine **Figure 2.** Remind students that although the same side of the moon always faces Earth, the moon's position in relation to the sun is not fixed. As the moon revolves around Earth, sunlight shines on the near and far sides of the moon at different times. Ask: **Why can't you see the far side of the moon from Earth?** *(The far side always faces away from Earth.)* Prompt students to connect each phase with how the moon looks from Earth. For example, Ask: **What do you see in the first quarter?** *(Half of the lighted side of the moon)* **What is happening in the waning gibbous phase?** *(You see more than half of the lighted side of the moon. The amount you can see from Earth decreases each day.)* **During which phases are the moon, Earth, and sun aligned?** *(A new moon and a full moon)*

21st Century Learning

CRITICAL THINKING Remind students that the moon waxes and wanes in each cycle of phases. Ask: **How can you tell whether the moon is waxing or waning?** *(Sample: Observe it over time to see whether it gets larger or smaller; a waxing moon gets larger, a waning moon gets smaller.)*

Elaborate

Apply It!

L1 Before beginning the activity, review the photographs of the moon, as seen from Earth, in **Figure 2.**

▲ **Make Models** Explain to students that a model is a picture, diagram, computer image, or other representation of a complex object or process.

Lab Resource: Quick Lab

L2 **MOON PHASES** Students will model phases of the moon.

Evaluate

Assess Your Understanding

Have students evaluate their understanding by completing the appropriate sentence.

R T I Response to Intervention

If students have trouble identifying the cause of moon phases, **then** review with them the images in **Figure 2.**

my science coach Have students go online for help in understanding the moon's phases.

Phases of the Moon Half the moon is almost always in sunlight. But since the moon orbits Earth, you see the moon from different angles. The phase of the moon you see depends on how much of the sunlit side of the moon faces Earth.

During the new moon phase, the side of the moon facing Earth is not lit. As the moon revolves around Earth, you see more of the lit side of the moon, until you see all of the lit side. As the month continues, you see less of the lit side. You can see these changes in Figure 2. About 29.5 days after the last new moon, a new moon occurs again.

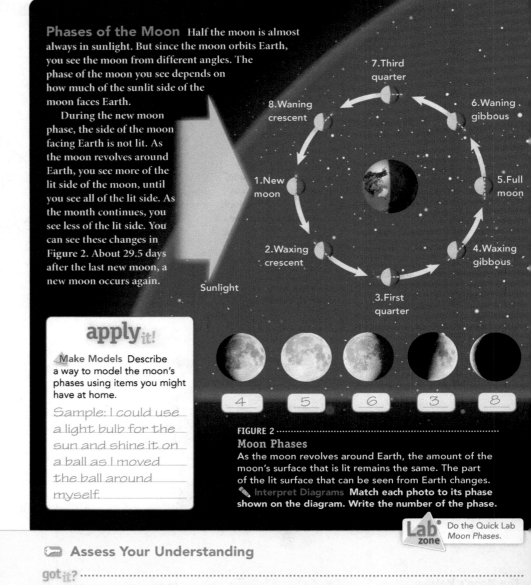

apply it!

Make Models Describe a way to model the moon's phases using items you might have at home.

Sample: I could use a light bulb for the sun and shine it on a ball as I moved the ball around myself.

FIGURE 2 ....
Moon Phases
As the moon revolves around Earth, the amount of the moon's surface that is lit remains the same. The part of the lit surface that can be seen from Earth changes.
✎ Interpret Diagrams **Match each photo to its phase shown on the diagram. Write the number of the phase.**

Lab zone Do the Quick Lab Moon Phases.

🔑 **Assess Your Understanding**

got it? ....

O I get it! Now I know that moon phases are caused by changes in the amount of the moon's lit half that can be seen from Earth.

O I need extra help with See TE note.

Go to **my science coach** online for help with this subject.

Digital Lesson: Assign the *Apply It* activity online and have students submit their work to you.

my science online.com | The Moon's Phases

What Are Eclipses?

The moon's orbit around Earth is slightly tilted with respect to Earth's orbit around the sun. As a result, the moon travels above and below Earth's orbit. But on rare occasions, Earth, the moon, and the sun line up.

When an object in space comes between the sun and a third object, it casts a shadow on that object, causing an **eclipse** (ih KLIPS) to take place. There are two types of eclipses: solar eclipses and lunar eclipses. (The words *solar* and *lunar* come from the Latin words for "sun" and "moon.")

Solar Eclipses During a new moon, the moon lies between Earth and the sun. A **solar eclipse** occurs when the moon passes directly between Earth and the sun, blocking sunlight from Earth. The moon's shadow then hits Earth.

Total Solar Eclipses The very darkest part of the moon's shadow is the **umbra** (UM bruh). You can see how the umbra strikes Earth in Figure 3. Within the umbra, the sun's light is completely blocked. Only people within the umbra experience a total solar eclipse. During a total solar eclipse, the sky grows as dark as night. The air gets cool and the sky becomes an eerie color. You can see the stars and the solar corona, which is the faint outer atmosphere of the sun.

Partial Solar Eclipses The moon casts another part of its shadow that is less dark than the umbra. This larger part of the shadow is called the **penumbra** (peh NUM bruh). In the penumbra, part of the sun is visible from Earth. During a solar eclipse, people in the penumbra see only a partial eclipse.

FIGURE 3 ································
Solar Eclipse
The diagram shows the moon's penumbra and umbra during an eclipse. It is not drawn to scale.

Relate Text and Visuals
Mark an X to show where a total solar eclipse would be visible. Circle the area in which a partial solar eclipse would be visible.

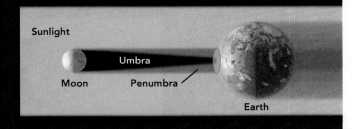

Sunlight
Umbra
Moon
Penumbra
Earth

25

Explain

Teach Key Concepts

Explain to students that a solar eclipse occurs when the moon passes directly between the sun and Earth. Ask: **Which side of the moon receives the light of the sun during a solar eclipse?** (The far side) **A solar eclipse lasts only a few minutes. Who can explain why?** (Because Earth rotates and carries you out of the moon's shadow)

Lead a Discussion

CAUSES AND EFFECTS OF ECLIPSES Have students examine **Figure 3.** Then, ask: **What causes an eclipse?** (When an object in space comes between the sun and a third object, it casts a shadow on the third object.) **Describe some events that occur when the moon blocks out the sun.** (Sample: Day becomes as dark as night, the air cools, and the sky becomes an eerie color.) **What has to happen to the relative positions of the sun, the moon, and Earth for an eclipse to occur?** (They all have to line up so that the moon blocks the sun from Earth or Earth blocks the sun from the moon.)

Relate Text and Visuals Tell students that as they relate text and visuals, they will learn that the two elements work together to convey information. Explain that visuals in a textbook may include photographs, diagrams, tables, and illustrations.

21st Century Learning

CRITICAL THINKING Tell students that the words *umbra* and *penumbra* come from Latin words meaning "shadow" and "almost shadow." Ask: **Would people in the moon's penumbra experience a total or a partial eclipse?** (Partial) Ask students to infer whether a solar eclipse can be viewed from a large area of Earth. (No; the sun's rays are blocked over only a small area.)

Differentiated Instruction

L1 **Define *Phase*** Have students brainstorm at least three different ways that the term *phase* is used in science. (Sample: Phases of the moon, phases of matter, and color phases in an animal or plant species) Use one of the meanings in a sentence, such as "The moon undergoes a cycle of phases." Have students write additional sentences incorporating other scientific meanings of *phase*.

L3 **Identifying How Full Moons Were Named** Before artificial lighting, the phases of the moon were important in planning activities. For example, the full moon nearest the fall equinox is called the harvest moon. Have students find out why it was so named. (It provides extra light during the early evening hours to help farmers gather their crops.) Encourage students to find out the names of other full moons.

Explain

Teach Key Concepts 🔑

Explain to students that a lunar eclipse occurs when Earth blocks sunlight from reaching the moon's surface. Ask: **Why do lunar eclipses occur only during a full moon?** *(Earth must come between the sun and moon during a lunar eclipse; this happens only during the full-moon phase.)* Sketch Earth and the moon, to approximate scale, on the board. Then, guide students to infer why lunar eclipses last much longer than solar eclipses. *(Earth is much larger than the moon, so its shadow is also larger. The moon may take several hours to pass completely through the complete shadow of Earth. By contrast, during a solar eclipse, the moon's shadow passes through a point on Earth's surface in a matter of minutes.)* Savvy students may ask why there isn't a solar and a lunar eclipse every month. Explain that the plane of the moon's orbit around Earth is tilted by 7° with respect to the ecliptic (the plane of Earth's orbit around the sun). In order for an eclipse to occur, you need the coincidence of the moon crossing the ecliptic at just the right time (when the moon, sun, and Earth all line up).

Teach With Visuals

Tell students to look at **Figure 4**. Ask: **What is the difference between the umbra and the penumbra?** *(Sample: During a lunar eclipse, the umbra is the darkest part of Earth's shadow. The penumbra is the larger, less dark part of Earth's shadow.)*

↻ **Relate Text and Visuals** Tell students that as they relate text and visuals, they will learn that the two elements work together to convey information. Explain that visuals in a textbook may include photographs, diagrams, tables, and illustrations.

Lunar Eclipses During most months, the moon moves near Earth's shadow but not quite into it. A lunar eclipse occurs at a full moon when Earth is directly between the moon and the sun. You can see a lunar eclipse in Figure 4. 🔑 During a lunar eclipse, Earth blocks sunlight from reaching the moon. Lunar eclipses occur only when there is a full moon because the moon is closest to Earth's shadow at that time.

↻ **Relate Text and Visuals** Mark an X on the photograph above that shows a total eclipse.

FIGURE 4
Lunar Eclipse
As the moon moves through Earth's shadow, total and partial eclipses occur. This diagram is not to scale.
✏️ **Infer** Draw a circle labeled *T* to show where the moon would be during a total eclipse. Draw two circles labeled *P* to show two places the moon could be during a partial eclipse.

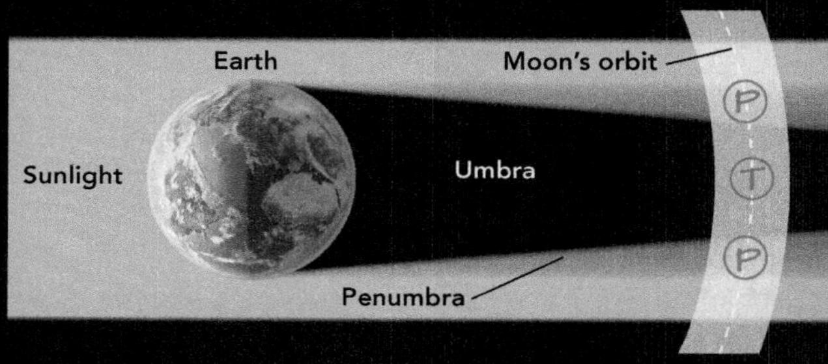

Total Lunar Eclipses Like the moon's shadow in a solar eclipse, Earth's shadow has an umbra and a penumbra. When the moon is in Earth's umbra, you see a total lunar eclipse. Unlike a total solar eclipse, a total lunar eclipse can be seen anywhere on Earth that the moon is visible. So you are more likely to see a total lunar eclipse than a total solar eclipse.

Partial Lunar Eclipses For most lunar eclipses, Earth, the moon, and the sun are not quite in line, and only a partial lunar eclipse results. A partial lunar eclipse occurs when the moon passes partly into the umbra of Earth's shadow. The edge of the umbra appears blurry, and you can watch it pass across the moon for two or three hours.

Earth   Moon's orbit
Sunlight   Umbra
Penumbra

Professional Development Note — **Teacher to Teacher**

Activity Try the "Solar Lab" to teach the phases of the moon and eclipses. Glue golf balls (moons) to golf tees. With lights out, except for a 100- or 200-watt light bulb in the center of the room, have the students face the "sun" holding the "moon" by the tee in their right hand extended. Their head is Earth. As they close one eye, they make the "sun" disappear. This is the new moon phase, when a solar eclipse can occur. As the students pivot slowly to their left, explain each phase. When their backs are to the "sun," remind them that lunar eclipses can occur at this phase, the full moon.

✏️ *Susan M. Pritchard, Ph.D.*
Washington Middle School
La Habra, California

Seasons and Shadows

How do Earth, the moon, and the sun interact?

FIGURE 5 ···

▷ **INTERACTIVE ART** Look at the diagram below. (The diagram is not to scale.) Identify what season it is in the Northern Hemisphere, what the phase of the moon is, and what kind of eclipse, if any, could occur.

Season	*Summer*
Moon Phase	*New*
Eclipse	*Solar eclipse*

Use the above diagram as a model. Draw the arrangement of Earth, the moon, and the sun during a total lunar eclipse in December.

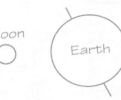 Moon

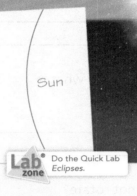 Earth

Sun

 Lab zone Do the Quick Lab *Eclipses.*

Assess Your Understanding

1a. Explain A (solar/~~lunar~~) eclipse occurs when the moon passes into Earth's shadow. A (~~solar~~/lunar) eclipse occurs when Earth passes into the moon's shadow.

b. **ANSWER** How do Earth, the moon, and the sun interact? *As Earth orbits the sun and the moon orbits Earth, their motions cause seasons, phases, and eclipses.*

got it? ···

○ I get it! Now I know that eclipses occur when *the moon passes into Earth's shadow or Earth passes into the moon's shadow.*

○ I need extra help with *See TE note.*

Go to **MY SCIENCE COACH** online for help with this subject.

27

Differentiated Instruction

L1 **Model Eclipses** Give students three different-sized balls. Tell them that the largest ball represents the sun, the second-largest ball represents Earth, and the smallest ball represents the moon. Have students arrange the balls in proper order to model the positions of the sun, the moon, and Earth during a solar eclipse and a lunar eclipse. *(During a solar eclipse, the balls should be arranged in the following order: sun, moon, Earth. During a lunar eclipse the balls should be arranged in the following order: sun, Earth, moon.)*

Elaborate

Support the Big Q

EARTH, MOON, AND SUN INTERACTIONS Remind students that the ends of Earth's axis tilt toward or away from the sun depending on the season. Ask: **In what direction does the south end of Earth's axis tilt during winter in the Northern Hemisphere?** *(Toward the sun)* **What season is it in the Southern Hemisphere when it is winter in the Northern Hemisphere?** *(Summer)* **How would the positions of the moon and Earth be different in a lunar eclipse?** *(Earth would be between the sun and the moon.)* **What phase would the moon be in then?** *(Full moon)*

Lab Resource: Quick Lab

L2 **ECLIPSES** Students will model solar and lunar eclipses.

Evaluate

Assess Your Understanding

After students answer the questions, have them evaluate their understanding by completing the appropriate sentence.

Answer the Big Q

To help students focus on the Big Question, lead a class discussion about what causes the seasons, the phases of the moon, solar eclipses, and lunar eclipses.

RTI Response to Intervention

1a. If students need help contrasting lunar and solar eclipses, **then** have them review the Key Concept statements.

b. If students have trouble making a generalization about the interactions of Earth, the moon, and the sun, **then** ask them to list changes they see in the positions and conditions of the sun and moon, then suggest reasons for those changes.

MY SCIENCE COACH Have students go online for help in understanding eclipses.

Interactive Art allows students to explore solar and lunar eclipses.

MY SCIENCE online.com | Eclipses |

Phases and Eclipses

Inquiry Warm-Up, *How Does the Moon Move?*

In the Inquiry Warm-Up, you investigated the moon's movement around Earth. Using what you learned from that activity, answer the questions below.

1. **INFER** What amount of time does the penny moving around the quarter model? Explain.

   _____

   _____

2. **DESIGN EXPERIMENTS** How could you use the coins to show what it would be like if the moon did not rotate?

   _____

   _____

3. **PREDICT** What would be different if the moon did not rotate?

   _____

   _____

4. **DRAW CONCLUSIONS** If the quarter is Earth, suppose you are standing on top of George Washington's head. Move the penny 180 degrees from where you are. What time is it where you are?

   _____

Phases and Eclipses

What Causes the Moon's Phases?

got it? ....

○ **I get it!** Now I know that moon phases are caused by _____

_____

_____

○ **I need extra help with** _____

_____

What Are Eclipses?

1a. **EXPLAIN** A (solar/lunar) eclipse occurs when the moon passes into
Earth's shadow. A (solar/lunar) eclipse occurs when Earth passes into
the moon's shadow.

b. **ANSWER** How do Earth, the moon, and the sun interact?

_____

_____

_____

_____

got it? ....

○ **I get it!** Now I know that eclipses occur when _____

_____

_____

○ **I need extra help with** _____

_____

Phases and Eclipses

What Causes the Moon's Phases?

The different shapes of the moon you see from Earth are called **phases.** Phases are caused by the motions of the moon around Earth. As the moon orbits Earth, the relative positions of the moon, Earth, and the sun change. **The changing relative positions of the moon, Earth, and the sun cause the phases of the moon.** The phase of the moon you see depends on how much of the sunlit side of the moon faces Earth.

What Are Eclipses?

The moon's orbit around Earth is slightly tilted with respect to Earth's orbit around the sun. As a result, the moon travels above and below Earth's orbit. But on rare occasions, Earth, the moon, and the sun line up.

When an object in space comes between the sun and a third object, it casts a shadow on that third object, causing an **eclipse** to take place. There are two types of eclipses: solar eclipses and lunar eclipses.

A **solar eclipse** occurs at a new moon when the moon passes directly between Earth and the sun, blocking sunlight from Earth. The moon's shadow then hits Earth.

The moon's shadow has two parts. The darker part is the **umbra.** The larger, lighter part is the **penumbra.**

During a solar eclipse, the sun's light is completely blocked to people within the umbra. They see a total solar eclipse. Part of the sun's light remains visible in the penumbra. So people within the penumbra see a partial solar eclipse.

A **lunar eclipse** occurs at a full moon when Earth is directly between the moon and the sun. **During a lunar eclipse, Earth blocks sunlight from reaching the moon.** Lunar eclipses occur only when there is a full moon, because the moon is closest to Earth at that time.

Earth's shadow also has an umbra and penumbra. When the moon is in Earth's umbra, you see a total lunar eclipse. For most lunar eclipses, Earth, the moon, and the sun are not quite in line, and only a partial lunar eclipse occurs.

On a separate sheet of paper, explain how interactions of the moon, Earth, and the sun cause the phases of the moon and eclipses.

Review and Reinforce

Phases and Eclipses

Understanding Main Ideas

Use the diagram below to answer Question 1 in the spaces provided.

1. What phase of the moon would someone on Earth see when the moon is at Positions A through F?

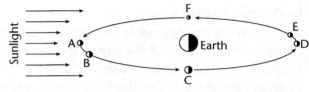

A: _____

B: _____

C: _____

D: _____

E: _____

F: _____

Building Vocabulary

Fill in the blank to complete each statement.

2. A(n) _____ occurs when the moon's shadow hits Earth or Earth's shadow hits the moon.

3. A person standing in the moon's _____ would see a partial solar eclipse.

4. A person standing in the moon's _____ would see a total solar eclipse.

5. The _____ of the moon you see depends on how much of the sunlit side of the moon faces Earth.

6. A(n) _____ eclipse occurs at a full moon when Earth is directly between the moon and the sun.

7. A(n) _____ occurs when the moon passes between Earth and the sun.

Enrich

Phases and Eclipses

> Read the passage. Then use a separate sheet of paper to answer the questions that follow.

Lunar Calendars

It is easy to see the changes in the appearance of the moon, so early peoples frequently based their calendars on the cycles of the moon. The word *month* comes from the same root as the word *moon*. Most Western societies use a calendar based on the solar year, called the Gregorian calendar. Other societies have also adopted the Gregorian calendar for civil and official purposes. It is divided into 12 months. These months do not exactly match the lunar months, since the moon takes about 29.5 days to complete a cycle of phases. Twelve lunar months is about 11 days short of a solar year. However, many people still organize their lives by lunar calendars. Two of the world's most widespread religions, Judaism and Islam, keep lunar calendars.

Most Muslims recognize a 12-lunar-month Islamic religious calendar for their private lives, even if they keep a different civil calendar. Originally, each lunar month began when the new moon was first sighted in the evening sky at sunset. Recently, however, many Muslims worldwide began recognizing official timekeepers in Cairo, Egypt, who announce the beginning of each month.

No attempt is made to keep the Islamic religious calendar synchronized with a solar calendar. So the holy month of Ramadan, a time of prayer and fasting among all Muslims, continually moves through the seasons, occurring about 11 days earlier each solar year. One year, Ramadan might be in the winter, and 16 solar years later, it would be in the summer.

The Jewish calendar has 12 or 13 lunar months. The standard year is 12 months, but an extra (or *intercalary*) month is inserted seven times during a 19-year cycle to keep the religious calendar closely aligned with the solar year. Thus, Jewish religious holidays always occur in the same season, although the exact dates vary. For example, the Jewish holiday Passover is always in spring.

1. How many days are in a lunar year of 12 lunar months? How many days are in a solar year?
2. Not counting leap years, how many days are in 19 solar years? How many days are in 19 lunar calendar years with an extra month added in seven times? How closely does the Jewish calendar coincide with the solar calendar every 19 years?
3. Why might it be important for farmers and hunters to keep their calendar aligned with the seasons?

Lesson Quiz

Phases and Eclipses

Write the letter of the correct answer on the line at the left.

1. ___ A solar eclipse occurs when the moon
   A passes into the penumbra of Earth
   B passes into the umbra of Earth
   C passes at a slight tilt between Earth and the sun
   D passes directly between Earth and the sun

2. ___ When Earth is directly between the moon and the sun,
   A a total solar eclipse occurs
   B a lunar eclipse occurs
   C a partial solar eclipse occurs
   D the penumbra of the moon shrivels

3. ___ As the moon moves through Earth's shadow,
   A a lunar eclipse occurs
   B the phases of the moon occur
   C a solar eclipse occurs
   D a new orbital path is formed

4. ___ Like Earth, the moon rotates and
   A waxes
   B goes through a cycle of phases each month
   C revolves
   D wanes

If the statement is true, write *true*. If the statement is false, change the underlined word or words to make the statement true.

5. _____ <u>Crescents</u> are the different shapes of the moon you see from Earth.

6. _____ The moon revolves around Earth and <u>revolves</u> on its own axis.

7. _____ One "day" on the moon is the same length as one <u>month</u> on Earth.

8. _____ As the moon orbits Earth, the <u>absolute</u> positions of the moon, Earth, and the sun change.

9. _____ The moon's orbit around Earth is <u>absolutely straight</u> with respect to Earth's orbit around the sun.

10. _____ The amount of the moon's surface that is lit by the sun <u>changes</u>.

Phases and Eclipses

Answer Key

After the Inquiry Warm-Up

1. a day; The moon goes around Earth once a day and appears in the same place in the sky each night.

2. Sample: Move the penny around the quarter without rotating it.

3. Some people on Earth would see the other side of the moon.

4. Accept all reasonable responses. Students should indicate that it is daytime because the moon is visible on the opposite side of the world so it is night there.

Key Concept Summaries

Sample: As the moon orbits Earth, the relative position of the moon, Earth, and sun change. Their changing relative positions cause the phases of the moon. When the moon passes directly between Earth and the sun, sunlight is blocked from Earth, so a solar eclipse occurs. When Earth passes directly between the moon and the sun, Earth blocks sunlight from reaching the moon, so a lunar eclipse occurs.

Review and Reinforce

1. A: new moon

   B: waxing crescent

   C: first quarter

   D: full moon

   E: waning gibbous

   F: third quarter

2. eclipse

3. penumbra

4. umbra

5. phase

6. lunar

7. solar

Enrich

1. A lunar year is 12 × 29.5 = 354 days. A solar year = 365 days.

2. 19 × 365 = 6,935 days
   19 × 354 + (7 × 29.5) = 6,932.5 days
   It is off by 2.5 days.

3. The planting and growth of crops and the movements of animals are seasonal, so it is important for farmers and hunters to be able to accurately predict the seasons.

Lesson Quiz

1. D
2. B
3. A
4. C
5. Phases
6. rotates
7. true
8. relative
9. slightly tilted
10. stays the same

Place the outside corner, the corner away from the dotted line, in the corner of your copy machine to copy onto letter-size paper.

5   How do Earth, the moon, and the sun interact?

Blended Path Active learning using Student Edition, Inquiry Path, and Digital Path

Lesson Pacing: 1–2 periods or $\frac{1}{2}$–1 block

⏱ **SHORT ON TIME?** To do this lesson in approximately half the time, do the Activate Prior Knowledge activity on page 28. A discussion of the Key Concepts on pages 29 and 30 will familiarize students with the lesson content. Have students do the Quick Lab. The rest of the lesson can be completed by students independently.

Preference Navigator, in the online Planning tools, allows you to customize *Interactive Science* to your own teaching style. You can also edit lesson plans by selecting the Lesson Planner option.

Digital Teacher's Edition allows you to access your Teacher's Edition and Resource materials online.

my science online

Lesson Vocabulary

- tide
- spring tide
- neap tide

Professional Development Note Content Refresher

Frequency of Tides One lunar day is 24 hours and 50 minutes, the time it takes for a specific spot on the surface of Earth to rotate once relative to a specific position under the moon.

One lunar day is 50 minutes longer than one solar day. There are two reasons why: Earth and the moon rotate and revolve in the same direction, and one complete moon revolution occurs 50 minutes faster than one complete rotation of Earth.

Because Earth rotates through two tidal bulges each lunar day, most coastal areas experience two high tides and two low tides every 24 hours and 50 minutes. Each high tide and low tide occurs in half that time, every 12 hours and 25 minutes. Water at the shore goes from high to low or low to high in 6 hours and 12.5 minutes, and there is relatively little difference between successive high and low water. These tides are called semi-diurnal. However, tides along some ʌsts do not follow this exact pattern. For instance, on the north ʌ the Gulf of Mexico, the tide is diurnal, meaning that it moves ʌgain only once in a 24-hour period. Likewise, the Pacific ʌriences mixed tides. While the area experiences two ʌes a day, those tides are characterized by a ʌen successive tides.

ENGAGE AND EXPLORE

Teach this lesson using a variety of resources. Begin by reading **My Planet Diary** as a class. Have students share what they already know about tides. Then have students do the **Inquiry Warm-Up activity.** Students will predict tide times for coastal cities. The **After the Inquiry Warm-Up worksheet** sets up a discussion about the high tide times at different cities on the same coast. Have volunteers share their answers to question 4 naming a city in Maine that would have about the same high tide time as Nantucket.

EXPLAIN AND ELABORATE

Teach Key Concepts by explaining that tides are caused by interactions between the moon and different parts of Earth. **Support the Big Q** by discussing the relationship between Earth's motion and tides. Continue to **Teach Key Concepts** by explaining that the position of the sun can also affect the heights of tides. Have students practice the inquiry skill in the **Apply It activity.**

Hand out the **Key Concept Summaries** as a review of each part of the lesson. Students can also use the online **Vocab Flash Cards** to review key terms.

EVALUATE

Have students take the **Lesson Quiz.** For an alternate assessment, see the **EXAM**VIEW® Assessment Suite, Progress Monitoring Assessments, or SuccessTracker™.

ⒺⓁⓁ Support

1 Content and Language

Write Cloze sentences for students to complete with the vocabulary terms for the lesson.

LESSON PLANNER 1.5

Lab zone Inquiry Path
Hands-on learning in the Lab zone

ENGAGE AND EXPLORE

To teach this lesson with an emphasis on inquiry, begin with the **Inquiry Warm-Up activity.** Students will predict tide times for coastal cities. The **After the Inquiry Warm-Up worksheet** sets up a discussion about the high tide times at different cities on the same coast. Have volunteers share their answers to question 4 naming a city in Maine that would have about the same high tide time as Nantucket.

EXPLAIN AND ELABORATE

Focus on the **Inquiry Skill** for the lesson. Remind students that an observation is what you can see, hear, smell, taste, or feel. Explain that information collected through observations is called evidence, or data. What data could be collected to make an observation in question 1 of the **Inquiry Warm-Up activity?** *(The distances between Portsmouth, Portland, and Bar Harbor)* **Support the Big Q** by discussing the relationship between Earth's motion and tides. Before students begin the **Apply It activity,** help them recall the factors that affect the strength of a gravitational force. Have students do the **Quick Lab** and share their models of the moon's pull of gravity. Students can use the online **Vocab Flash Cards** to review key terms.

EVALUATE

Have students take the **Lesson Quiz.** For an alternate assessment, see the **EXAM**VIEW® Assessment Suite, Progress Monitoring Assessments, or SuccessTracker™.

Digital Path
Online learning at my science online.com

ENGAGE AND EXPLORE

Teach this lesson using digital resources. Begin by having students learn more about tides and explore real-world connections to tides at **My Planet Diary** online. Have them access the Chapter Resources to find the **Unlock the Big Question activity.** There they can answer the questions and refine their responses as they continue through the lesson. You can re-assign the activity and have students submit their work so you can track their progress.

EXPLAIN AND ELABORATE

Students reading above, at, or below the lexile measure of this lesson can access basic content readings at their level at **My Reading Web.** Encourage students to use the online **Vocab Flash Cards** to preview key terms. **Support the Big Q** by discussing the relationship between Earth's motion and tides. The **Art in Motion activity** online allows students to explore a moving model of how tides occur. Assign the **Apply It activity** online and have students submit their work to you. Have students do the **Quick Lab.** The **Key Concept Summaries** online allow students to read a summary and see an image associated with each part of the lesson. Online remediation is available at **My Science Coach.**

EVALUATE

Have students take the **Lesson Quiz.** For an alternate assessment, see the **EXAM**VIEW® Assessment Suite, Progress Monitoring Assessments, or SuccessTracker™.

2 Frontload the Lesson

In the visual on page 30, have students identify the sun, the moon, and Earth. Then, read the first sentence for each of the first three boxes, aloud. Have students trace the alignment with their fingers. Have them describe the positions of the three elements in their own words.

3 Comprehensible Input

Have students use a Venn Diagram to compare and contrast a spring tide and a neap tide.

4 Language Production

Pair or group students with varied language abilities to complete labs collaboratively for language practice. Have each student copy the completed written lab for personal reference.

5 Assess Understanding

Make true or false statements using lesson content and have students indicate if they agree or disagree with a thumbs up or thumbs down gesture to check whole-class comprehension.

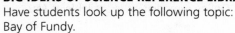

LESSON 1.5

Tides

Establish Learning Objective

After this lesson, students will be able to:

🔑 Explain what causes tides.

Engage

Activate Prior Knowledge

MY PLANET DIARY Read *A River in Reverse* with the class. Tell students that in some locations, there can be dramatic differences between the heights of high and low tides. Ask: **Have you ever built a sand castle that got washed away by the ocean?** *(Sample: Yes)* **What do you think caused the sand castle to wash away?** *(Rising tide)*

BIG IDEAS OF SCIENCE REFERENCE LIBRARY 📖
Have students look up the following topic:
Bay of Fundy.

Explore

Lab Resource: Inquiry Warm-Up

L2 **WHEN IS HIGH TIDE?** Students will use a map and high tide times in coastal cities to predict high tide times in other coastal cities.

🔑 **What Are Tides?**

MY PLANET DIARY

FUN FACT

A River in Reverse

If you were visiting New Brunswick in Canada, you might see the Saint John River flowing into the ocean. But six hours later, you might find that the river changed direction while you were gone! How could this happen? The Saint John River really does reverse course twice a day. At low tide, it empties into the Bay of Fundy, shown below. At high tide, the Bay of Fundy's tide pushes into the river, forcing the river to run in the opposite direction. The Bay of Fundy's tides are among the highest in the world.

Use your experience to answer the questions.

1. Why does the Saint John River change direction?

The tides from the Bay of Fundy push the river's water backward.

2. Have you ever seen a natural event that surprised you? Why was it surprising?

Answers should describe students' observations.

> **PLANET DIARY** Go to **Planet Diary** to learn more about tides.

 Do the Inquiry Warm-Up *When Is High Tide?*

High tide

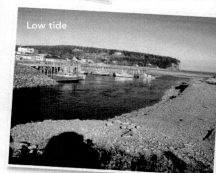
Low tide

28 Earth, Moon, and Sun

SUPPORT ALL READERS

Lexile Measure = 900L   Lexile Word Count = 698

Prior Exposure to Content: May be the first time students have encountered this topic

Academic Vocabulary: *cause, effect, observe, interpret, infer*

Science Vocabulary: *tide, spring tide, neap tide*

Concept Level: May be difficult for students who struggle with abstract ideas

Preteach With: My Planet Diary "A River in Reverse" and Figure 1 activity

Go to **My Reading Web** to access leveled readings that provide a foundation for the content.

my science online.com

Vocabulary
- tide
- spring tide
- neap tide

Skills
- ⟳ Reading: Relate Cause and Effect
- △ Inquiry: Observe

What Are Tides?

The reversing Saint John River is caused by ocean **tides,** the rise and fall of ocean water that occurs every 12.5 hours or so. The water rises for about six hours, then falls for about six hours.

The Tide Cycle The force of gravity pulls the moon and Earth (including the water on Earth's surface) toward each other. ▬ **Tides are caused mainly by differences in how much gravity from the moon and the sun pulls on different parts of Earth.**

At any one time on Earth, there are two places with high tides and two places with low tides. As Earth rotates, one high tide occurs on the side of Earth that faces the moon. The second high tide occurs on the opposite side of Earth. **Figure 1** explains why.

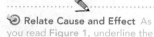

✏ ⟳ **Relate Cause and Effect** As you read **Figure 1**, underline the causes of high and low tides.

FIGURE 1 ··········
▶ ART IN MOTION **Tides**

You can think of Earth as a ball surrounded by a layer of water, as shown here. The layer is really much thinner than this, but is drawn thicker so it is easier to see.

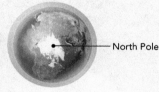

— North Pole

The Near Side The moon's gravity pulls a little more strongly on the water on the side closest to the moon than on Earth as a whole. This difference causes a bulge of water on the side of Earth closest to the moon. This bulge causes high tide.

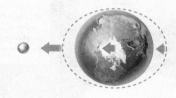

The Far Side The moon's gravity pulls more weakly on the water on the far side of Earth than on Earth as a whole. Since Earth is pulled more strongly, the water is "left behind." Water flows toward the far side, causing high tide. Halfway between the high tides, water flows toward the high tides, causing low tide.

✏ **Interpret Diagrams**
Write an *H* where high tides occur and an *L* where low tides occur.

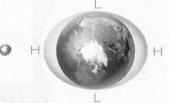

L

H — — H

L

29

(E)(L)(L) Support

1 Content and Language
Write the terms *tide* and *time* on the board. Explain that the word *tide* comes from the Old English word *tid,* meaning "time." Encourage students to see that the rising and falling of ocean water occurs at regular intervals of time.

2 Frontload the Lesson
Invite students to study the pair of photographs showing high tide and low tide at the Bay of Fundy. Then invite students to use descriptive words and phrases to explain how the appearance of a sandy beach would change at high tide and again at low tide.

3 Comprehensible Input
Have students use a cycle diagram to show the sequence of events involved in the tide cycle during one day. Remind students that ocean water rises for about six hours, then falls for about six hours twice daily.

Explain

Introduce Vocabulary

Point out the three vocabulary terms. Inform students that they will learn about *tides* in general and about the two specific tides, *spring tides* and *neap tides,* that occur during particular phases of the moon.

Teach Key Concepts ▬

Explain to students that tides are caused by interactions between the moon and different parts of Earth. Ask: **How does the moon cause a high tide?** *(The force of gravity from the moon pulls on Earth. The water on the side of Earth facing the moon is pulled toward the moon more strongly than is the rest of Earth. The water on the other side of Earth is pulled least of all, and is left behind. This produces "bulges" of water.)*

⟳ **Relate Cause and Effect** Tell students that science involves many cause-and-effect relationships. A cause makes something happen. An effect is what happens. When they recognize that one event causes another, they are relating cause and effect.

Support the Big Q ❓▶

EARTH'S MOTION AND THE TIDES Remind students that Earth has two basic types of motion. Ask: **Which of Earth's two basic types of motion affect the tide cycle?** *(Rotation)* **How?** *(Sample: As Earth rotates, one high tide stays on the side of Earth facing the moon. The second high tide stays on the opposite side of Earth.)* **Why might it be useful to know when high and low tides occur?** *(Samples: People who fish need to know the tide cycle because it affects when they fish and what they catch; people walking along a narrow beach need to know the tide cycle to stay safe)* Inform students that each location on Earth sweeps through two high tides, and two low tides every 25 hours or so.

My Planet Diary provides an opportunity for students to explore real-world connections to tides.

Art in Motion allows students to explore a moving model of how tides occur.

my science online.com | Tides

Explain

Teach Key Concepts 🔑

Explain to students that in addition to the positions of Earth and the moon, the position of the sun can also affect the heights of tides. Ask: **The sun is a great distance (about 150 million kilometers) from Earth, so why does its gravity affect the tides?** *(In addition to distance, mass affects the force of strength of a gravitational force. The sun's mass is immense.)*

Teach With Visuals

Tell students to look at the diagram. Ask: **Why do most coastal regions have two high tides and two low tides each day?** *(High tides occur on both the side of Earth closest to the moon and the side farthest from the moon. Every point on Earth moves through these two locations each day. Low tides occur between each high tide.)* **How does the size of high and low tides in a spring tide compare with the size of high and low tides in a neap tide?** *(During a spring tide, high tides are higher than usual, and low tides are lower than usual. During a neap tide, the situation is reversed: High tides are lower than usual, and low tides are higher than usual.)* **What causes the difference?** *(The difference is caused by the different positions of Earth, the moon, and the sun relative to each other. When the sun, the moon, and Earth are in a straight line, spring tides occur.)*

21st Century Learning 📖

CREATIVITY Life on the Mudflats. Have students read *Bay of Fundy* in the **Big Ideas of Science Reference Library.** Ask them to choose one mudflat-dwelling creature and create a storyboard that shows what happens to the animal over the course of one high and one low tide. Students should include an explanation of what is causing the tidal changes.

The Sun's Role Even though the sun is about 150 million kilometers from Earth, it is so massive that its gravity affects the tides. The sun pulls the water on Earth's surface toward it.
🔑 Changes in the positions of Earth, the moon, and the sun affect the heights of the tides during a month.

New Moon
The sun, the moon, and Earth are nearly in a line during a new moon. The gravity of the sun and the moon pull in the same direction. Their combined forces produce a tide with the greatest difference between consecutive low and high tides, called a **spring tide.** The term "spring tide" comes from an Old English word, *springen*, meaning "to jump."

First Quarter
During the moon's first-quarter phase, the line between Earth and the sun is at right angles to the line between Earth and the moon. The sun's pull is at right angles to the moon's pull. This arrangement produces a **neap tide**, a tide with the least difference between consecutive low and high tides. Neap tides occur twice a month.

Full Moon
At full moon, the moon and the sun are on opposite sides of Earth. Since there are high tides on both sides of Earth, a spring tide is also produced. It doesn't matter in which order the sun, Earth, and the moon line up.

Third Quarter
✏️ **Infer** Draw the position of the moon and the tide bulges at third quarter. What kind of tide occurs?

Neap tide

30 Earth, Moon, and Sun

Digital Lesson: Assign the *Apply It* activity online and have students submit their work to you.

 Tides

30 Earth, Moon, and Sun

apply it!

The table shows high and low tides at four times in May 2008, in St. John, New Brunswick. St. John is on the Bay of Fundy.

High and Low Tides at St. John, New Brunswick		
Date	High Tide (meters)	Low Tide (meters)
May 6–7	8.7	0.0
May 13–14	7.1	1.7
May 21	7.5	1.2
May 26	6.9	2.0

1 Interpret Data Spring tides occurred at two of the times shown. Which two? How do you know?

May 6–7 and May 21; the difference between high and low tides was greatest on those days.

2 [CHALLENGE] Would the tide be higher when the moon is on the same side of Earth as New Brunswick or on the opposite side? Why?

Sample: The tides would be highest when the moon is on the same side because then the pull of gravity from the moon is strongest.

 Vocabulary Identify Multiple Meanings Does a spring tide always happen in the season of spring? Explain your answer.

No; a spring tide happens whenever Earth, the moon, and the sun are in a line. This can occur in any month.

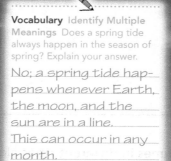

 Lab zone Do the Quick Lab Modeling the Moon's Pull of Gravity.

Assess Your Understanding

1a. Review Most coastal areas have ___two___ high tides and ___two___ low tides each day.

b. Relate Cause and Effect What causes tides?

Tides are caused by differences in how the moon and sun pull on different parts of Earth.

c. Observe Look at the diagrams on the previous page. What is the angle formed by the sun, Earth, and the moon during a neap tide? A spring tide?

During a neap tide, the angle is 90°. During a spring tide, the angle is 0° or 180°.

got it? ....

○ I get it! Now I know that tides are _changes in the level of oceans due to the pull of the moon's and sun's gravity on Earth._

○ I need extra help with _See TE note._

Go to **MY SCIENCE COACH** online for help with this subject.

31

Differentiated Instruction

L1 **Outline** Instruct students to outline the passage *What Are Tides?* writing the two subheads and listing details under each one.

L3 **Track the Tides** Have students use a daily newspaper or the Internet to track the height of high and low tides at a location of their choice for at least two weeks. If possible, have students use local tide tables and track tide heights for 30 days to see a full monthly tide cycle. Tell students to make a graph of their data, with the date as the *x*-axis and tide height as the *y*-axis. Have students also find the dates of the new moon and full moon and add them to the graph. Invite students to share and interpret their graphs in class discussion. If students use the Internet, remind them to follow prescribed guidelines for Internet use.

Elaborate

Apply It!

L1 Before students begin the activity, help them recall the factors that affect the strength of a gravitational force. Ask: **What two factors determine how strong the force of gravity is between two objects?** (The mass of the objects and the distance between them) **Which of those two factors explains variations in how much gravity from the moon pulls on each side of Earth?** (Distance) **How do you know?** (The masses of the moon and Earth are always the same, but the distance between the moon and each side of Earth changes as Earth rotates.)

Lab Resource: Quick Lab

L1 **MODELING THE MOON'S PULL OF GRAVITY** Students will model the moon's effect on Earth's tides.

Evaluate

Observe Remind students that an observation is what you can see, hear, smell, taste, or feel. Explain that information collected through observations is called evidence, or data.

Assess Your Understanding

After students answer the questions, have them evaluate their understanding by completing the appropriate sentence.

R T I Response to Intervention

1a. If students have trouble naming the numbers of high and low tides per day, **then** have them skim the first section of the lesson.

b. If students need help explaining what causes tides, **then** have them review **Figure 1.**

c. If students have difficulty describing the angle formed by the sun, Earth, and moon during neap and spring tides, **then** review with them the possible alignments of Earth, the moon, and the sun.

MY SCIENCE COACH Have students go online for help in understanding tides.

Lab zone After the Inquiry Warm-Up

Tides

Inquiry Warm-Up, *When Is High Tide?*
In the Inquiry Warm-Up, you investigated high tide times in different cities along the same coast. Using what you learned from that activity, answer the questions below.

1. **OBSERVE** Where is Portland in relation to Portsmouth and Bar Harbor?

_____

2. **PREDICT** Would a city located west of Portsmouth have an earlier or later high tide? Would a city located east of Bar Harbor have an earlier or later high tide?

_____

_____

3. **INTERPRET DATA** Compare the differences between the morning and evening high tide times in Portsmouth and Bar Harbor. What does this tell you about the tides in these cities?

_____

_____

4. **OBSERVE** Locate Nantucket on the map. Which city in Maine would have about the same high tide times as Nantucket?

_____

Name _____ Date _____ Class _____

Tides

What Are Tides?

1a. **REVIEW** Most coastal areas have _____ high tides and

_____ low tides each day.

b. ⟳ **RELATE CAUSE AND EFFECT** What causes tides?

_____

_____

c. **OBSERVE** Look at the diagrams on page 30 of your textbook. What is the angle formed by the sun, Earth, and the moon during a neap tide? A spring tide?

_____

_____

gotit? ....

○ **I get it!** Now I know that tides are _____

_____

_____

○ **I need extra help with** _____

_____

Key Concept Summary

Tides

What Are Tides?

The force of gravity pulls the moon and Earth (including the water on Earth's surface) toward each other. **Tides are caused mainly by differences in how much gravity from the moon and the sun pulls on different parts of Earth.**	The sun is so massive that, even though it is about 150 million kilometers from Earth, its gravity also affects the tides. The sun pulls the water on Earth's surface toward it. **Changes in the positions of Earth, the moon, and the sun affect the heights of the tides during a month.**
At any one time on Earth, there are two places with high tides and two places with low tides. As Earth rotates, one high tide occurs on the side of Earth that faces the moon. The second high tide occurs on the opposite side of Earth. Halfway between the high tides, water flows toward the high tides, causing low tides.	The sun, the moon, and Earth are nearly in a line during a new moon. The gravity of the sun and moon pull in the same direction. Their combined forces produce a tide with the greatest difference between consecutive low and high tides, called a **spring tide.**
The moon's gravity pulls a little more strongly on the water on the side of Earth closest to the moon than on Earth as a whole. This difference causes a bulge of water on the side of Earth closest to the moon. The bulge causes high tide.	During the moon's first-quarter phase, the line between Earth and the sun is at right angles to the line between Earth and the moon. The sun's pull is at right angles to the moon's pull. This arrangement produces a **neap tide,** a tide with the least difference between consecutive low and high tides. Neap tides occur twice a month.
The moon's gravity pulls more weakly on the water on the far side of Earth than on Earth as a whole. Since Earth is pulled more strongly, the water is "left behind." Water flows toward the far side, causing high tide.	At full moon, the moon and the sun are on opposite side of Earth. Since there are high tides on both sides of Earth, a spring tide is also produced. It doesn't matter in which order the sun, Earth, and the moon line up.

On a separate sheet of paper, draw two diagrams showing the relative positions of Earth, the sun, and the moon during a spring tide. Show the phase of the moon in each diagram.

Review and Reinforce

Tides

Understanding Main Ideas
Use the diagram at right to answer Question 1 in the spaces provided.

1. What kind of tide will occur when the moon is at positions A, C, D, and F?

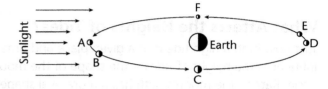

_____

_____

_____

Building Vocabulary
Fill in the blank to complete each statement.

2. A(n) _____ tide occurs when the sun is at right angles to the line between Earth and the moon.

3. Differences in the moon's and sun's pull on different sides of Earth cause _____.

4. A(n) _____ tide occurs when the sun, Earth and the moon are nearly in a line.

5. _____ pulls all objects in the universe, including the moon and Earth and the sun and Earth, toward each other.

6. The term _____ comes from an Old English word, *springen,* meaning "to jump."

Enrich

Tides

> The diagram below shows the moon's path around Earth is not a perfect circle. Read the passage and study the diagram. Then answer the questions that follow on a separate sheet of paper.

What Affects the Heights of Tides?

Just how high a high tide is at a given place and time depends on many factors. One factor that influences the height of tides is the shape of the moon's orbit. Its path around Earth is not a perfect circle. Rather, the moon's path has a more oval shape, closer to Earth at some points and farther at others. Because of this, the distance between Earth and the moon ranges from 375,000 kilometers to 408,000 kilometers. This difference is greater than the distance from New York City to Los Angeles. When the moon is closest to Earth, tides are usually high because the moon's pull is stronger when it is closer to Earth. These tides are called **perigee tides.** When the moon is farthest away from Earth, tides are usually low. These are **apogee tides.**

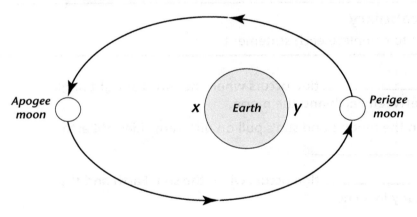

1. Would the daily tides at points *x* and *y* be higher during a perigee moon or an apogee moon? Explain.

2. Compare and contrast perigee tides and spring tides.

3. Like the moon's orbit, Earth's orbit is not a perfect circle, but an oval. How do you think this might affect Earth's tides?

Lesson Quiz

Tides

Write the letter of the correct answer on the line at the left.

1. ___ The bulge of water on the side of Earth closest to the moon produces

   A low tide

   B neap tide

   C high tide

   D rip tide

2. ___ Water flows toward the high tides, halfway between them causing

   A low tides

   B neap tides

   C high tides

   D rip tides

3. ___ Tides are the cycle of rising and falling ocean water that repeats approximately

   A every 24 hours

   B every 12.5 hours

   C every 25 hours

   D every 6.25 hours

4. ___ A spring tide can occur

   A in any month after March

   B in March, April, or May

   C in late February–early June

   D in any month of the year

If the statement is true, write *true*. If the statement is false, change the underlined word or words to make the statement true.

5. _____ A neap tide has the greatest difference between consecutive low and high tides.

6. _____ Neap tides occur once a month.

7. _____ Spring tides are produced during a new moon and crescent moon.

8. _____ The sun's gravity affects the tides, even though it is about 150 million miles from Earth.

9. _____ Changes in the positions of Earth, the moon, and the sun affect the number of high tides during a month.

10. _____ Tides are caused mainly by differences in how much gravity from the moon and the sun pulls on different parts of Earth.

Tides

Answer Key

After the Inquiry Warm-Up

1. The distance between Portland and Bar Harbor is about three times the distance between Portland and Portsmouth.

2. A city west of Portsmouth would have a later high tide. A city east of Bar Harbor would have an earlier high tide.

3. The differences are the same for morning and evening. High tide arrives at about the same time in each city in the morning and evening.

4. Portland

Key Concept Summary

The sun, moon, and Earth should be in a line in each diagram. One diagram should show the sun at the left, a new moon in the center, and Earth at the right. The other diagram should show the sun at the left, Earth is in the center, and a full moon at the right.

Review and Reinforce

1. At positions A and D, a spring tide will occur. At positions C and F, a neap tide will occur.

2. neap

3. tides

4. spring

5. gravity

6. spring tide

Enrich

1. The daily high tides at points *x* and *y* would be higher during a perigee moon because the moon's pull is stronger when it is closer to Earth.

2. Both perigee and spring tides are tides with an unusually large range between high and low tide. Perigee tides occur twice a month when the moon's orbit passes closest to Earth. Spring tides occur twice a month when the moon, the sun, and Earth are in a straight line.

3. Students may say that when Earth is closest to the sun, the sun's influence on tides would be greater. As a result, there would be more difference between spring and neap tides. Similarly, when Earth is farthest from the sun, the sun's influence on tides would be less, and there would be less difference between spring and neap tides.

Lesson Quiz

1. C
2. A
3. B
4. D
5. least
6. twice
7. full
8. kilometers
9. heights
10. true

Earth's Moon

THE BIG ? — How do Earth, the moon, and the sun interact?

Lesson Pacing: 1–2 periods or $\frac{1}{2}$–1 block

🕐 **SHORT ON TIME?** To do this lesson in approximately half the time, do the Activate Prior Knowledge activity on page 32. A discussion of the Key Concepts on page 33 will familiarize students with the lesson content. Have students do the Quick Lab. The rest of the lesson can be completed by students independently.

> **Preference Navigator,** in the online Planning tools, allows you to customize *Interactive Science* to your own teaching style. You can also edit lesson plans by selecting the Lesson Planner option.
>
> **Digital Teacher's Edition** allows you to access your Teacher's Edition and Resource materials online.

Lesson Vocabulary

• maria   • crater   • meteoroid

Content Refresher

Moon Photos In 1994, an uncrewed NASA spacecraft, *Clementine*, took images of the moon through different filters specifically chosen to identify different types of minerals on the moon. Using this technology, scientists were able to produce maps showing the moon's mineralogy. The spacecraft was named in honor of the prospector's daughter in the old song "My Darlin' Clementine."

In 1998, the American *Lunar Prospector* mapped the entire moon from an altitude of only 100 kilometers. The spacecraft found evidence suggesting the existence of ice frozen in the lunar soil near the moon's poles. The ice might exist in permanently shaded regions at the bottom of large craters. The *Lunar Prospector* mission ended when the probe was intentionally crashed into a large crater. Scientists hoped that the impact would liberate water vapor that could be detected from Earth. The results of the test were inconclusive.

In 2009, NASA sent the Lunar Crater Observation Sensing Satellite (LCROSS) to blast chunks out of the Cabeus crater at the moon's south pole. The LCROSS probe separated from the launching rocket and sent the spent module to the moon's surface to throw up a plume of debris. The LCROSS probe then flew through the plume and analyzed the contents for traces of water and ice.

LESSON OBJECTIVE

🔑 Describe the features and characteristics of the moon.

Blended Path
Active learning using Student Edition, Inquiry Path, and Digital Path

ENGAGE AND EXPLORE

Teach this lesson using a variety of resources. Begin by reading **My Planet Diary** as a class. Have students share their reactions to the primary source document of Galileo's observations. Then have students do the **Inquiry Warm-Up activity.** Students will model the formation of craters and develop hypotheses about how the speeds and masses of objects that hit the moon affect crater size. The **After the Inquiry Warm-Up worksheet** sets up a discussion about how different-sized craters on the moon are formed. Have volunteers share their answers to question 4 about a crater created by a 1-meter drop.

EXPLAIN AND ELABORATE

Teach Key Concepts by explaining that the moon and Earth differ in size, temperature, and surface features. **Lead a Discussion** comparing the diameters, masses, and relative densities of the moon and Earth. **Support the Big Q** by comparing the temperature extremes on Earth with those on the moon and discuss the reasons for the differences. Have students practice the inquiry skill in the **Apply It activity.**

Hand out the **Key Concept Summaries** as a review of each part of the lesson. Students can also use the online **Vocab Flash Cards** to review key terms.

EVALUATE

Have students take the **Lesson Quiz.** For an alternate assessment, see the **EXAM**VIEW® Assessment Suite, Progress Monitoring Assessments, or SuccessTracker™.

ELL Support

1 Content and Language

Write simple sentences using the terms *maria, crater,* and *meteoroid*. Read the sentences aloud, prompting students to repeat after you. Then have students write their own sentences using each term.

Lab zone Inquiry Path
Hands-on learning in the Lab zone

Digital Path
Online learning at my science online.com

ENGAGE AND EXPLORE

To teach this lesson with an emphasis on inquiry, begin with the **Inquiry Warm-Up activity.** Students will model the formation of craters and develop hypotheses about how the speeds and masses of objects that hit the moon affect crater size. The **After the Inquiry Warm-Up worksheet** sets up a discussion about how different-sized craters on the moon are formed. Have volunteers share their answers to question 4 about a crater created by a 1-meter drop.

EXPLAIN AND ELABORATE

Focus on the **Inquiry Skill** for the lesson. Remind students that a hypothesis is one possible explanation for a set of observations. It is not a guess but is often based on an inference. What hypothesis could be made in question 4 of the **Inquiry Warm-Up activity?** (*A 1-meter drop would create a larger crater.*) **Support the Big Q** by comparing the temperature extremes on Earth with those on the moon and discuss the reasons for the differences. Before beginning the **Apply It activity,** have students review the characteristics of the moon described under the subheads *Temperature* and *Water*. Have students do the **Quick Lab** and share their sketches of the features they see on the moon. Students can use the online **Vocab Flash Cards** to review key terms.

EVALUATE

Have students take the **Lesson Quiz.** For an alternate assessment, see the **EXAM**VIEW® Assessment Suite, Progress Monitoring Assessments, or SuccessTracker™.

ENGAGE AND EXPLORE

Teach this lesson using digital resources. Begin by having students learn more about Earth's moon and explore real-world connections to Earth's moon at **My Planet Diary** online. Have them access the Chapter Resources to find the **Unlock the Big Question activity.** There they can answer the questions and refine their responses as they continue through the lesson. You can re-assign the activity and have students submit their work so you can track their progress.

EXPLAIN AND ELABORATE

Students reading above, at, or below the lexile measure of this lesson can access basic content readings at their level at **My Reading Web.** Encourage students to use the online **Vocab Flash Cards** to preview key terms. **Support the Big Q** by comparing the temperature extremes on Earth with those on the moon and discuss the reasons for the differences. Have students do the **Apply It activity** online and submit their work to you. Have students do the **Quick Lab** and share their sketches of the features they see on the moon.

The **Key Concept Summaries** online allow students to read a summary and see an image associated with each part of the lesson. Online remediation is available at **My Science Coach.**

EVALUATE

Have students take the **Lesson Quiz.** For an alternate assessment, see the **EXAM**VIEW® Assessment Suite, Progress Monitoring Assessments, or SuccessTracker™.

2 Frontload the Lesson
Preview the lesson title and heads with students. Ask them to use this information to predict what they will learn about in the lesson.

3 Comprehensible Input
Have students use a Venn diagram to compare the features and characteristics of Earth and the moon. Encourage them to use information from the chapter as well as from their own knowledge base.

4 Language Production
Pair or group students with varied language abilities to complete labs collaboratively for language practice. Have each student copy the completed written lab for personal reference.

5 Assess Understanding
Divide the class into small groups. Have each student identify a Key Concept from the lesson to discuss in his or her group. After the discussion, have students talk about the Key Concepts as a group.

LESSON 1.6

Earth's Moon

Establish Learning Objective

After this lesson, students will be able to:

🔑 Describe the features and characteristics of the moon.

Engage

Activate Prior Knowledge

MY PLANET DIARY Read *Galileo Galilei* with the class. Tell students that Galileo's observations made people question beliefs that had been held for centuries about objects in the night sky and how they move. Ask: **How do you like reading Galileo's observations in his own words?** (*Sample: I like reading primary sources. They make history more immediate and historical figures easier to relate to.*)

BIG IDEAS OF SCIENCE REFERENCE LIBRARY 📖 Have students look up the following topic: Moon.

Explore

Lab Resource: Inquiry Warm-Up 🧪

L2 WHY DO CRATERS LOOK DIFFERENT FROM EACH OTHER? Students will model the formation of craters and develop hypotheses about how the speeds and masses of objects that hit the moon affect crater size.

 UNLOCK THE BIG Q?

🔑 **What Is the Moon Like?**

MY PLANET DIARY

VOICES FROM HISTORY

Galileo Galilei

In 1609, the Italian astronomer Galileo Galilei turned a new tool—the telescope—toward the moon. What he saw amazed him: wide dark areas and strange spots and ridges.

> I have been led to that opinion ... that I feel sure that the surface of the Moon is not perfectly smooth ... but that, on the contrary, it is ... just like the surface of the Earth itself, which is varied everywhere by high mountains and deep valleys.

Today, scientists know that Galileo was right. Powerful telescopes have shown the mountains and craters on the moon, and astronauts have walked and driven over the moon's surface.

✏️ **Communicate Discuss Galileo's observations with a partner. Then answer the questions below.**

1. What conclusions did Galileo draw about the moon?

He concluded that the moon's surface was varied.

2. How do you think it would feel to make an observation that no one had made before?

Sample: It would be exciting, but also scary because people might not believe me.

▶ **PLANET DIARY** Go to **Planet Diary** to learn more about Earth's moon.

🧪 **Lab zone** Do the Inquiry Warm-Up *Why Do Craters Look Different From Each Other?*

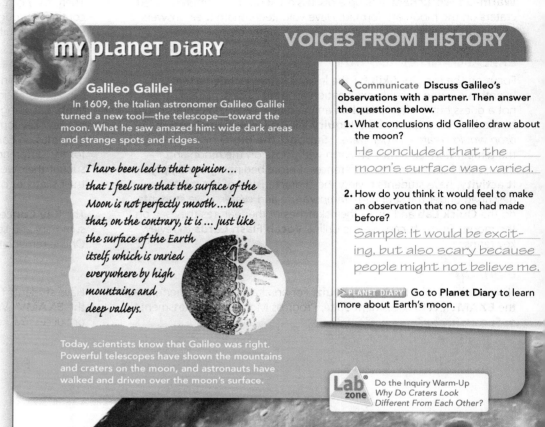

SUPPORT ALL READERS

Lexile Measure = 900L   Lexile Word Count = 720

Prior Exposure to Content: May be the first time students have encountered this topic

Academic Vocabulary: *compare, contrast, develop, hypotheses*

Science Vocabulary: *maria, crater, meteoroid*

Concept Level: Generally appropriate for most students in this grade

Preteach With: My Planet Diary "Galileo Galilei" and Figure 1 activity

Go to **My Reading Web** to access leveled readings that provide a foundation for the content.

MY SCIENCE online.com

Vocabulary
* maria • crater
* meteoroid

Skills
- Reading: Compare and Contrast
- Inquiry: Develop Hypotheses

What Is the Moon Like?

For thousands of years, people could see the moon, but didn't know much about it. Galileo's observations were some of the first to show details on the moon's surface. Scientists have since learned more about the moon's features. **The moon is dry and airless and has an irregular surface. Compared to Earth, the moon is small and has large variations in its surface temperature.**

Surface Features As **Figure 1** shows, the moon has many unusual structures, including maria, craters, and highlands.

Maria Dark, flat areas, called **maria** (MAH ree uh), are hardened rock formed from huge lava flows that occurred 3–4 billion years ago. The singular form of *maria* is *mare* (MAH ray).

Craters Large round pits called **craters** can be hundreds of kilometers across. These craters were caused by the impacts of **meteoroids,** chunks of rock or dust from space. Maria have relatively few craters. This means that most of the moon's craters formed from impacts early in its history, before maria formed.

Highlands Some of the light-colored features you can see on the moon's surface are highlands, or mountains. The peaks of the lunar highlands and the rims of the craters cast dark shadows. The highlands cover most of the moon's surface.

FIGURE 1 ·······················
Moon Features
This photograph shows the features of the northern part of the side of the moon that you can see from Earth.

✎ **Relate Diagrams and Photos** How is the photograph different from Galileo's drawing on the previous page?

Sample: The photo-graph shows more details than the drawing.

33

Explain

Introduce Vocabulary

Write the term *maria* on the board. Inform students that Galileo named the dark, flat areas he observed on the moon's surface after a Latin word meaning "seas." Galileo thought incorrectly that the maria were oceans.

Teach Key Concepts 🔑

Explain to students that the moon and Earth differ in size, temperature, and surface features. Ask: **What is found on Earth that is not found on the moon?** *(Air and abundant water)* Point out that when you observe a full moon, you can see both light and dark areas. These areas are maria and highlands. Ask: **Which moon features are linked to ancient volcanic activity?** *(Dark, flat areas called maria)* **What are highlands?** *(Mountains that cover most of the moon's surface)* **What causes craters?** *(The impact of meteoroids, which are chunks of rock or dust from space)* Display an image that shows the near and far sides of the moon. Have students compare and contrast the features both sides of the moon.

My Planet Diary provides an opportunity for students to explore real-world connections to Earth's moon.

my science online.com | Earth's Moon

ELL Support

1 Content and Language
Write the term *meteoroid* on the board, and circle the suffix *-oid.* Explain that this Latin suffix means "having the appearance of." Tell students that meteoroids are small bodies moving in the solar system. If a meteoroid enters Earth's atmosphere, it is called a *meteor.* Meteors that land on Earth's surface are called *meteorites.*

2 Frontload the Lesson
Invite students to share their ideas about the moon's characteristics, including its size in relation to Earth, its landforms, and its temperature.

3 Comprehensible Input
Provide pairs or small groups of students with modeling clay to create models showing the relative sizes and contrasting surfaces of Earth and the moon.

Lead a Discussion

MOON SIZE Have students locate the sentence that describes the moon's size. Ask: **How do the diameters of the moon and Earth compare?** *(Earth's diameter is four times greater than the moon's diameter.)* **How do the masses of the moon and Earth compare?** *(The moon has only one eightieth as much mass as Earth.)* **How does this difference in mass affect the relative densities of the moon and Earth?** *(Overall, Earth is denser. The density of the moon is similar to that of Earth's crust. Earth's very dense core makes Earth's overall density greater than that of the moon.)*

⤵ **Compare and Contrast** Remind students that when you compare and contrast, you examine the similarities and differences between things, such as Earth and the moon.

Support the Big Q ❓

HEATING THE MOON Tell students that the highest temperature recorded on Earth was less than 60°C and the lowest was about −90°C. Have students compare these temperatures to the extremes on the moon. Ask: **How is the moon warmed?** *(By energy in sunlight)* **How is Earth warmed?** *(By energy in sunlight)* **Why do temperatures on the moon vary so much more than on Earth?** *(The moon has no atmosphere.)* Briefly explain to students that our atmosphere moderates temperature on Earth because gases in the atmosphere trap heat at Earth's surface. Because some of the sun's heat does not escape, nights on Earth are much warmer than nights on the moon.

21st Century Learning

CRITICAL THINKING Summarize the collision-ring theory for students. Then, ask: **What evidence do you think might be used to support a theory that the moon was formed from material from Earth's outer layers?** *(Sample: The moon's average density is similar to the density of Earth's outer layers.)*

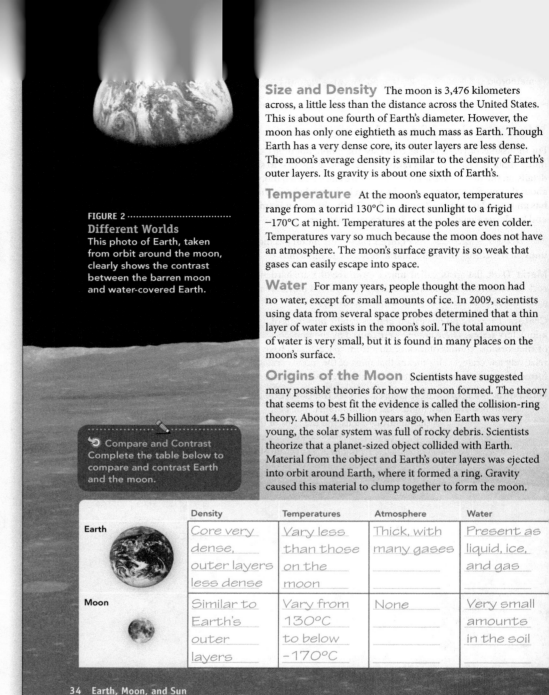

FIGURE 2
Different Worlds
This photo of Earth, taken from orbit around the moon, clearly shows the contrast between the barren moon and water-covered Earth.

⤵ **Compare and Contrast**
Complete the table below to compare and contrast Earth and the moon.

Size and Density The moon is 3,476 kilometers across, a little less than the distance across the United States. This is about one fourth of Earth's diameter. However, the moon has only one eightieth as much mass as Earth. Though Earth has a very dense core, its outer layers are less dense. The moon's average density is similar to the density of Earth's outer layers. Its gravity is about one sixth of Earth's.

Temperature At the moon's equator, temperatures range from a torrid 130°C in direct sunlight to a frigid −170°C at night. Temperatures at the poles are even colder. Temperatures vary so much because the moon does not have an atmosphere. The moon's surface gravity is so weak that gases can easily escape into space.

Water For many years, people thought the moon had no water, except for small amounts of ice. In 2009, scientists using data from several space probes determined that a thin layer of water exists in the moon's soil. The total amount of water is very small, but it is found in many places on the moon's surface.

Origins of the Moon Scientists have suggested many possible theories for how the moon formed. The theory that seems to best fit the evidence is called the collision-ring theory. About 4.5 billion years ago, when Earth was very young, the solar system was full of rocky debris. Scientists theorize that a planet-sized object collided with Earth. Material from the object and Earth's outer layers was ejected into orbit around Earth, where it formed a ring. Gravity caused this material to clump together to form the moon.

	Density	Temperatures	Atmosphere	Water
Earth	Core very dense, outer layers less dense	Vary less than those on the moon	Thick, with many gases	Present as liquid, ice, and gas
Moon	Similar to Earth's outer layers	Vary from 130°C to below −170°C	None	Very small amounts in the soil

34 Earth, Moon, and Sun

Digital Lesson: Assign the *Apply It* activity online and have students submit their work to you.

MY SCIENCE online.com ▷ Earth's Moon

apply it!

Within your lifetime, tourists may be able to travel to the moon. If you were taking a trip to the moon, what would you pack? Remember that the moon is dry, has almost no liquid water, and has no atmosphere.

1 **Solve Problems** On the packing list to the right, list five items you would need on the moon.

2 **CHALLENGE** List two items that you could not use on the moon. Why would they not work?

Sample: I could not use my
hair dryer because there
is no source of electric-
ity; I could not use a candle
because there is no oxygen
for it to burn.

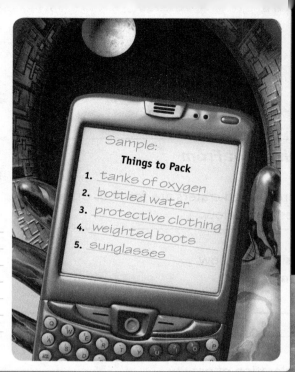

Sample:
Things to Pack
1. tanks of oxygen
2. bottled water
3. protective clothing
4. weighted boots
5. sunglasses

 Do the Quick Lab
Moonwatching.

Assess Your Understanding

1a. **List** What are the three main surface features on the moon?
Maria, craters, and highlands

b. **Compare and Contrast** How does the moon's gravity compare with Earth's?
It is much less than Earth's.

c. **Develop Hypotheses** Write a hypothesis explaining why the moon has very little liquid water.
Sample: The moon has very
little liquid water because it
either evaporated or froze.

got it?

○ **I get it!** Now I know that the characteristics of Earth's moon are that it is small, dry, airless, and has low gravity. Its surface includes maria, craters, and highlands.

○ **I need extra help with** See TE note.

Go to **MY SCIENCE COACH** *online for help with this subject.*

35

Elaborate

Apply It!

L1 Before beginning the activity, have them review the characteristics of the moon described under the subheads *Temperature* and *Water*.

Lab Resource: Quick Lab

L1 **MOONWATCHING** Students will observe the moon and sketch the features that they see.

Evaluate

Develop Hypotheses Explain to students that a hypothesis is one possible explanation for a set of observations. It is *not* a guess but is often based on an inference.

Assess Your Understanding

After students answer the questions, have them evaluate their understanding by completing the appropriate sentence.

RTI Response to Intervention

1a. If students have trouble identifying the three main surface features on the moon, **then** have them find and reread the relevant portion of the text.

b. If students need help comparing the moon's gravity with Earth's, **then** remind them that the moon has only one eightieth as much mass as Earth.

c. If students have trouble hypothesizing why the moon has almost no water, **then** remind them of the extreme temperatures and lack of atmosphere on the moon.

MY SCIENCE COACH Have students go online for help in understanding the moon.

Differentiated Instruction

L1 **Make a Diagram** Have students use their completed tables comparing the moon and Earth to make a Venn diagram comparing and contrasting the properties of the moon and Earth.

L3 **Aitken Basin** Tell students that a crater on the far side of the moon called the South Pole-Aitken Basin is the largest and deepest impact crater known in the solar system. Have students work in pairs to research to find a topographical map of the giant far side basin. Have partners present and interpret their maps, citing their source for the map and explaining what features of the basin it shows.

35

Lab zone **After the Inquiry Warm-Up**

Earth's Moon

> **Inquiry Warm-Up, *Why Do Craters Look Different From Each Other?***
>
> In the Inquiry Warm-Up, you investigated how different-sized craters are formed. Using what you learned from that activity, answer the questions below.

1. **COMPARE AND CONTRAST** How is your experiment similar to how craters are created on the moon? How is it different?

   _____

   _____

2. **MEASURE** Velocity is found by multiplying the acceleration of gravity, 9.81 m/s², by the time it takes an object to reach the ground. Repeat the drops from 20 and 50 cm with the same marble and record the time each drop takes.

   _____

   _____

3. **CALCULATE** What is the velocity for each height?

   _____

   _____

4. **PREDICT** How would craters created by a 1-meter drop differ from those in your experiment?

   _____

Earth's Moon

What Is the Moon Like?

1a. **LIST** What are the three main surface features on the moon?

_____

b. 🎯 **COMPARE AND CONTRAST** How does the moon's gravity compare with Earth's?

_____

_____

c. **DEVELOP HYPOTHESES** Write a hypothesis explaining why the moon has no liquid water.

_____

_____

gotit? ....

○ **I get it!** Now I know that the characteristics of Earth's moon are _____

_____

_____

○ **I need extra help with** _____

_____

Earth's Moon

What Is the Moon Like?

Galileo Galilei's observations in the early 1600s were some of the first to show details on the moon's surface. Scientists have since learned more about the moon's features. **The moon is dry and airless and has an irregular surface. Compared to Earth, the moon is small and has large variations in its surface temperature.**

The moon has many unusual structures. Dark, flat areas called **maria** are hardened rock formed from huge lava flows that occurred 3–4 billion years ago. The singular form of *maria* is *mare*. Large round pits called **craters** can be hundreds of kilometers across. The moon's craters were caused by the impacts of *meteoroids,* chunks of rock or dust from space. Some of the light-colored features you can see on the moon's surface are highlands, or mountains. Highlands cover most of the moon's surface.

The moon is smaller and less dense than Earth. Its diameter is about one fourth of Earth's diameter. It has only one eightieth as much mass as Earth. Temperatures on the moon vary greatly because the moon does not have an atmosphere. The moon's surface gravity is so weak that gases can easily escape into space. The moon has no liquid water. However, there may be patches of ice near the moon's poles.

Scientists have suggested many possible theories for how the moon formed. The collision-ring theory seems best to fit the evidence. This theory holds that a planet-sized rocky object collided with Earth to form the moon. Material from the object and Earth's outer layers was ejected into orbit around Earth, where it formed a ring. Gravity caused this material to clump together to form the moon.

On a separate sheet of paper, write a paragraph comparing the moon and Earth.

Review and Reinforce

Earth's Moon

Understanding Main Ideas
Answer the following questions on a separate sheet of paper.

1. How are the size and mass of the moon different from that of Earth?
2. How do astronomers think the moon was formed?
3. Who was the first person to observe the moon through a telescope?
4. How do temperatures on the moon differ from those on Earth?

Building Vocabulary
Answer the following questions in the spaces provided.

5. What feature covers much of the moon's surface?

_____

6. What are moon craters? How were they formed?

_____

_____

7. What are maria? How were they formed?

_____

_____

8. What are meteoroids?

_____

_____

Enrich

Earth's Moon

Read the passage and study the map of one area on the surface of the moon below.
Then use a separate sheet of paper to answer the questions that follow.

The Evolution of Lunar Landscapes

One way that astronomers estimate the age of a region on the moon is by counting the craters. If meteors are equally likely to hit any spot on the moon, older regions should have more craters per square kilometer because more meteors would have had the chance to strike them. This simple rule, along with a few others, enables astronomers to learn the order in which features on the moon were formed. Use this rule in the following activity.

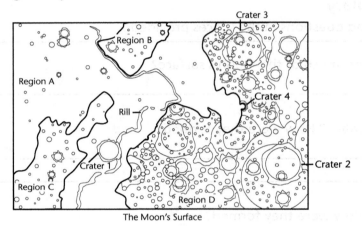

The Moon's Surface

1. In the map above, the heavy black lines mark the boundaries of four basic regions: A, B, C, and D. The circular features are craters. Based on the number of craters per unit of area, which region is probably the oldest? Which is probably the youngest?

2. Several small craters lie in the floor and on the walls of crater 2. Which is older, crater 2 or the small craters inside it?

3. Craters 2 and 3 have about the same area. Which one is probably older? Why?

4. Region A is a mare. (*Mare* is the singular form of *maria*.) The others are highlands. Notice how the material of region A fills crater 4. Which formed first, region A or crater 4? Why?

5. The long structures in region A are *rills*. A rill is a kind of valley formed when an underground tube collapses. Is the labeled rill older or younger than region A? List the following in order of age, from oldest to youngest: crater 1, crater 4, the labeled rill, and the floor of region A.

Name _____ Date _____ Class _____

Earth's Moon

Write the letter of the correct answer on the line at the left.

1. ___ The collision-ring theory seems best to describe how

   A   craters were formed

   B   highlands were formed

   C   the moon was formed

   D   maria were formed

2. ___ At the moon's equator, daytime and nighttime temperatures range from

   A   130° C to –170° C

   B   120° C to –110° C

   C   75° C to –30° C

   D   40° C to 10° C

3. ___ At 3,476 kilometers, the moon's diameter is slightly less than the distance across

   A   Texas

   B   France

   C   Russia

   D   the United States

4. ___ Craters were caused by the impact of

   A   meteoroids

   B   meteors

   C   meters

   D   meteorites

If the statement is true, write *true*. If the statement is false, change the underlined word or words to make the statement true.

5. _____ The moon is <u>humid</u> and airless, and has an irregular surface.

6. _____ Compared to Earth, the moon has <u>small</u> variations in its surface temperature.

7. _____ Maria have relatively <u>large numbers of</u> craters.

8. _____ The highlands cover <u>a little</u> of the moon's surface.

9. _____ The moon has <u>no</u> liquid water.

10. _____ The moon's average density is similar to the density of <u>the sun's</u> outer layers.

Earth's Moon

Answer Key

After the Inquiry Warm-Up

1. Accept all reasonable responses. Students may say they are similar because the marbles hitting the sand make craters the way objects colliding with the surface of the moon would. They may say the two are different because the moon and Earth have different levels of gravity.

2. Answers will vary based on experiment results.

3. Answers will vary based on experiment results. Students should multiply both times from question 2 by 9.81. The drop from 50 cm should have a greater velocity.

4. They would be larger.

Key Concept Summary

Sample: The moon is smaller and less dense than Earth and has larger variations in its surface temperature. The moon has no liquid water. It does have unusual surface features such as maria and craters. Both Earth and the moon have mountains; lunar mountains are called highlands.

Review and Reinforce

1. The moon's diameter is about one fourth that of Earth. Its mass is much less than that of Earth, about one eightieth.

2. Sample: When Earth was very young, a planet-sized object collided with it. Material from this collision was thrown into orbit around Earth. Eventually the materials combined to form the moon.

3. Galileo Galilei

4. The moon has much larger variations in its surface temperature than Earth has.

5. highlands

6. Craters are pits on the moon's surface that were caused by the impact of meteoroids.

7. Maria are flat, dark parts of the moon's surface formed by lava flows billions of years ago.

8. Meteoroids are chunks of rock or dust from space.

Enrich

1. Region D is probably the oldest, and region A is probably the youngest.

2. Crater 2 is older.

3. Crater 3 is probably older, because many more meteoroids have struck it than have struck crater 2.

4. Crater 4 must be older than region A because the material of region A could not have filled its floor if it hadn't already been there.

5. It must be younger. Had the rill been older, it would have been filled with molten rock when region A formed. From oldest to youngest they are crater 4, the floor of region A, the labeled rill, crater 1.

Lesson Quiz

1. C
2. A
3. D
4. A
5. dry
6. large
7. few
8. most
9. true
10. Earth's

Place the outside corner, the corner away from the dotted line, in the corner of your copy machine to copy onto letter-size paper.

Study Guide

Review the Big Q

Have students complete the statement at the top of the page. These Key Concepts support their understanding of the chapter's Big Question. Have students return to the chapter opener question. What is different about how students view the image of the moon's phases now that they have completed the chapter? Thinking about this will help them prepare for the *Apply the Big Q* activity in the Review and Assessment.

Partner Review

Have partners review definitions of vocabulary terms by using the Study Guide to quiz each other. Students could read the Key Concept statements and leave out words for their partner to fill in, or change a statement so that it is false and then ask their partner to correct it.

Class Activity: Concept Map

Have students develop a concept map to show how the information in this chapter is related. (The movements and relative positions of Earth, the moon, and the sun cause Earth to experience day and night, years, seasons, moon phases, and eclipses.) Have students brainstorm to identify the Key Concepts, vocabulary, details, and examples, then write each one on a sticky note and attach it at random on chart paper or on the board. Explain that the concept map will begin at the top with Key Concepts. Ask students to use the following questions to help them organize the information on the notes:

- How does Earth move in space?
- What keeps Earth and the moon in orbit?
- What causes the Moon's phases?
- What are two types of eclipses?
- What causes eclipses?

My Science Coach allows students to complete the *Practice Test* online.

The Big Question allows students to complete the *Apply the Big Q* activity about how Earth, the moon, and the sun interact.

Vocab Flash Cards offer a way to review the chapter vocabulary words.

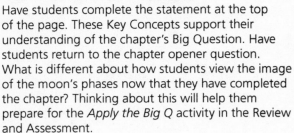
Earth, Moon, and Sun

Study Guide

Interactions between Earth, the moon, and the sun cause <u>tides</u>, <u>phases</u>, <u>seasons</u>, and <u>eclipses</u>.

LESSON 1 The Sky From Earth

🔑 On a clear night, you may see stars, the moon, planets, meteors, and comets.

🔑 A constellation is a pattern or grouping of stars imagined by people to represent figures.

🔑 The apparent motion of objects in the sky depends on the motions of Earth.

Vocabulary
- satellite • planet • meteor • comet
- star • constellation

LESSON 2 Earth in Space

🔑 Earth moves in space in two major ways: rotation and revolution.

🔑 Earth has seasons because its axis is tilted as it revolves around the sun.

Vocabulary
- axis • rotation
- revolution
- orbit • calendar
- solstice • equinox

LESSON 3 Gravity and Motion

🔑 The strength of the force of gravity between two objects depends on two factors: the masses of the objects and the distance between them.

🔑 Newton concluded that inertia and gravity combine to keep Earth in orbit around the sun and the moon in orbit around Earth.

Vocabulary
- force • gravity • law of universal gravitation
- mass • weight • inertia
- Newton's first law of motion

LESSON 4 Phases and Eclipses

🔑 The changing relative positions of the moon, Earth, and sun cause the phases of the moon.

🔑 A solar eclipse occurs when the moon passes directly between Earth and the sun, blocking sunlight from Earth. During a lunar eclipse, Earth blocks sunlight from reaching the moon.

Vocabulary
- phase • eclipse • solar eclipse • umbra
- penumbra • lunar eclipse

LESSON 5 Tides

🔑 Tides are caused by differences in how much gravity from the moon and the sun pulls on different parts of Earth.

🔑 Changes in the positions of Earth, the moon, and the sun affect the heights of the tides during a month.

Vocabulary
- tide • spring tide • neap tide

LESSON 6 Earth's Moon

🔑 The moon is dry and airless and has an irregular surface. Compared to Earth, the moon is small and has large variations in its surface temperature.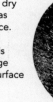

Vocabulary
- maria • crater
- meteoroid

ELL Support

4 Language Production

Divide the class into four groups. Post four large sheets of paper or poster board with the essential questions from each lesson at the top of each sheet. Position each group at one poster. Have them write down all they have learned that responds to the questions. Then have them rotate to the next poster to add information until all groups have worked with all posters.

Beginning
LOW/HIGH Allow students to answer with drawings, single words, or short phrases.

Intermediate
LOW/HIGH Have students draft sentences to answer the questions.

Advanced
LOW/HIGH Have students assist and/or edit the work of classmates with lower language proficiency.

Review and Assessment

LESSON 1 The Sky From Earth

1. Which of the following objects is found in Earth's atmosphere?

   a. comet   **b.** meteor

   c. moon   **d.** planet

2. Over time, people have given names to groups of stars, called _constellations._

3. **Predict** The constellation Orion appears in the eastern sky in December. Where would you expect it to appear in March? Why?

It would appear in the western sky, because Earth's position in its orbit has changed.

4. **Write About It** Suppose you were camping on a summer night. Describe what objects you might see in the sky and how the sky would change throughout the night.
See TE rubric.

LESSON 2 Earth in Space

5. What is Earth's annual motion around the sun called?

   a. month   **b.** revolution

   c. rotation   **d.** seasons

6. The _June solstice_ occurs when the sun is farthest north of the equator.

7. **Infer** Mars's axis is tilted at about the same angle as Earth's axis. Do you think Mars has seasons? Explain your answer.

Yes, because the tilt will cause changes in the amount of sunlight reaching Mars.

8. **Write About It** Write a guide for younger children explaining how Earth's motions are related to the lengths of days and years.
See TE rubric.

LESSON 3 Gravity and Motion

9. The tendency of an object to resist a change in motion is called

   a. force.   **b.** gravity.

   c. inertia.   **d.** weight.

10. An object is kept in orbit by _gravity_ and _inertia._

11. **Relate Cause and Effect** If you move two objects farther apart, how does the force of gravity between the two objects change?
The force decreases.

12. **Compare and Contrast** How are weight and mass different? _Weight is the force due to gravity. Mass is the amount of matter in an object._

13. **Explain** Explain Newton's first law of motion in your own words. _Sample: An object at rest will not move, and an object in motion will keep moving in the same way, unless a force acts on it._

Use this illustration to answer Question 14.

450 N

14. **math!** How much would the person above weigh on the moon? _about 75 N_

37

Review and Assessment

Assess Understanding

Have students complete the answers to the Review and Assessment questions. Have a class discussion about what students find confusing. Write Key Concepts on the board to reinforce knowledge.

RTI Response to Intervention

2. If students cannot explain the term *constellations*, **then** have them locate the highlighted term in the text and reread the definition.

7. If students need help relating the tilt of a planet's axis to Earth's seasons, **then** have them find and review the information about what causes seasons on Earth.

11. If students have trouble describing what happens to a gravitational force as distance increases, **then** have them find and review the appropriate Key Concept statement.

Alternate Assessment

L1 **MAKE A MODEL** Have students work in groups to make dioramas with moveable components that demonstrate an understanding of the chapter content. Assign each group one of the following topics: why Earth has days and seasons, what keeps Earth and the moon in orbit, and what causes solar and lunar eclipses. Invite groups to present their completed dioramas to the class and explain the process shown in their models.

Write About It Assess student's writing using this rubric.

SCORING RUBRIC	SCORE 4	SCORE 3	SCORE 2	SCORE 1
Describe objects seen in the sky and how they would change during the night	Student identifies stars, the moon, planets, meteors, and comets, and correctly explains their apparent motion.	Student identifies most of the objects seen in the sky and adequately explains their apparent motion.	Student identifies one or two objects and explains their apparent motion with assistance.	Student cannot identify any objects in the sky or explain their apparent motion.

Write About It Assess student's writing using this rubric.

SCORING RUBRIC	SCORE 4	SCORE 3	SCORE 2	SCORE 1
How Earth's motions relate to the length of days and years	Student clearly explains that Earth's rotation causes day and night, and that Earth's revolution around the sun takes one full year.	Student adequately explains how Earth's rotation and revolution affect the lengths of days and years.	Student unclearly or incompletely explains how Earth's rotation and revolution affect the lengths of days and years.	Student does not explain how Earth's rotation and revolution affect the lengths of days and years.

Review and Assessment, Cont.

RTI Response to Intervention

17. If students need help explaining why the moon has phases, **then** have them review **Figure 2.**

20. If students cannot explain what a neap tide is, **then** have them locate the highlighted term and restate the definition in their own words.

24. If students cannot account for the temperature differences on the moon, **then** have them reread the information for the red heading *Temperature.*

Apply the Big Q

TRANSFER Students should be able to demonstrate understanding of how Earth, the moon, and the sun interact by answering this question. See the scoring rubric below.

Connect to the Big Idea

BIG IDEA Earth is part of a system of objects that orbit the sun. Send students back to the Big Ideas of Science at the beginning of their student edition. Have them read what they wrote before they started the chapter. Lead a class discussion about how their thoughts have changed. If all chapters have been completed, have students fill in the bottom section for the Big Idea.

L3 WRITING IN SCIENCE Ask students to write a radio interview with an astronomer that explains how Earth, the moon, and the sun interact during solar and lunar eclipses.

Review and Assessment

LESSON 4 Phases and Eclipses

15. The moon's shadow falling on Earth causes a

  a. full moon.   **b.** lunar eclipse.

  c. phase.   **d.** solar eclipse.

16. The darkest part of the moon's shadow is the
umbra.

17. Relate Cause and Effect Why does the moon have phases? The amount of the lit half of the moon that is seen from Earth changes.

18. Make Generalizations Which occurs more often, a partial or a total lunar eclipse? Why? Partial; the penumbra is larger than the umbra, so the moon enters it more often.

LESSON 5 Tides

19. About how long passes between high tides?

  a. 6 hours   **b.** 12 hours

  c. 24 hours   **d.** 48 hours

20. The least difference between high and low tides occurs during a neap tide.

Use the diagram to answer Question 21.

21. Interpret Diagrams Does the diagram show a spring or a neap tide? How do you know? A spring tide; Earth, the moon, and the sun are in a line.

LESSON 6 Earth's Moon

22. What caused the moon's craters?

  a. maria   **b.** meteoroids

  c. tides   **d.** volcanoes

23. The moon's light-colored highlands are
mountains.

24. Explain Why do temperatures vary so much on the moon? The moon has no atmosphere, so it does not hold the heat from the sun.

25. Write About It Suppose you were hired to design a spacesuit for use on the moon. What characteristics of the moon would be important for you to consider? Explain. See TE rubric.

APPLY THE BIG How do Earth, the moon, and the sun interact?

26. Can more people see a total solar eclipse or a total lunar eclipse? Explain your answer. Sample: More people can see a total lunar eclipse. A lunar eclipse can be seen from anywhere that the moon is visible, because Earth's shadow is larger than the moon. The moon's shadow during a solar eclipse is very small, so only people in that small area can see the solar eclipse.
See TE rubric.

Write About It Assess student's writing using this rubric.

SCORING RUBRIC	SCORE 4	SCORE 3	SCORE 2	SCORE 1
Characteristics of the moon	Identifies lack of atmosphere, temperature swings, lack of water, and decreased gravity as critical to the design of a spacesuit	Identifies most characteristics relevant to the design of a spacesuit	Identifies at least one characteristic relevant to the design of a spacesuit	Identifies no characteristics relevant to the design of a spacesuit

How do Earth, the moon, and the sun interact?
Assess student's response using this rubric.

SCORING RUBRIC	SCORE 4	SCORE 3	SCORE 2	SCORE 1
Comparative visibility of solar and lunar eclipses	Student fully and clearly explains why more people can see a total lunar eclipse.	Student explains why more people can see a total lunar eclipse.	Student unclearly explains why more people can see a total lunar eclipse.	Student does not explain why more people can see a total lunar eclipse.

Standardized Test Prep

Multiple Choice

Circle the letter of the best answer.

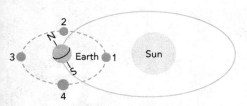

1. Which of the following can occur when the moon is at location 1?

   A   only a lunar eclipse
   Ⓑ   only a solar eclipse
   C   both a solar and a lunar eclipse
   D   neither a solar nor a lunar eclipse

2. On what does the force of gravity between two objects depend?

   A   mass and weight
   B   speed and distance
   C   weight and speed
   Ⓓ   mass and distance

3. What happens at a spring tide?

   A   There is only one high tide each day.
   B   There is only one low tide each day.
   Ⓒ   There is the most difference between consecutive high and low tides.
   D   There is the least difference between consecutive high and low tides.

4. The dark, flat areas on the moon are called

   A   craters.
   B   highlands.
   Ⓒ   maria.
   D   meteoroids.

5. Which type of object visible from Earth orbits the sun and has cleared the area of its orbit?

   A   star
   Ⓑ   planet
   C   moon
   D   meteor

Constructed Response

Use the diagram below to answer the question.

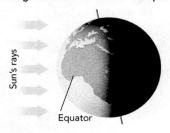

6. In the Northern Hemisphere, is it the summer solstice, winter solstice, or one of the equinoxes? Explain how you know.

See TE note.

39

Standardized Test Prep

Test-Taking Skills

INTERPRETING DIAGRAMS Tell students that when they need to answer a question about diagrams, they should first examine the diagram carefully. The numbers on the diagram shown above Question 1 give key information; they indicate the locations of the moon in its orbit around Earth. Students should note that at location 1, the moon is directly between Earth and the sun, blocking sunlight from Earth. Therefore, a solar eclipse (and only a solar eclipse) can occur. The answer is choice **B**.

Constructed Response

6. It is the summer solstice. I can tell because the Northern Hemisphere is tilted toward the sun.

Additional Assessment Resources

Chapter Test
EXAMVIEW® Assessment Suite
Performance Assessment
Progress Monitoring Assessments
SuccessTracker™

CHAPTER 1

ⒺⓁⓁ Support

5 Assess Understanding

Have ELLs complete the Alternate Assessment. Provide guidelines on the information it must cover, and a rubric for assessment. You may wish to have students work in small groups to complete the activity.

Beginning

LOW/HIGH Students can use single words and short phrases in their explanations.

Intermediate

LOW/HIGH Allow students extra time to complete their explanations.

Advanced

LOW/HIGH Students can write down their explanations in the form of a journal entry.

Remediate If students have trouble with...

QUESTION	SEE LESSON	STANDARDS
1	4	
2	3	
3	5	
4	6	
5	1	
6	2	

Science Matters

Museum of Science

Have students read *Keeping Track of Time*. Ask students to name patterns they have noticed with the sun and moon. They may point out the phases of the moon or the times of sunrise and sunset being different at different times of year. Explain that these patterns occur because of the orbit of the moon around Earth and Earth around the sun.

Ask students when Thanksgiving occurs. Point out that, if there were no calendar, or many different calendars, it would be difficult to tell when the fourth Thursday in November is. Without a standard calendar, people across the U.S. might celebrate Thanksgiving on different days.

The Gregorian calendar is a reform of the Julian calendar, named for Julius Caesar. Have students identify whether this year is a leap year. Point out that leap years occur almost every four years because the Earth takes approximately 365.25 days to orbit the sun. So adding an extra day every four years accounts for that 0.25 remainder of a day in the orbit.

As students research historical calendars, ask them to note which important events are shown on it. Have them detail how time is divided on the calendar they chose.

Ask: **Why do you think early people chose to use the sun and moon to help measure time?** *(Sample: They followed patterns that were easily observed by people who did not have advanced calculating methods.)* **What type of yearly events might be recorded on an early calendar?** *(Sample: Seasons, harvest time, holidays for early religions)*

Hot Science

SCIENCE MATTERS

KEEPING TRACK OF TIME

▲ This sun stone is sometimes called the Aztec calendar. It shows the 20 days in the Aztec month. The Aztec calendar was a solar calendar, with a total of 365 days in a year.

What day of the week is your birthday this year? Better check the calendar.

Calendars were invented to keep track of important events, such as planting schedules and festivals.

Early people noticed certain patterns in nature. The seasons change. The sun rises and sets. The moon changes phases. These patterns became the basis for calendars even before people understood that Earth rotates on an axis and revolves around the sun or that the moon revolves around Earth.

Calendars were lunar (based on the moon), solar (based on the sun), or lunisolar (based on a combination). But none was completely accurate—important events shifted around from one year to the next.

The Gregorian calendar, introduced in 1582, is the standard calendar in use today. It is more accurate than most calendars, but even it requires some tinkering. We add an extra day almost every four years, giving us a leap year. Century years (like 2000) are not leap years unless they are divisible by 400.

Research It There are about 40 different kinds of calendars in use today. Pick one and research it. Write an essay describing the calendar and how it is different from the Gregorian calendar. What does the calendar tell you about the society that uses it?

Quick Facts

On July 20, 1969, astronauts from the *Apollo 11* mission were the first people to set foot on a celestial body other than Earth. *Apollo 11* was the name of the rocket that took the astronauts into space. The lunar module was called *Eagle* and the command module was called *Columbia*. The *Eagle* landed in an area on the moon known as the Sea of Tranquility. When it landed, the module had less than 30 seconds worth of fuel left. The astronauts explored the surface for two and a half hours and left a flag and a plaque declaring that they had been there and reading "We came in peace for all mankind." Since this historic mission, 10 other astronauts have walked on the surface of the moon.

AFTER APOLLO: EXPLORING THE MOON

This is no ordinary footprint. It was made by an astronaut on the moon's dusty surface. Because there is no wind to weather it, it could last for a very long time.

No one has set foot on the moon since the two Apollo 17 astronauts did in 1972. But the moon has not been abandoned. Robotic spacecraft and rovers have taken over from humans.

In 2007, China and Japan sent robotic space probes to photograph and map the moon. In late 2008, India launched its moon orbiter and released a briefcase-sized probe onto the moon's surface, where it beamed back images. Next up? The National Aeronautic and Space Administration's Lunar Reconnaissance Orbiter, which will search for good landing sites and resources. Its goal is to help put humans back on the moon in the near future.

Research It Choose one of the international moon missions and prepare a timeline, from initial design to moon orbit.

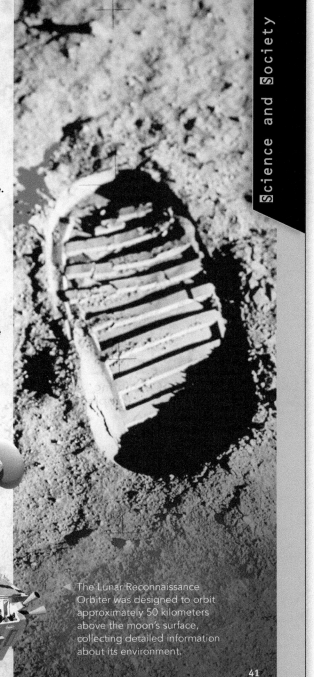

The Lunar Reconnaissance Orbiter was designed to orbit approximately 50 kilometers above the moon's surface, collecting detailed information about its environment.

Science and Society

41

Science and Society

Have students read *After Apollo: Exploring the Moon.* Tell students that space exploration was very heated in the 1960s. Russia and the United States raced against each other for years to reach the moon first. In 1969, Americans Buzz Aldrin and Neil Armstrong were the first people to set foot on the moon.

Explain that lunar expeditions could be difficult, dangerous, and expensive. Because the moon has no atmosphere and much lower gravity than the Earth, astronauts need a lot of special equipment to help them survive and move around as they explore the lunar surface. Because of this, scientists have invented robots and satellites that can gather data about the moon more efficiently than people can. Some scientists are eager to get people back to the moon. If robots or satellites break, it's very difficult to fix them remotely. Also, human astronauts are able to interpret the data they collect and may be able to design new experiments while they are already on the moon. Robots or rovers may not be equipped to do the same. By having people involved first-hand in space exploration, we can learn a lot more and learn it faster.

As students research their moon mission, have them include the purpose of the mission and ask them to name ways having an astronaut on this mission might help us learn more.

Ask: **How could human observation tell us more than a picture?** *(Sample: A picture only tells what something looks like, humans can use other senses to make observations.)* **What is an advantage of using rovers and robots?** *(Sample: Robots do not need breathing equipment or other protection from the lack of atmosphere in space.)*

Exploring Space

Introduce the Big Q

Have students look at the image and read the Engaging Question and description. Ask students to think about how the swimsuit might be similar to a spacesuit. Have volunteers share their hypotheses. Point out that the swimsuit compresses the swimmer's body and a space suit holds compressed air or oxygen around an astronaut. Ask: **Why would a competitive swimmer and an astronaut each want garments made of compressible, ultralight material?** *(Sample: A swimmer would want to minimize water resistance and an astronaut would want to allow mobility and reduce mass in space.)* Tell students that NASA, which engineered and created the spacesuit, assisted in the development of this swimsuit. NASA tested the suit's fabric and the ultrasonically welded seams in a wind tunnel. Wind tunnels are used to test viscous drag, or the force of friction through air or water. They are used to test the space shuttle and airplanes. This analysis helps engineers reduce drag for maximum efficiency, whether it's in a space shuttle, an airplane, or this swimsuit.

Untamed Science Video

A LITTLE OUTER SPACE HERE ON EARTH Before viewing, invite students to discuss what they know about outer space. Then play the video. Lead a class discussion and make a list of questions that this video raises. You may wish to have students view the video again after they have completed the chapter to see if their questions have been answered.

> **To access the online resources for this chapter, search on or navigate to *Exploring Space.***
>
> **Untamed Science Video** explores space spinoffs, or items used on Earth that were originally developed for use in space.
>
> **The Big Question** allows students to answer the Engaging Question about how people on Earth, such as competitive swimmers, benefit from products developed through space exploration.

my science online > Exploring Space

HOW IS THIS SWIMSUIT LIKE A SPACESUIT?

? THE BIG **How does exploring space benefit people on Earth?**

This high-tech swimsuit is made of a specially developed lightweight fabric with ultrasonically fused seams that make the suit very sleek. The swimsuit compresses the body to help the athletes go faster.

Develop Hypotheses **How might this swimsuit be similar to a spacesuit?**

This swimsuit and a spacesuit are pieces of clothing that are specially made for a specific purpose.

> UNTAMED SCIENCE Watch the **Untamed Science** video to learn more about exploring space.

Professional Development Note **From the Author**

Why does our government spend money in space when we have so many problems here on Earth? My first and perhaps flippant response to that question is that no one spends money in space. All the money is spent here on Earth. My second, more serious response is that the challenge of exploration and discovery, whether in space or elsewhere, nourishes the human spirit and brings out the best of our uniquely human abilities. President Kennedy expressed this most eloquently when he said, "We choose to go to the moon in this decade, not because it is easy but because it is hard, because that goal will serve to organize and measure the best of our energies and skills...."

Kathryn Thornton

Exploring Space

Chapter at a Glance

CHAPTER PACING: 8–10 periods or 4–5 blocks

INTRODUCE THE CHAPTER: Use the Engaging Question and the opening image to get students thinking about space exploration. Activate prior knowledge and preteach vocabulary using the Getting Started pages.

Lesson 1: The Science of Rockets

Lesson 2: The History of Space Exploration

Lesson 3: Using Space Science on Earth

ASSESSMENT OPTIONS: Chapter Test, **EXAM**VIEW® Assessment Suite, Performance Assessment, Progress Monitoring Assessments, SuccessTracker™

Preference Navigator, in the online Planning tools, allows you to customize *Interactive Science* to your own teaching style. You can also edit lesson plans by selecting the Lesson Planner option.

Digital Teacher's Edition allows you to access your Teacher's Edition and Resource online.

my science online.com

Differentiated Instruction

L1 Make a Word Web Draw a word web with "Space Exploration" at the center. Invite students to call out words that that they associate with space exploration. Underline any vocabulary terms from this chapter that students provide.

L3 Share Prior Knowledge Have students write two or three paragraphs summarizing what they have learned about space exploration in previous grades or through outside reading. Ask students to read their paragraphs aloud.

Getting Started

Check Your Understanding

This activity assesses students' understanding of forces involved in a rocket launch. After students have shared their answers, point out that gravity pulls downward on the rocket as the rocket pushes upward against gravity.

Preteach Vocabulary Skills

Explain to students that words from just about every subject area have related word forms—for example *history, historian, historical,* and *historiography; math, mathematical,* and *mathematician*. Point out that learning to identify related word forms can make it easier to learn new vocabulary words. Also mention that brainstorming related word forms is a fun game to play when you're on a long car ride.

Check Your Understanding

1. **Background** Read the paragraph below and then answer the question.

> Bill wonders how a rocket gets off the ground. His sister Jan explains that the rocket's engines create a lot of **force.** The force causes the rocket to travel upward with great **speed.** The force helps the rocket push against **gravity** and have enough speed to rise into space.

> A **force** is a push or pull.
>
> **Speed** is the distance an object moves per unit of time.
>
> **Gravity** is the force that pulls objects toward each other.

- What force is pulling down on the rocket as it pushes off the ground?

  Gravity

> **MY READING WEB** If you had trouble completing the question above, visit **My Reading Web** and type in *Exploring Space*.

Vocabulary Skill

Identify Related Word Forms You can expand your vocabulary by learning the related forms of a word. If you know that the verb *collect* means "to gather together," then you can figure out the meaning of the noun *collection* and the adjective *collective*.

Verb	Noun	Adjective
probe to examine something carefully	probe an unmanned space vehicle	probing serving to test or try
vacuum to clean with a vacuum cleaner	vacuum a place empty of all matter	vacuum partially or completely empty of all matter

2. **Quick Check** Circle the sentence below that uses the noun form of the word *probe.*
   - The satellite *probes* Earth's surface thoroughly.
   - The *probe* collected photographs and data for the scientists to analyze.

My Reading Web offers leveled readings that offer a foundation for the chapter content.

Vocab Flash Cards offer extra practice with the chapter vocabulary words.

Digital Lesson
- Assign the *Check Your Understanding* activity online and have students submit their work to you.
- Assign the *Vocabulary Skill* activity online and have students submit their work to you.

my science online.com ▶ **Exploring Space**

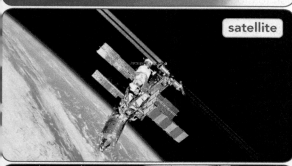
rocket

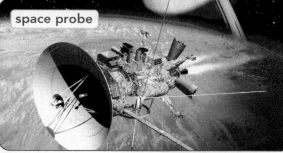
satellite

space probe

space spinoff

Chapter Preview

LESSON 1
- rocket
- thrust
- velocity
- orbital velocity
- escape velocity
- Relate Text and Visuals
- Interpret Data

LESSON 2
- satellite
- space shuttle
- space station
- space probe
- rover
- Ask Questions
- Make Models

LESSON 3
- vacuum
- microgravity
- space spinoff
- remote sensing
- geostationary orbit
- Identify the Main Idea
- Draw Conclusions

> **VOCAB FLASH CARDS** For extra help with vocabulary, visit **Vocab Flash Cards** and type in **Exploring Space**.

45

CHAPTER 2

Preview Vocabulary Terms

Have students work together to create a word wall to display the vocabulary terms for the chapter. Be sure to discuss and analyze each term before posting it on the wall. As the class progresses through the chapter, the words can be sorted and categorized in different ways. A list of Academic Vocabulary for each lesson can be found in the Support All Readers box at the start of the lesson.

L1 Have students look at the images on this page as you pronounce the vocabulary word. Have students repeat the word after you. Then read the definition. Use the sample sentence in italics to clarify the meaning of the term.

rocket *(RAWK it)* Device that expels gas in one direction to move it in the opposite direction. *A rocket works like a balloon that is propelled through the air by releasing gas.*

satellite *(SAT ul yt)* Object that revolves around another object in space. Sputnik I, *launched by the Soviet Union in 1957, was the first artificial satellite.*

space probe *(spays prohb)* Spacecraft that carries scientific instruments that collect data but has no human crew. *A space probe can explore places astronauts can't survive.*

space spinoff *(spays SPIN awf)* Item that has uses on Earth but was originally developed for use in space. *A space spinoff can be used in a consumer product, such as headphones.*

LESSON

1

How does exploring space benefit people on Earth?

Blended Path Active learning using Student Edition, Inquiry Path, and Digital Path

Lesson Pacing: 2–3 periods or 1–1½ blocks

🕐 **SHORT ON TIME?** To do this lesson in approximately half the time, do the Activate Prior Knowledge activity on page 46. A discussion of the Key Concepts on pages 47, 48, and 50 will familiarize students with the lesson content. Have students do the Quick Labs. The rest of the lesson can be completed by students independently.

> **Preference Navigator,** in the online Planning tools, allows you to customize *Interactive Science* to your own teaching style. You can also edit lesson plans by selecting the Lesson Planner option.
>
> **Digital Teacher's Edition** allows you to access your Teacher's Edition and Resource materials online.

Lesson Vocabulary

• rocket • thrust • velocity • orbital velocity • escape velocity

Content Refresher

Professional Development Note

***Atlas* Rockets** Since the late 1950s, NASA has used Atlas rockets to launch probes into space and satellites into orbit around Earth. Originally designed and built in 1946 as an intercontinental missile for the US Air Force, the Atlas missiles were subsequently adapted for space use. Approximately 350 Atlas missiles were built at a cost of three million dollars each. The first successful test launch of an Atlas rocket was on December 17, 1967. Many were eventually converted to orbital launch vehicles after they were removed from service as missiles.

Recent versions of the rockets are approximately 58 meters high. They are usually made up of three stages. The first stage, simply called Atlas, uses both solid-fuel boosters and liquid-fuel engines to launch the payload into space. The second stage, known as Centaur, uses liquid-fuel engines to maneuver into proper orbit. The third stage is the payload—the satellite or spacecraft carried by the rocket. The payload is released from the Centaur, which falls back to Earth and burns up on reentry into the atmosphere.

Atlas rockets have been regularly upgraded over time. They were used to launch the Surveyor missions to the moon and the early Pioneer missions. More recently, they have been used to launch satellites into space for both governmental and commercial enterprises.

LESSON OBJECTIVES

🔑 Explain how rockets were developed.

🔑 Demonstrate how a rocket works.

🔑 Explain the main advantage of a multistage rocket.

ENGAGE AND EXPLORE

Teach this lesson using a variety of resources. Begin by reading **My Planet Diary** as a class. Have students discuss the drawbacks of a jet pack flight. Then have students do the **Inquiry Warm-Up activity.** Students will use a balloon to model a rocket and infer how it works. The **After the Inquiry Warm-Up worksheet** sets up a discussion about the force of air escaping a balloon. Have volunteers share their answers to question 4 telling how they would attempt to control the flight path of the balloon.

EXPLAIN AND ELABORATE

Teach Key Concepts by explaining the technology behind modern rockets is based on earlier inventions.

Teach Key Concepts by explaining that a rocket is propelled forward by gases that shoot out the back of a rocket. **Lead a Discussion** about the two forces that act on a rocket: gravity and thrust.

Teach Key Concepts by explaining to students that a multistage rocket has advantages over a rocket with a single fuel chamber. **Support the Big Q** by discussing the uses of satellites.

Hand out the **Key Concept Summaries** as a review of each part of the lesson. Students can also use the online **Vocab Flash Cards** to review key terms.

EVALUATE

Have students take the **Lesson Quiz.** For an alternate assessment, see the **EXAM**VIEW® Assessment Suite, Progress Monitoring Assessments, or SuccessTracker™.

ELL Support

1 Content and Language

Write the term *thrust* on the board and say the word aloud. Point out that some English words have more than one meaning. Have students find the term in a dictionary. Read the definitions and then choose the definition for the term as it is used in the lesson.

Lab zone Inquiry Path
Hands-on learning in the Lab zone

ENGAGE AND EXPLORE

To teach this lesson with an emphasis on inquiry, begin with the **Inquiry Warm-Up activity.** Students will use a balloon to model a rocket and infer how it works. The **After the Inquiry Warm-Up worksheet** sets up a discussion about the force of air escaping a balloon. Have volunteers share their answers to question 4 telling how they would attempt to control the flight path of the balloon.

EXPLAIN AND ELABORATE

Focus on the **Inquiry Skill** for the lesson. Remind students that at the end of an experiment, scientists need to analyze their data to look for any patterns or trends. What pattern could be observed in the **Inquiry Warm-Up activity?** *(As air escaped the opening, the balloon was pushed in the opposite direction.)* Have students do the **Quick Lab** and share their findings about the history of rockets.

Do the **Build Inquiry** to allow students to draw conclusions about rocket propulsion technologies. Have students do the **Quick Lab** building a rocket propelled by a chemical reaction of antacid and water.

Support the Big Q by discussing the uses of satellites. Have students do the **Quick Lab** to make and launch a rocket model with two stages. Students can use the online **Vocab Flash Cards** to review key terms.

EVALUATE

Have students take the **Lesson Quiz.** For an alternate assessment, see the **EXAM**VIEW® Assessment Suite, Progress Monitoring Assessments, or SuccessTracker™.

Digital Path
Online learning at my science online.com

ENGAGE AND EXPLORE

Teach this lesson using digital resources. Begin by having students learn more about rockets and explore real-world connections to rocket science at **My Planet Diary** online. Have them access the Chapter Resources to find the **Unlock the Big Question activity.** There they can answer the questions and refine their responses as they continue through the lesson. You can re-assign the activity and have students submit their work so you can track their progress.

EXPLAIN AND ELABORATE

Students reading above, at, or below the lexile measure of this lesson can access basic content readings at their level at **My Reading Web.** Encourage students to use the online **Vocab Flash Cards** to preview key terms. Have students do the **Quick Lab** and share their findings about the history of rockets.

Use the **Virtual Lab activity** online to allow students to launch projectiles with rockets to get objects into orbit around Earth. Assign the **Do the Math activity** online and have students submit their work to you. Have students do the **Quick Lab** building a rocket propelled by a chemical reaction of antacid and water.

Support the Big Q by discussing the uses of satellites. Use the **Interactive Art activity** online to show how a multistage rocket works. Have students do the **Quick Lab** to make and launch a rocket model with two stages. The **Key Concept Summaries** online allow students to read a summary and see an image associated with each part of the lesson. Online remediation is available at **My Science Coach.**

EVALUATE

Have students take the **Lesson Quiz.** For an alternate assessment, see the **EXAM**VIEW® Assessment Suite, Progress Monitoring Assessments, or SuccessTracker™.

2 Frontload the Lesson
Use the lesson title, section headings, and visuals to help students predict what the lesson will be about. Make sure students confirm their predictions as they read the lesson.

3 Comprehensible Input
Divide the class into three groups. Assign a lesson objective to each group. Have the groups prepare a presentation to explain or demonstrate the objective and present their presentations to the class.

4 Language Production
Pair or group students with varied language abilities to complete labs collaboratively for language practice. Have each student copy the completed written lab for personal reference.

5 Assess Understanding
Have students keep a content area log for this lesson using a two-column format with the headings "What I Understand" and "What I Don't Understand." Follow up so that students can move items from the "Don't Understand" to the "Understand" column.

LESSON 2.1

The Science of Rockets

Establish Learning Objectives

After this lesson, students will be able to:

- 🔑 Explain how rockets were developed.
- 🔑 Demonstrate how a rocket works.
- 🔑 Explain the main advantage of a multistage rocket.

Engage

Activate Prior Knowledge

MY PLANET DIARY Read *Jet Packs* with the class. Inform students that adventurers and "daredevils" have used jet packs to cross the Grand Canyon, the Alps, and the English Channel. Ask: **What are some drawbacks to consider before attempting a jet pack flight?** *(Samples: The fuel could burn you; you could hurt yourself in a crash landing.)*

BIG IDEAS OF SCIENCE REFERENCE LIBRARY 📖 Have students look up the following topic: Jet Packs.

Explore

Lab Resource: Inquiry Warm-Up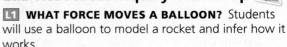

L1 **WHAT FORCE MOVES A BALLOON?** Students will use a balloon to model a rocket and infer how it works.

LESSON
1 The Science of Rockets

- 🔑 **How Were Rockets Developed?**
- 🔑 **How Does a Rocket Work?**
- 🔑 **What Is the Main Advantage of a Multistage Rocket?**

MY PLANET DIARY

Jet Packs

It's been snowing all day and the roads haven't been plowed yet. No problem. Just strap on a jet pack and fly over the snow.

Does this sound like something out of a science fiction movie? Actually, manufacturers have already started making one-person jet packs. The jet packs are very expensive. They also use a lot of heavy fuel—about 10 gallons of gasoline per hour. And jet packs can carry a person for only about 30 minutes before they have to be refueled. However, 30 minutes is long enough to get many people to work—if they can find a place to land and park the jet pack once they get there.

FUN FACT

Study the picture of the person using a jet pack. Use your knowledge of science to answer the question.

What would be the advantages and disadvantages of using a jet pack for transportation?

Using a jet pack, you could fly over snowy roads and other obstacles. However, the fuel is costly and heavy, and trips would have to be short.

▶ **PLANET DIARY** Go to Planet Diary to learn more about rockets.

 Lab zone Do the Inquiry Warm-Up *What Force Moves a Balloon?*

How Were Rockets Developed?

You've probably seen rockets at fireworks displays. As the rockets moved skyward, you may have noticed a fiery gas rushing out of the back. A **rocket** is a device that expels gas in one direction to move the rocket in the opposite direction. 🔑 **Rocket technology originated in China hundreds of years ago and then gradually spread to other parts of the world.** Rockets were developed for military use as well as for fireworks.

SUPPORT ALL READERS

Prior Exposure to Content: May be the first time students have encountered this topic

Academic Vocabulary: *data, interpret, relate, explain, apply*

Science Vocabulary: *rocket, thrust, velocity*

Concept Level: Generally appropriate for most students in this grade

Preteach With: My Planet Diary "Jet Packs" and Figure 2 activity

Go to **My Reading Web** to access leveled readings that provide a foundation for the content.

my science online.com

Vocabulary
- rocket
- thrust
- velocity
- orbital velocity
- escape velocity

Skills
- Reading: Relate Text and Visuals
- Inquiry: Interpret Data

Origins of Rockets The first rockets were made in China in the 1100s. These early "rockets" weren't rockets, but simply arrows coated with a flammable powder that were lighted and shot with bows. By about 1200, the Chinese were using gunpowder inside their rockets.

The British greatly improved rocketry in the early 1800s. British ships used rockets against American troops in the War of 1812. "The Star-Spangled Banner" contains the words "the rockets' red glare, the bombs bursting in air." These words describe a British rocket attack on Fort McHenry in Baltimore, Maryland.

Development of Modern Rockets Modern rockets were first developed by scientists in the early 1900s. One such scientist was the Russian physicist Konstantin Tsiolkovsky. He described in scientific terms how rockets work and proposed designs for advanced rockets. The American physicist Robert Goddard also designed rockets. Beginning around 1915, he built rockets to test his designs.

Scientists made major advances in rocket design during World War II. The Germans used a rocket called the V-2 to destroy both military and civilian targets. The V-2 was a large rocket that could travel about 300 kilometers. The designer of the V-2, Wernher von Braun, was brought to the United States after the war ended. Von Braun used his experience to direct the development of many rockets used in the United States space program.

FIGURE 1 ....
Rocket Timeline
A legend claims the Chinese official Wan-Hoo tried to fly to the moon around the year 1500 by tying rockets to his chair.

✏️ On the cards below, write a brief entry for the events that took place in the development of rockets.

- 1100s — Chinese arrows
- 1200s — Chinese gunpowder
- 1300s
- 1400s
- 1500s
- 1600s
- 1700s
- 1800s — British rockets
- 1900s — Tsiolkovsky, Goddard, von Braun

Lab zone — Do the Quick Lab History of Rockets.

⛊ Assess Your Understanding
got it? ....

○ I get it! Now I know that rocket technology originated __in China hundreds of years ago__ and gradually spread to __other parts of the world.__

○ I need extra help with __See TE note.__

Go to my science COACH *online for help with this subject.*

47

ⒺⓁⓁ Support

1 Content and Language
Write *velocity* on the board. Explain that *velocity* comes from the Latin word *velox,* meaning "quick." Point out that, in the context of science, *velocity* and *speed* are not synonyms, since *velocity* is a measurement of speed in one particular direction.

2 Frontload the Lesson
Encourage volunteers to share what they know about rockets. Then have students conduct a picture walk of the lesson. Remind them to use detailed phrases to describe each concept or term.

3 Comprehensible Input
Have students create a timeline that shows important people, devices, and events in the history of rockets. Encourage students to locate additional information to help them present a more comprehensive account than appears in **Figure 1.**

Explain ——————————
Introduce Vocabulary
Inform students that *velocity* means "speed in a given direction." Tell them that they will read about two kinds of velocity, *orbital velocity* and *escape velocity*, one or both of which a rocket launched into space must achieve.

Teach Key Concepts
Explain to students that modern technology often builds on or improves on earlier inventions. Ask: **Who developed the first rockets?** *(The Chinese)* Draw students' attention to the description in their books of the first rockets. Explain that "arrows coated with a flammable powder" are technically not rockets but were the start of rocket technology. Ask: **When were modern rockets first developed?** *(In the early 1900s)*

Explore ——————————
Lab Resource: Quick Lab
L2 HISTORY OF ROCKETS Students will build a simple rocket.

Evaluate ——————————
Assess Your Understanding
Have students evaluate their understanding by completing the appropriate sentence.

ⓇⓉⒾ Response to Intervention
If students have trouble describing the beginnings of rocket technology, **then** have them find and reread the boldfaced Key Concept statement.

my science ⑤ COACH Have students go online for help in understanding how rockets were developed.

My Planet Diary provides an opportunity for students to explore real-world connections to rocket science.

my science online | Development of Rockets

Explain

Teach Key Concepts 🗝

Explain to students that a rocket is propelled forward by gases that shoot out the back of the rocket. Ask: **How are the gases produced?** *(In most rockets, they are produced by burning a fuel.)* **What are the three types of rockets?** *(Solid-fuel rocket, liquid-fuel rocket, ion rocket)* Inform students that the English scientist Isaac Newton explained the concept of action and reaction forces. The relationship between action and reaction forces is stated in Newton's third law of motion. Ask: **What is the term for the reaction force that moves a rocket?** *(Thrust)* Blow up a balloon and release it to show students Newton's third law in action. Ask students to brainstorm other examples of this law and classify the forces as action or reaction.

Lead a Discussion

OVERCOMING GRAVITY Explain to students that two forces act on a rocket. Gravity pulls the rocket toward the ground. Thrust pushes the rocket up away from Earth. The more thrust a rocket can develop, the greater the velocity it reaches. Ask: **What is orbital velocity?** *(The velocity a rocket must achieve to establish an orbit around Earth)* **What do you think would happen to a rocket that cannot go this fast?** *(It will fall back to Earth.)*

Elaborate

Build Inquiry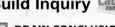

L3 DRAW CONCLUSIONS ABOUT ROCKET PROPULSION TECHNOLOGIES

Materials reference materials or computers with Internet connection

Time 30 minutes

Inform students that three types of fuel are used to power modern spacecraft: solid fuel, liquid fuel, and electrically charged particles of gas (ions). Then, organize students in small groups to research developments in rocket propulsion. Have students chart their findings chronologically. Brief descriptions should accompany each development. Encourage students to include emerging technologies. If students do their research on the Internet, remind them to follow prescribed guidelines for Internet use.

Ask: **What were early rockets powered by?** *(Gunpowder)*

How Does a Rocket Work?

A rocket can be as small as your finger or as large as a skyscraper. An essential feature of any rocket, though, is that it expels gas in one direction. 🗝 **A rocket moves forward when gases shooting out the back of the rocket push it in the opposite direction.**

A rocket works like a balloon that is propelled through the air by releasing gas. In most rockets, fuel is burned to make hot gas. The gas pushes in every direction, but it can leave the rocket only through openings at the back. This moves the rocket forward.

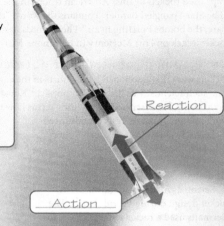

Reaction

Action

> **Action and Reaction Forces**
>
> A rocket demonstrates a basic law of physics: For every force, or action, there is an equal and opposite force, or reaction. Look at **Figure 2**. The force of the gas shooting out of the rocket is an action force. An equal force—the reaction force—pushes the rocket forward.
>
> The reaction force that propels a rocket forward is called **thrust.** The amount of thrust depends on the mass and speed of the gases propelled out of the rocket. The greater the thrust, the greater a rocket's velocity. **Velocity** is speed in a given direction.

FIGURE 2 ·····························

▶VIRTUAL LAB Rocket Action and Reaction

The force of gas propelled out the back of a rocket produces an opposing force that propels the rocket forward.

✎ **Label the action force and the reaction force in the figure, and explain how this causes the rocket to fly.**

The gases shooting out of the back of the rocket push the rocket in the opposite direction.

> **Rocket Fuels**
>
> Three types of fuel are used to power modern rockets.
>
> **Solid-fuel rocket:**
> • Oxygen is mixed with the fuel (a dry explosive chemical).
> • The rocket can be triggered from a distance by an igniter.
> • Once the fuel is ignited, it burns until all of it is gone.
>
> **Liquid-fuel rocket:**
> • Oxygen and the fuel are in liquid form, stored separately.
> • When the rocket fires, the fuel and oxygen are pumped into the same chamber and ignited.
> • The burning of fuel can be controlled.
>
> **Ion rocket:**
> • This type expels charged gas particles out of the engine.
> • Ion rockets are very fuel-efficient.

48 Exploring Space

Virtual Lab allows students to launch projectiles with rockets to get objects into orbit around Earth.

Digital Lesson: Assign the *Do the Math* activity online and have students submit their work to you.

my science online.com ▷ | Rocket Science

Orbital and Escape Velocity

In order to lift off the ground, a rocket must have more upward thrust than the downward force of gravity. Once a rocket is off the ground, it must reach a certain velocity in order to go into orbit. **Orbital velocity** is the velocity a rocket must achieve to establish an orbit around Earth. If the rocket has an even greater velocity, it can fly off into space. **Escape velocity** is the velocity a rocket must reach to fly beyond a planet's gravitational pull. The escape velocity a rocket needs to leave Earth is about 40,200 km per hour. That's more than 11 kilometers every second!

do the math!

Rocket Altitude

A rocket's altitude is how high it rises above the ground. Use the graph to answer the questions about a model rocket with a parachute packed inside, such as the one in the photo above.

1 Interpret Data What was the altitude after 2 seconds?

About 120 m

2 CHALLENGE Did the rocket rise or fall faster? How do you know?

It rose faster; the graph is steeper going up
than coming down

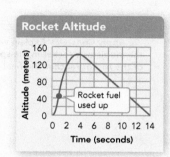

Rocket Altitude

Altitude (meters) vs Time (seconds)

Rocket fuel used up

Assess Your Understanding

1a. Explain What is thrust?
The reaction force that propels
a rocket forward

b. Interpret Diagrams Use **Figure 2** to explain how a rocket moves forward.
Burning fuel makes hot gas
that pushes outward in every
direction. The gas shoots out
the openings in the back of the
rocket. This action force results
in an equal reaction force that
pushes the rocket forward.

Lab zone | Do the Quick Lab Be a Rocket Scientist.

got it?

○ I get it! Now I know that a rocket moves forward when _gases shooting out_
the back of the rocket push it
in the opposite direction.

○ I need extra help with _See TE note._

Go to **my science COACH** online for help with this subject.

49

Do the Math!

L1 Remind students that line graphs often show how something changes over time. This graph shows how the rocket's altitude changes.

△ **Interpret Data** Explain that at the end of an experiment, scientists need to analyze their data to look for any patterns or trends. Patterns often become clear when the data is organized in a line graph or data table. Point out that students need to interpret the graph in two ways to answer the questions.

See *Math Skill and Problem-Solving Activities* for support.

Lab Resource: Quick Lab

L2 **BE A ROCKET SCIENTIST** Students will build a rocket propelled by a chemical reaction of antacid and water.

Evaluate

Assess Your Understanding

After students answer the questions, have them evaluate their understanding by completing the appropriate sentence.

RTI Response to Intervention

1a. If students have trouble defining *thrust,* **then** have them locate and reread the sentence that contains the highlighted vocabulary term.

b. If students need help interpreting **Figure 2** to explain how a rocket moves forward, **then** have them review the boldfaced Key Concept statement.

my science COACH Have students go online for help in understanding how a rocket works.

Differentiated Instruction

L1 **Make a Word Knowledge Chart** Have students construct a chart with four columns labeled *Term, Can Define or Use It, Have Heard or Seen It,* and *Don't Know* to rate their knowledge of each lesson term. Then, ask students to share what they know about *orbital velocity* and other terms in this lesson.

L3 **Write an Essay** Have students write a short essay using the following sentence as a thesis statement: In a sense, the development of spacecraft began with the launching of simple rockets in the 1100s. Tell students to use their textbook for background information and to do and incorporate additional research.

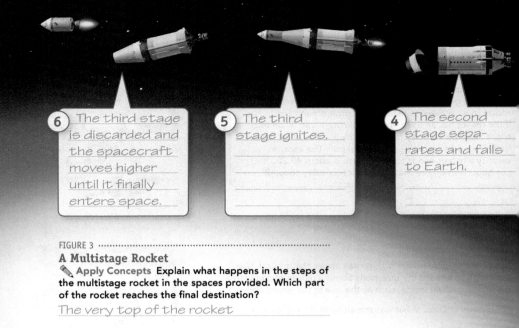

Explain

Teach Key Concepts 🔑

Explain to students that a multistage rocket has advantages over a rocket with a single fuel chamber. Ask: **Why is a multistage rocket more efficient than a single-stage rocket?** *(Because the weight of a multistage rocket is gradually reduced as fuel is used up and empty fuel containers are cast off)* Help students understand that the more mass an object has, the more force is needed to accelerate it to orbital velocity. As fuel is burned and empty stages of a multistage rocket are discarded, the rocket's mass is reduced. Thus, less force—and less fuel—is needed to accelerate the final rocket stage to orbital velocity.

Support the Big Q ❓

SATELLITES Direct students' attention to **Figure 3.** Point out that only the spacecraft at the top of the rocket goes into orbit or could leave Earth behind. Remind students that a satellite is any object that orbits a planet. Ask: **What uses of satellites have you heard of?** *(Students will likely have heard of satellite television or satellite radio. Some students may be aware of weather satellites or GPS satellites.)* Tell students that all of these useful satellites were lifted into orbit by rockets.

21st Century Learning

COMMUNICATION Invite students to imagine they can interview a panel made up of scientists who helped to develop modern rockets. Have each student write two questions they would like to ask. Then have students pose their questions to the class and, using what they have learned, work together to construct answers.

21st Century Learning 📖

COMMUNICATION Have students read *Jet Packs* in the **Big Ideas of Science Reference Library** and create a short handout or multimedia presentation on how to use a jetpack. Students should use graphics, such as yellow warning signs, to convey important safety tips. They should include an explanation of the force that propels the jetpack forward, the function of the control handles, and the maximum amount of time a rider can stay in flight.

6 The third stage is discarded and the spacecraft moves higher until it finally enters space.

5 The third stage ignites.

4 The second stage separates and falls to Earth.

FIGURE 3 ....
A Multistage Rocket

✏️ **Apply Concepts** Explain what happens in the steps of the multistage rocket in the spaces provided. Which part of the rocket reaches the final destination?

The very top of the rocket

What Is the Main Advantage of a Multistage Rocket?

A rocket can carry only so much fuel. As the fuel in a rocket burns, its fuel chambers begin to empty. Even though much of the rocket is empty, the whole rocket must still be pushed upward by the remaining fuel. But what if the empty part of the rocket could be thrown off? Then the remaining fuel wouldn't have to push a partially empty rocket. This is the idea behind multistage rockets.

Konstantin Tsiolkovsky proposed multistage rockets in 1924. **The main advantage of a multistage rocket is that the total weight of the rocket is greatly reduced as the rocket rises.**

In a multistage rocket, smaller rockets, or stages, are placed one on top of the other and then fired in succession. **Figure 3** shows how a multistage rocket works. As each stage of the rocket uses up its fuel, the empty fuel container falls away. The next stage then ignites and continues powering the rocket toward its destination. At the end, there is just a single stage left, the very top of the rocket.

Multistage rockets were used in the 1960s to send astronauts to the moon. Today, they are used to launch a variety of satellites and space probes.

50 Exploring Space

Interactive Art shows how a multistage rocket works.

my science online.com 〉 **Multistage Rockets**

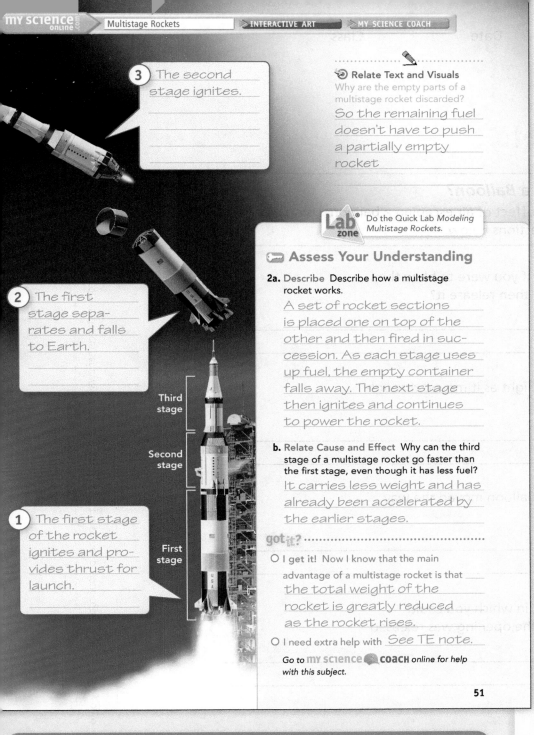

3 The second stage ignites.

✏️ Relate Text and Visuals
Why are the empty parts of a multistage rocket discarded?
So the remaining fuel doesn't have to push a partially empty rocket

2 The first stage separates and falls to Earth.

Third stage

Second stage

1 The first stage of the rocket ignites and provides thrust for launch.

First stage

Lab zone Do the Quick Lab *Modeling Multistage Rockets.*

🔑 Assess Your Understanding

2a. Describe Describe how a multistage rocket works.
A set of rocket sections is placed one on top of the other and then fired in succession. As each stage uses up fuel, the empty container falls away. The next stage then ignites and continues to power the rocket.

b. Relate Cause and Effect Why can the third stage of a multistage rocket go faster than the first stage, even though it has less fuel?
It carries less weight and has already been accelerated by the earlier stages.

got it? ....

○ I get it! Now I know that the main advantage of a multistage rocket is that the total weight of the rocket is greatly reduced as the rocket rises.

○ I need extra help with See TE note.

Go to **my science ⬤ coach** *online for help with this subject.*

51

Teach With Visuals

Tell students to look at **Figure 3.** Make sure students understand that this figure includes four illustrations of the same rocket—on the launch pad, dropping the first stage, dropping the second stage, and dropping the third stage. Ask: **Why is the first stage the largest rocket?** *(It has to lift the greatest mass so it contains the most fuel.)* **What is the smallest part of the rocket?** *(The actual spacecraft)*

✏️ Relate Text and Visuals Explain that visuals include photographs, graphs, tables, diagrams, and illustrations. Stress that visuals contain important information that supplement the text or help readers better understand it.

Lab Resource: Quick Lab **Lab zone**

L3 MODEL MULTISTAGE ROCKETS Students will make and launch a rocket model with two stages.

Evaluate ───────

Assess Your Understanding

After students answer the questions, have them evaluate their understanding by completing the appropriate sentence.

RTI Response to Intervention

2a. If students have trouble describing how a multistage rocket works, **then** review with them **Figure 3** and the related text.

b. If students need help explaining the relative speed of an rocket's third stage, **then** have them reread the boldfaced Key Concept statement.

my science ⬤ coach Have students go online for help in understanding multistage rockets.

Differentiated Instruction

L3 Multimedia Presentation
Have students work in groups to research ion propulsion and prepare a multimedia presentation for the class. You may wish to give students research questions such as the following: **What is ion propulsion? How is it similar to and different from chemical fuels? How is it used?**

L1 Make an Illustration Have students sequence and illustrate the steps in a rocket launch.

Lab zone **After the Inquiry Warm-Up**

The Science of Rockets

Inquiry Warm-Up, *What Force Moves a Balloon?*
In the Inquiry Warm-Up, you investigated the effect of air escaping a balloon. Using what you learned from that activity, answer the questions below.

1. **PREDICT** What do you expect would happen if you were to blow the balloon up larger than you did in Step 1 and then release it?

_____

_____

2. **OBSERVE** Describe the path of the balloon's flight as it moved through the air.

_____

_____

3. **DEVELOP HYPOTHESES** Why do you think the balloon moved the way it did?

_____

_____

4. **DESIGN EXPERIMENTS** Describe an experiment in which you could control the flight path of the balloon when the opening was released.

_____

_____

Place the outside corner, the corner away from the dotted line, in the corner of your copy machine to copy onto letter-size paper.

Assess Your Understanding

The Science of Rockets

How Were Rockets Developed?

got it? ···

○ **I get it!** Now I know that rocket technology originated _____

and gradually spread to _____

○ **I need extra help with** _____

_____

How Does a Rocket Work?

1a. **EXPLAIN** What is thrust?

_____

_____

b. **INTERPRET DIAGRAMS** Use Figure 2 to explain how a rocket moves
forward.

_____

_____

_____

_____

got it? ···

○ **I get it!** Now I know that a rocket moves forward when _____

_____

○ **I need extra help with** _____

_____

Assess Your Understanding

The Science of Rockets

What Is the Main Advantage of a Multistage Rocket?

2a. DESCRIBE Describe how a multistage rocket works.

_____

_____

_____

_____

b. RELATE CAUSE AND EFFECT Why can the third stage of a multistage
rocket go faster than the first stage, even though it has less fuel?

_____

_____

gotit? ....

○ **I get it!** Now I know that the main advantage of a multistage rocket is that _____

_____

_____

○ **I need extra help with** _____

_____

The Science of Rockets

How Were Rockets Developed?

A **rocket** is a device that expels gas in one direction to move in the opposite direction. **Rocket technology originated in China hundreds of years ago and gradually spread to other parts of the world.**

The first "rockets" weren't rockets, but simply arrows, coated with a flammable powder, that were lighted and shot with bows. By about 1200, the Chinese were using gunpowder inside their rockets. The British greatly improved rocketry in the early 1800s and used rockets against American troops in the War of 1812. Modern rockets were developed in the early 1900s.

How Does a Rocket Work?

A rocket moves forward when gases shooting out the back of the rocket push it in the opposite direction. A rocket demonstrates a basic law of physics. The force of the gas shooting out of the rocket is an action force. An equal force—the reaction force—pushes the rocket forward.

The reaction force that propels a rocket forward is called **thrust.** The amount of thrust depends on the mass and speed of the gases propelled out of the rocket. The greater the thrust, the greater a rocket's velocity. **Velocity** is speed in a given direction.

In order to lift off the ground, a rocket must have more upward thrust than the downward force of gravity. **Orbital velocity** is the velocity a rocket must achieve to establish an orbit around Earth. **Escape velocity** is the velocity a rocket must reach to fly beyond a planet's gravitational pull.

What Is the Main Advantage of a Multistage Rocket?

The main advantage of a multistage rocket is that the total weight of the rocket is greatly reduced as the rocket rises. In a multistage rocket, smaller rockets, or stages, are placed one on top of the other and then fired in succession. As each stage of the rocket uses up its fuel, the empty fuel container falls away. The next stage then ignites and continues powering the rocket toward its destination. Multistage rockets were used in the 1960s to send astronauts to the moon. Today, they are used to launch satellites and space probes.

On a separate sheet of paper, explain how a multistage rocket works.

Name _____ Date _____ Class _____

The Science of Rockets

Understanding Main Ideas
Fill in the blanks to identify the two forces.

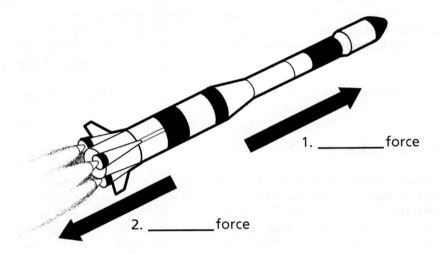

1. _____ force

2. _____ force

Building Vocabulary
Match each term with its definition by writing the letter of the correct definition in the right column on the line beside the term in the left column.

3. ___ thrust

4. ___ orbital velocity

5. ___ multistage rocket

6. ___ escape velocity

7. ___ reaction force

8. ___ rocket

9. ___ velocity

a. equal and opposite to the action force

b. speed in a given direction

c. velocity a rocket must achieve to orbit Earth

d. consists of stages placed on top of one another that drop off as fuel is consumed

e. reaction force that propels an object forward

f. velocity a rocket must reach to fly beyond a planet's gravitational pull

g. device that expels gas in one direction to move in the opposite direction

Enrich

The Science of Rockets

Read the passage and study the diagram below. Then use a separate sheet of paper to answer the questions that follow.

Rocket Thrust

Rockets fly by producing thrust. Thrust is the force that moves the rocket forward. Thrust occurs because forces always come in pairs. This is stated in Newton's third law of motion. According to this law, if one object exerts a force on a second object, the second object exerts a force of equal strength in the opposite direction on the first object. So, if you push on an object, the object pushes back on you with the same force.

You know that fuel burns in a rocket engine. When the fuel burns, hot gases form. The burning occurs in an area called the combustion chamber, which is attached to the rocket nozzle. The molecules of hot gas from the burning fuel are moving. These moving molecules hit the inside of the combustion chamber and nozzle, except at the back, where the molecules are able to escape. As the gas molecules hit the rocket, the rocket pushes back on the gas. Because the back of the rocket is open, this pushing back, or thrust, propels the rocket forward. The amount of thrust depends on several factors, including the mass and speed of the gases pushed out of the rocket. The greater the mass of the gas that is pushed outward and the faster the gas moves, the greater the thrust that pushes the rocket.

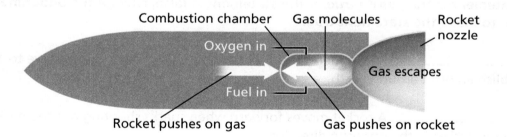

1. What is thrust?
2. What is Newton's third law of motion?
3. What happens when gas molecules hit the inside of a rocket's combustion chamber?
4. How is thrust produced in a rocket?
5. What are two ways to increase the amount of thrust a rocket produces?

Name _____ Date _____ Class _____

The Science of Rockets

Write the letter of the correct answer on the line at the left.

1. ___ The speed of a rocket in a given direction is the rocket's
   A velocity
   B thrust
   C momentum
   D power

2. ___ Rockets were invented in ancient
   A Britain
   B China
   C America
   D Egypt

3. ___ Two famous modern rocket scientists were
   A Robert Hooke and Joseph Priestly
   B Albert Einstein and Stephen Hawking
   C Konstantin Tsiolkovsky and Robert Goddard
   D Isaac Newton and Hans Christian Oersted

4. ___ The "stages" in a multistage rocket are
   A tanks of fuel
   B smaller rockets
   C separate operations
   D historical developments

If the statement is true, write *true*. If the statement is false, change the underlined word or words to make the statement true.

5. _____ Rotational velocity is the velocity a rocket must achieve to establish an orbit around Earth.

6. _____ A rocket moves forward when sparks shooting out the back push the rocket in the opposite direction.

7. _____ The total weight of a multistage rocket is greatly reduced as the rocket lands.

8. _____ The greater the mass, the greater a rocket's velocity.

9. _____ Warp speed is the velocity a rocket must reach to fly beyond a planet's gravitational pull.

10. _____ The amount of inertia depends on the mass and speed of the gases propelled out of the rocket.

The Science of Rockets

Answer Key

After the Inquiry Warm-Up

1. Accept all reasonable responses. Students will likely say the balloon would fly further.

2. The balloon flew in different directions.

3. The opening of the balloon fluttered as air escaped it. This caused the escaping air to repeatedly change directions. And for each of those directions, the balloon moved in the opposite direction.

4. Sample: Pass a long string through a straw. Tie the ends of the string to two points. Tape the straw to the side of an inflated balloon. Release the opening of the balloon.

Key Concept Summaries

Sample: A multistage rocket moves forward when gases shooting out its back thrust it in the opposite direction. It is made up of smaller rockets, called stages. The stages are stacked and fired in succession. As one stage is fired, the fuel container powering the previous stage falls away. So the total weight of the rocket is greatly reduced as the rocket rises into space.

Review and Reinforce

1. reaction
2. action
3. e
4. c
5. d
6. f
7. a
8. g
9. b

Enrich

1. the force that moves the rocket forward

2. If one object exerts a force on a second object, then the second object exerts a force of equal strength in the opposite direction on the first object.

3. The inside of the combustion chamber pushes in the opposite direction on the molecules of gas.

4. As gas molecules hit the inside of the combustion chamber and nozzle, the combustion chamber and nozzle push back on the gas. This reaction force is the rocket's thrust.

5. Increase the mass of gas by adding fuel or cause the gas molecules to move faster.

Lesson Quiz

1. A
2. B
3. C
4. B
5. Orbital
6. gases
7. rises
8. thrust
9. Escape velocity
10. thrust

The History of Space Exploration

Lesson Pacing: 3–4 periods or 1½–2 blocks

🕐 **SHORT ON TIME?** To do this lesson in approximately half the time, do the Activate Prior Knowledge activity on page 52. A discussion of the Key Concepts on pages 53, 54, 57, 58, and 59 will familiarize students with the lesson content. Have students do the Quick Labs. The rest of the lesson can be completed by students independently.

> **Preference Navigator,** in the online Planning tools, allows you to customize *Interactive Science* to your own teaching style. You can also edit lesson plans by selecting the Lesson Planner option.
>
> **Digital Teacher's Edition** allows you to access your Teacher's Edition and Resource materials online.

my science online

Lesson Vocabulary

- satellite
- space shuttle
- space station
- space probe
- rover

 Professional Development Note

Content Refresher

History of NASA The National Aeronautics and Space Administration (NASA) was created in 1958. Its mission was to explore space which, in 1958, meant human space flight. NASA immediately embarked on Project Mercury to see whether humans could survive in space. The project involved sending an astronaut into Earth's orbit on board a small craft. The success of the program led to Project Gemini, which involved using spacecraft built for a crew of two astronauts. During Project Gemini, NASA learned about living and working in space, as well as how to maneuver spacecraft in orbit. This last lesson became important later in the space program when spacecraft had to dock, or join up, with each other. Project Gemini was quickly followed by Project Apollo, which put astronauts on the surface of the moon in 1969. Although the last Apollo mission was in 1972, NASA began human space missions again in 1981 with the birth of the space shuttle program. Since that time, NASA has launched from one to nine space shuttle flights each year, with the exception of 1987 when no flights were undertaken.

LESSON OBJECTIVES

▭ Describe the history of human spaceflight, including the space race.

▭ Describe modern and future plans for crewed space exploration.

▭ Summarize past and future uses of space probes in space exploration.

Blended Path
Active learning using Student Edition, Inquiry Path, and Digital Path

ENGAGE AND EXPLORE

Teach this lesson using a variety of resources. Begin by reading **My Planet Diary** as a class. Have students discuss the questions scientists hope to answer through space exploration. Then have students do the **Inquiry Warm-Up activity.** Students will use a map of the moon to identify locations where astronauts landed and speculate on what astronauts saw at each place. The **After the Inquiry Warm-Up worksheet** sets up a discussion about the surface of the moon. Have volunteers share their answers to question 4 about why the far side of the moon has not been chosen as a landing site.

EXPLAIN AND ELABORATE

Teach Key Concepts explaining that the Space Race was a rivalry between the Soviet Union and the United States to explore space and develop technology. Continue to **Teach Key Concepts** by describing the Apollo Program. **Lead a Discussion** about man's first landing on the moon, the Apollo 11 mission, and the information NASA later gathered. Then **Lead a Discussion** about possible new missions to the moon.

Teach Key Concepts by explaining how NASA uses space shuttles to perform any important tasks. Continue to **Teach Key Concepts** by explaining that astronauts and scientists can carry out long-term observations in space from a space station.

Teach Key Concepts by explaining that a space probe uses scientific instruments, instead of humans, to collect data. **Support the Big Q** by discussing how scientists use information from space probes to better understand weather patterns on Earth. Have students practice the inquiry skill in the **Apply It activity.**

Hand out the **Key Concept Summaries** as a review of each part of the lesson. Students can also use the online **Vocab Flash Cards** to review key terms.

EVALUATE

Have students take the **Lesson Quiz.** For an alternate assessment, see the **EXAM**VIEW® Assessment Suite, Progress Monitoring Assessments, or SuccessTracker™.

ELL Support

1 Content and Language

Explain to students that the terms *shuttle, station,* and *probe* have multiple meanings. Have them find the first term in a dictionary, read the definitions, and then use the visuals in the chapter to predict which of the meanings fits the way the term will be used in the chapter. Repeat for the other two terms. Have students check their predictions as they read.

Lab zone Inquiry Path
Hands-on learning in the Lab zone

Digital Path
Online learning at **my science online**.com

ENGAGE AND EXPLORE

To teach this lesson with an emphasis on inquiry, begin with the **Inquiry Warm-Up activity.** Students will use a map of the moon to identify locations where astronauts landed and speculate on what astronauts saw at each place. The **After the Inquiry Warm-Up worksheet** sets up a discussion about the surface of the moon. Have volunteers share their answers to question 4 about why the far side of the moon has not been chosen as a landing site.

EXPLAIN AND ELABORATE

Focus on the **Inquiry Skill** for the lesson. Remind students that a model does not have to be three-dimensional. For example, a computer image and an illustration are models. What kind of model was used in the **Inquiry Warm-Up activity?** (A map of the moon's surface) Do the **Build Inquiry** to allow students to apply the concept of moon exploration by brainstorming the survival requirements and technical factors involved in landing safely on the moon and returning to Earth. Have students do the **Quick Lab** about humans in space.

Do the **Build Inquiry** to allow students to research the space station the experiments conducted on the ISS, how people live and work on the ISS, and transportation to and from the ISS. Have students do the **Quick Lab** about tools used in space.

Do the **Build Inquiry** to explore the advantages and disadvantages of probes and crewed missions. **Support the Big Q** by discussing how scientists use information from space probes to better understand weather patterns on Earth. Before beginning the **Apply It activity** review the different types of probes and how each is used. Have students do the **Quick Lab** about remote control and share their results. Students can use the online **Vocab Flash Cards** to review key terms.

EVALUATE

Have students take the **Lesson Quiz.** For an alternate assessment, see the **EXAM**VIEW® Assessment Suite, Progress Monitoring Assessments, or SuccessTracker™.

ENGAGE AND EXPLORE

Teach this lesson using digital resources. Begin by having students learn more about space probes and explore real-world connections to space exploration at **My Planet Diary** online. Have them access the Chapter Resources to find the **Unlock the Big Question activity.** There they can answer the questions and refine their responses as they continue through the lesson. You can re-assign the activity and have students submit their work so you can track their progress.

EXPLAIN AND ELABORATE

Students reading above, at, or below the lexile measure of this lesson can access basic content readings at their level at **My Reading Web.** Encourage students to use the online **Vocab Flash Cards** to preview key terms. Have students do the **Quick Lab** about humans in space.

Have students do the **Quick Lab** about tools used in space.

Use the **Interactive Act activity** online to allow students to build their own orbiters. **Support the Big Q** by discussing how scientists use information from space probes to better understand weather patterns on Earth. Assign the **Apply It activity** online and have students submit their work to you. Have students do the **Quick Lab** about remote control and share their results. The **Key Concept Summaries** online allow students to read a summary and see an image associated with each part of the lesson. Online remediation is available at **My Science Coach.**

EVALUATE

Have students take the **Lesson Quiz.** For an alternate assessment, see the **EXAM**VIEW® Assessment Suite, Progress Monitoring Assessments, or SuccessTracker™.

2 Frontload the Lesson
Have students create a word map by writing the vocabulary terms in the top box. As they read the chapter, they should fill in the bottom boxes with terms, phrases, or images associated with the vocabulary term.

3 Comprehensible Input
Have students use a Venn diagram to compare and contrast a space probe with the space shuttle.

4 Language Production
Pair or group students with varied language abilities to complete labs collaboratively for language practice. Have each student copy the completed written lab for personal reference.

5 Assess Understanding
Ask students to make notes about Key Concepts in the lesson and use the notes to prepare an oral presentation of the concepts. Encourage students to use the visuals in the lesson to support their presentations.

The History of Space Exploration

Establish Learning Objectives

After this lesson, students will be able to:

🔑 Describe the history of human spaceflight, including the space race.

🔑 Describe modern and future plans for crewed space exploration.

🔑 Summarize past and future uses of space probes in space exploration.

Engage

Activate Prior Knowledge

MY PLANET DIARY Read *The* Cassini *Space Probe* with the class. Point out that, while it's possible that Enceladus might support life, Enceladus does not have plants or animals. The *Cassini* probe found simple organic chemicals and indications of complex organic chemicals. Ask: **What questions do scientists hope to answer through space exploration?** *(Sample: How did the planets form?)*

BIG IDEAS OF SCIENCE REFERENCE LIBRARY 📖 Have students look up the following topic: Space Technology.

Explore

Lab Resource: Inquiry Warm-Up

L1 **WHERE ON THE MOON DID THE ASTRONAUTS LAND?** Students will use a map of the moon to identify locations where astronauts landed and speculate on what astronauts saw at each place.

The History of Space Exploration

 UNLOCK THE BIG ❓

🔑 **What Was the Space Race?**

🔑 **How Are Space Shuttles and Space Stations Used?**

🔑 **How Are Space Probes Used?**

MY PLANET DIARY   DISCOVERY

The *Cassini* Space Probe

Scientists believe that for life to emerge on a planet or moon, there needs to be liquid water and just the right amount of heat. In 2005, NASA's *Cassini* space probe sent back evidence that one of Saturn's moons, Enceladus, might fit the bill. *Cassini* photographed geysers spewing plumes of water hundreds of kilometers above the moon's surface.

Scientists found that the best explanation for these geysers was liquid water below the surface. So it's possible that there is both enough water and heat within Enceladus to support life.

Communicate Use what you know about life on Earth to answer the question below. Then discuss your answer with a partner.

Why do scientists think that conditions for life might exist within Enceladus?

It has liquid water and heat.

▶ **PLANET DIARY** Go to Planet Diary to learn more about space probes.

 Lab zone Do the Inquiry Warm-Up *Where on the Moon Did the Astronauts Land?*

What Was the Space Race?

In the 1950s, the Soviet Union was the greatest rival to the United States in politics and military power. The tensions between the two countries were so high that they were said to be in a "cold war." 🔑 The space race was the rivalry between the United States and the Soviet Union to explore space. It began in 1957, when the Soviets launched the satellite *Sputnik I* into orbit. The United States responded by speeding up its own space program, which led to the Apollo moon missions in the 1960s and the early 1970s.

SUPPORT ALL READERS
Lexile Measure = 1020L   Lexile Word Count = 1875

Prior Exposure to Content: May be the first time students have encountered this topic

Academic Vocabulary: *model, question, generalization, summarize*

Science Vocabulary: *satellite, space station, rover*

Concept Level: Generally appropriate for most students in this grade

Preteach With: My Planet Diary "The *Cassini* Space Probe" and Figure 1 activity

Go to **My Reading Web** to access leveled readings that provide a foundation for the content.

MY SCIENCE online.com

Vocabulary

- satellite
- space shuttle
- space station
- space probe
- rover

Skills

- 🔊 Reading: Ask Questions
- △ Inquiry: Make Models

The First Artificial Satellites A **satellite** is an object that revolves around another object in space. The moon is a natural satellite of Earth. A spacecraft orbiting Earth is an artificial satellite. *Sputnik I* was the first artificial satellite. This success by the Soviets caused great alarm in the United States.

The United States responded in early 1958 by launching its own satellite, *Explorer 1*, into orbit. Over the next few years, the United States and the Soviet Union launched many more satellites.

Later in 1958, the United States created a government agency in charge of its space program called the National Aeronautics and Space Administration (NASA). NASA brought together the talents of many scientists and engineers. They solved the difficult technical problems of space flight.

Humans in Space In 1961, the Soviets launched the first human into space. Yuri Gagarin flew one orbit around Earth aboard *Vostok 1*. Less than a month later, Alan Shepard became the first American in space, but did not orbit Earth. His spacecraft, *Freedom 7*, was part of the Mercury space program.

The first American to orbit Earth was John Glenn. He was launched into space aboard the space capsule *Friendship 7* in 1962. The tiny capsule orbited Earth three times.

FIGURE 1 ....
Space Race Timeline
✎ **Relate Text and Visuals** Write the name and historic first of each spacecraft with its picture.

Name: *Friendship 7*
First: *American to orbit Earth*

1962

Name: *Freedom 7*
First: *American in space*

1961

1961

Name: *Vostok 1*
First: *Human in space*

Name: *Sputnik 1*
First: *Satellite*

57

1958

Name: *Explorer 1*
First: *U.S. satellite*

53

Explain ──────────

Introduce Vocabulary

Write the term *rover* on the board. Tell students that *rover* means "wanderer." Point out that, capitalized, *Rover,* is a common dog name. Explain that in science *rover* denotes a small robot used in space exploration.

Teach Key Concepts 🔑

Explain to students that in the 1950s, the United States and the Soviet Union were the two most powerful countries in the world. Tell students that when the Soviet Union launched a satellite, U.S. leaders interpreted the launch as a sign that the Soviets were ahead in math and science and possessed technology that could make the Soviet Union more powerful than the United States. Ask: **How did the United States respond to the launching of *Sputnik I*?** *(The United States established a government agency to take charge of its space program and launched its first satellite in 1958.)* **What caused the space race to become even more competitive after the United States launched a satellite?** *(The Soviet Union launched the first human-occupied spacecraft.)* **How did the United States respond?** *(Less than a month after the Soviets, the Americans launched a human-occupied spacecraft.)*

Teach With Visuals

L1 Tell students to look at **Figure 1.** Ask: **Who is this astronaut?** *(John Glenn, the first American to orbit Earth)* Inform students that there were seven astronauts in the first group, so the name of each capsule ended in 7. The capsule Glenn traveled in was so small only one astronaut could fit inside it. **Where on the rocket do you think the space capsule was located?** *(At the top)*

My Planet Diary provides an opportunity for students to explore real-world connections to space exploration.

Explain

Teach Key Concepts 🔑

Explain to students that landing a person on the moon was a goal that grew out of the space race between the United States and the Soviet Union. Ask: **What was the Apollo program?** *(The American effort to land astronauts on the moon and return them to Earth)* **How did astronauts explore the moon's surface?** *(Apollo 11 astronauts walked on the surface and collected rock samples. In later missions, astronauts used lunar buggies.)*

Lead a Discussion

Tell students that launches of Mercury, Gemini, and Apollo missions were usually shown live on television. Millions of people across the country watched the launch of *Apollo 11* and followed the progress of the mission. Television cameras on the Eagle broadcast images of the astronauts back to Earth. Students may wonder who the third astronaut was. Michael Collins was the astronaut who stayed on the command module while Armstrong and Aldrin landed on the moon in the *Eagle*. Ask: **What did Armstrong and Aldrin do while on the moon?** *(They collected samples, planted an American flag, and left seismograph equipment.)* **What did later studies of "moonquakes" reveal to scientists?** *(That the moon may have a small core of molten material at its center)*

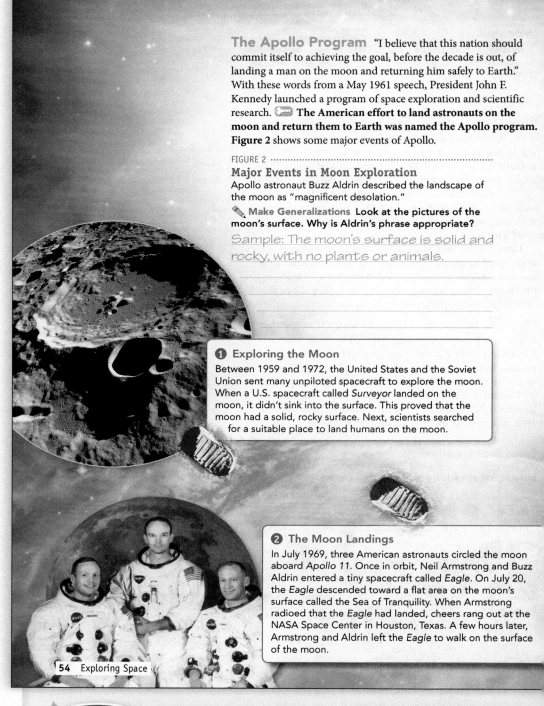

The Apollo Program "I believe that this nation should commit itself to achieving the goal, before the decade is out, of landing a man on the moon and returning him safely to Earth." With these words from a May 1961 speech, President John F. Kennedy launched a program of space exploration and scientific research. 🔑 **The American effort to land astronauts on the moon and return them to Earth was named the Apollo program. Figure 2** shows some major events of Apollo.

FIGURE 2 ···

Major Events in Moon Exploration
Apollo astronaut Buzz Aldrin described the landscape of the moon as "magnificent desolation."

✎ **Make Generalizations** Look at the pictures of the moon's surface. Why is Aldrin's phrase appropriate?

Sample: The moon's surface is solid and rocky, with no plants or animals.

❶ Exploring the Moon
Between 1959 and 1972, the United States and the Soviet Union sent many unpiloted spacecraft to explore the moon. When a U.S. spacecraft called *Surveyor* landed on the moon, it didn't sink into the surface. This proved that the moon had a solid, rocky surface. Next, scientists searched for a suitable place to land humans on the moon.

❷ The Moon Landings
In July 1969, three American astronauts circled the moon aboard *Apollo 11*. Once in orbit, Neil Armstrong and Buzz Aldrin entered a tiny spacecraft called *Eagle*. On July 20, the *Eagle* descended toward a flat area on the moon's surface called the Sea of Tranquility. When Armstrong radioed that the *Eagle* had landed, cheers rang out at the NASA Space Center in Houston, Texas. A few hours later, Armstrong and Aldrin left the *Eagle* to walk on the surface of the moon.

54 Exploring Space

Professional Development Note | Teacher to Teacher

Satellite Technology: "Eyes in the Sky" Since *Sputnik* was launched in 1957, satellite technology has become more advanced with each satellite placed in orbit. Satellites are used for Earth observation, weather prediction, and communication, along with other uses. Your students can use the NASA Web site to explore the various satellites and their uses over the years. Remind students to follow prescribed guidelines for Internet use.

✏ *Treva Jeffries*
Scott High School
Toledo, Ohio

3 Moon Rocks and Moonquakes

The astronauts collected 382 kilograms of lunar samples, commonly called "moon rocks," for analysis. Scientists such as Andrea B. Mosie and astronaut Jack Schmitt studied these rocks. They learned that the minerals that make up moon rocks are the same minerals that are found on Earth. However, in some moon rocks these minerals combine to form kinds of rocks that are not found on Earth.

One way Apollo astronauts explored the structure of the moon was to study the many moonquakes that occur there. Instruments they left behind, called seismometers, identified more than 7,000 moonquakes. By measuring these waves, scientists found that the moon may have a small core of molten rock or metal at its center.

4 On the Moon's Surface

Everything that the *Apollo 11* astronauts found was new and exciting. For about two hours, Armstrong and Aldrin explored the moon's surface, collecting samples to take back to Earth. They also planted an American flag.

Over the next three years, five more Apollo missions landed on the moon. In these later missions, astronauts were able to stay on the moon for days instead of hours. Some astronauts even used a lunar rover, or buggy, to explore larger areas of the moon.

✏️ **Summarize** After reading through the story of the Apollo program, list three discoveries that scientists made about the moon.

Sample: The moon has a solid, rocky surface. The minerals that make up moon rocks are among the same ones found on Earth. The moon may have a small core of molten rock or metal at its center.

55

Elaborate

21st Century Learning

CRITICAL THINKING Tell students that the Soviets' launch of *Sputnik I* spurred the United States to make educational reforms. Ask: **What subject areas do you think were the focus of the reforms?** *(Science and math)* **At what grade level do you think science was especially emphasized? Why?** *(Sample: In elementary school because a new generation would grow up with greater skills and interest in pursuing a career in science)*

Build Inquiry

L2 APPLY THE CONCEPT OF MOON EXPLORATION

Materials none

Time 15 minutes

Ask a student volunteer to read aloud the quote by President John F. Kennedy. Then, organize students in small groups. Tell them to suppose that they are NASA scientists during the early 1960s. Have students brainstorm how to send a crew of humans to the moon. Encourage students to consider survival requirements and technical factors involved in landing safely on the moon and returning to Earth. Have small groups designate a spokesperson to share their ideas with the class.

Ask: **Which items would be necessary for survival? How did you decide?** *(Sample: Water and oxygen; The lack of oxygen and water on the moon means that supplies of those items would have to last the entire trip.)*

Differentiated Instruction

L3 Communicate the First Moon Landing Acquire a recording or videotape of the first moon landing. Have students listen to or watch the recording. Ask them to act as newscasters creating a broadcast of the event. Students can present live broadcasts or record their broadcasts on audio- or videotape.

L1 Make a Timeline Have students make a timeline listing key accomplishments of the Apollo program.

Explain

Lead a Discussion

MISSIONS BEYOND THE MOON Point out that interest in moon exploration briefly revived in recent years. Ask: **What evidence in the text shows that interest in the moon revived?** *(In 2003, the European Space Agency launched an unpiloted spacecraft to orbit the moon and collect data for a lunar map.)*

Teach With Visuals

Tell students to look at **Figure 3.** Ask: **How might a lunar base be useful for the future human exploration of Mars?** *(Sample: A lunar base would provide a proving ground for new technologies that could then be used on Mars. Also, from a lunar base, missions could be launched to carry people to Mars.)*

Elaborate

Lab Resource: Quick Lab

L2 HUMANS IN SPACE Students will select materials they might use to build a spacesuit.

Evaluate

Assess Your Understanding

After students answer the questions, have them evaluate their understanding by completing the appropriate sentence.

RTI Response to Intervention

1a. If students have trouble identifying the Apollo program, **then** have them review **Figure 2.**

b. If students need help evaluating the Apollo program, **then** have them reread the subsection that describes its achievements.

MY SCIENCE COACH Have students go online for help in understanding missions to the moon.

FIGURE 3 ·······································

Lunar Base
A possible future base on the moon is shown in this artist's conception.

✎ **Describe** Explain how living on the moon would be similar to going camping.

<u>People living on the</u>
<u>moon would have</u>
<u>to bring their own</u>
<u>supplies.</u>

Missions Beyond the Moon The Apollo missions were a tremendous achievement. They yielded fascinating information and memorable images. Yet, the cost of those missions was high. There were few immediate benefits beyond the knowledge gained about the moon and Earth's formation. NASA moved on to other projects. For many years after, the moon was largely ignored.

In the first decade of the 21st century, interest in the moon revived for a brief period of time. In 2003, the European Space Agency launched an unpiloted spacecraft to orbit the moon. Its main purpose was to collect data for a lunar map. Such a map could be used in the future to select the best location for a possible lunar base. Figure 3 shows what a lunar base might look like.

Today, the United States is looking beyond the moon. In 2010, the country announced plans to launch a crewed spacecraft to Mars by the mid-2030's. The first missions would follow in the footsteps of the Apollo program that sent humans to the moon. A crewed mission would orbit Mars and then return. Only later would the United States attempt to land astronauts on Mars.

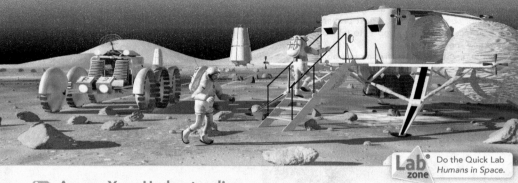

Lab zone® Do the Quick Lab
Humans in Space.

🔑 Assess Your Understanding

1a. Identify What was the Apollo program?
<u>The American effort to land</u>
<u>astronauts on the moon</u>

b. Draw Conclusions Was the Apollo program successful in meeting President Kennedy's challenge?
<u>Yes; the program was success-</u>
<u>ful because Americans landed</u>
<u>on the moon in 1969.</u>

got it?

○ I get it! Now I know that the space race began when the Soviets launched _____ <u>Sputnik 1</u> and continued with the American program called <u>Apollo.</u>
○ I need extra help with <u>See TE note.</u>

Go to **MY SCIENCE COACH** online for help with this subject.

56 Exploring Space

How Are Space Shuttles and Space Stations Used?

After the great success of the moon landings, the question for space exploration was, "What comes next?" Scientists and public officials decided that one goal should be to build space shuttles and space stations where astronauts can live and work.

Space Shuttles Before 1981, spacecraft could be used only once. In contrast, a space shuttle is like an airplane—it can fly, land, and then fly again. A **space shuttle** is a spacecraft that can carry a crew into space, return to Earth, and then be reused for the same purpose. Because it can be reused, NASA doesn't have to build a new spacecraft for each mission. **NASA has used space shuttles to perform many important tasks. These include taking satellites into orbit, repairing damaged satellites, and carrying astronauts and equipment to and from space stations.**

During a shuttle mission, astronauts live in a pressurized crew cabin at the front of the shuttle. There, they can wear regular clothes and breathe without an oxygen tank. Behind the crew cabin is a large, open area called the payload bay. A shuttle payload bay might carry a satellite to be released into orbit. It could also carry a laboratory in which astronauts can perform experiments. **Figure 4** shows the main parts of the space shuttle.

Vocabulary Identify Related Word Forms In science, the word *pressure* means "force per a given area." Why does the word *pressurized* mean that a crew cabin is filled with air?

The air exerts pressure on the walls.

FIGURE 4

A Space Shuttle
A space shuttle has a crew cabin, a payload bay, and rockets.

✎ **Interpret Diagrams** On the diagram, label the main parts of the space shuttle and explain their use.

Crew cabin: crew lives there
Payload bay: carries equipment
Rockets: move the shuttle

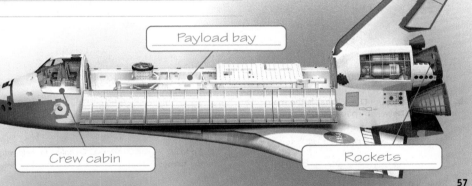

Payload bay

Crew cabin

Rockets

57

Explain

Teach Key Concepts

Explain to students that NASA uses space shuttles to perform many important tasks. Ask: **What functions do space shuttles serve?** (They take satellites into orbit, repair damaged satellites, and carry astronauts and equipment to and from space stations.) **How is the space shuttle different from previous spacecraft?** (The shuttle can be reused. Other spacecraft could not.) **What is an advantage of having a pressurized crew cabin?** (Astronauts do not have to wear pressurized space suits all the time.)

Teach With Visuals

Tell students to look at **Figure 4.** Ask: **What is the largest part of the space shuttle?** (Payload bay) **How is the space shuttle like an airplane?** (It has wings and a tail.) Make sure students understand that the rockets on the shuttle are for maneuvering, not for achieving orbit. Ask: **What do you think is missing from this illustration?** (The rocket that lifts the shuttle into orbit)

Differentiated Instruction

L3 Challenger and Columbia Tell students that, tragically, two shuttles built by NASA—*Challenger* and *Columbia*—were destroyed during flights. Have students research and report on the debate that occurred after the *Columbia* disaster in 2003, about whether to continue the space shuttle program.

L1 The Space Shuttle Draw students' attention to **Figure 4.** As they interpret and label the diagram, have them point to places in the text that indicate what label or description goes where.

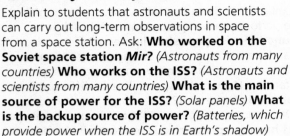

Explain

Teach Key Concepts

Explain to students that astronauts and scientists can carry out long-term observations in space from a space station. Ask: **Who worked on the Soviet space station *Mir*?** *(Astronauts from many countries)* **Who works on the ISS?** *(Astronauts and scientists from many countries)* **What is the main source of power for the ISS?** *(Solar panels)* **What is the backup source of power?** *(Batteries, which provide power when the ISS is in Earth's shadow)*

Elaborate

Build Inquiry

L2 COMMUNICATE KNOWLEDGE ABOUT THE INTERNATIONAL SPACE STATION (ISS)

Materials poster board, markers, NASA Web site

Time 30 minutes

Ask students to suppose that they are scientists from different countries, working together on the ISS. Organize them in four groups, and assign each group to research the ISS and summarize one of the following: its design; experiments conducted there; life on board; and getting to and from the ISS. Groups can present their findings to the class.

Ask: **How does the information learned from living and working on the ISS benefit society as a whole?** *(Sample: Developing more efficient ways of recycling water helps people on Earth.)*

Lab Resource: Quick Lab

L1 WHICH TOOL WOULD YOU USE IN SPACE?
Students will explore how to adapt tools for space.

Evaluate

Assess Your Understanding

After students answer the questions, have them evaluate their understanding by completing the appropriate sentence.

RTI Response to Intervention

2a. If students have trouble identifying a space shuttle and space station **then** have them find and review the descriptions of each in this subsection.

b. If students have trouble contrasting space shuttles and space stations, **then** have them think about the amount of time astronauts spend in each.

MY SCIENCE COACH Have students go online for help in understanding space shuttles and space stations

58 Exploring Space

FIGURE 5 ······
International Space Station

✎ **CHALLENGE** State one advantage of building a space station in orbit instead of sending it up all in one piece.

People can start working in the space station even though it is unfinished.

Space Stations Have you ever wondered what it would be like to live in space? A **space station** is a large artificial satellite on which people can live and work for long periods. **A space station provides a place where long-term observations and experiments can be carried out in space.** In the 1970s and 1980s, both the United States and the Soviet Union placed space stations in orbit. The Soviet space station *Mir* stayed in orbit for 15 years before it fell to Earth in 2001. Astronauts from many countries spent time aboard *Mir*.

In the 1990s, the United States and 15 other countries began constructing the International Space Station (ISS). The first module, or section, of the station was placed into orbit in 1998. Since then, many other modules have been added. On board, astronauts from many countries are carrying out experiments in various fields of science. They are also learning more about how humans adapt to space.

The main source of power for the International Space Station is its eight large arrays of solar panels, as shown in **Figure 5.** Together, the solar panels contain more than 250,000 solar cells, each capable of converting sunlight into electricity. At full power, the solar panels produce enough electricity to power about 55 houses on Earth. The ISS carries large batteries to provide power when it is in Earth's shadow.

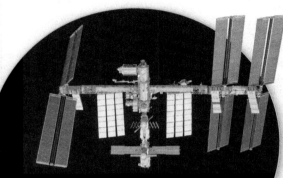

 Lab zone Do the Quick Lab *Which Tool Would You Use in Space?*

Assess Your Understanding

2a. Describe What is a space shuttle? What is a space station?

Space shuttle: a spacecraft that can carry people into space and back; space station: a place for long-term observations and experiments in space

b. Compare and Contrast What is the main difference between space shuttles and space stations?

Space stations permit long-term living in space.

got it?

○ I get it! Now I know that space shuttles are used to *take satellites into orbit and carry astronauts to space stations,*

and a space station is used to *provide a place where people can live and work for long periods in space.*

○ I need extra help with *See TE note.*

Go to **MY SCIENCE COACH** *online for help with this subject.*

58 Exploring Space

How Are Space Probes Used?

Since space exploration began in the 1950s, only 24 people have traveled as far as the moon. No one has traveled farther. Yet, during this period, space scientists have gathered a great deal of information about other parts of the solar system. This data was collected by space probes. A **space probe** is a spacecraft that carries scientific instruments that can collect data, but has no human crew.

Each space probe is designed for a specific mission. Some are designed to land on a certain planet, as shown in **Figure 6**. Others are designed to fly by and collect data about more than one planet. **A space probe collects data about the solar system and sends the information back to Earth.**

Each space probe has a power system to produce electricity and a communication system to send and receive signals. Probes also carry scientific instruments to collect data and perform experiments. Some probes, called orbiters, are equipped to photograph and analyze the atmosphere of a planet. Other probes, called landers, are equipped to land on a planet and analyze the materials on its surface. Some have small robots called **rovers** that move around on the surface. A rover typically has instruments that collect and analyze soil and rock samples.

Ask Questions What is one question about another planet you would want information from a space probe to answer?

Sample: Is there water on the surface?

FIGURE 6 ....
> **INTERACTIVE ART** Space Probe Mission
The postcards show the steps of a space probe mission.

✎ Write captions to tell the story of the space probe.

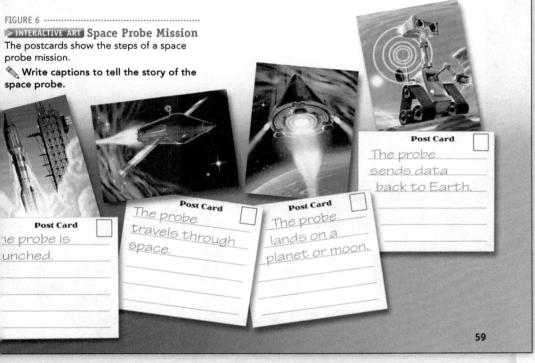

Post Card
ne probe is unched.

Post Card
The probe travels through space.

Post Card
The probe lands on a planet or moon.

Post Card
The probe sends data back to Earth.

59

Differentiated Instruction

L3 Design a Mural Have interested students collaborate to make a classroom mural giving information about the *Lunar Prospector, Cassini,* Mars Exploration Rover (*Opportunity* and *Spirit*), and *New Horizons* probes. Students can organize themselves in pairs or small groups of researchers, photo researchers, caption writers, editors, and layout designers.

L1 Make a Chart Draw a chart on the board, and write three column heads: *Shuttles, Stations,* and *Probes.* Have students provide details to compare and contrast these spacecraft as you list them.

Explain

Teach Key Concepts 🔑

Explain to students that a space probe has no human crew. Instead, it uses scientific instruments to collect data. Ask: **What are two different kinds of probes?** (*Orbiters, which photograph and analyze the atmosphere of a planet and landers, which land on a planet and analyze the materials on its surface*) **What are rovers?** (*Rovers are small robots, with which some landers are equipped. Rovers usually have instruments that collect and analyze soil and rock samples.*)

Ask Questions Explain to students that asking themselves questions as they read is an excellent way to engage with and get more out of a text.

Elaborate

Build Inquiry 🧪

L1 SPACE PROBES VERSUS CREWED MISSIONS

Materials diagram of the solar system

Time 10 minutes

Tell students that both probes and crewed missions have advantages and disadvantages. Point out Earth and the moon on the diagram. Then point out Mars.

Ask: **Which trip would involve the longer traveling time: a trip to Mars or to the moon?** (*A trip to Mars*) Tell students that a trip to Mars would take several months but a trip to the moon would take only a few days. Ask: **How would such a long journey to Mars affect people in space?** (*Sample: It would be very hard for the crew; they might get homesick or cranky and have difficulty working with others.*)

Interactive Art allows students to build their own orbiters.

my science online | Space Probes

Explain

Support the Big Q

INFORMATION FROM SPACE PROBES Space probes send a wealth of information back to Earth. Some space probes have studied weather conditions on other climates. Explain to students that this information allows scientists to better understand weather patterns on Earth. Ask: **How would a better understanding of our weather patterns be useful?** *(It could help farmers better plan when to plant crops. It could help meteorologists to be able to detect conditions that lead to storms sooner.)*

Elaborate

Apply It!

L1 Before beginning the activity, have them review the different types of probes and how each is used.

Make Models Be sure students understand that a model does not have to be three-dimensional. For example, a computer image and an illustration are models.

Space probes such as the ones pictured here have now visited or passed near all of the planets. They have also explored many moons, asteroids, and comets.

1 Make Models Choose a type of probe, either orbiter or lander, and draw your probe in the space provided below. List by number the tools required by each type of probe.

Lander: Sample: 1, 2, 3, 4, 5, 6, 7, 8

Orbiter: Sample: 1, 4, 5, 8

2 CHALLENGE On the note paper, explain why you chose each item.

Design Your Own Space Probe

Students should draw a space probe with a range of features adapted to its purpose.

1. Solar panel
2. Wheels
3. Parachute
4. Camera
5. Antenna
6. Robotic arm
7. Landing pad
8. Mini lab

Lunar Prospector, 1998
Lunar Prospector found evidence of water ice and identified other minerals on the moon's surface.

60 Exploring Space

Digital Lesson: Assign the *Apply It* activity online and have students submit their work to you.

my science online.com   Space Probes

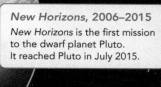

New Horizons, 2006–2015
New Horizons is the first mission to the dwarf planet Pluto. It reached Pluto in July 2015.

Cassini, 2004
Cassini explored Saturn's moons. It launched a smaller probe, *Huygens*, which explored Titan, Saturn's largest moon.

✎ *Sample for a lander: solar panel for energy; wheels to move around; parachute to land; robotic arm to pick up soil; camera to take pictures; antenna to send data to Earth; robotic arm to pick up rocks; landing pads to land*

Mars Exploration Rovers, 2004
Two rovers, *Opportunity* and *Spirit*, explored Mars's surface and found evidence of ancient water.

Lab zone Do the Quick Lab *Remote Control*.

🗝 Assess Your Understanding

3a. Summarize What is a space probe?
A spacecraft with scientific instruments but no crew

b. Make Judgments What are the advantages and disadvantages of a space probe compared to a piloted spacecraft?
Sample: A probe costs less but has no one on board to repair problems.

got it? ⋯⋯⋯⋯⋯⋯⋯⋯⋯⋯⋯

○ **I get it!** Now I know that a space probe *collects data about the solar system and sends the data back to Earth.*

○ **I need extra help with** *See TE note.*

Go to MY SCIENCE 🌐 **COACH** *online for help with this subject.*

61

21st Century Learning

CRITICAL THINKING Tell students that probes launched during the 1970s moved faster through space than later probes. Challenge students to infer why NASA slowed down its probes. *(A fast-moving probe is difficult to stop—it speeds past its destination, giving it little time to gather data. A slow-moving spacecraft is more easily controlled and can be made to swing around a planet, allowing plenty of time to gather data.)*

Lab Resource: Quick Lab

L2 REMOTE CONTROL Students will explore what it is like to control an exploratory device by remote.

Evaluate ⎯⎯⎯⎯⎯⎯

Assess Your Understanding

After students answer the questions, have them evaluate their understanding by completing the appropriate sentence.

R T I Response to Intervention

3a. If students need help identifying a space probe, **then** have them find and reread the sentence that contains the highlighted vocabulary term.

b. If students have trouble assessing the advantages and disadvantages of a space probe and a piloted spacecraft, **then** remind them that interest in moon exploration waned for many years, partly due to its high cost.

MY SCIENCE Ⓢ **COACH** Have students go online for help in understanding space probes.

Differentiated Instruction

L3 Write a News Report Have students pretend that, as a newspaper reporter, they are covering the launch of a new space probe. Tell them to write a brief news story that includes details on the probe's mission and how it works. What planet will it explore? What questions will it try to answer?

L1 Research Have students research to find artists' views of different space probes. Encourage students to share and explain the images they find.

Labzone **After the Inquiry Warm-Up**

The History of Space Exploration

Inquiry Warm-Up, *Where on the Moon Did the Astronauts Land?*
In the Inquiry Warm-Up, you investigated the surface of the moon. Using what you learned from that activity, answer the questions below.

1. **OBSERVE** What features are closest to the landing site you chose?

_____

2. **COMPARE AND CONTRAST** How does your landing site compare to the landing site chosen for *Eagle*?

_____

_____

3. **APPLY CONCEPTS** What area might make a poor choice for a landing site? Explain.

_____

_____

4. **DRAW CONCLUSIONS** These landmarks are all on the near side of the moon that can be seen from Earth. Why do you think that astronauts chose not to land on the far side of the moon?

_____

_____

_____

Assess Your Understanding

The History of Space Exploration

What Was the Space Race?

1a. IDENTIFY What was the Apollo program?

_____

b. DRAW CONCLUSIONS Was the Apollo program successful in meeting President Kennedy's challenge?

_____

_____

_____

got it? ....

○ **I get it!** Now I know that the space race began when the Soviets launched _____ and continued with the American program called _____

○ **I need extra help with** _____

_____

How Are Space Shuttles and Space Stations Used?

2a. DESCRIBE What is a space shuttle? What is a space station?

_____

_____

_____

b. COMPARE AND CONTRAST What is the main difference between space shuttles and space stations?

_____

got it? ....

○ **I get it!** Now I know that space shuttles are used to _____

_____

and a space station is used to _____

_____

○ **I need extra help with** _____

_____

The History of Space Exploration

How Are Space Probes Used?

3a. **SUMMARIZE** What is a space probe?

_____

b. **MAKE JUDGMENTS** What are the advantages and disadvantages of a space probe compared to a piloted spacecraft?

_____

_____

got it? ···

○ **I get it!** Now I know that a space probe _____

_____

○ **I need extra help with** _____

_____

The History of Space Exploration

What Was the Space Race?

The space race was the rivalry between the United States and the Soviet Union to explore space. It began in 1957, when the Soviets launched the satellite Sputnik I into orbit. The United States responded by speeding up its own space program, which led to the Apollo moon missions in the 1960s.

A **satellite** is an object that revolves around another object in space. *Sputnik I*, launched by the Soviets, was the first artificial satellite to orbit Earth. Greatly alarmed, the United States launched its own satellite, *Explorer I*, in 1958. Later that same year, the United States created the National Aeronautics and Space Administration (NASA).

The American effort to land astronauts on the moon and return them to Earth was named the Apollo program. Today, the United States is looking beyond the moon. In 2010, the country announced plans to launch a crewed spacecraft to Mars by the mid-2030's.

How Are Space Shuttles and Space Stations Used?

A **space shuttle** is a spacecraft that can carry a crew into space, return to Earth, and be reused for the same purpose. **NASA has used space shuttles to perform many important tasks. These include taking satellites into orbit, repairing damaged satellites, and carrying astronauts and equipment to and from space stations.**

A **space station** is a large artificial satellite. **A space station provides a place where long-term observations and experiments can be carried out in space.** In the 1980s, the United States and 15 other countries decided to construct the International Space Station (ISS).

How Are Space Probes Used?

A **space probe** carries scientific instruments but has no human crew. **A space probe collects data about the solar system and sends the information back to Earth.** Probes called orbiters are equipped to photograph and analyze the atmosphere of a planet.

Probes called landers are equipped to land on a planet and analyze the materials on its surface. Some probes have small robots called **rovers** that move around on the surface.

On a separate sheet of paper, explain what space shuttles, space probes, and space stations are and how they are used.

Name _____ Date _____ Class _____

The History of Space Exploration

Understanding Main Ideas
Identify each of the drawings below. Then answer the questions that follow in the spaces provided.

  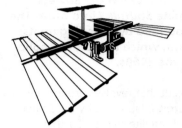 

1. _____ 2. _____ 3. _____ 4. _____

5. Compare and contrast a space shuttle and a space station.

   _____

   _____

   _____

6. What opportunities do space probes offer scientists?

   _____

   _____

   _____

Building Vocabulary
On a separate sheet of paper, write a definition for each of these terms.

7. space station
8. space probe
9. rover
10. space shuttle

Enrich

The History of Space Exploration

> The illustrations below show how lunar regolith forms. Read the passage and study the illustrations. Then use a separate sheet of paper to answer the questions that follow.

Moon Dust

When the Apollo astronauts stepped onto the moon's surface, they left footprints in the thick layer of dust and rubble. This loose material is called lunar regolith, and it covers most of the moon's surface. Its thickness ranges from a few centimeters at some places to several meters at others.

Meteoroid — Moon's surface

The moon has been struck by many meteoroids. When meteoroids hit the moon, some rock is melted and thrown upward from the moon's surface. Pieces of rock that don't melt also get thrown upward.

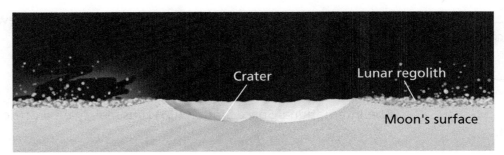
Crater — Lunar regolith — Moon's surface

The pieces of molten rock cool, forming volcanic glass, and fall back to the moon's surface. Pieces of rock and dust that don't melt also fall back to the moon. This loose, broken material accumulates on the surface. After many meteoroid impacts, the dust and rubble become a thick layer of lunar regolith.

1. What is lunar regolith?
2. How does lunar regolith form?
3. Why do you think some rock melts during meteoroid collisions?
4. Why does the material thrown upward during meteoroid collisions fall back to the moon's surface?
5. Which region of the moon is probably older—one covered by a thick layer of regolith or one covered by a thin layer of regolith?

Lesson Quiz

The History of Space Exploration

Fill in the blank to complete each statement.

1. A spacecraft that has various scientific instruments that can collect data but has no human crew is called a(n) _____.

2. A(n) _____ is a large artificial satellite on which people can live and work for long periods.

3. Some probes have small robots called _____ that can move about on the surface of another planet or moon.

4. A(n) _____ is a spacecraft that can carry a crew into space, return to Earth, and then be reused for the same purpose.

If the statement is true, write *true*. If the statement is false, change the underlined word or words to make the statement true.

5. _____ The cost of the *Apollo 11* mission was <u>almost nothing</u>.

6. _____ In 2010, the United States announced plans to launch a crewed spacecraft to <u>Mars</u>.

7. _____ An advantage of a space shuttle is that it can be <u>recycled</u>.

8. _____ The International Space Station (ISS) runs mainly on <u>electric</u> power.

9. _____ Probes called <u>rovers</u> are equipped to photograph and analyze the atmosphere of a planet.

10. _____ In 1969, an American spacecraft called the *<u>Beagle</u>* became the first to bring a crew to the surface of the moon.

The History of Space Exploration

Answer Key

After the Inquiry Warm-Up

1. Accept all reasonable responses. Answers will vary based on the site chosen by students.

2. Accept all reasonable responses. Answers will vary based on the site chosen by students.

3. Accept all reasonable responses. Students may say the Apennine Mountains would make a poor landing site because it would be difficult to find a stable area on which to land.

4. Accept all reasonable responses. Students may say that the astronauts would find it more useful to explore the side of the moon scientists are more familiar with.

Key Concept Summaries

Sample: A space shuttle is a spacecraft that can carry a crew into space, return to Earth, and be reused for the same purpose. It is used to perform tasks such as taking satellites into orbit, repairing damaged satellites, and carrying astronauts and equipment to and from space stations. A space station is a large artificial satellite used for making long-term observations and carrying out experiments in space. A space probe (unlike a space shuttle or space station) has no human crew. A space probe collects data about the solar system and sends the information back to Earth.

Review and Reinforce

1. space shuttle
2. space probe
3. space station
4. rover

5. Sample: A space shuttle and a space station are both spacecraft. People can work on a space station for a relatively long period of time, whereas a space shuttle is a transportation vehicle that carries a crew to and from space.

6. Sample: Space probes allow scientists to gather information from places that are too far away for piloted spacecraft.

7. large artificial satellite on which people can live and work for long periods.

8. spacecraft that carries scientific instruments that can collect data, but no human crew

9. a small robot on some landers, which moves around on the surface and typically has instruments that collect and analyze soil and rock samples

10. a spacecraft that can carry a crew into space, return to Earth, and then be reused again for the same purpose

Enrich

1. a deposit of dust and rubble on the moon's surface

2. Meteoroids strike the moon and throw debris up and away from the crater. The debris falls back to the surface to form the lunar regolith.

3. Some of the energy from the impact is changed to heat, which melts some rock.

4. The moon's gravity pulls almost all of the material back to the surface.

5. The region covered by a thick layer of regolith; it probably has been exposed to more impacts over a longer period of time.

Lesson Quiz

1. space probe
2. space station
3. rovers
4. space shuttle
5. high
6. true
7. reused
8. solar
9. orbiters
10. *Eagle*

Using Space Science on Earth

How does exploring space benefit people on Earth?

Lesson Pacing: 2–3 periods or 1–1½ blocks

🕐 **SHORT ON TIME?** To do this lesson in approximately half the time, do the Activate Prior Knowledge activity on page 62. A discussion of the Key Concepts on pages 63, 64, and 66 will familiarize students with the lesson content. **Explore the Big Q** by reviewing the items developed in space that benefit people on Earth and discussing whether or not there are compelling arguments against space exploration. Do the Quick Labs and have students do the **Interactive Art activity** online. The rest of the lesson can be completed by students independently.

Preference Navigator, in the online Planning tools, allows you to customize *Interactive Science* to your own teaching style. You can also edit lesson plans by selecting the Lesson Planner option.

Digital Teacher's Edition allows you to access your Teacher's Edition and Resource materials online.

my science online.com

Lesson Vocabulary

- vacuum
- microgravity
- space spinoff
- remote sensing
- geostationary orbit

Content Refresher

Benefits of Space Science According to NASA, less than 1 percent of the U.S. budget is spent on the space program. NASA officials estimate that for every dollar invested in its ventures, the U.S. economy receives a $7 return in the form of job creation, economic growth, and taxes.

NASA stresses its contribution to the country's economic welfare because many people argue against funding the space program. Opponents of the space program say that the money could be better spent, for example, on education or medical research.

To counter such arguments, NASA provides on its Web site a detailed justification of space exploration. NASA points out that the basic knowledge about the universe gained through space exploration gives humans a better understanding of Earth. They also point to the areas in which NASA-developed technologies benefit society, such as: health and medicine, transportation, public safety, consumer goods, environmental and agricultural resources, computer technology, and industrial productivity.

LESSON OBJECTIVES

▭ Describe conditions in space, including near vacuum, extreme temperatures, and microgravity.

▭ Identify the benefits that space technology has provided for modern society.

▭ Describe some uses of satellites orbiting Earth.

ENGAGE AND EXPLORE

Teach this lesson using a variety of resources. Begin by reading **My Planet Diary** as a class. Have students the educational requirements for an electrical engineer. Then have students do the **Inquiry Warm-Up activity.** Students will examine a number of everyday items and materials and try to determine which of them were developed based on space science research. The **After the Inquiry Warm-Up worksheet** sets up a discussion about the objects that were developed from technologies originally used by the space program. Have volunteers share their answers to question 4 telling why astronauts needed cordless tools with portable power sources.

EXPLAIN AND ELABORATE

Teach Key Concepts by explaining that space has no air and different gravity conditions than Earth.

Teach Key Concepts by explaining that the space program has provided many benefits beyond space exploration. Have students practice the inquiry skill in the **Apply It activity.**

Teach Key Concepts by explaining that satellites are used for communications and for collecting scientific data. **Explore the Big Q** by reviewing the items developed in space that benefit people on Earth and discussing whether or not there are compelling arguments against space exploration. **Answer the Big Q** by leading a class discussion about the benefits of space exploration.

Hand out the **Key Concept Summaries** as a review of each part of the lesson. Students can also use the online **Vocab Flash Cards** to review key terms.

EVALUATE

Have students take the **Lesson Quiz.** For an alternate assessment, see the **EXAM**VIEW® Assessment Suite, Progress Monitoring Assessments, or SuccessTracker™.

ⒺⓁⓁ Support

1 Content and Language

Tell students that the term *vacuum* comes from a Latin word that means "to be empty." Ask them to name a common household appliance that has the term in its name. Discuss why that term might have been used to name the appliance. *(It creates a state of emptiness.)* Review the definition of *vacuum* as it is used in the lesson. Discuss how remembering the function of a vacuum cleaner can help them remember the meaning of the term as it is used in the lesson.

Lab zone Inquiry Path
Hands-on learning in the Lab zone

ENGAGE AND EXPLORE

To teach this lesson with an emphasis on inquiry, begin with the **Inquiry Warm-Up activity.** Students will examine a number of everyday items and materials and try to determine which of them were developed based on space science research. The **After the Inquiry Warm-Up worksheet** sets up a discussion about the objects that were invented from technologies originally used by the space program. Have volunteers share their answers to question 4 telling why astronauts needed cordless tools with portable power sources.

EXPLAIN AND ELABORATE

Focus on the **Inquiry Skill** for the lesson. Remind students that a conclusion is a statement that sums up what you have learned. What conclusion could be drawn in question 4 of the **Inquiry Warm-Up activity?** *(That using long cords on power tools would not be practical in space.)* Have students do the **Quick Lab** to understand what is needed to survive in space.

Before beginning the **Apply It activity,** have students identify each item shown in the eight numbered photographs and then have students explain the reasons for the connections they made. Have students do the **Lab Investigation** to draw conclusions about which type of blanket gives better protection against heat loss. **Explore the Big Q** by reviewing the items developed in space that benefit people on Earth and discussing whether or not there are compelling arguments against space exploration. Have students do the **Quick Lab** about the usefulness of satellites. **Answer the Big Q** by leading a class discussion about the benefits of space exploration. Students can use the online **Vocab Flash Cards** to review key terms.

EVALUATE

Have students take the **Lesson Quiz.** For an alternate assessment, see the **EXAM**VIEW® Assessment Suite, Progress Monitoring Assessments, or SuccessTracker™.

Digital Path
Online learning at my science online.com

ENGAGE AND EXPLORE

Teach this lesson using digital resources. Begin by having students learn more about space technology and explore real-world connections to conditions in space at **My Planet Diary** online. Have them access the Chapter Resources to find the **Unlock the Big Question activity.** There they can answer the questions and refine their responses as they continue through the lesson. You can re-assign the activity and have students submit their work so you can track their progress.

EXPLAIN AND ELABORATE

Students reading above, at, or below the lexile measure of this lesson can access basic content readings at their level at **My Reading Web.** Encourage students to use the online **Vocab Flash Cards** to preview key terms.

Assign the **Apply It activity** online and have students submit their work to you.

Use the **Interactive Art activity** online to allow students to match everyday objects to the space technology used to develop them. **Explore the Big Q** by reviewing the items developed in space that benefit people on Earth and discussing whether or not there are compelling arguments against space exploration. Have students do the **Quick Lab** about the usefulness of satellites. **Answer the Big Q** by leading a class discussion about the benefits of space exploration. Online remediation is available at **My Science Coach.** The **Key Concept Summaries** online allow students to read a summary and see an image associated with each part of the lesson.

EVALUATE

Have students take the **Lesson Quiz.** For an alternate assessment, see the **EXAM**VIEW® Assessment Suite, Progress Monitoring Assessments, or SuccessTracker™.

2 Frontload the Lesson

Preview the lesson questions. Ask students if there are any words they do not understand. Explain the specific meanings these words have in this science lesson.

3 Comprehensible Input

Have students use the information in the table on page 64 to write sentences about the uses of space spinoffs in consumer products.

4 Language Production

Pair or group students with varied language abilities to complete labs collaboratively for language practice. Have each student copy the completed written lab for personal reference.

5 Assess Understanding

Divide the class into small groups. Have each student identify a Key Concept from the lesson to discuss in his or her group. After the discussion, have the students talk about the Key Concepts as a group.

Using Space Science on Earth

Establish Learning Objectives

After this lesson, students will be able to:

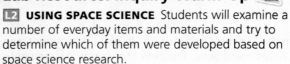 Describe conditions in space, including near vacuum, extreme temperatures, and microgravity.

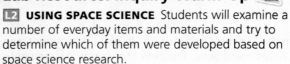 Identify the benefits that space technology has provided for modern society.

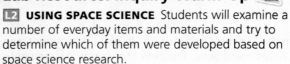 Describe some uses of satellites orbiting Earth.

Engage

Activate Prior Knowledge

MY PLANET DIARY Read *Ellen Ochoa* with the class. Inform students that in April 2002 Ochoa flew on *Discovery* to the ISS and, along with two colleagues, operated the space station's robotic arm for the first time. Ask: **What kinds of degrees, beyond her high school diploma, do you suppose Ochoa has earned?** (*A bachelor of science degree in physics and a master of science degree and doctorate in electrical engineering.*)

BIG IDEAS OF SCIENCE REFERENCE LIBRARY 📖
Have students look up the following topic: Space Technology.

Explore

Lab Resource: Inquiry Warm-Up Lab zone

L2 **USING SPACE SCIENCE** Students will examine a number of everyday items and materials and try to determine which of them were developed based on space science research.

Using Space Science on Earth

 UNLOCK THE BIG ?

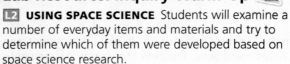 **What Are Conditions Like in Space?**

 How Has Space Technology Benefited People?

 What Are Some Uses of Satellites Orbiting Earth?

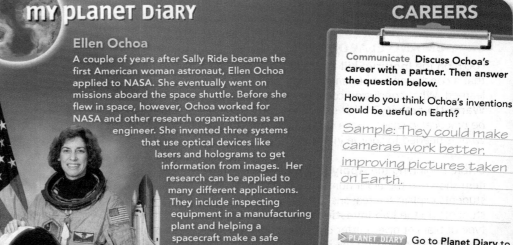

my planet diary

CAREERS

Ellen Ochoa

A couple of years after Sally Ride became the first American woman astronaut, Ellen Ochoa applied to NASA. She eventually went on missions aboard the space shuttle. Before she flew in space, however, Ochoa worked for NASA and other research organizations as an engineer. She invented three systems that use optical devices like lasers and holograms to get information from images. Her research can be applied to many different applications. They include inspecting equipment in a manufacturing plant and helping a spacecraft make a safe landing on Mars.

Communicate Discuss Ochoa's career with a partner. Then answer the question below.

How do you think Ochoa's inventions could be useful on Earth?

Sample: They could make cameras work better, improving pictures taken on Earth.

> **PLANET DIARY** Go to **Planet Diary** to learn more about space technology.

Lab zone Do the Inquiry Warm-Up Using Space Science.

What Are Conditions Like in Space?

Astronauts who travel into space face conditions that are very different from those on Earth. **Conditions in space that differ from those on Earth include near vacuum, extreme temperatures, and microgravity. Many types of engineers and scientists have worked together to respond to the challenges of space.**

SUPPORT ALL READERS
Lexile Measure = 960L   Lexile Word Count = 858

Prior Exposure to Content: May be the first time students have encountered this topic

Academic Vocabulary: *conclusions, identify, main idea*

Science Vocabulary: *vacuum, microgravity, geostationary orbit*

Concept Level: Generally appropriate for most students in this grade

Preteach With: My Planet Diary "Ellen Ochoa" and Figure 1 activity

Go to **My Reading Web** to access leveled readings that provide a foundation for the content.

my science online.com

Vocabulary
- vacuum
- microgravity
- space spinoff
- remote sensing
- geostationary orbit

Skills
- Reading: Identify the Main Idea
- Inquiry: Draw Conclusions

Vacuum Even though you can't see the air, it fills every room in your house. But space has no air and is nearly a vacuum. A **vacuum** is a place that is empty of all matter. Except for a few stray atoms and molecules, space is mostly empty. Since there is no air in space, there is no oxygen for astronauts to breathe. To protect astronauts, spacecraft must be airtight.

Because there is no air, there is nothing to hold the sun's heat. In direct sunlight, the surface of a spacecraft heats up to high temperatures. But in shadow, temperatures fall to very low levels. Spacecraft must be well insulated to protect astronauts against the extreme temperatures outside.

Microgravity Have you ever floated in a swimming pool? Astronauts in orbit experience a similar feeling of weightlessness, or **microgravity**. Their mass is the same as it was on Earth, but on a scale their weight would register as zero. Although they are in microgravity, they are still under the influence of Earth's gravity. In fact, Earth's gravity is holding them in orbit. Astronauts in orbit feel weightless because they are falling through space with their spacecraft. They don't fall to Earth because their inertia keeps them moving forward. Recall that inertia is the tendency of an object to resist a change in motion.

Figure 1 shows astronaut Steve Frick experiencing microgravity. Engineers must create devices that are capable of working in microgravity. Drink containers must be designed so that their contents do not float off. Long periods spent in microgravity can cause health problems. Scientists are trying to discover how to reduce the effects of microgravity on people.

FIGURE 1 ·····················

Eating in Space
Astronaut Steve Frick eats a snack in orbit.

✎ **Draw Conclusions**
How is eating in space different from eating on Earth?

In space, food and drink will float away because of microgravity.

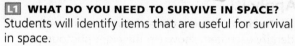
Do the Quick Lab *What Do You Need to Survive in Space?*

Assess Your Understanding
got it? ·······················

○ I get it! Now I know conditions in space that differ from those on Earth include near vacuum, extreme temperatures, and microgravity.

○ I need extra help with See TE note.

Go to my science coach *online for help with this subject.*

63

ELL Support

1 Content and Language
Write the term *vacuum* on the board, and tell students that the word comes from the Latin word *vacare*, "to be empty." Explain that a *vacuum* is a place that is empty of all matter. Point out that a vacuum cleaner is a device that uses an air pump to create a partial vacuum.

2 Frontload the Lesson
Invite students to brainstorm examples of special equipment or clothing that

allow people to survive in extreme cold or extreme heat. Tell students that they will learn about conditions in space that make such items necessary.

3 Comprehensible Input
Have students create a main-ideas-and-details chart that contains space in the left column for three main ideas. Have pairs or small groups of students work together to fill in the chart as they read the three sections of the lesson.

Explain

Introduce Vocabulary
Inform students that the prefix *micro-* means "extremely small." Explain that *microgravity* is a state of "extremely small" gravity. Microgravity—that is, gravity reduced to almost nothing—produces a near-weightless environment such as astronauts experience during space flight.

Teach Key Concepts 🔑
Explain to students that space has no air and different gravity conditions than Earth. Ask: **What is a vacuum?** *(A place that is empty of all matter)* **Why are there extreme temperatures in space?** *(There is virtually no matter, so there is nothing to hold the sun's heat.)* **Is it true that no gravity acts on astronauts orbiting Earth?** *(No. Gravity acts on the astronauts, but they and the spacecraft are falling through space together, which produces a feeling of weightlessness. Although they are falling, their inertia carries them forward, so they don't crash onto Earth's surface.)*

△ **Draw Conclusions** Explain to students that a conclusion is a statement that sums up what you have learned.

Elaborate

Lab Resource: Quick Lab 🧪
L1 WHAT DO YOU NEED TO SURVIVE IN SPACE?
Students will identify items that are useful for survival in space.

Evaluate

Assess Your Understanding
Have students evaluate their understanding by completing the appropriate sentence.

RTI Response to Intervention
If students have trouble contrasting conditions in space and on Earth, **then** have them review the Key Concept statement.

my science coach Have students go online for help in understanding conditions in space.

My Planet Diary provides an opportunity for students to explore real-world connections to conditions in space.

my science online.com | Conditions in Space

Explain

Teach Key Concepts

Explain to students that the space program has provided many benefits beyond space exploration. Ask: **What is a space spinoff?** *(An item that has uses on Earth but was developed for use in space)* **What types of space spinoffs are used in medicine?** *(Samples: lasers, pacemakers, and computer-aided imaging techniques)* **What are some spinoffs that benefit consumers?** *(Sample: Joystick controllers, scratch-resistant lenses, freeze-dried foods, shock-absorbing helmets, and shock-absorbing sneakers)*

21st Century Learning

CRITICAL THINKING Explain to students that many of the devices developed by the space program are miniaturized and lightweight. Many of these miniature parts have been developed for use on Earth. For example, artificial limbs have been made with controls as small as coins. Ask: **Why do you think so many of the devices developed by the space program are tiny and weigh very little?** *(Spacecraft travel faster and use less fuel when they carry less mass. Also, smaller devices take up less room.)*

Elaborate

Apply It!

L1 Before beginning the activity, have students identify each item shown in the eight photographs.

▲ **Draw Conclusions** Explain to students that a conclusion is a statement that sums up what they have learned. Suggest that students think about how the function of each item shown in the bottom row, or the material from which it is made, would be useful in space.

21st Century Learning

INTERPERSONAL SKILLS Have students read *Space Technology* in the **Big Ideas of Science Reference Library.** Ask partners to work together to create a chart that organizes the discoveries that have resulted from space exploration. Categories may include Sports, Safety, Medicine, Entertainment, Transportation, and any others. Items may be placed in more than one category. Have the pair identify which invention they think is the most important and state why.

How Has Space Technology Benefited People?

The scientists and engineers who have worked on the space program have developed thousands of new materials and devices for use in space. Many of these items have proved useful on Earth as well. An item that has uses on Earth but was originally developed for use in space is called a **space spinoff.** Often such spinoffs are modified somewhat for use on Earth.

The space program has led to the development of many **thousands of products, among them consumer products, new materials, medical devices, and communications satellites.** The tables on these pages show a few familiar examples.

Consumer Products Space spinoffs include many devices used in consumer products.

Materials	Use
Joystick controllers	Wheelchairs and video games
Scratch-resistant lenses	To make eyeglasses
Freeze-dried foods	Eaten by campers
Shock-absorbing helmets	Worn by cyclists
Shock-absorbing sneakers	Worn by runners

apply it!

Draw Conclusions Three items are shown in the top row that were developed for use in space. In the bottom row, write in the number for each item that corresponds to the space spinoff. Explain why you made each connection.

Sample: 1. The astronaut's radio system led to the head-phones. 2. Communications satellites are used for cell phones. 3. Shock-absorbing materials made for the boots are used in athletic shoes.

① ② ② ③

Digital Lesson: Assign the *Apply It* activity online and have students submit their work to you.

my science online.com | Space Spinoffs

New Materials
A variety of materials were first developed by chemists and engineers for use in spacecraft.

Materials	Use
Composite materials	Tennis rackets and golf clubs
Memory metals	Flexible metal eyeglass frames
Clear, ceramic materials	Dental braces
Shielding materials	Houses, cars and trucks

Medical Devices
Medical science has benefited greatly from the technology of the space program.

Materials	Use
Computer-aided imaging techniques	By hospitals
Lasers	To clean clogged arteries
Pacemakers with longer-life batteries	For hearts

Lab zone Do the Lab Investigation *Space Spinoffs.*

Assess Your Understanding

1a. Define What is a space spinoff?

An item originally designed for use in space that has uses on Earth

b. Summarize How has medical science benefited from the space program?

Medical spinoffs include lasers to clean clogged arteries, pacemakers for hearts, and computer-aided imaging for hospitals.

c. Compare and Contrast Choose one space spinoff and compare how it is used in space and on Earth.

Sample: Insulating materials that protect spacecraft from radiation are used in houses.

got it? ....

○ I get it! Now I know that the space program has developed *thousands of products that have many uses in modern society.*

○ I need extra help with *See TE note.*

Go to **my science COACH** online for help with this subject.

65

Make Analogies

MEMORY METALS Inform students that memory metals "remember" their former shape when bent. Memory metals were developed by chemists and engineers for use in space, to make spacecraft components lightweight yet strong. Have a volunteer squeeze a rubber ball and then release it. Ask: **What happened to the ball's shape when it was squeezed?** *(The shape changed.)* **What happened when the ball was released?** *(It regained its former shape.)* **How is the ball like a memory metal?** *(Memory metals also regain their former shape after being compressed.)*

Lab Resource: Lab Investigation **Lab zone**

L2 SPACE SPINOFFS Students will draw conclusions about which type of blanket gives better protection against heat loss.

Evaluate

Assess Your Understanding

After students answer the questions, have them evaluate their understanding by completing the appropriate sentence.

RTI Response to Intervention

1a. If students have trouble giving a definition for *space spinoff,* **then** have them find and reread the sentence that contains the highlighted vocabulary term.

b. If students have trouble explaining how medical science has benefited from the space program, **then** direct them to the table that lists three ways in which medical science has benefited.

c. If students need help comparing how a space spinoff is used on Earth and in space, **then** help them review the images in the *Apply It* activity.

my science COACH Have students go online for help in understanding space spinoffs.

Differentiated Instruction

L1 Write a Personal Essay Have students write one- to three-paragraph personal essays telling how space spinoffs have affected their lives. Encourage students to use the tables in their books to help them remember products, materials, and devices developed in space.

L3 Research Spinoffs Have students work with partners to find and learn about three space spinoffs that are not discussed in the text. Tell students to identify one spinoff for each of the following categories: consumer products, new materials, and medical devices. Invite partners to share their findings in class discussion.

Explain

Teach Key Concepts 🔑

Explain to students that satellites are used for communications and for collecting scientific data. Remind students that observation satellites use remote sensing. Ask: **What types of scientific data do satellites collect?** *(Sample: Information about the atmosphere, such as weather systems; information about Earth's surface, such as patterns of rainfall)* **What might be the advantage of gathering such data from above Earth's surface?** *(Sample: More area is visible from above; large-scale patterns can be seen; no obstacles are in the way.)*

🔍 **Identify the Main Idea** Explain to students that the main idea is the most important—or biggest—idea in every paragraph or section. If students have difficulty finding the main idea, suggest that they list all of the ideas in the paragraph and then choose the idea that is big enough to include all the others.

21st Century Learning

L1 **CRITICAL THINKING** Remind students that satellites are used by many people for many purposes. Ask: **In what professions do people rely on data collected by satellites?** *(Sample: Meteorology, geology, climatology, cartography)* **Who benefits from satellites in daily life?** *(Sample: Just about everyone; for example, if you have cable television, you benefit from satellites whenever you watch TV.)*

What Are Some Uses of Satellites Orbiting Earth?

When a World Cup soccer final is played, almost the entire world can watch! Today, hundreds of satellites are in orbit, relaying television signals from one part of the planet to another. Satellites also relay telephone signals and computer data. 🔑 **Satellites are used for communications and for collecting weather data and other scientific data.**

Observation satellites are used for many purposes, including tracking weather systems, mapping Earth's surface, and observing changes in Earth's environment. Observation satellites collect data using **remote sensing,** which is the collection of information about Earth and other objects in space without being in direct contact. Modern computers take the data collected by satellites and produce images for various purposes. For example, **Figure 2** shows a scientist studying weather data. Satellite data might also be used to analyze the amount of rainfall over a wide area, or to discover where oil deposits lie underground.

Satellite orbits depend on their purpose. Most communications satellites are placed in a geostationary orbit. In a **geostationary orbit,** (jee oh STAY shuh ner ee) a satellite orbits Earth at the same rate as Earth rotates and thus stays over the same place over Earth's equator all the time.

🖉 **Identify the Main Idea**
In the paragraph at the right, underline the uses of observation satellites.

FIGURE 2

Remote Sensing and Forest Fires
The scientist shown is studying weather data taken from a satellite by remote sensing.
🖉 **CHALLENGE** How can remote sensing help fight forest fires?

Remote sensing allows scientists to detect the conditions for fires before fires begin. It also allows scientists to monitor the fires safely.

66 Exploring Space

Interactive Art allows students to match everyday objects to the space technology used to develop them.

my science ONLINE.com ▶ Space Science on Earth

EXPLORE THE BIG ?

Space Spinoffs

How does exploring space benefit people on Earth?

FIGURE 3 ....

> **INTERACTIVE ART** The word bank below shows space spinoffs.

✎ **Demonstrate Consumer Literacy** Choose three items, and describe three ways you might use them on Earth. Label the items shown on the page.

GPS

Space helmet

Freeze-dried food	Solar panels	Space helmet
Communications satellites	Radio telescope	Scratch-resistant lenses
Global Positioning System (GPS)	Light-emitting diodes	Tiny fuel pumps
Gas detector	Infrared cameras	Pressurized ink

Sample: Freeze-dried foods might be used for camping, long-term storage, and emergency rations. Scratch-resistant lenses might be used in eyeglasses, binoculars, and cameras. Communications satellites might be used for cell phones, television, and satellite radio.

Lab zone — Do the Quick Lab *Useful Satellites*.

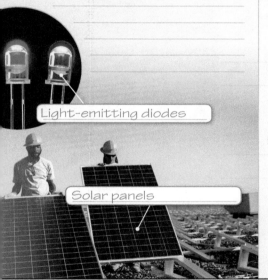

Light-emitting diodes

Solar panels

🔲 Assess Your Understanding

2a. Listing Name two uses of satellites that affect everyday life.

Sample: transmitting TV signals, collecting weather data

b. Infer What advantage would there be to placing a satellite in geostationary orbit?

The satellite would always be in the same place in the sky.

c. ANSWER THE BIG ? How does exploring space benefit people on Earth?

Technology developed for space science has spinoffs for people on Earth.

got it? ....

○ I get it! Now I know that satellites are used for *communications and for collecting scientific data.*

○ I need extra help with *See TE note.*

Go to **my science COACH** online for help with this subject.

67

Elaborate ——————

Explore the Big Question

Direct students' attention to **Figure 3.** Point out the word bank. Ask: **What information does the word bank give?** *(The word bank lists items developed in space that benefit people on Earth.)* **After reading this chapter, can you think of a way to argue convincingly that space exploration does *not* benefit people on Earth? Explain.** *(Sample: Although I can see why some Americans argue that there are greater priorities, I cannot think of a compelling argument against space exploration. The benefits in so many areas of life on Earth seem well worth the cost of the space program.)*

Lab Resource: Quick Lab

L1 USEFUL SATELLITES Students will explore how satellites are used to study Earth.

Evaluate ——————

Assess Your Understanding

After students answer the questions, have them evaluate their understanding by completing the appropriate sentence.

Answer the Big Q

To help students focus on the Big Question, lead a class discussion about the benefits of space exploration.

R T I Response to Intervention

2a. If students have trouble identifying two everyday uses of satellites, **then** review with them the information in this section.

b. If students have trouble inferring an advantage of a geostationary satellite, **then** use a globe and ping-pong ball to model the synchronous orbit of the satellite and rotation of Earth.

c. If students need help explaining how exploring space benefits people on Earth, **then** suggest that they focus on a single area, such as medicine.

my science COACH Have students go online for help in understanding space science on Earth.

Differentiated Instruction

L3 Design an Experiment Have students think of and write about a way scientists can use satellites to determine whether a rainforest is becoming smaller over time. *(Scientists can examine satellite images of an area taken over a period of years to find out whether the area covered by rainforest is changing.)*

L1 Make a Concept Map Have students make a concept map that shows different space spinoffs and their uses.

Lab **zone** **After the Inquiry Warm-Up**

Using Space Science on Earth

Inquiry Warm-Up, *Using Space Science*
In the Inquiry Warm-Up, you investigated objects that were developed from technologies originally used by the space program. Using what you learned from that activity, answer the questions below.

1. **EXPLAIN** Land-line telephones were invented long before the space program began. How do you think space exploration led to improvements in telephone communications?

   _____

   _____

2. **RELATE CAUSE AND EFFECT** What condition of working in space made it necessary to create new materials for astronauts' space boots that led to improvements in running shoes?

   _____

   _____

3. **INFER** How do you think astronauts use joystick controllers? Explain.

   _____

   _____

4. **DRAW CONCLUSIONS** The space program led to the development of cordless tools with portable power sources. Why do you think astronauts needed these?

   _____

   _____

Place the outside corner, the corner away from the dotted line, in the corner of your copy machine to copy onto letter-size paper.

Using Space Science on Earth

What Are Conditions Like in Space?

got it? ··

○ **I get it!** Now I know that conditions in space that differ from those on Earth include _____

_____

○ **I need extra help with** _____

_____

How Has Space Technology Benefited People?

1a. DEFINE What is a space spinoff?

_____

_____

b. SUMMARIZE How has medical science benefited from the space program?

_____

_____

_____

c. COMPARE AND CONTRAST Choose one space spinoff and compare how it is used in space and on Earth.

_____

_____

got it? ··

○ **I get it!** Now I know that the space program has developed _____

_____

○ **I need extra help with** _____

_____

Using Space Science on Earth

> **What Are Some Uses of Satellites Orbiting Earth?**

2a. **LISTING** Name two uses of satellites that affect everyday life.

_____

_____

b. **INFER** What advantage would there be to placing a satellite in geostationary orbit?

_____

_____

c. **ANSWER** ❓ How does exploring space benefit people on Earth?

_____

_____

gotit? ···

○ **I get it!** Now I know that satellites are used for _____

_____

○ **I need extra help with** _____

_____

Name _____ Date _____ Class _____

Using Space Science on Earth

What Are Conditions Like in Space?

Conditions in space that differ from those on Earth include near vacuum, extreme temperatures, and microgravity. Many types of engineers and scientists have worked together to respond to the challenges of space. Space has no air and is nearly a **vacuum,** a place that is empty of all matter. Since there is no air in space, there is no oxygen for astronauts to breathe. So spacecraft must be airtight. Spacecraft must also be well insulated to protect astronauts against the extreme temperatures outside.

Astronauts in orbit experience a feeling of weightlessness, or **microgravity.** Space engineers must create devices that can work in microgravity. Astronauts feel weightless because they are falling through space with their spacecraft. They don't fall to Earth because their inertia keeps them moving forward.

How Has Space Technology Benefited People?

A **space spinoff** is an item that has been used on Earth but was originally developed for use in space. Often such spinoffs are modified somewhat for use on Earth. **The space program has led to the**

development of many thousands of products, among them consumer products, new materials, medical devices, and communications satellites.

What Are Some Uses of Satellites Orbiting Earth?

Satellites are used for communications and for collecting weather data, and other scientific data. Observation satellites are used for many purposes, including tracking weather systems, mapping Earth's surface, and observing changes in Earth's environment. Observation satellites collect data using **remote sensing,** which is the collection of information about Earth and other objects in space without being in direct contact.

Satellites are placed in different orbits depending on their purpose. Most communications satellites are placed in a geostationary orbit. In a **geostationary orbit,** a satellite orbits Earth at the same rate as Earth rotates and thus stays over the same place on Earth's equator all the time.

On a separate sheet of paper, explain what space spinoffs are, list three categories of space spinoffs, and provide an example in each category.

Name _____ Date _____ Class _____

Using Space Science on Earth

Understanding Main Ideas
Answer the following questions in the spaces provided.

1. Name three conditions in space that are different from those on Earth.

   _____

   _____

2. Name a space spinoff for each category.

   Medical _____

   Material _____

   Consumer _____

3. What are some of the benefits of satellites in everyday life?

   _____

   _____

4. Name three ways in which observation satellites are used.

   _____

   _____

Building Vocabulary
On a separate sheet of paper, write a definition for each of these terms.

5. geostationary orbit
6. remote sensing
7. vacuum
8. microgravity
9. space spinoff

Enrich

Using Space Science on Earth

Read the passage and study the map below. Then use a separate sheet of paper to answer the questions that follow.

Geostationary Orbits and Polar Orbits

When a satellite is in a geostationary orbit, it is in orbit over the equator. Another kind of orbit is called a *polar* orbit. This is an orbit that passes over both the North Pole and the South Pole.

On the map below, draw a line to represent the path a satellite in a low polar orbit might take as it passes over the United States. An easy way to do this is to start with your pencil on the **X** (a place in Canada) and begin to move it straight south (down) to represent the direction of movement of the satellite. At the same time, move the paper to the east (right) to represent the motion of Earth. Your result will be a line moving from northeast to southwest. You can see that it is the combination of the satellite's motion and Earth's rotation that determines the path a satellite in polar orbit takes over Earth.

1. A satellite in a polar orbit traces a curved path over the surface of Earth. Explain why.

2. Why does a geostationary satellite not trace a path over the surface of Earth?

3. Suppose that the satellite in polar orbit whose path you drew takes two hours to complete one orbit. After two hours, Earth will have rotated two hours to the east, and the satellite will be passing over the place represented by the **Y** on the map. About where will it be in two more hours?

4. How often would the satellite in question 3 pass over the same point on Earth?

5. Television signals cannot pass through Earth. If you wanted to launch a satellite that would be used to transmit television images from the United States to Europe 24 hours a day, would you put it into a geostationary orbit or a polar orbit? Explain.

6. If you wanted to launch a satellite that could take photographs of the entire surface of Earth, what kind of orbit would you put it in? Explain.

Name _____ Date _____ Class _____

Using Space Science on Earth

Write the letter of the correct answer on the line at the left.

1. ___ Most communications satellites are

   A in a temporary orbit

   B in a geostationary orbit

   C in a mobile orbit

   D in their own unique orbit

2. ___ Observation satellites collect data by

   A remote sensing

   B direct observation

   C scientific experimentation

   D rotation and revolution

3. ___ Because space has almost no air, it is nearly a

   A desert

   B black hole

   C vacuum

   D wasteland

4. ___ A communications satellite is a space

   A spinoff

   B station

   C telephone

   D shuttle

If the statement is true, write _true_. If the statement is false, change the underlined word or words to make the statement true.

5. _____ Shock-absorbing sneakers are an example of a space <u>byproduct</u>.

6. _____ The space program has spurred development of <u>hundreds</u> of products that benefit people on Earth.

7. _____ Space has a much <u>wider</u> range of temperatures than Earth.

8. _____ An astronaut's <u>mass</u> is the same in space and on Earth.

9. _____ <u>Consumer product</u> space spinoffs include computer-aided imaging techniques.

10. _____ Engineers and <u>fabric designers</u> have developed a variety of materials for use in spacecraft that are also useful on Earth.

Using Space Science on Earth

Answer Key

After the Inquiry Warm-Up

1. Sample: With the advent of space travel, people needed to be able to communicate over much longer distances. This led to improvements in long-distance telecommunications.

2. a different level of gravity

3. Sample: to control probes and rovers; They send probes and rovers to places they cannot go themselves and need a way to control those devices remotely.

4. They needed to use the tools in places far from a place where they could plug them in; using long cords would not be practical.

Key Concept Summaries

Sample: "Space spinoffs" refers to the many thousands of products that were first developed in the space program and usually modified for use on Earth. They include consumer products, such as scratch-resistant lenses; new materials, such as "memory metals;" medical devices, such as computer-imaging techniques; and communications satellites.

Review and Reinforce

1. Space has greater temperature extremes and microgravity. Space has no air and is nearly a vacuum.

2. Sample: Medical—pacemaker; Material— memory materials; Consumer— shock-absorbing helmets

3. Sample: relaying of television and telephone signals and scientific data around the world

4. Sample: tracking weather systems, mapping Earth's surface, and observing changes in the environment

5. an orbit in which a satellite orbits Earth at the same rate as Earth rotates and thus stays over the same place all the time

6. the collection of information about Earth and other objects in space without being in direct contact

7. place that is empty of all matter

8. gravity reduced to almost nothing

9. item that has uses on Earth but was originally developed for use in space

Enrich

1. The path is a combination of the movement of the satellite and the movement of Earth.

2. Relative to any point on Earth, a satellite in geostationary orbit does not move, so it can't trace a path.

3. It would be the same distance to the west of Y that Y is from X.

4. once every twelve hours

5. The satellite should be in a geostationary orbit from which both the United States and Europe would be visible. The satellite would stay in the same relative position in the sky and could transmit from the United States to Europe 24 hours a day.

6. The satellite should be put into polar orbit because it would eventually pass over the entire surface of Earth. A satellite in geostationary orbit "sees" only one side of Earth.

Lesson Quiz

1. B
2. A
3. C
4. A
5. spinoff
6. thousands
7. true
8. true
9. Medical
10. chemists

Study Guide

Review the Big Q

Have students complete the statement at the top of the page. These Key Concepts support their understanding of the chapter's Big Question. Have students return to the chapter opener pages. What is different about how students view the image of the high-tech swimsuit now that they have completed the chapter? Thinking about this will help them prepare for the *Apply the Big Q* activity in the Review and Assessment.

Partner Review

Have partners review definitions of vocabulary terms by using the Study Guide to quiz each other. Students could read the Key Concept statements and leave out words for their partner to fill in, or change a statement so that it is false and then ask their partner to correct it.

Class Activity: Concept Map

Have students develop a concept map to show how the main ideas in this chapter are related. Have students brainstorm to identify the Key Concepts, vocabulary, details, and examples; write each on a sticky note; and attach the note at random on chart paper or on the board. Explain that the concept map will begin at the top with Key Concepts. Ask students to use the following questions to help them organize the information on the notes:

- What key events, developments, and achievements in the history of space exploration can you recall?
- What was the space race?
- What past and ongoing space programs involving the United States and/or other countries can you identify?
- How do people use satellites?
- How do space spinoffs benefit people on Earth?

My Science Coach allows students to complete the *Practice Test* online.

The Big Question allows students to complete the *Apply the Big Q* activity about how space exploration benefits people on Earth.

Vocab Flash Cards offer a way to review the chapter vocabulary words.

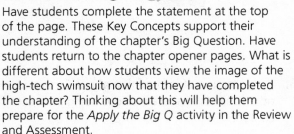

> Exploring Space

Space science benefits people on Earth through *space spinoffs and space satellites for communications and collecting data.*

LESSON 1 The Science of Rockets

🔑 Rocket technology originated in China hundreds of years ago and gradually spread to other parts of the world.

🔑 A rocket moves forward when gases shooting out the back of the rocket push it in the opposite direction.

🔑 The main advantage of a multistage rocket is that the total weight of the rocket is greatly reduced as the rocket rises.

Vocabulary
- rocket • thrust • velocity
- orbital velocity • escape velocity

LESSON 2 The History of Space Exploration

🔑 The space race was the rivalry between the United States and the Soviet Union to explore space, including the Apollo missions.

🔑 NASA has used space shuttles to take satellites into orbit, repair damaged satellites, and carry astronauts to and from space stations.

🔑 A space station provides a place for experiments in space.

🔑 Space probes collect data about the solar system.

Vocabulary
- satellite • space shuttle
- space station • space probe • rover

LESSON 3 Using Space Science on Earth

🔑 Conditions in space that differ from those on Earth include near vacuum, extreme temperatures, and microgravity.

🔑 The space program has led to the development of many thousands of products, among them consumer products, new materials, medical devices, and communications satellites.

🔑 Satellites are used for communications and for collecting weather data and other scientific data.

Vocabulary
- vacuum • microgravity • space spinoff
- remote sensing • geostationary orbit

ⒺⓁⓁ Support

4 Language Production

Arrange the class in small-group circles. Introduce a question based on the Essential Questions from the chapter. Then have one member of each circle give a fact or detail that helps answer the question. The student to his or her right should then provide a different fact or detail. The cycle continues until there is no new information to share and all questions have been discussed.

Beginning
LOW/HIGH Students can refer to their books or notes during the discussion.

Intermediate
LOW/HIGH Allow students extra time to share their facts and details.

Advanced
LOW/HIGH Challenge students to use vocabulary terms during the discussion.

Review and Assessment

LESSON 1 The Science of Rockets

1. Which term names a device that expels gas in one direction in order to move in the opposite direction?

a. space station   b. rover

c. space probe   **d.** rocket

2. Classify A jet airplane uses liquid fuel and oxygen from the atmosphere. The engine expels hot gases to the rear and the airplane moves forward. Is a jet a type of rocket? Explain.

Yes; a jet expels gas in one direction to move in the opposite direction, like a rocket.

Use the illustration to answer the question below.

3. Apply Concepts The diagram shows a rocket lifting off. What does each arrow represent?

Red arrow: action force; blue arrow: reaction force called thrust

4. math! For every force there is an equal and opposite force. Describe a line graph that shows the relationship between a rocket's reaction force and thrust.

The graph would be a straight line at a 45-degree angle.

LESSON 2 The History of Space Exploration

5. What is any object that revolves around another object in space?

a. rocket   b. vacuum

c. satellite   d. shuttle

6. Relate Cause and Effect After the Soviet Union launched *Sputnik I*, American educators improved math and science education. What explains this decision?

They believed that better math and science education would help Americans compete in space exploration.

7. Make Generalizations Give one way in which the International Space Station could help with further exploration of the solar system.

Research on the space station will teach us more about how humans might adapt to long periods of space travel.

8. Compare and Contrast How is a space shuttle different from a space probe?

A space shuttle is a reusable craft that carries astronauts into space and back. A space probe is an unmanned spacecraft that collects data in places where people cannot easily go.

9. Write About It Suppose you are planning a Mars mission. List some major challenges the mission would face and suggest possible solutions. How will the crew's basic needs be met on the long journey?

See TE rubric.

69

Review and Assessment

Assess Understanding

Have students complete the answers to the Review and Assessment questions. Have a class discussion about what students find confusing. Write Key Concepts on the board to reinforce knowledge.

RTI Response to Intervention

3. If students cannot explain the arrows in the diagram, **then** have them review **Figure 2.**

7. If students have trouble determining how the ISS could help with further exploration of the solar system, **then** suggest that they think about what the ISS has taught us so far about humans' capacity to live in space.

Alternate Assessment

L3 THEATRICAL PRESENTATION Have students form three groups to present the information from one of the lessons in this chapter: rocket technology, the history of space exploration, and the uses of space technology on Earth. Students should explain the key ideas from each lesson and use vocabulary terms whenever possible.

CHAPTER 2

| Write About It | Assess student's writing using this rubric. | | | |

SCORING RUBRIC	SCORE 4	SCORE 3	SCORE 2	SCORE 1
Plan a Mars mission	Student describes how basic needs will be met and lists probable challenges and logical solutions.	Student describes how basic needs will be met and lists plausible challenges and solutions.	Student describes how some basic needs will be met and lists at least one challenge and solution.	Student neither describes how basic needs will be met nor lists challenges and solutions.

Review and Assessment, Cont.

RTI Response to Intervention

11. If students need help interpreting the graph, **then** remind them that a geostationary satellite doesn't move. Call on volunteers to tell what coordinates to find on the graph and explain.

Apply the Big Q

TRANSFER Students should be able to demonstrate understanding of how space spinoffs benefit people on Earth by answering this question. See the scoring rubric below.

Connect to the Big Idea

BIG IDEA Science, society, and technology affect each other.

Send students back to the Big Ideas of Science at the beginning of their student edition. Have them read what they wrote about how science, society, and technology affect each other before they started the chapter. Lead a class discussion about how their thoughts have changed. If all chapters have been completed, have students fill in the bottom section for the Big Idea.

L3 WRITING IN SCIENCE Ask students to write a blog entry that explains to readers how exploring space benefits people on Earth.

LESSON 3 Using Space Science on Earth

10. Classify Name a space spinoff in each of the following categories: medical devices, materials, consumer products.

Sample: medical devices: pacemaker; materials: clear dental braces; consumer products: eyeglasses

Use the graph to answer Questions 11 and 12.

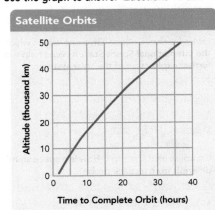

Satellite Orbits

Altitude (thousand km) vs *Time to Complete Orbit (hours)*

11. Reading Graphs A geostationary satellite orbits Earth once every 24 hours. At what altitude does such a satellite orbit?

About 36,000 km

12. Making Generalizations What is the relationship between satellite altitude and the time needed to complete one orbit?

Orbital time increases with altitude.

APPLY **How does exploring space benefit people on Earth?**

13. Suppose your car broke down in an unfamiliar place. Explain two ways that satellites in orbit could help you get assistance.

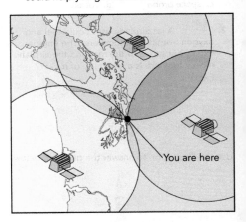

You are here

First, communications satellites can be used to relay phone calls. Second, satellites are also used in the Global Positioning System (GPS). If you have a GPS device in the car, you can use it to find your location and share that information with emergency crews. See TE rubric.

 How does exploring space benefit people on Earth?
Assess student's response using this rubric.

SCORING RUBRIC	SCORE 4	SCORE 3	SCORE 2	SCORE 1
Explain how orbiting satellites can help in a car breakdown	Student thoroughly and accurately explains two ways in which satellites can help.	Student accurately explains two ways in which satellites can help.	Student accurately explains one way in which satellites can help.	Student does not explain how satellites can help.

Standardized Test Prep

Multiple Choice

Circle the letter of the best answer.

1. The diagram below shows a rocket and the direction of four forces.

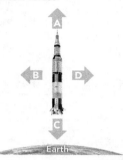

Which force represents an equal and opposite force to the thrust of the rocket?

A Force A   B Force B
Ⓒ Force C   D Force D

2. Which of the following is most responsible for rockets reaching the moon?

A explosives
B single-stage rockets
C gunpowder
Ⓓ multistage rockets

3. How often does a satellite in geostationary orbit revolve around Earth?

A once per hour
Ⓑ once per day
C once per month
D once per year

4. Which of these did the United States accomplish first during the space race?

A sending the first human being into space
B sending the first living creature into space
Ⓒ landing the first human on the moon
D launching the first satellite into space

5. What force must a rocket overcome to reach space?

Ⓐ gravity
B escape velocity
C thrust
D orbital velocity

Constructed Response

Use the diagram below and your knowledge of science to help you answer Question 6. Write your answer on a separate sheet of paper.

Object	Escape velocity (km/s)
MERCURY	4.3
VENUS	10.3
MOON	2.4
MARS	5.0

Object	Escape velocity (km/s)
JUPITER	59.5
SATURN	35.6
URANUS	21.2
NEPTUNE	23.6

6. The table shows the escape velocity for a rocket leaving different objects in the solar system. Explain why it might be easier to launch a rocket to Mars from the moon rather than from Earth. What would be the problem with sending astronauts to explore Jupiter?

See TE note.

Standardized Test Prep

Test-Taking Skills

INTERPRETING A DIAGRAM Point out that a diagram may have several components, such as drawings, arrows, and labels. Question 1 requires students carefully to examine the arrows—and labels—in order to identify the equal and opposite force to the upward thrust of the rocket.

Constructed Response

6. The escape velocity for the moon is less than that of Earth, so it would take less force to launch a rocket from the moon than from Earth. As for sending astronauts to explore Jupiter, it would be very difficult for them to return. A rocket launched from Jupiter would require a lot of thrust to escape.

Additional Assessment Resources

Chapter Test
EXAMVIEW® Assessment Suite
Performance Assessment
Progress Monitoring Assessments
SuccessTracker™

ⒺⓁⓁ Support

5 Assess Understanding

Have ELL students complete the Alternate Assessment. Provide guidelines on the information it must cover, and a rubric for assessment. You may wish to have them complete the activity in small groups of varying language proficiencies.

Beginning

LOW/HIGH Allow students extra time to complete their presentations.

Intermediate

LOW/HIGH Allow students to refer to their books or notes when completing their presentations.

Advanced

LOW/HIGH Challenge students to use vocabulary terms from the lesson in their presentations.

Remediate If students have trouble with...

QUESTION	SEE LESSON	STANDARDS
1	1	
2	1	
3	3	
4	2	
5	1	
6	1	

Science Matters

Museum of Science

Have students read *One Ticket to Space, Please.* Point out to students that, at one time, the prospect of people traveling in space was thought of as impossible, but in the future it could become commonplace.

Explain that space tourists would be able to see a rare sight: Earth as seen from high above the highest altitude at which any airplane can fly. They would also get to experience what it is like to be an astronaut and how exiting and re-entering Earth's atmosphere would feel. In some countries, customers can travel deeper into space for more prolonged flights. These people have to train as astronauts before they leave Earth's atmosphere, so they can become accustomed to life in space and travel safely.

As students work on their ads, encourage them to think about the practicality of such trips. Flights into space would be very expensive and could be riskier than other kinds of travel. Suggest they brainstorm to come up with a list of benefits that would outweigh these costs. Also, encourage them to tailor their ads to their audience, such as people who enjoy exciting risks. Tell them to include a list of fun activities customers could participate in while experiencing zero gravity.

Ask: **Why do you think the time outside the Earth's atmosphere is so short?** *(Sample: It could be expensive and dangerous to stay in space for very long.)* **Why do you think the aircraft needs to travel at three times the speed of sound?** *(It has to travel that fast to escape Earth's gravity.)*

SCIENCE MATTERS

TECH & DESIGN

Museum of Science

One Ticket to Space, Please

Soon, tourists could be lining up to visit . . . space?

Right now, highly trained astronauts who work with space agencies such as the National Aeronautics and Space Administration (NASA), the Japan Aerospace Exploration Agency, or the European Space Agency travel to space. But a small number of companies have started testing space flights that will take paying passengers the way airplanes and trains do. Passengers will be able to fly to space. Companies hope to make space travel available to many people.

So what can you look forward to as a space tourist? The aircraft will fly to the edge of the atmosphere at three times the speed of sound. Then, the aircraft will launch two rockets carrying passengers. The rockets will enter space and float for about 5 minutes. Passengers will experience total weightlessness—with enough time to do flips in zero gravity! The rockets will then return to Earth. Space tourism—it's going to be out of this world!

Write About It Create a magazine ad promoting the flights. Think about who you are targeting, where your ad should be placed, and what design will convince the most people.

Museum of Science.

72 Exploring Space

Quick Facts

Students might think eating in space would be strange. Explain that astronauts eat many of the same things we do. They must bring enough food to last them between supply trips. Some foods, such as fruits, can be eaten in space just as they are on Earth. Others, such as pasta, are dehydrated and must have water added in order to be eaten. Astronauts can cook in an oven on a space shuttle, but they do not have refrigerators, so they can't save leftovers. Astronauts make sandwiches on tortillas instead of bread because they take up less room and don't crumble as easily. They have condiments, but salt and pepper come in liquid form because if you sprinkled regular salt and pepper in space, it would float away and could clog air vents. Think about your favorite foods and how eating them might be different in space.

Living in Space:
THE EXPEDITION 18 CREW

Far above Earth, astronauts from different countries are working together to build a research facility in space.

In 1998, a Russian rocket launched the first piece of the International Space Station (ISS). Ten years later, the eighteenth crew to make the station their home arrived at the ISS.

The crew of Expedition 18 included members from the United States, Russian, and Japanese space programs. Each member of the crew had specific jobs to do in space. Flight Engineer Sandra Magnus installed a new toilet. When Magnus's stay was completed, Flight Engineer Koichi Wakata and his crew installed a system to recycle the crew's water.

The work of these astronauts represents a step toward the colonization of space. The crews who work on the ISS are learning how to address human needs in space. They are also teaching us about the effects that life in space can have on human bodies.

Research It Will a boomerang return to its thrower in zero gravity? For a fun experiment to do in his own time, Japanese astronaut Takao Doi took one to the ISS and found out. Make a hypothesis, then write a report on his results.

Frontiers of Technology

Have students read *Living in Space: The Expedition 18 Crew*. Tell students the ISS is a project shared between many different countries. The ISS includes places for the astronauts to sleep, eat, and work. They do experiments in laboratories and conduct spacewalks outside the ISS.

Explain that astronauts living on the ISS do not have ready access to a lot of resources. They rely on supplies being brought from Earth. They must also find ways to be self-sufficient such as recycling the water they use and the air they breathe. These methods do not just help the astronauts survive in space, they teach them how many people can survive and live in space. Point out that this will be helpful as mankind explores further into space. The more self-sufficient they can become, the further into space, away from Earth, people will be able to travel.

Astronauts in space must become used to living in microgravity. Everything floats in space, including liquids. The astronauts on the ISS have developed special means of drinking liquids and using water to get clean.

As students research the boomerang experiment, have them think of other things they might like to test out in space. Have them guess how their trial activity might turn out, based on the results of the boomerang experiment.

Ask: **What are some conditions astronauts on the ISS must learn to live under?** *(Sample: weightlessness, being isolated from Earth, needing to recycle water and air)* **How are the astronauts living on the ISS helping people?** *(They are learning how to make it easier for people to live in space for long periods of time.)*

CHAPTER 2

The Solar System

Introduce the Big Q

Have students look at the image and read the Engaging Question and description. Ask students to infer what Saturn's rings are made of and how they formed. Have volunteers explain their inferences. Point out that Saturn's rings are widely regarded as the planet's most distinctive trait. Ask: **How is Saturn like other objects in our solar system?** *(Sample: It orbits the sun.)* **In what way is it different, besides in its rings?** *(Sample: The composition of its atmosphere is different.)* Explain to students that the glowing ring at the southern pole of Saturn are auroras caused by solar wind from the sun. Auroras also occur at Saturn's north pole. These auroras are similar to the ones that occur on Earth.

Untamed Science Video

100 METERS TO NEPTUNE Before viewing, invite students to discuss what they know about our solar system. Then play the video. Lead a class discussion and make a list of questions that this video raises. You may wish to have students view the video again after they have completed the chapter to see if their questions have been answered.

> **To access the online resources for this chapter, search on or navigate to *The Solar System.***
>
> **Untamed Science Video** explores the distance between objects in the solar system.
>
> **The Big Question** allows students to answer the Engaging Question about Saturn's distinctive rings.

mY SCIENCE online.com   **The Solar System**

WHAT MIGHT SATURN'S RINGS BE MADE OF?

Why are objects in the solar system different from each other?

This photograph from the *Cassini* space probe shows Saturn and part of its magnificent system of rings. Space probes such as *Cassini* have helped scientists learn more about the objects in the solar system.

Infer **What do you think Saturn's rings are made of? How might they have formed?**

Sample: I think the rings are made of chunks of rock and ice. They may have formed from a moon that broke apart.

> **UNTAMED SCIENCE** Watch the **Untamed Science** video to learn more about the solar system.

Professional Development Note   From the Author

My children used to sing a song about the solar system, *The Family of the Sun,* which has since been revised to account for Pluto's reclassification. When they were young our solar system was the only one, as far as we knew. Although the existence of other solar systems had been suspected for at least 200 years, it was not until 1995 that we first began to meet our extended family. Today more than 300 *extrasolar* planets (planets that orbit a star other than our sun) have been discovered through indirect means, and the first extrasolar planet has been imaged.

✎ *Kathryn Thornton*

The Solar System **3**

Chapter at a Glance

CHAPTER PACING: 13–19 periods or $6\frac{1}{2}$–$9\frac{1}{2}$ blocks

INTRODUCE THE CHAPTER: Use the Engaging Question and the opening image to get students thinking about the solar system. Activate prior knowledge and preteach vocabulary using the Getting Started pages.

Lesson 1: Models of the Solar System

Lesson 2: Introducing the Solar System

Lesson 3: The Sun

Lesson 4: The Inner Planets

Lesson 5: The Outer Planets

Lesson 6: Small Solar System Objects

ASSESSMENT OPTIONS: Chapter Test, **EXAM**VIEW® Assessment Suite, Performance Assessments, Progress Monitoring Assessments, SuccessTracker™

Preference Navigator, in the online Planning tools, allows you to customize *Interactive Science* to your own teaching style. You can also edit lesson plans by selecting the Lesson Planner option.

Digital Teacher's Edition allows you to access your Teacher's Edition and Resource online.

my science online.com

my science online.com > The Solar System > UNTAMED SCIENCE > THE BIG QUESTION 75

Differentiated Instruction

L3 **The Kepler Mission** Have students research to learn about NASA's exoplanet-hunting *Kepler* space telescope, which was launched in March, 2009. Tell students to find information about the mission and its significance. *(The Kepler Mission was designed to find out whether there are other planets orbiting other stars, with characteristics similar to Earth.)*

L1 **Night Sky** Invite students to examine a photograph of the night sky. Ask them to identify the objects that they see. Encourage students to describe each object, whether or not they know its name. Then have students count the different types of objects they observed.

Getting Started

Check Your Understanding

This activity assesses students' understanding of rotation, revolution, and gravitational force. After students have shared their answers, remind them that gravity attracts all the different objects in our solar system to each other.

Preteach Vocabulary Skills

Explain to students that when you identify a word's origin, you identify the language from which the word came into English and the meaning of the original word. Inform students that learning to identify Greek (and Latin) word parts can make it easier for them to figure out the meaning of unfamiliar words, not only in science but in other content areas.

Check Your Understanding

1. **Background** Read the paragraph below and then answer the question.

Tyrone is watching a movie. He sees astronauts explore a planet that **revolves** around a star. As the astronauts travel, they notice that the planet **rotates.** Tyrone knows that **gravity** holds the planet in orbit around the star.

- What causes day and night on a planet?

The planet's rotation on its axis

> **Revolution** is the motion of one object around another.
>
> An object **rotates** when it spins around a central axis.
>
> **Gravity** is the force that attracts all objects toward each other.

> MY READING WEB If you had trouble completing the question above, visit **My Reading Web** and type in *The Solar System.*

Vocabulary Skill

Greek Word Origins Many science words come to English from Greek. In this chapter, you will learn the term *geocentric. Geocentric* comes from the Greek word parts *ge,* meaning "Earth," and *kentron,* meaning "center."

$$\underset{\text{Earth}}{ge} + \underset{\text{center}}{kentron} = \underset{\text{having Earth at the center}}{geocentric}$$

Learn these Greek word parts to help you remember the vocabulary terms.

Greek Word	Meaning	Example
helios	sun	heliocentric, *adj.*
chromas	color	chromosphere, *n.*
sphaira	sphere	photosphere, *n.*

2. **Quick Check** Predict the meaning of *heliocentric.*

Having the sun at the center

My Reading Web offers leveled readings that offer a foundation for the chapter content.

Vocab Flash Cards offer extra practice with the chapter vocabulary words.

Digital Lesson
- Assign the *Check Your Understanding* activity online and have students submit their work to you.
- Assign the *Vocabulary Skill* activity online and have students submit their work to you.

my science online.com > The Solar System

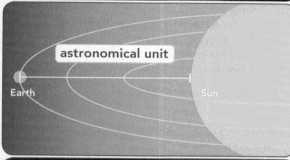

planet

astronomical unit

Earth   Sun

solar system

asteroid belt

Chapter Preview

LESSON 1
- geocentric • heliocentric
- ellipse
- ⊘ Sequence
- △ Make Models

LESSON 2
- solar system • astronomical unit
- planet • dwarf planet
- planetesimal
- ⊘ Identify Supporting Evidence
- △ Calculate

LESSON 3
- core • nuclear fusion
- radiation zone • convection zone
- photosphere • chromosphere
- corona • solar wind • sunspot
- prominence • solar flare
- ⊘ Relate Cause and Effect
- △ Interpret Data

LESSON 4
- terrestrial planet
- greenhouse effect
- ⊘ Compare and Contrast
- △ Communicate

LESSON 5
- gas giant • ring
- ⊘ Outline
- △ Pose Questions

LESSON 6
- asteroid belt • Kuiper belt
- Oort cloud • comet
- coma • nucleus • asteroid
- meteoroid • meteor • meteorite
- ⊘ Summarize
- △ Classify

> VOCAB FLASH CARDS For extra help with vocabulary, visit **Vocab Flash Cards** and type in *The Solar System.*

77

CHAPTER 3

Preview Vocabulary Terms

Have students create a personalized science glossary for the vocabulary terms in this chapter. In their glossaries, students should define each term and reference the pages in the chapter that define and explain the term. Encourage students to include drawings and diagrams that help explain the meaning of the terms and concepts. A list of Academic Vocabulary for each lesson can be found in the Support All Readers box at the start of the lesson.

L1 Have students look at the images on this page as you pronounce the vocabulary word. Have students repeat the word after you. Then read the definition. Use the sample sentence in italics to clarify the meaning of the term.

planet *(PLAN it)* object that orbits the sun and has cleared out the region of the solar system along its orbit. *Each planet has a day and a year.*

astronomical unit *(as truh NAHM ih kul YOO nit)* The average distance between Earth and the sun, about 150,000,000 kilometers. *Since Mercury is closer to the sun than Earth is, its distance from the sun is equal to less than one astronomical unit.*

solar system *(SOH lur SIS tum)* The sun, the planets, their moons, and a variety of smaller objects. *The sun is at the center of our solar system, with other objects orbiting around it.*

asteroid belt *(AS tur oyd belt)* Region of the solar system between Mars and Jupiter. *Most asteroids orbit the sun in the asteroid belt.*

Have students complete the **Preview Vocabulary Terms** activity either alone or in pairs. Before students begin creating their science glossaries, write each word and introduce it to students by pointing and saying it aloud.

Beginning
LOW Draw a picture or other visual aid for each vocabulary term in the glossary to associate the term with its definition.

HIGH Include words and phrases in their native language to help students remember specific terms.

Intermediate
LOW/HIGH Include English pronunciations for each term.

Advanced
LOW/HIGH For each vocabulary term in the glossary, write a sentence that uses the term correctly.

Models of the Solar System

Why are objects in the Solar System different from each other?

Lesson Pacing: 1–2 periods or $\frac{1}{2}$–1 block

🕐 **SHORT ON TIME?** To do this lesson in approximately half the time, do the Activate Prior Knowledge activity on page 78. A discussion of the Key Concepts on pages 79 and 80 will familiarize students with the lesson content. Have students do the Quick Labs. The rest of the lesson can be completed by students independently.

Preference Navigator, in the online Planning tools, allows you to customize *Interactive Science* to your own teaching style. You can also edit lesson plans by selecting the Lesson Planner option.

Digital Teacher's Edition allows you to access your Teacher's Edition and Resource materials online.

my science online.com ▸

Lesson Vocabulary

- geocentric
- heliocentric
- ellipse

 Content Refresher

Observing the Solar System Until the early 1600s, scientists dating back to the ancient Greeks assumed that all of the planets moved in perfect circles, which were considered to be the most perfect geometric shape. From 1576 to 1597, the Danish astronomer Tycho Brahe made detailed measurements of planetary positions. Tycho's assistant, Johannes Kepler, found that Tycho's data were inconsistent with the assumption that the planets moved in circular orbits. Kepler used the data to develop three laws of planetary motion: *1) The orbit of each planet around the sun is an ellipse, with the sun at one of the foci of the ellipse; 2) A planet sweeps out equal areas in equal times as it orbits the sun; and 3) The square of the period of a planet orbiting the sun is proportional to the cube of its mean (average) distance from the sun.*

Kepler could say *how* the planets moved, but not *why*. In 1687, 57 years after Kepler died, Isaac Newton provided the explanation in his book, the *Principia*. Newton's three laws of motion and the law of universal gravitation provided the physical explanation for Kepler's laws and the movement of the planets.

LESSON OBJECTIVES

▸ Describe the geocentric model of the solar system.

▸ Recognize how scientists such as Copernicus, Kepler, and Galileo contributed to acceptance of the heliocentric model of the solar system.

Blended Path
Active learning using Student Edition, Inquiry Path, and Digital Path

ENGAGE AND EXPLORE

Teach this lesson using a variety of resources. Begin by reading **My Planet Diary** as a class. Have students share ideas about how Mr. Myers artwork is similar to a model. Then have students do the **Inquiry Warm-Up activity.** Students will investigate what is at the center of the solar system. Discuss why early astronomers believed the sun revolved around Earth. The **After the Inquiry Warm-Up worksheet** sets up a comparison between the two models of the solar system. Have volunteers share their answers to question 4 about what astronomers would have needed to better understand the position of Earth and the sun.

EXPLAIN AND ELABORATE

Teach Key Concepts by explaining what the ancient Greeks observed in the sky and how they believed the planets moved. Reinforce the idea that the objects in the solar system are always moving before assigning the **Apply It activity.**

Teach Key Concepts by explaining how Kepler developed the heliocentric model of the solar system. Continue to **Teach Key Concepts** by helping students understand why Galileo's discovery of Jupiter's moons was important to proving that Earth was not the center of the universe. To **Support the Big Q,** discuss how technological advances have impacted astronomers' understanding of the solar system. Hand out the **Key Concept Summaries** as a review of each part of the lesson. Students can also use the online **Vocab Flash Cards** to review key terms.

EVALUATE

Have students take the **Lesson Quiz.** For an alternate assessment, see the **EXAM**VIEW® Assessment Suite, Progress Monitoring Assessments, or SuccessTracker™.

E L L Support

1 Content and Language

The word part *-centric* means "concentrated around." In a *geocentric* model of the solar system, the planets were thought to be concentrated around Earth; however, in a *heliocentric* model the planets are concentrated around the sun. Knowing this, help students determine the meanings of *geo-* and *helio-*. (*Earth; sun*)

Lab zone Inquiry Path
Hands-on learning in the Lab zone

Digital Path
Online learning at my science online.com

ENGAGE AND EXPLORE

To teach this lesson with an emphasis on inquiry, begin with the **Inquiry Warm-Up activity.** Students will investigate what is at the center of the solar system. Discuss why early astronomers believed the sun revolved around Earth. Have students do the **After the Inquiry Warm-Up worksheet.** Talk about the diagrams they drew of the two models. Have volunteers share their answers to question 4 about what would have helped astronomers to better understand the position of the sun and Earth.

EXPLAIN AND ELABORATE

Focus on the **Inquiry Skill** for the lesson. Point out that when you make models, you create a representation of a complex situation or object in order to better understand it. What models did students draw in the **Inquiry Warm-Up activity?** *(One model of the solar system as geocentric and one as heliocentric.)* Review the location of the sun and moon in the night sky before beginning the **Apply It activity.** Ask volunteers to share their experiences. Have students do the **Quick Lab** to model a geocentric solar system and then share their results.

To **Support the Big Q,** discuss how Galileo's improvements to the telescope had an impact on astronomers' understanding of our solar system. To **Build Inquiry,** have students model the movements of the inner planets around the sun. The **Teacher Demo** reinforces understanding of what happens to the distance between a planet and the sun in an elliptical orbit. Do the **Quick Lab** to reinforce understanding of planetary orbits. Students can use the online **Vocab Flash Cards** to review key terms.

EVALUATE

Have students take the **Lesson Quiz.** For an alternate assessment, see the **EXAM**VIEW® Assessment Suite, Progress Monitoring Assessments, or SuccessTracker™.

ENGAGE AND EXPLORE

Teach this lesson using digital resources. Begin by having students explore real-world connections to solar system models at **My Planet Diary** online. Have them access the Chapter Resources to find the **Unlock the Big Question activity.** There they can answer the questions and refine their responses as they continue through the lesson. You can re-assign the activity and have students submit their work so you can track their progress.

EXPLAIN AND ELABORATE

Students reading above, at, or below the lexile measure of this lesson can access basic content readings at their level at **My Reading Web.** Have students use the online **Vocab Flash Cards** to preview key terms. Review the idea that the objects in our solar system are always moving before assigning the online **Apply It activity.** Ask volunteers to share their experiences. Have students submit their work to you. Do the **Quick Lab** to model a geocentric solar system and then ask students to share their results.

Support the Big Q by discussing how improvements to technology allowed Galileo and other astronomers to better understand the solar system. Have students do the **Quick Lab** to model planetary orbits.

The **Key Concept Summaries** online allow students to read a summary and see an image associated with each part of the lesson. Online remediation is available at **My Science Coach.**

EVALUATE

Have students take the **Lesson Quiz.** For an alternate assessment, see the **EXAM**VIEW® Assessment Suite, Progress Monitoring Assessments, or SuccessTracker™.

2 Frontload the Lesson
Preview the lesson visuals, labels, and captions. Ask students what they know about the words *geocentric* and *heliocentric.* Explain the specific meanings these words have in science.

3 Comprehensible Input
Have students study the visuals and their captions on pages 80 and 81 to support the Key Concepts of the lesson.

4 Language Production
Pair or group students with varied language abilities to complete labs collaboratively for language practice. Have each student copy the completed written lab for personal reference.

5 Assess Understanding
Have students keep a content area log for this lesson using a two-column format with the headings "What I Understand" and "What I Don't Understand." Follow up so that students can move items from the "Don't Understand" to the "Understand" column.

LESSON 3.1

Models of the Solar System

Establish Learning Objectives

After this lesson, students will be able to:

🔑 Describe the geocentric model of the solar system.

🔑 Recognize how scientists such as Copernicus, Kepler, and Galileo contributed to acceptance of the heliocentric model of the solar system.

Engage

Activate Prior Knowledge

MY PLANET DIARY Read *Picturing the Solar System* with the class. Point out that using a computer allows Mr. Myers to depict people and objects much more realistically than using a pencil. Ask: **What other kinds of artists make images that explain or clarify scientific concepts?** (Sample: Medical illustrators)

BIG IDEAS OF SCIENCE REFERENCE LIBRARY 📖 Have students look up the following topic: Astronomy Myths.

Explore

Lab Resource: Inquiry Warm-Up 🧪

L2 **WHAT IS AT THE CENTER?** Partners will represent Earth and the sun and make two sets of observations.

---

1 Models of the Solar System

🔑 **What Was the Geocentric Model?**

🔑 **How Did the Heliocentric Model Develop?**

MY PLANET DIARY   CAREER

Picturing the Solar System

When Walter Myers was seven years old, he found a book with drawings of astronauts walking on the moons of Saturn. Ever since, he's been making space pictures himself. At first, he used pencil. Today, he works on computers. He likes using computers because he can create images that are more like photographs, such as the ones below.

As an artist, Mr. Myers can show scenes that haven't been photographed, such as ideas for future spacecraft and the views from another planet's moons. Mr. Myers especially likes creating views of what human visitors to other planets might see. His work has appeared in books, magazines, Web sites, and even on television!

Use what you have read to answer these questions.

1. What tool does Walter Myers use?

   Computers

2. Why do people use art or other models to show objects in the solar system?

   Sample: It is difficult to photograph objects in the solar system, and we can't visit them ourselves.

> **PLANET DIARY** Go to **Planet Diary** to learn more about models of the solar system.

Lab zone — Do the Inquiry Warm-Up *What Is at the Center?*

78   The Solar System

SUPPORT ALL READERS
Lexile Measure = 910L   Lexile Word Count = 734

Prior Exposure to Content: May be the first time students have encountered this topic

Academic Vocabulary: *models, observations, sequence*

Science Vocabulary: *geocentric, heliocentric, ellipse*

Concept Level: May be difficult for students who struggle with abstract ideas

Preteach With: My Planet Diary "Picturing the Solar System" and Figure 1 activity

Go to **My Reading Web** to access leveled readings that provide a foundation for the content.

my science online.com

Vocabulary
- geocentric
- heliocentric
- ellipse

Skills
- Reading: Sequence
- Inquiry: Make Models

What Was the Geocentric Model?

From here on Earth, it seems as if our planet is stationary and that the sun, moon, and stars are moving around Earth. But is the sky really moving above you? Centuries ago, before there were space shuttles or even telescopes, people had no easy way to find out.

Ancient Observations Ancient observers, including the Greeks, Chinese, and Mayans, noticed that the patterns of the stars didn't change over time. Although the stars seemed to move, they stayed in the same position relative to one another. These people also observed planets, which moved among the stars.

Many early observers thought Earth was at the center of the universe. Some Chinese observers thought Earth was under a dome of stars. Many Greek astronomers thought that Earth was inside rotating spheres nested inside each other. These spheres contained the stars and planets. Since *ge* is the Greek word for "Earth," an Earth-centered model is known as a **geocentric** (jee oh SEN trik) model. **In a geocentric model, Earth is at the center of the revolving planets and stars.**

Ptolemy's Model About A.D. 140, the Greek astronomer Ptolemy (TAHL uh mee) further developed the geocentric model. Like the earlier Greeks, Ptolemy thought that Earth was at the center of the universe. In Ptolemy's model, however, the planets moved in small circles carried along in bigger circles.

Ptolemy's geocentric model explained the motions observed in the sky fairly accurately. As a result, the geocentric model of the universe was widely accepted for nearly 1,500 years after Ptolemy.

 apply it!

Critique Scientific Explanations and Models Describe an experience from everyday life that appears to support the geocentric model.

Sample: If I stand
and watch the stars,
they appear to move,
but the ground under
my feet does not.

Lab zone Do the Quick Lab *Going Around in Circles.*

Assess Your Understanding

got it?

○ I get it! Now I know that the geocentric model is _a model of the solar system in_ _which Earth is at the center and stars and planets revolve around it._

○ I need extra help with _See TE note._

Go to **my science COACH** online for help with this subject.

79

ELL Support

1 Content and Language
Write the words *ellipse* and *eclipse* on the board. Have students pronounce each word aloud. Explain that *ellipse* comes from the Greek word for "oval." It is unrelated to the word *eclipse*.

2 Frontload the Lesson
Urge students to reflect on the concept of point of view as it relates to the solar system. Ask them why they think people might consider Earth as "the center

of the universe." Tell students they will learn how scientists developed a different view of the solar system.

3 Comprehensible Input
Have students create a cluster diagram. In large circles, students can write the topics *geocentric model* and *heliocentric model.* Encourage students to add details relating to Ptolemy, Aristarchus, Copernicus, Brahe, Kepler, and Galileo.

Explain

Introduce Vocabulary

Write *heliocentric* on the board. Remind students that the terms origin indicates its meaning. *Helios* refers to the sun, so *heliocentric* means a sun-centered model.

Teach Key Concepts

Explain to students that a model that puts Earth at the center of the revolving planets is a geocentric model. Inform students that the ancient Greeks observed planets in the sky—but only Mercury, Venus, Mars, Jupiter, and Saturn. Ask: **Why could the ancient Greeks see only five planets?** *(They did not have telescopes and could not see the other planets because those planets are so far away.)* **How do Earth and the other planets move in a geocentric model?** *(Earth stays in one place, and the other planets revolve around Earth.)*

Elaborate

Apply It

L1 Before beginning the activity, have students examine a photograph of the night sky that shows stars and the moon. Ask: **Where was the sun when this picture was taken?** *(The sun was in its usual position but could not be seen because it was on the other side of Earth.)*

Lab Resource: Quick Lab

L1 GOING AROUND IN CIRCLES Students will model a geocentric solar system.

Evaluate

Assess Your Understanding

Have students evaluate their understanding by completing the appropriate sentence.

RTI Response to Intervention

If students have trouble identifying the geocentric model, **then** have them reread the Key Concept statement.

my science COACH Have students go online for help in understanding the geocentric model.

My Planet Diary provides an opportunity for students to explore real-world connections to solar system models.

Digital Lesson: Assign the *Apply It* activity online and have students submit their work to you.

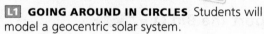

LESSON 3.1

Explain

Teach Key Concepts 🔑

Explain to students that Johannes Kepler developed the heliocentric model by applying his knowledge of mathematics to Brahe's data. Ask: **What did Kepler discover through his calculations?** *(The orbit of each planet is not a circle but an ellipse.)* **What skills did Kepler use to reach his conclusion?** *(Sample: Making measurements, interpreting data, making models, verifying hypotheses, communicating)* **Which earlier model did Kepler change?** *(Copernicus's model)*

🔄 **Sequence** Explain that a sequence is the order in which a series of events occurs. Tell students to use the timeline to help them visualize a sequence.

Teach Key Concepts

Tell students that Galileo did not alter the previous version of the heliocentric model, but he collected additional data, which supported this model. Ask: **What did Galileo discover through his telescope?** *(Four moons of Jupiter)* **Why was this discovery important?** *(He could show that they orbited Jupiter, not Earth, which proved that objects could orbit something other than Earth.)*

🔺 **Make Models** Explain to students that a model is a picture, diagram, computer image, or other representation of a complex object or process. Be sure students understand that a model does not have to be three-dimensional.

Support the Big Q ❓

TECHNOLOGICAL ADVANCES Galileo, who had made significant improvement to the telescope, could observe Venus in a way that no other astronomer before him could do. Galileo noted the phases of Venus and this fact revealed the flaws of the geocentric model, which had been based on less accurate observations of the sun and other objects in the sky. Discuss with students how technological advances have had had an impact on astronomers' understanding of our solar system.

21st Century Learning 📖

COMMUNICATION Have students read *Astronomy Myths* in the **Big Ideas of Science Reference Library.** Ask students to write about their earliest memories of what they thought existed in the night sky. For example, did they think people lived on stars? Where did they think the sun went at night? Are their views similar in any way to the myths featured on the pages?

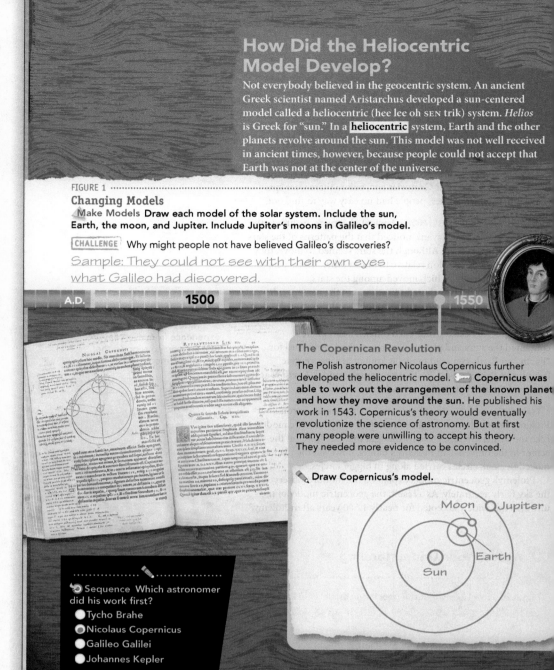

How Did the Heliocentric Model Develop?

Not everybody believed in the geocentric system. An ancient Greek scientist named Aristarchus developed a sun-centered model called a heliocentric (hee lee oh SEN trik) system. *Helios* is Greek for "sun." In a **heliocentric** system, Earth and the other planets revolve around the sun. This model was not well received in ancient times, however, because people could not accept that Earth was not at the center of the universe.

FIGURE 1 ··········

Changing Models

🔺Make Models Draw each model of the solar system. Include the sun, Earth, the moon, and Jupiter. Include Jupiter's moons in Galileo's model.

[CHALLENGE] Why might people not have believed Galileo's discoveries?

Sample: They could not see with their own eyes what Galileo had discovered.

A.D. ———— **1500** ———————— 1550

The Copernican Revolution

The Polish astronomer Nicolaus Copernicus further developed the heliocentric model. 🔑 **Copernicus was able to work out the arrangement of the known planet and how they move around the sun.** He published his work in 1543. Copernicus's theory would eventually revolutionize the science of astronomy. But at first many people were unwilling to accept his theory. They needed more evidence to be convinced.

✏️ **Draw Copernicus's model.**

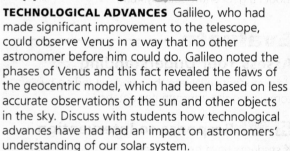

Moon ⦿Jupiter

Earth

Sun

················· ✏️ ·················

🔄 Sequence Which astronomer did his work first?
⦿ Tycho Brahe
◉ Nicolaus Copernicus
⦿ Galileo Galilei
⦿ Johannes Kepler

Brahe and Kepler

Ptolemy and Copernicus both assumed that planets moved in perfect circles. Their models fit existing observations fairly well. But in the late 1500s, the Dutch astronomer Tycho Brahe (TEE koh BRAH uh) made much more accurate observations. Brahe's assistant, Johannes Kepler, used the observations to figure out the shape of the planets' orbits. When he used circular orbits, his calculations did not fit the observations. 🗝 **After years of detailed calculations, Kepler found that the orbit of each planet is an ellipse.** An **ellipse** is an oval shape.

✏ Draw Kepler's model.

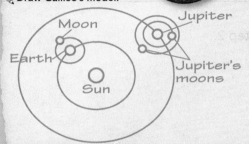

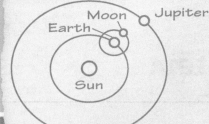
Tycho Brahe's Observatory

○ 1600   ● 1650

Galileo's Evidence

In the 1500s and early 1600s, most people still believed in the geocentric model. 🗝 **However, evidence collected by the Italian scientist Galileo Galilei gradually convinced others that the heliocentric model was correct.** In 1610, Galileo used a telescope to discover four moons around Jupiter. These moons proved that not everything in the sky revolves around Earth. Galileo also discovered that Venus goes through a series of phases similar to the moon's. But Venus would not have a full set of phases if both it and the sun circled around Earth. Therefore, Galileo reasoned, the geocentric model must be incorrect.

✏ Draw Galileo's model.

Moon   Jupiter
Earth
Sun   Jupiter's moons

Lab zone Do the Quick Lab *A Loopy Ellipse.*

🗝 Assess Your Understanding

1a. Review ((Kepler)/Copernicus) discovered that planets move in ellipses.

b. Relate Evidence and Explanation What discoveries by Galileo support the heliocentric model?

The moons of Jupiter and the
phases of Venus

got it?

○ I get it! Now I know that the heliocentric model was developed _through the_
work of Copernicus, Brahe,
Kepler, and Galileo.

○ I need extra help with _See TE note._

Go to MY SCIENCE ⬤ COACH online for help with this subject.

81

Differentiated Instruction

L1 Label Diagrams Find online and photocopy a geocentric and heliocentric model of the solar system, or create your own blackline models. Give each student one copy of each model. Write on the board terms such as *geocentric, planet, moon, stationary, center, heloiocentric,* and *sun.* Have students label their diagrams using these and/or additional relevant terms.

L3 Dramatization Have interested students read Bertolt Brecht's play *Galileo,* then, working in collaborative groups, have students choose an important scene to present to the class. Tell students to provide an introduction to the scene that they perform, using a narrator to set the scene in the context of the whole play.

Elaborate

Build Inquiry **Lab zone**

L1 MODEL THE MOVEMENTS OF THE INNER PLANETS

Materials chalk, metric ruler

Time 15 minutes

Have students in groups of four use chalk to draw concentric circles in a playground or parking lot. The circles should have radii of 3.5 m, 5.0 m, and 7.5 m. Tell students they will represent the sun and the orbits of Venus, Earth, and Mars, respectively.

Ask: **Where will the sun stand?** *(In the center)* **Where are the orbits of the other planets?** *(Inner circle: Venus; middle circle: Earth; outer circle: Mars)* Have students model the movements of the planets by walking around the "sun." **If everyone moved at a constant speed, which planet orbited the sun the fastest?** *(Venus)* **The slowest?** *(Mars)*

Teacher Demo **Lab zone**

L1 ELLIPTICAL ORBITS

Materials chalk

Time 15 minutes

To help students understand elliptical orbits, diagram Mars, its orbit, and the sun on the board. The sun should be slightly offset from the center of the orbit. The orbit itself should be slightly flattened.

Ask: **In an elliptical orbit, what happens to the distance between a planet and the sun?** *(It changes as the planet revolves.)*

Lab Resource: Quick Lab **Lab zone**

L2 A LOOPY ELLIPSE Students will draw different ellipses to model planetary orbits.

Evaluate

Assess Your Understanding

After students answer the questions, have them evaluate their understanding by completing the appropriate sentence.

RTI Response to Intervention

1a. If students have difficulty identifying Kepler's contribution, **then** have them locate and review an entry in the timeline that can help them.

b. If students need help explaining how Galileo's discoveries supported the heliocentric model, **then** discuss with them the importance of combining the work of many scientists to build a model or theory.

MY SCIENCE ⬤ COACH Have students go online for help in understanding the heliocentric model.

Lab zone After the Inquiry Warm-Up

Models of the Solar System

Inquiry Warm-Up, *What Is at the Center?*
In the Inquiry Warm-Up, you investigated whether Earth or the sun is at the center of the solar system. Using what you learned from that activity, answer the questions below.

1. **INFER** Why did early astronomers believe the sun revolved around Earth?

   _____

   _____

2. **COMMUNICATE** Draw and label a diagram of Step 2.

3. **COMMUNICATE** Draw and label a diagram of Step 4.

4. **ANALYZE SOURCES OF ERROR** What would early astronomers have needed in order to have a better understanding of the positions of Earth and the sun?

   _____

   _____

Assess Your Understanding

Models of the Solar System

What Was the Geocentric Model?

gotit? ···

○ **I get it!** Now I know that the geocentric model is _____

_____

_____

○ **I need extra help with** _____

_____

How Did the Heliocentric Model Develop?

1a. **REVIEW** (Kepler/Copernicus) discovered that planets move in ellipses.

b. **RELATE EVIDENCE AND EXPLANATION** What discoveries by Galileo support the heliocentric model?

_____

_____

gotit? ···

○ **I get it!** Now I know that the heliocentric model was developed _____

_____

_____

○ **I need extra help with** _____

_____

Models of the Solar System

What Was the Geocentric Model?

Ancient observers noticed that the positions of the stars did not change over time. They believed Earth was at the center of the universe. An Earth-centered model is known as a **geocentric** model. (*Ge* is the Greek word for "earth.") **In a geocentric model, Earth is at the center of the revolving planets and stars.**

About A.D. 140, the Greek astronomer Ptolemy developed the geocentric model. It was widely accepted for almost 1,500 years after his death.

How Did the Heliocentric Model Develop?

An ancient Greek scientist, Aristarchus, developed a sun-centered model. This is called a heliocentric system. (*Helios* is Greek for "sun.") In a **heliocentric** system, Earth and the other planets revolve around the sun.

In 1543, Nicolaus Copernicus further developed the heliocentric model. **Copernicus was able to work out the arrangement of the known planets and how they move around the sun.**

Many people believed the planets moved in perfect circles, but Tycho Brahe made accurate observations of their movements. His assistant, Johannes Kepler, used the observations to figure out the shape

of the planets' orbits. **After years of detailed calculations, Kepler found that the orbit of each planet is an ellipse.** An **ellipse** is an oval shape.

For many years, people continued to believe the geocentric model. **However, evidence collected by the Italian scientist Galileo Galilei gradually convinced others that the heliocentric model was correct.** In 1610, Galileo discovered moons orbiting Jupiter, proving that not everything in the sky travels around Earth. He also discovered that Venus goes through phases similar to the moon's, meaning it too travels around the sun. Therefore, Galileo reasoned, the heliocentric model is correct.

On a separate sheet of paper, compare and contrast the geocentric model and the heliocentric model. Underline the name of the model that is correct.

Name _____ Date _____ Class _____

Models of the Solar System

Understanding Main Ideas

Use the diagrams below to answer the questions in the spaces provided.

Ancient Greek Model

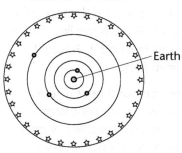

Earth

Ptolemy's Geocentric Model

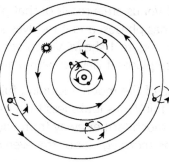

Copernicus's Heliocentric Model

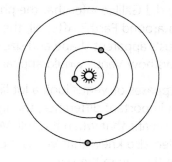

1. What is the main difference between the geocentric and heliocentric models?

_____

_____

2. How do the ancient Greek model and Ptolemy's model differ?

_____

3. How did Galileo's observations of Jupiter and Venus support Copernicus's model?

_____

_____

_____

Building Vocabulary

On a separate sheet of paper, write a definition for each of these terms.

4. heliocentric

5. ellipse

6. geocentric

Enrich

Models of the Solar System

> Read the passage and study the diagram below. Then use a separate sheet of paper to answer the questions that follow.

The Phases of Venus

Why did Galileo infer that the phases of Venus are a result of that planet's moving around the sun rather than around Earth? After all, the moon has phases, and it revolves around Earth. The answer lies in how Venus's apparent shape and size change. Figure 1 shows Venus at several places in its orbit. Figure 2 shows how Venus would appear at these places if viewed with a telescope from Earth.

The phases of Venus look a lot like those of the moon, including full, half, crescent, and new. There is an important difference, though. The full Venus looks less than half as wide as the crescent Venus. This means that when it is full, Venus is much farther away from Earth than when it is crescent or new. Galileo also knew that Venus is called the *morning star* or the *evening star* because it is never very far from the sun in the sky.

Combining these observations, Galileo reasoned that Venus must revolve around the sun.

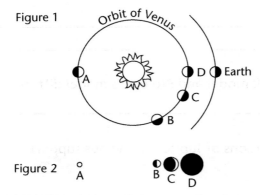

1. How is the position of the full moon in relation to Earth and the sun different from the position of the full Venus in relation to Earth and the sun? Does the apparent size of the moon change with its phases?

2. Where is the moon located, relative to Earth and the sun, when it is new? What about Venus?

3. The moon has phases too. Why doesn't that make us think the moon revolves around the sun, rather than around Earth?

Lesson Quiz

Models of the Solar System

If the statement is true, write *true*. If the statement is false, change the underlined word or words to make the statement true.

1. _____ *Ge* is the <u>Greek</u> word for "Earth."

2. _____ *Helios* is the <u>Latin</u> word for "sun."

3. _____ A(n) <u>octagon</u> is an oval shape, such as the planets' orbits.

4. _____ Galileo discovered <u>six</u> moons around Jupiter.

5. _____ Ptolemy's model explained the motions observed in the sky <u>fairly accurately</u>.

6. _____ In ancient times, people could not accept that <u>the sun</u> was the center of the universe.

Write the letter of the correct answer on the line at the left.

7. ___ In the late 1500s, Ptolemy's observations were supplanted by those of
   A later Greek astronomers
   B later Polish astronomers
   C Edwin Hubble
   D Tycho Brahe

8. ___ The arrangement of the known planets and how they move around the sun was first worked out by
   A Galileo Galilei
   B Nicolaus Copernicus
   C Tycho Brahe
   D Johannes Kepler

9. ___ People became convinced that the heliocentric model is correct after evaluating evidence collected by
   A Galileo Galilei
   B Nicolaus Copernicus
   C Tycho Brahe
   D Johannes Kepler

10. ___ Earth is at the center of the revolving planets and stars in a(n)
   A heliocentric model
   B astrological model
   C geocentric model
   D Copernican model

Models of the Solar System

Answer Key

After the Inquiry Warm-Up

1. The sun, moon, and stars seemed to move around Earth, which doesn't feel like it is moving.

2. Students should draw a circular diagram with the sun in the center and Earth moving around the sun.

3. Students should draw a circular diagram with Earth in the center and the sun moving around Earth.

4. Answers will vary. Sample: Early astronomers needed better technology to see the real motions of objects in space.

Key Concept Summaries

Sample: Both models describe the motions of objects in our solar system. In a geocentric model, Earth is at the center of the revolving planets and stars. In a heliocentric model, Earth and the other planets revolve around the sun.

Review and Reinforce

1. In the geocentric model, the planets and the sun revolve around Earth. In the heliocentric model, Earth and the planets revolve around the sun.

2. In Ptolemy's model, the planets move on small circles that move on bigger circles.

3. Galileo observed moons orbiting around Jupiter. This showed that not everything revolves around Earth. He also observed phases of Venus that are similar to those of Earth's moon. Copernicus's heliocentric model could easily explain those observations.

4. having the sun at the center

5. an oval shape

6. having Earth at the center

Enrich

1. The full moon is on the opposite side of Earth from the sun. The full Venus is in almost the same direction as the sun. The apparent size of the moon does not change with its phases.

2. The new moon is between Earth and the sun. So is the new Venus.

3. Because its size does not appear to change, we know the moon is always about the same distance from Earth. Also, the moon is sometimes between Earth and the sun and sometimes on the opposite side of Earth from the sun.

Lesson Quiz

1. true
2. Greek
3. ellipse
4. four
5. true
6. Earth
7. D
8. B
9. A
10. C

Place the outside corner, the corner away from the dotted line, in the corner of your copy machine to copy onto letter-size paper.

Introducing the Solar System

Why are objects in the Solar System different from each other?

Lesson Pacing: 2–3 periods or 1–1½ blocks

🕐 **SHORT ON TIME?** To do this lesson in approximately half the time, do the Activate Prior Knowledge activity on page 82. A discussion of the Key Concepts on pages 83 and 86 will familiarize students with the lesson content. Use the Explore the Big Q to help students understand why objects in the Solar System are different from each other. Do the Quick Lab and have students do the Art in Motion activity online. The rest of the lesson can be completed by students independently.

Preference Navigator, in the online Planning tools, allows you to customize *Interactive Science* to your own teaching style. You can also edit lesson plans by selecting the Lesson Planner option.

Digital Teacher's Edition allows you to access your Teacher's Edition and Resource materials online.

Lesson Vocabulary

- solar system
- astronomical unit
- planet
- dwarf planet
- planetesimal

 Content Refresher

Planets, Dwarf Planets, and the IAU The International Astronomical Union (IAU) defines *planet* as "a celestial body that is in orbit around the Sun; has sufficient mass for its self-gravity to overcome rigid body forces so that it assumes a hydrostatic equilibrium (nearly round) shape; and has cleared the neighborhood around its orbit." The IAU defines *dwarf planet* as "a celestial body that is in orbit around the Sun; has sufficient mass for its self-gravity to overcome rigid body forces so that it assumes a hydrostatic equilibrium (nearly round) shape; has not cleared the neighborhood around its orbit; and is not a satellite."

A *plutoid* is a type of dwarf planet, distinguished by having an orbital path around the sun beyond the orbit of Neptune. Plutoids' satellites are not themselves plutoids. The first three named plutoids were Pluto, Eris and Makemake.

Founded in 1919, the IAU is made up of almost 10,000 astronomers from around the world. It is the internationally recognized authority for assigning designations to celestial bodies.

LESSON OBJECTIVES

🔑 Identify the objects that make up the solar system.

🔑 Explain how the solar system formed.

ENGAGE AND EXPLORE

Teach this lesson using a variety of resources. Begin by reading **My Planet Diary** as a class. Have students share ideas about how they keep cool in extreme heat. Then have students do the **Inquiry Warm-Up activity.** Students will investigate the relative size of the sun and Earth. Discuss why the sun and moon appear to be similar in size in the sky. The **After the Inquiry Warm-Up worksheet** sets up a discussion comparing how long it takes to travel around Earth and the moon when moving at 110 km/h. Have volunteers share their answers to question 4 about how many times light would travel around Earth in 4 seconds.

EXPLAIN AND ELABORATE

Teach Key Concepts by explaining the characteristics of our solar system. **Lead a Discussion** about the size of our sun in comparison to other objects in the solar system and in comparison to other stars. **Lead a Discussion** about the planetary objects in the solar system.

Then **Lead a Discussion** about satellites, comets and asteroids.

Continue to **Teach Key Concepts** by explaining that scientists think the solar system formed, about 4.6 billion years ago, when the sun formed from energy produced by nuclear fusion. Use **Figure 2** to illustrate the formation of the solar system. **Lead a Discussion** about how planets formed as a result of planetesimals colliding. To **Explore the Big Q,** have students identify differences between the main categories of objects in the solar system. Also discuss the differences between objects within each category. Help students **Answer the Big Q** by discussing why objects in the solar system are different from each other. Hand out the **Key Concept Summaries** as a review of each part of the lesson. Students can also use the online **Vocab Flash Cards** to review key terms.

EVALUATE

Have students take the **Lesson Quiz.** For an alternate assessment, see the **EXAM**VIEW® Assessment Suite, Progress Monitoring Assessments, or SuccessTracker™.

E L L Support

1 Content and Language

The word *comet* comes from the Greek word *komētēs,* which means having long hair. Discuss how a comet often looks like a furry head with lengthy tails.

Lab zone Inquiry Path
Hands-on learning in the Lab zone

Digital Path
Online learning at my science online.com

ENGAGE AND EXPLORE

To teach this lesson with an emphasis on inquiry, begin with the **Inquiry Warm-Up activity.** Students will investigate the size of the sun and Earth. Discuss why the sun appears to be the same size as the moon in the sky. Have students do the **After the Inquiry Warm-Up worksheet.** Talk about the amount of time it takes to travel around the moon and Earth when moving at 110 km/h. Have volunteers share their answers to question 4 about how many times light would travel around Earth in 4 seconds.

EXPLAIN AND ELABORATE

Focus on the **Inquiry Skill** for the lesson. Point out that when you calculate, you describe a situation using mathematical computations. What did students calculate in the **Inquiry Warm-Up activity?** *(The amount of time it takes to travel around Earth and the moon at 110 km/h)* Students will design an experiment, to determine how a planet's distance from the sun affects its period of revolution, in the **Lab Investigation.**

To **Explore the Big Q,** have students compare and contrast the properties of the categories of objects in the solar system. Also have them compare the properties of the objects within a category. Have students do the **Quick Lab** to investigate planetary formation and then share their results. Have students **Answer the Big Q** and then share their responses. Students can use the online **Vocab Flash Cards** to review key terms.

EVALUATE

Have students take the **Lesson Quiz.** For an alternate assessment, see the **EXAM**VIEW® Assessment Suite, Progress Monitoring Assessments, or SuccessTracker™.

ENGAGE AND EXPLORE

Teach this lesson using digital resources. Begin by having students explore real-world connections to the solar system's composition and formation at **My Planet Diary** online. Have them access the Chapter Resources to find the **Unlock the Big Question activity.** There they can answer the questions and refine their responses as they continue through the lesson. You can re-assign the activity and have students submit their work so you can track their progress.

EXPLAIN AND ELABORATE

Students reading above, at, or below the lexile measure of this lesson can access basic content readings at their level at **My Reading Web.** Have students use the online **Vocab Flash Cards** to preview key terms. Assign the **Do the Math activity** online and have students submit their work to you. Have students do the **Interactive Art activity** to explore the objects in the solar system.

Have students do the online **Art in Motion activity** to show the formation of the solar system. To **Explore the Big Q,** discuss the main categories of objects in the solar system and their characteristics. Do the **Quick Lab** to investigate planetary formation and then ask students to share their results. Have students **Answer the Big Q** and then share their responses. The **Key Concept Summaries** online allow students to read a summary and see an image associated with each part of the lesson. Online remediation is available at **My Science Coach.**

EVALUATE

Have students take the **Lesson Quiz.** For an alternate assessment, see the **EXAM**VIEW® Assessment Suite, Progress Monitoring Assessments, or SuccessTracker™.

2 Frontload the Lesson
Preview the lesson visuals, labels, and captions. Ask students what they know about the words *astronomical unit* and *planetesimal.* Explain the specific meanings these words have in science.

3 Comprehensible Input
Have students study the visuals and their captions on pages 84, 85, and 86 to support the Key Concepts of the lesson.

4 Language Production
Pair or group students with varied language abilities to complete labs collaboratively for language practice. Have each student copy the completed written lab for personal reference.

5 Assess Understanding
Divide the class into small groups. Have each student identify a Key Concept from the lesson to discuss in his or her group. After the discussions, have students talk about the Key Concepts as a group.

Introducing the Solar System

Establish Learning Objectives

After this lesson, students will be able to:

🔑 Identify the objects that make up the solar system.

🔑 Explain how the solar system formed.

Engage

Activate Prior Knowledge

MY PLANET DIARY Read *Extreme Conditions* with the class. Explain that the material from which the sunshade is made is integral to its design. Ask: **Do you think a sunshade is a good idea? Why or why not?** *(Sample: Yes; I've used an umbrella when sitting on the beach. It provides excellent protection for my skin.)*

BIG IDEAS OF SCIENCE REFERENCE LIBRARY 📖
Have students look up the following topics: Earth, Space Probes.

Explore

Lab Resource: Inquiry Warm-Up

L2 HOW BIG IS EARTH? Students will investigate the relative sizes of the sun and Earth.

LESSON 2

Introducing the Solar System

🔑 **What Makes Up the Solar System?**

🔑 **How Did the Solar System Form?**

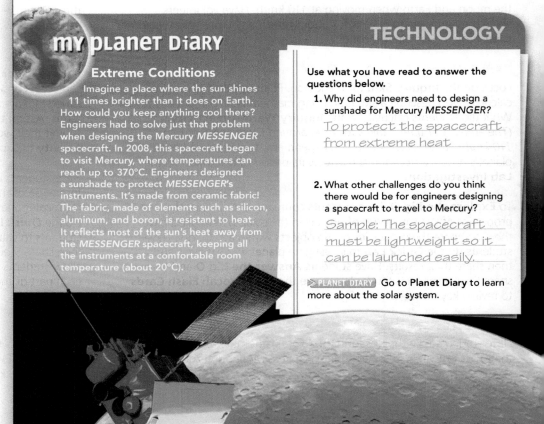

MY PLANET DIARY

Extreme Conditions

Imagine a place where the sun shines 11 times brighter than it does on Earth. How could you keep anything cool there? Engineers had to solve just that problem when designing the Mercury *MESSENGER* spacecraft. In 2008, this spacecraft began to visit Mercury, where temperatures can reach up to 370°C. Engineers designed a sunshade to protect *MESSENGER*'s instruments. It's made from ceramic fabric! The fabric, made of elements such as silicon, aluminum, and boron, is resistant to heat. It reflects most of the sun's heat away from the *MESSENGER* spacecraft, keeping all the instruments at a comfortable room temperature (about 20°C).

TECHNOLOGY

Use what you have read to answer the questions below.

1. Why did engineers need to design a sunshade for Mercury *MESSENGER*?

   To protect the spacecraft from extreme heat

2. What other challenges do you think there would be for engineers designing a spacecraft to travel to Mercury?

   Sample: The spacecraft must be lightweight so it can be launched easily.

▶ PLANET DIARY Go to **Planet Diary** to learn more about the solar system.

Lab zone — Do the Inquiry Warm-Up *How Big Is Earth?*

82 The Solar System

SUPPORT ALL READERS

Lexile Measure = 870L   Lexile Word Count = 1082

Prior Exposure to Content: Most students have encountered this topic in earlier grades

Academic Vocabulary: *calculate, supporting evidence, sequence*

Science Vocabulary: *solar system, astronomical unit, planet*

Concept Level: May be difficult for students who struggle with abstract ideas

Preteach With: My Planet Diary "Extreme Conditions" and Figure 1 activity

Go to **My Reading Web** to access leveled readings that provide a foundation for the content.

MY SCIENCE online.com

LESSON 3.2

Vocabulary

- solar system
- astronomical unit
- planet
- dwarf planet
- planetesimal

Skills

- Reading: Identify Supporting Evidence
- Inquiry: Calculate

What Makes Up the Solar System?

Mercury is just one of many objects that make up the solar system. **Our solar system consists of the sun, the planets, their moons, and a variety of smaller objects**. The sun is at the center of the solar system, with other objects orbiting around it. The force of gravity holds the solar system together.

Distances in the Solar System Distances within the solar system are so large that they cannot be easily measured in meters or kilometers. Instead, scientists often use a unit called the astronomical unit. One **astronomical unit** (AU) equals the average distance between Earth and the sun, about 150,000,000 kilometers. The solar system extends more than 100,000 AU from the sun.

do the math!

Converting Units

To convert from astronomical units (AU) to kilometers (km), you can multiply the number of AU by 150,000,000.

1 **Calculate** Mars is 1.52 AU from the sun. About how many kilometers is Mars from the sun? _228,000,000 km_

2 **Apply Concepts** If you know an object's distance from the sun in kilometers, how can you find its distance in AU? _Divide the distance in kilometers by 150,000,000._

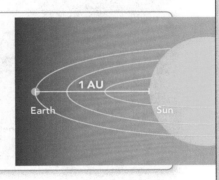

Earth — 1 AU — Sun

The Sun At the center of our solar system is the sun. The sun is much larger than anything else in the solar system. About 99.85 percent of the mass of the solar system is contained within the sun. Despite being more than a million times the volume of Earth, our sun is actually a very ordinary mid-sized star. Using telescopes, we see stars that have volumes a thousand times greater than the sun's! This turns out to be a very good thing for us. Large stars burn out and die quickly, but our sun will last for five billion more years.

Identify Supporting Evidence Underline a sentence that supports the statement, "The sun is much larger than anything else in the solar system."

83

ELL Support

1 Content and Language

Write the term *dwarf planet* on the board. Explain that the word *dwarf* is sometimes used to identify an object, plant, or person who is significantly smaller than most others of its kind.

2 Frontload the Lesson

Use **Figure 1** to help show the relationship of the planets to the sun. Point to the sun and Earth, urging students to note the huge difference in

their sizes. Have students identify other planets, their positions relative to the sun, and their sizes relative to Earth.

3 Comprehensible Input

Have students complete a flowchart to show the sequence of steps to the formation of our solar system. Urge students to use verbs to identify each step, such as "Gravity *pulls* hydrogen, helium, rocks, ice, and other materials into a cloud."

Explain

Introduce Vocabulary

Write *planetesimal* on the board, and read it aloud. Explain that the ending *-tesimal* means "much, much less." Inform students that an individual planetesimal had much, much less mass and was much, much smaller in size than a planet.

Teach Key Concepts

Explain to students that our solar system is made up of four basic types of objects. Ask: **What makes up our solar system?** *(The sun, planets, their moons, and smaller objects)* **What is at the center of the solar system?** *(The sun)* **How do you describe a model of the solar system with the sun at the center?** *(Heliocentric)* **What holds the solar system together?** *(Gravity)* **What unit is used to measure large distances in space?** *(Astronomical units)* Tell students that one astronomical unit is equal to the distance between Earth and the sun. Ask: **How large is one AU?** *(150,000,000 km)*

Lead a Discussion

THE SUN Make sure that students understand that the sun is the largest object in our solar system, but not the largest object in the universe. Ask: **How much of the mass of the solar system is contained in the sun?** *(About 99.85 percent)*

Identify Supporting Evidence Explain that evidence consists of facts—information whose accuracy is confirmed by observation or testing.

Elaborate

Do the Math!

L1 Ask students why scientists use astronomical units (AUs) instead of kilometers to measure distances within the solar system. *(The distances are too large to measure in kilometers.)* Tell students they will get a sense of how useful astronomical units are as they do the activity.

Calculate Explain that converting one unit to another involves multiplying or dividing. After students have made their calculations, have them check the place value of their answer.

See *Math Skill and Problem-Solving Activities* for support.

My Planet Diary provides an opportunity for students to explore real-world connections to the solar system's composition and formation.

Digital Lesson: Assign the *Do the Math* activity online and have students submit their work to you.

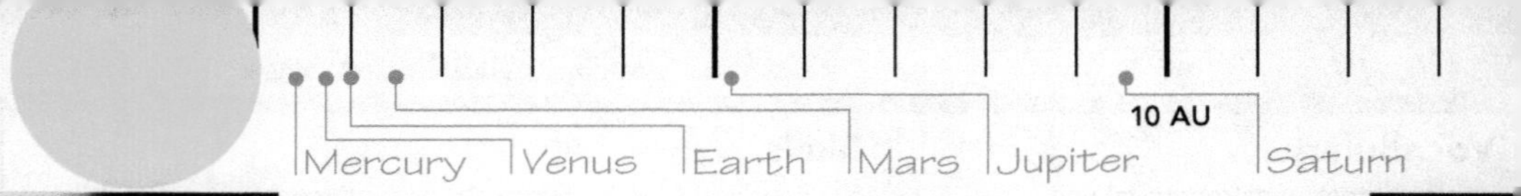

Explain

Lead a Discussion

PLANETS AND DWARF PLANETS Point out the subheads, which name all the main types of objects in the solar system, except the sun. Ask: **Which two kinds of objects are planetary?** *(Planets and dwarf planets)* **What are the characteristics of a planet?** *(It is round, it orbits the sun, and has cleared out other objects from the area around its orbit.)* **What are the eight planets?** *(Mercury, Venus, Earth, Mars, Jupiter, Saturn, Uranus, and Neptune)* **How many dwarf planets are there?** *(Five)*

21st Century Learning

CRITICAL THINKING: Compare and Contrast
Point out that Pluto was, for many years, considered the ninth planet in the solar system. Ask: **How is Pluto classified now?** *(As a dwarf planet)* **How are planets and dwarf planets alike?** *(Sample: Both orbit the sun.)* **How are they different?** *(Sample: Dwarf planets have less gravity—not enough to clear their orbital area of other objects.)*

---

					10 AU	
Mercury	Venus	Earth	Mars	Jupiter		Saturn

FIGURE 1

> **INTERACTIVE ART** **The Solar System**
The planets' sizes are shown to scale, but their distances from the sun are not.

✎ **Mark the position of each planet on the distance scale above.**

1. **Interpret Data** Where is the largest gap between planets?

   Between Uranus and Neptune

2. **CHALLENGE** Could you show the planets' relative sizes and distances from the sun in the same diagram on one page? Why or why not?

   No; If you showed the distances to scale, the
   planets would be too small to see.

Mercury
Diameter: 4,879 km
Distance from the sun: 0.39 AU
Orbital period: 87.97 Earth days
Moons: 0

Earth
Diameter: 12,756 km
Distance from the sun: 1 AU
Orbital period: 365.26 Earth days
Moons: 1

Venus
Diameter: 12,104 km
Distance from the sun: 0.72 AU
Orbital period: 224.7 Earth days
Moons: 0

Mars
Diameter: 6,794 km
Distance from the sun: 1.52 AU
Orbital period: 687 Earth days
Moons: 2

Planets

There are many different objects in the solar system. How do you decide what is a planet and what isn't? In 2006, astronomers decided that a **planet** must be round, orbit the sun, and have cleared out the region of the solar system along its orbit. The first four planets are small and are mostly made of rock and metal. The last four planets are very large and are mostly made of gas and liquid. Like Earth, each planet has a "day" and a "year." Its day is the time it takes to rotate on its axis. Its year is the time it takes to orbit the sun. **Figure 1** shows some basic facts about the planets.

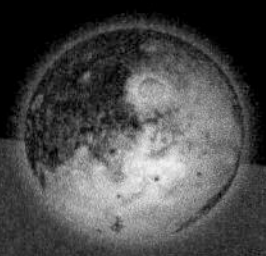

Dwarf Planets

For many years, Pluto was considered the ninth planet in the solar system. But Pluto shares the area of its orbit with other objects. Pluto is now considered a dwarf planet. A **dwarf planet** is an object that orbits the sun and has enough gravity to be spherical, but has not cleared the area of its orbit. There are five known dwarf planets in our solar system: Pluto, Eris, Ceres, Makemake (MAH keh MAH keh), and Haumea (how MAY uh). As scientists observe more distant objects, the number of dwarf planets might grow.

84 The Solar System

Professional Development Note **Teacher to Teacher**

Activity Many students have a misconception that the solar system is a crowded place. I introduce the solar system by having students create a scale model that is accurate both in spacing and size of the planets. We scale the average diameter of the orbit of Pluto to about 92 meters. This allows us to lay it out on the football field. The sun is about the size of a large nightlight bulb (21.5 mm) and Earth has a diameter of 0.2 mm, about 2.3 meters from the sun.

✉ *Joel Palmer, Ed.D.*
Mesquite ISD
Mesquite, Texas

20 AU
Uranus

30 AU
Neptune

Satellites

Except for Mercury and Venus, every planet in the solar system has at least one natural satellite, or moon. Earth has the fewest moons, with just one. Jupiter and Saturn each have more than 60! Some dwarf planets also have satellites.

Smaller Objects

The solar system also includes many smaller objects that orbit the sun. Some, called asteroids, are small, mostly rocky bodies. Many asteroids are found in an area between the orbits of Mars and Jupiter. Comets are another large group of solar system objects. Comets are loose balls of ice and rock that usually have very long, narrow orbits.

Saturn
Diameter: 120,536 km
Distance from the sun: 9.54 AU
Orbital period: 29.47 Earth years
Moons: 60+

Neptune
Diameter: 49,258 km
Distance from the sun: 30.07 AU
Orbital period: 163.72 Earth years
Moons: 13+

Uranus
Diameter: 51,118 km
Distance from the sun: 19.19 AU
Orbital period: 83.75 Earth years
Moons: 20+

Jupiter
Diameter: 142,984 km
Distance from the sun: 5.20 AU
Orbital period: 11.86 Earth years
Moons: 60+

 Lab zone Do the Lab Investigation *Speeding Around the Sun.*

Assess Your Understanding

1a. **Sequence** List the planets in order of increasing distance from the sun.

Mercury, Venus, Earth, Mars, Jupiter, Saturn, Uranus, Neptune

b. **Make Generalizations** What is the relationship between a planet's distance from the sun and the length of its year?

The farther the planet is from the sun, the longer its year.

got it?

O **I get it!** Now I know that the solar system includes the sun, planets, satellites, asteroids, comets, and dwarf planets.

O **I need extra help with** See TE note.

Go to **MY SCIENCE COACH** online for help with this subject.

85

Lead a Discussion

SATELLITES AND SMALLER OBJECTS Remind students that Earth's moon is a satellite. Ask: **Which planets do not have satellites?** *(Mercury and Venus)* **Which planets have the most satellites?** *(Jupiter and Saturn)* **What kinds of objects are in the category of smaller objects?** *(Asteroids and comets)*

Elaborate

Lab Resource: Lab Investigation **Lab zone**

L3 **SPEEDING AROUND THE SUN** Students will design an experiment to determine how a planet's distance from the sun affects its period of revolution.

Evaluate

Assess Your Understanding

After students answer the questions, have them evaluate their understanding by completing the appropriate sentence.

RTI Response to Intervention

1a. If students have trouble listing the planets in order of increasing distance from the sun, **then** have them consult the text boxes that give facts about each planet.

b. If students have trouble explaining how a planet's distance from the sun affects the length of its year, **then** have them make a two-column chart to organize the data about distances and length of a year.

MY SCIENCE COACH Have students go online for help in understanding the solar system.

Interactive Art allows students to explore the objects in the solar system.

MY SCIENCE online.com | The Solar System

Differentiated Instruction

L1 **Make Flashcards** Give each student eight note cards. Have students write the names of the eight planets on the cards, one name per card. On the other side of the appropriate card, have students copy from the text that planet's diameter, distance from the sun, and number of moons. Then have partners take turns using their flashcards to test each other's knowledge of the planets' relative size, distance from the sun, and number of moons. If time allows, have teams of students compete in a quiz game in which you serve as the moderator.

Explain

Teach Key Concepts 🔊

Explain to students the scientific theory of how the solar system formed Ask: **When do scientists think the solar system formed?** *(About 4.6 billion years ago)* **From what do scientists think the solar system formed?** *(From a cloud pulled together by gravity)* **What was the cloud made of?** *(Hydrogen, helium, rock, ice, and other materials)*

Teach With Visuals

Tell students to look at **Figure 2.** Ask: **What do the images show?** *(Sample: The formation of the sun and planets from a cloud pulled together by gravity)*

Lead a Discussion

PLANET FORMATION Remind students that one of the defining characteristics of a planet is that it has cleared out the area around the path of its orbit. Ask: **What are planetismals?** *(Small bodies made of rock and ice)* **How did planetismals form planets?** *(They collided and stuck together)* **How do you think this is related to the definition of planet?** *(By colliding with and sticking to other matter in their path, planetismals cleared out the area around their orbits. They also became larger in the process.)*

FIGURE 2 ·

⊳ART IN MOTION **Formation of the Solar System**

✎ **Sequence** Write the numbers 1 through 4 in the circles to put the images in order.

86 The Solar System

How Did the Solar System Form?

Where did the objects in the solar system come from? 🔊 **Scientists think the solar system formed about 4.6 billion years ago from a cloud of hydrogen, helium, rock, ice, and other materials pulled together by gravity.**

A Spinning Disk The process began as gravity pulled the cloud's material together. The cloud collapsed and started to rotate, forming a disk. Most of the material was pulled to the center. As this material became tightly packed, it got hotter and the pressure on it increased.

Eventually, the temperature and pressure became so high that hydrogen atoms were pressed together to form helium. This process, called nuclear fusion, releases large amounts of energy. Once nuclear fusion began, the sun gave off light and became a stable star. Sunlight is one form of the energy produced by fusion.

The Planets Form Away from the sun, planets began to form as gravity pulled rock, ice, and gas together. The rock and ice formed small bodies called **planetesimals** (pla nuh TE suh muhlz). Over time, planetesimals collided and stuck together, eventually combining to form all the other objects in the solar system.

Inner Planets Close to the sun, the solar system was very hot. Most water evaporated, preventing ice from forming. The bodies that formed in this region were comparatively low in mass. Their gravity was too weak to hold on to light gases such as hydrogen and helium. This is why the inner planets are small and rocky.

Outer Planets At greater distances from the sun, temperatures were cooler. Ice formed, adding mass to the planets that formed at these distances. As the planets grew, their gravity was strong enough to hold hydrogen and helium, forming the gas giant planets. Beyond the gas giants, temperatures were even lower. Ice and other materials produced comets and dwarf planets.

Art in Motion shows the formation of the solar system.

my science online.com ⟩ The Early Solar System

Solve THE SOLAR SYSTEM

Why are objects in the solar system different from each other?

FIGURE 3 ....

Use the clues to complete the puzzle.
Then answer the question.

ACROSS

3 The planet farthest from the sun
4 A loose, icy body with a long, narrow orbit
6 A gas giant planet that is smaller than Jupiter but larger than Neptune
7 The smallest planet in the solar system
8 An object that orbits a planet

DOWN

1 The largest planet in the solar system
2 A planet that formed closer to the sun than Earth but not closest to the sun
5 A small rocky body that orbits the sun

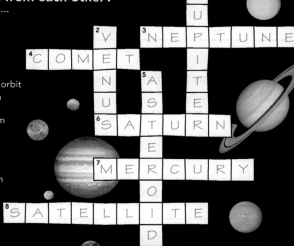

Crossword puzzle solution:
- 1 Down: JUPITER
- 2 Down: VENUS
- 3 Across: NEPTUNE
- 4 Across: COMET
- 5 Down: ASTEROID
- 6 Across: SATURN
- 7 Across: MERCURY
- 8 Across: SATELLITE

Why are the objects in clues 2 and 6 so different?

Sample: Venus formed very close to the sun, where conditions were hot.
It was too small to hold onto hydrogen and helium. Saturn formed where
ice could form, and had enough mass to hold on to hydrogen and helium.

Lab zone — Do the Quick Lab *Clumping Planets.*

Assess Your Understanding

2a. Explain What force formed the solar system?

Gravity

b. ANSWER Why are objects in the solar system different from each other?

The objects formed from different materials and at different distances from the sun.

got it?

○ I get it! Now I know that the solar system formed when gravity pulled together a cloud of gas and dust.

○ I need extra help with See TE note.

Go to **my science COACH** online for help with this subject.

87

Elaborate

Explore the Big Q

Direct students' attention to the crossword puzzle. As they work the puzzle, encourage students to think about how varied objects in the solar system are. Ask: **What main categories of objects in the solar system are different from each other?** *(Sample: Planets, dwarf planets, moons, asteroids, and comets)* **Are objects within each category alike?** *(Sample: No, for example the inner and outer planets are quite different, and each planet has distinct characteristics.)* **What determined the main differences between the inner and outer planets?** *(Their distance from the sun when they formed)* **Why is this distance important?** *(The inner planets were hot because they were close to the sun. Water evaporated and light gases escaped. The outer planets were cooler, so water froze. These planets had strong enough gravity to hold onto the lighter gases, and they became gas giants.)*

Lab Resource: Quick Lab

L1 CLUMPING PLANETS Students will investigate planetary formation.

Evaluate

Assess Your Understanding

After students answer the questions, have them evaluate their understanding by completing the appropriate sentence.

Answer the Big Q

To help students focus on the Big Question, lead a class discussion about why objects in the solar system are different from each other.

RTI Response to Intervention

2a. If students need help identifying the force that formed the solar system, **then** have them locate and reread the Key Concept statement, paying particular attention to the last phrase.

b. If students have difficulty explaining why objects are different from each other, **then** review with them the way the planets and other objects formed.

my science COACH Have students go online for help in understanding the early solar system.

Differentiated Instruction

L1 Make a Puzzle After students solve the crossword puzzle to answer the Big Question, challenge them to create similar puzzles about objects in the solar system. Pair visual and verbal learners for this activity. Encourage them to use the puzzle in the text as a model and information in the text for clues. Have partners exchange completed puzzles with another pair and work the puzzle that they received.

L3 Research Solar System Formation Inform students that some scientists think energy from a nearby supernova started the collapse of the gas cloud that formed the solar system. Have interested students research this hypothesis and share their findings with the class.

Lab zone **After the Inquiry Warm-Up**

Introducing the Solar System

Inquiry Warm-Up, *How Big Is Earth?*

In the Inquiry Warm-Up, you investigated the relative sizes of the sun and Earth. Using what you learned from that activity, answer the questions below.

1. **INFER** Why do you think the sun and the moon seem to be the same size in the sky even though the sun is much larger?

   _____

   _____

2. **CALCULATE** Earth's circumference is about 46,350 kilometers. If you're traveling at 110 km/h, how long in days, hours, and minutes would it take to make one trip around Earth?

   _____

   _____

3. **CALCULATE** The moon has approximately one-fourth the circumference of Earth. Assuming you're traveling at 110 km/h, how long would it take to make one trip around the moon?

   _____

   _____

4. **CALCULATE** Light travels at about 300,000 kilometers per second. About how many times would light travel around Earth in 4 seconds?

   _____

   _____

Assess Your Understanding

Introducing the Solar System

What Makes Up the Solar System?

1a. SEQUENCE List the planets in order of increasing distance from the sun.

_____

_____

b. MAKE GENERALIZATIONS What is the relationship between a planet's distance from the sun and the length of its year?

_____

got it? ....

○ **I get it!** Now I know that the solar system includes _____

_____

○ **I need extra help with** _____

_____

How Did the Solar System Form?

2a. EXPLAIN What force formed the solar system?

_____

b. ANSWER Why are objects in the solar system different from each other?

_____

_____

got it? ....

○ **I get it!** Now I know that the solar system formed when _____

_____

○ **I need extra help with** _____

_____

Introducing the Solar System

What Makes Up the Solar System?

Our solar system consists of the sun, the planets, their moons, and a variety of smaller objects. The sun is at the center of the solar system, with other objects orbiting it. Gravity holds the solar system together. About 99.85 percent of the mass of the entire solar system is contained within the sun.

Distances in the solar system are so large that they are measured in astronomical units. One **astronomical unit** (AU) equals the average distance between Earth and the sun, about 150,000,000 kilometers.

There are many different types of objects in the solar system. A **planet** is round, orbits the sun, and has cleared out the region of the solar system along its orbit. All except Mercury and Venus have at least one natural satellite, or moon. A **dwarf planet** is an object that orbits the sun and has enough gravity to be spherical, but has not cleared the area of its orbit.

The solar system also includes many smaller objects that orbit the sun, such as asteroids and comets.

How Did the Solar System Form?

Scientists think the solar system formed about 4.6 billion years ago from a cloud of hydrogen, helium, rock, ice, and other materials pulled together by gravity. Eventually, the temperature and pressure in the cloud became so high that, through nuclear fusion, hydrogen atoms were pressed together to form helium, a process that produces light and heat.

Away from the sun, planets began to form as gravity pulled rock, ice, and gas together. The rock and ice

formed small bodies called **planetesimals.** Over time, planetesimals collided and stuck together, eventually combining to form all the other objects in the solar system.

Close to the sun, the inner planets are small and rocky. At greater distances from the sun, planets became gas giants. Beyond the gas giants, ice and other materials produced comets and dwarf planets.

On a separate sheet of paper, list six types of bodies that the solar system includes, and describe the material from which the solar system formed.

Review and Reinforce

Introducing the Solar System

Understanding Main Ideas
Answer the following questions in the spaces provided.

1. What makes up our solar system?

_____

_____

2. From what did the solar system form?

_____

_____

3. When was the solar system formed?

_____

Building Vocabulary
Match each term with its definition by writing the letter of the correct definition in the right column on the line beside the term in the left column.

4. ___ dwarf planet

5. ___ astronomical unit

6. ___ solar system

7. ___ planetesimal

8. ___ planet

a. small body that combined with like bodies to form all the other objects in our solar system

b. the sun, the planets, their moons, and a variety of smaller objects

c. object that orbits the sun, is spherical, but has not cleared the area of its orbit

d. used to measure distances within the solar system

e. object that orbits the sun, is round, and has cleared the area of its orbit

Introducing the Solar System

> The table below gives information about the mass, gravity, and day length of Earth, Venus, Mars, and three imaginary planets. Read the passage and study the table. Then use a separate sheet of paper to answer the questions that follow.

Planets for Human Settlement

Will humans ever travel to other solar systems? Will we ever find an Earthlike planet on which humans could easily live?

Humans need several things, such as water, oxygen, light, and comfortable temperatures to support life. Whether a planet can supply what we need to live depends on many factors. Let's look at two important factors.

- **A planet's rotation rate** A planet with a slow rotation rate has long days, which would be harmful to humans. It would get very hot in the afternoon and very cold at night. Humans probably could not live comfortably on a planet whose day was greater than four Earth days.

- **A planet's mass** Mass determines many of the other characteristics of a planet. Larger planets have stronger gravity. Humans cannot stand gravity greater than 1.5 times Earth's gravity for very long. Also, a planet's surface water and atmosphere originally come from beneath its surface. For this reason, a planet must be massive enough to have a large volume compared to its surface area. A planet smaller than 0.4 times Earth's mass would probably not have enough air and water to support human life.

	Earth	Mars	Planet A	Planet B	Planet C
Mass (Earth = 1)	1	0.107	2.5	0.7	1
Gravity (Earth = 1)	1	0.38	1.65	0.87	1
Length of Day (hrs)	24	24.62	30	60	255

1. Planets A, B, and C revolve around stars like the sun in orbits like that of Earth. Could planet A possibly support human life? Explain.

2. Could planet B possibly support human life? Explain.

3. Could planet C possibly support human life? Explain.

4. If Mars were located in Earth's orbit, could it support human life? Explain.

Lesson Quiz

Introducing the Solar System

Write the letter of the correct answer on the line at the left.

1. ___ One day is the time it takes a planet to rotate on its

   A equator

   B axis

   C poles

   D moon

2. ___ Scientists think the solar system formed about

   A 4.6 thousand years ago

   B 4.6 hundred thousand years ago

   C 4.6 million years ago

   D 4.6 billion years ago

3. ___ The sun is a(n)

   A asteroid

   B planet

   C planetesimal

   D star

4. ___ Planetesimals collided, stuck together, and eventually combined to form all the other objects in the

   A galaxy

   B universe

   C solar system

   D zodiac

Fill in the blank to complete each statement.

5. Scientists use the _____ to measure distances within the solar system.

6. About 99.85 percent of the mass of the solar system is contained within the

   _____.

7. All but two planets in the solar system have a natural satellite, or

   _____.

8. The four outermost planets in the sun's orbit are mostly made of liquid and

   _____.

9. _____, once the ninth planet in the solar system, is now considered a dwarf planet.

10. The solar system began to form as _____ pulled rock, ice, and gas together.

Introducing the Solar System

Answer Key

After the Inquiry Warm-Up

1. The sun is much farther away than the moon, so it appears smaller than it actually is.

2. 17 days, 13 hours, 22 minutes

3. 4 days, 9 hours, 21 minutes

4. about 26 times

Key Concept Summaries

Sample: The sun (a star), planets, dwarf planets, satellites, asteroids, comets. The solar system formed from a cloud of hydrogen, helium, ice, rock, and other materials pulled together by gravity.

Review and Reinforce

1. the sun, the planets, their moons, and a variety of smaller objects such as comets and asteroids

2. a cloud of hydrogen, helium, rock, ice, and other materials pulled together by gravity

3. about 4.6 billion years ago

4. c   5. d

6. b   7. a

8. e

Enrich

1. Planet A could not support human life for an extended period. Its gravity is too great.

2. Planet B might be able to support human life. Its mass is over 0.4 times that of Earth, so it might have water and an atmosphere. Its length of day is 2.5 times that of Earth. Its gravity is slightly less than Earth's, so humans wouldn't be harmed.

3. Planet C could not support human life for long. Its day is too long.

4. Even though its day is only slightly longer than Earth's, Mars could not support human life because it is too small to have a sufficient thick atmosphere or enough surface water.

Lesson Quiz

1. B   2. D
3. D   4. C
5. astronomical unit   6. sun
7. moon   8. gas
9. Pluto   10. gravity

Place the outside corner, the corner away from the dotted line, in the corner of your copy machine to copy onto letter-size paper.

The Sun

3 Why are objects in the Solar System different from each other?

Lesson Pacing: 1–2 periods or $\frac{1}{2}$–1 block

🕐 **SHORT ON TIME?** To do this lesson in approximately half the time, do the Activate Prior Knowledge activity on page 88. A discussion of the Key Concepts on pages 89, 90, and 92 will familiarize students with the lesson content. Have students do the Quick Labs. The rest of the lesson can be completed by students independently.

Preference Navigator, in the online Planning tools, allows you to customize *Interactive Science* to your own teaching style. You can also edit lesson plans by selecting the Lesson Planner option.

Digital Teacher's Edition allows you to access your Teacher's Edition and Resource materials online.

Lesson Vocabulary

- core
- nuclear fusion
- radiation zone
- convection zone
- photosphere
- chromosphere
- corona
- solar wind
- sunspot
- prominence
- solar flare

Content Refresher
Professional Development Note

Sunspot Cycles Some scientists theorize that sunspot cycles influence Earth's climate. Among the evidence for this hypothesis is the so-called Little Ice Age, which lasted from approximately 1550 until 1850. During this time, most parts of the world experienced cooler and harsher weather.

The Little Ice Age has been associated with a period of low sunspot activity that occurred between 1645 and 1715. This period is known as the Maunder minimum after the English astronomer who described it. Sunspots were first detected around 1600, but there are few recorded sightings during the Maunder minimum. Sunspot sightings resumed after 1715.

There is evidence that times of low sunspot activity occur in cycles of 500 years. If there is such a cycle, another "Little Ice Age" could possibly begin in about 2050.

Scientists have also analyzed the average number of visible sunspots per month. They found that the number of visible sunspots skyrockets to nearly 150 on occasion and then decreases to less than ten, there is a pattern to these highs and lows that can be seen over the course of about an 11-year cycle. In the times of high sunspot activity, the sun is more active which scientists hypothesize contributes to changes in Earth's outermost layers.

LESSON OBJECTIVES

- 🔑 Identify the layers of the sun's interior and atmosphere.
- 🔑 Describe the features that form on or above the sun's surface.

Blended Path
Active learning using Student Edition, Inquiry Path, and Digital Path

ENGAGE AND EXPLORE

Teach this lesson using a variety of resources. Begin by reading **My Planet Diary** as a class. Have students share ideas about what happens during an electrical power outage. Then have students do the **Inquiry Warm-Up activity.** Students will learn how to safely observe the sun. Discuss the objects that can affect their observations of the sun. The **After the Inquiry Warm-Up worksheet** sets up a discussion about why they should not look directly at the sun. Have volunteers share their predictions of how the sun would look different if the moon were between the sun and Earth.

EXPLAIN AND ELABORATE

Teach Key Concepts by explaining how energy moves through the three zones of the sun. **Lead a Discussion** about how heat is transferred by convection in the corresponding zone of the sun. **Teach Key Concepts** by telling students about the properties of the sun's atmospheres.

Continue to **Teach Key Concepts** by asking students what sunspots, prominences, and solar flares are. Look at the images in **Figure 3** to compare and contrast sunspots and prominences. **Support the Big Q** by discussing how auroras and magnetic storms are formed by the interaction between solar wind and Earth's magnetic field. Hand out the **Key Concept Summaries** as a review of each part of the lesson. Students can also use the online **Vocab Flash Cards** to review key terms.

EVALUATE

Have students take the **Lesson Quiz.** For an alternate assessment, see the **EXAM**VIEW® Assessment Suite, Progress Monitoring Assessments, or SuccessTracker™.

ELL Support

1 Content and Language
Photosphere contains the Greek word part *photo-* meaning "light," so the *photosphere* is the "light sphere."

Lab zone Inquiry Path
Hands-on learning in the Lab zone

ENGAGE AND EXPLORE

To teach this lesson with an emphasis on inquiry, begin with the **Inquiry Warm-Up activity.** Students will investigate how to safely observe the sun. Discuss how clouds affect their observations of the sun. Have students do the **After the Inquiry Warm-Up worksheet.** Talk about why they should not look directly at the sun. Have volunteers share their predictions of how the sun would look different if the moon were between the sun and Earth.

EXPLAIN AND ELABORATE

Focus on the **Inquiry Skill** for the lesson. Point out that when you interpret data, you look for patterns in facts and figures in order to analyze the information. In the **Inquiry Warm-Up activity,** what data was it necessary to know to make a prediction for question 4? *(That the moon looks like it is nearly the same size as the sun when looking in the sky)* Do the **Teacher Demo** to show students that energy from the sun warms Earth. Have students do the **Quick Lab** to investigate the layers of the sun and then share their results.

To **Support the Big Q,** discuss how auroras and magnetic storms are created by the interaction between solar wind and Earth's magnetic field. Do the **Quick Lab** to reinforce understanding of sunspots. Students can use the online **Vocab Flash Cards** to review key terms.

EVALUATE

Have students take the **Lesson Quiz.** For an alternate assessment, see the **EXAM**VIEW® Assessment Suite, Progress Monitoring Assessments, or SuccessTracker™.

Digital Path
Online learning at my science online.com

ENGAGE AND EXPLORE

Teach this lesson using digital resources. Begin by having students explore real-world connections to the sun at **My Planet Diary** online. Have them access the Chapter Resources to find the **Unlock the Big Question activity.** There they can answer the questions and refine their responses as they continue through the lesson. You can re-assign the activity and have students submit their work so you can track their progress.

EXPLAIN AND ELABORATE

Students reading above, at, or below the lexile measure of this lesson can access basic content readings at their level at **My Reading Web.** Have students use the online **Vocab Flash Cards** to preview key terms. Have students do the **interactive Art activity** online to explore the structure of the sun. Assign the **Do the Math activity** online and have students submit their work to you. Do the **Quick Lab** to investigate the layers of the sun and then ask students to share their results.

To **Support the Big Q,** ask students to describe what is created when solar wind and Earth's magnetic fields interact. Do the **Quick Lab** to explore sunspots. The **Key Concept Summaries** online allow students to read a summary and see an image associated with each part of the lesson. Online remediation is available at **My Science Coach.**

EVALUATE

Have students take the **Lesson Quiz.** For an alternate assessment, see the **EXAM**VIEW® Assessment Suite, Progress Monitoring Assessments, or SuccessTracker™.

2 Frontload the Lesson
Preview the lesson visuals, labels, and captions. Ask students what they know about the terms *core* and *prominence.* Explain the specific meanings these words have in science.

3 Comprehensible Input
Have students study the visuals and their captions on pages 89, 90, 91, 92, and 93 to support the Key Concepts of the lesson.

4 Language Production
Pair or group students with varied language abilities to complete labs collaboratively for language practice. Have each student copy the completed written lab for personal reference.

5 Assess Understanding
Have students develop a portfolio of their notes and then do oral presentations of lesson content.

The Sun

Establish Learning Objectives

After this lesson, students will be able to:

🔑 Identify the layers of the sun's interior and atmosphere.

🔑 Describe features that form on or above the sun's surface.

Engage

Activate Prior Knowledge

MY PLANET DIARY Read *Left in the Dark* with the class. Inform students that an electrical surge through the circuits in a building or house can cause a power outage. Ask: **Raise your hand if you have experienced an electric power outage. What caused the outage?** *(Sample: My sister turned on a blow dryer and overloaded the circuit.)* **How did you get the power to return?** *(Sample: By resetting the circuit breaker)*

BIG IDEAS OF SCIENCE REFERENCE LIBRARY Have students look up the following topic: Solar Power.

Explore

Lab Resource: Inquiry Warm-Up 🧪Lab zone

L2 HOW CAN YOU SAFELY OBSERVE THE SUN? Students will use binoculars to project an image of the sun onto a sheet of paper.

The Sun

🔑 **What Is the Structure of the Sun?**

🔑 **What Features Can You See on the Sun?**

MY PLANET DIARY

DISASTER

Left in the Dark

On March 13, 1989, a flood of electric particles from the sun reached Earth, causing a magnetic storm. Bright streamers of color filled the sky as far south as Jamaica. But in Quebec, Canada, the storm brought problems. At 2:45 A.M., the entire electric power system collapsed. People woke up with no heat or light. Traffic snarled as traffic lights and subways stopped working.

How could particles from the sun take out a power system? The magnetic storm caused an electrical surge through the power lines. Electric stations couldn't handle the extra electricity, and they blew out, taking the power system with them.

✏️ **Communicate** Discuss the Quebec blackout with a partner. Then answer the questions below.

1. What caused the Quebec blackout of 1989?

   An electrical surge due to a magnetic storm

2. How would your life be affected if a magnetic storm shut down electricity in your area?

   Sample: I would not be able to charge my cell phone.

▶ **PLANET DIARY** Go to **Planet Diary** to learn more about the sun.

🧪Lab zone Do the Inquiry Warm-Up *How Can You Safely Observe the Sun?*

SUPPORT ALL READERS

Lexile Measure = 940L   Lexile Word Count = 1096

Prior Exposure to Content: May be the first time students have encountered this topic

Academic Vocabulary: *cause, data, effect, interpret, relate*

Science Vocabulary: *core, nuclear fusion, corona, sunspot*

Concept Level: May be difficult for students who struggle with abstract ideas

Preteach With: My Planet Diary "Left in the Dark" and Figure 1 activity

Go to **My Reading Web** to access leveled readings that provide a foundation for the content.

 my science online.com

Vocabulary

- core
- nuclear fusion
- radiation zone
- convection zone
- photosphere
- chromosphere
- corona
- solar wind
- sunspot
- prominence
- solar flare

Skills

- Reading: Relate Cause and Effect
- Inquiry: Interpret Data

What Is the Structure of the Sun?

Unlike Earth, the sun has no solid surface. About three fourths of the sun's mass is hydrogen, and about one fourth is helium. There are tiny amounts of other elements. **The sun has an interior and an atmosphere. The interior includes the core, the radiation zone, and the convection zone.** Figure 1 shows the sun's interior.

FIGURE 1 ·······················
Layers of the Sun
The diagram shows the layers of the sun's interior.

✎ **Apply Concepts** Draw arrows to show energy as it passes from the sun's core through the radiation and convection zones. Underline clues in the text that help you determine the path.

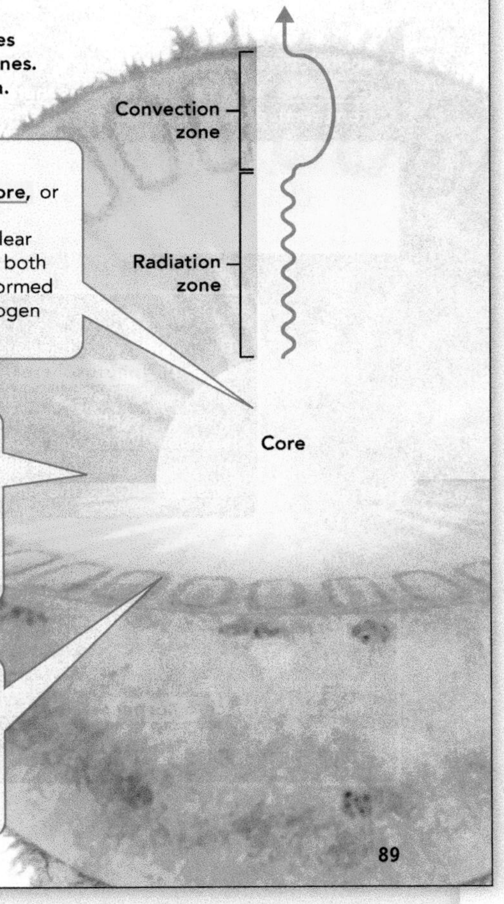

The Core
The sun produces an enormous amount of energy in its **core,** or central region, through nuclear fusion. In the process of **nuclear fusion,** hydrogen atoms join to form helium. Nuclear fusion requires extremely high temperature and pressure, both of which are found in the core. The total mass of helium formed by nuclear fusion is slightly less than the mass of the hydrogen that goes into it. The remaining mass becomes energy.

The Radiation Zone
The energy produced in the sun's core moves outward through the radiation zone. The **radiation zone** is a region of very tightly packed gas where energy moves mainly in the form of electromagnetic radiation. Because the radiation zone is so dense, energy can take more than 100,000 years to move through it.

The Convection Zone
The **convection zone** is the outermost layer of the sun's interior. Hot gases rise from the bottom of the convection zone and gradually cool as they approach the top. Cooler gases sink, forming loops of gas that move energy toward the sun's surface.

Convection zone

Radiation zone

Core

89

E L L Support

1 Content and Language
Write the word *prominence* on the board. Explain that we use this word in daily life to mean "something that stands out." Tell students that solar *prominences* are loops of gas that stand out because of their large size.

2 Frontload the Lesson
Invite students to share their knowledge and experiences about the sun. Ask student volunteers to give concise explanations of the sun's position in the solar system and the time it takes Earth to complete one orbit of the sun.

3 Comprehensible Input
Have students use paper and scissors to make a model of the structure of the sun cutting paper in increasingly large concentric circles to represent the core, radiation zone, and convection zone. Have students use colored pencils and markers to label each part of the sun.

Explain

Introduce Vocabulary
Write the terms *solar wind* and *solar flare* on the board. Underline *solar.* Inform students that the adjective *solar* may be used to refer to anything about the sun, including eclipses, flares, winds, and prominences.

Teach Key Concepts
Remind students that the sun does not have a solid surface. Explain that the sun's interior includes three layers. Ask: **What are the layers of the sun?** *(Core, radiation zone, and convection zone)* **In which layer does nuclear fusion occur?** *(The core)* **How is energy transferred in the radiation zone?** *(Mainly in the form of electromagnetic radiation)* **What happens to the temperature of gases as they reach the top of the convection zone?** *(Their temperature decreases.)* **What happens to the gases as they become cooler?** *(They sink to the bottom of the convection zone.)*

Lead a Discussion
CONVECTION Students may have encountered the process of convection in their study of science. Review the process of convection. Ask: **What is convection?** *(The transfer of heat by the movement of currents in a fluid)* **Where do convection currents in the sun absorb heat?** *(From the radiation zone)* **Where do the convections currents carry this heat?** *(Toward the surface of the sun)* Tell students that this heat is transferred to the bottom of the sun's atmosphere.

Elaborate

21st Century Learning

L3 CRITICAL THINKING Point out that nuclear fusion is not used as an energy source on Earth. Nuclear power plants generate power through nuclear fission. The energy released by nuclear fusion is three to four times greater than that of nuclear fission. Ask: **Why do you think that nuclear fusion is not used as an energy source on Earth?** *(Sample: Nuclear fusion occurs only under conditions of extremely high temperature and pressure. We do not now have the technology to generate electricity by fusion in a cost-effective way.)*

My Planet Diary provides an opportunity for students to explore real-world connections to the sun.

my science online.com | Structure of the Sun

Explain

Teach Key Concepts

Remind students that Earth's atmosphere is divided into layers. Explain that, similarly, the sun's atmosphere has layers. Ask: **What are the layers of the sun's atmosphere, from innermost to outermost?** *(The photosphere, the chromosphere, and the corona)* **If you look at a typical image of the sun, which layer to you see?** *(The photosphere)* **Why are you able to see this layer?** *(The gases are very thick.)*

Elaborate

Teacher Demo

L1 ENERGY FROM THE SUN

Materials 2 glass jars with lids, 2 plastic thermometers, black plastic, waterproof glue (hot glue works well)

Time 45 minutes

Remind students that most energy on Earth comes from the sun. Glue black plastic on one-half of the *inside* of each jar. Glue a plastic thermometer to the inside of each jar so that it can be read without opening the jar. Fill the jars with cold water, leaving 1.0 cm for expansion, and cap tightly. Take the class outside, and place one jar in a shady spot and the other in direct sun, propped up so that sunlight fully illuminates the inside of the jar. Read the temperature of each jar every five minutes for thirty minutes. Back in the classroom, have students graph the temperature versus time for each container.

Ask: **What happened to the temperature of the jars?** *(The shady jar may have gone up or down slightly; the sunny jar rose several degrees.)* **What caused the temperature to rise?** *(Energy from the sun)*

Vocabulary Greek Word Origins The Greek word *photos* means "light." What does *photosphere* mean?

Light sphere

The Sun's Atmosphere The sun has an atmosphere that stretches far into space, as you can see in Figure 2. The layers of the atmosphere become less dense the farther they are from the radiation zone. Like the sun's interior, the atmosphere is primarily composed of hydrogen and helium. The sun's atmosphere includes the photosphere, the chromosphere, and the corona. Each layer has unique properties.

FIGURE 2 ....
▶ INTERACTIVE ART The Sun's Atmosphere
This image is a combination of two photographs of the sun. One shows the sun's surface and was taken through a special filter that shows the sun's features. The other shows the corona and was taken during an eclipse.

✎ Relate Text and Visuals On the photograph, label the photosphere and corona. Shade in the area of the chromosphere.
CHALLENGE Why can the chromosphere and corona only be seen from Earth during an eclipse?

The glare from the photosphere normally outshines the other layers.
During an eclipse, the photosphere is blocked.

The Photosphere
The inner layer of the sun's atmosphere is called the photosphere (FOH tuh sfeer). The sun does not have a solid surface, but the gases of the photosphere are thick enough to be visible. When you look at an image of the sun, you are looking at the photosphere. It is considered to be the sun's surface layer.

The Chromosphere
At the start and end of a total eclipse, a reddish glow is visible just around the photosphere. This glow comes from the middle layer of the sun's atmosphere, the chromosphere (KROH muh sfeer). The Greek word *chroma* means "color," so the chromosphere is the "color sphere."

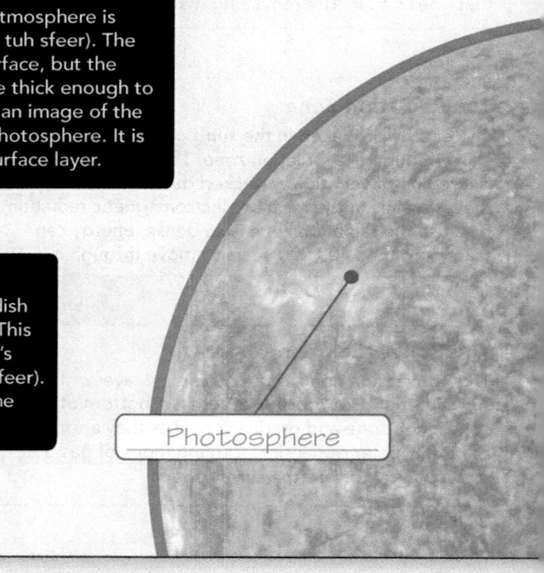

Photosphere

90 The Solar System

Interactive Art allows students to explore the structure of the sun.

Digital Lesson: Assign the *Do the Math* activity online and have students submit their work to you.

my science online.com **Structure of the Sun**

do the math! Analyzing Data

Solar Temperature

Use the table to answer the questions.

Layer	Temperature (°C)
Core	About 15,000,000
Radiation and Convection Zones	About 4,000,000
Photosphere	About 6,000
Inner Chromosphere	About 4,300
Outer Chromosphere	About 8,300
Corona	About 1,000,000

1 Interpret Data Which layer is hottest?

The core

2 Compare and Contrast How does the temperature change in the sun's atmosphere differ from the temperature change in the sun's interior?

As you move outward, the atmosphere becomes hotter instead of cooler.

The Corona

During a total solar eclipse, an even fainter layer of the sun becomes visible, as you can see in **Figure 2.** This outer layer, which looks like a white halo around the sun, is called the **corona,** which means "crown" in Latin. The corona extends into space for millions of kilometers. It gradually thins into streams of electrically charged particles called the **solar wind.**

Corona

Lab zone Do the Quick Lab Layers of the Sun.

📖 Assess Your Understanding

1a. List List the layers of the sun's interior and atmosphere, starting from the center.

Core, radiation zone, convection zone, photosphere, chromosphere, corona

b. Compare and Contrast What is one key difference between the radiation and convection zones?

In the radiation zone, energy moves slowly by radiation. In the convection zone, it moves by convection.

got it? ....

O I get it! Now I know that the sun's structure includes layers in its interior and its atmosphere.

O I need extra help with See TE note.

Go to **my science COACH** online for help with this subject.

91

L1 Remind students that organizing data in a table can help show patterns or trends. Point out that Question 2 asks students to use the table to identify a pattern. Work through the question with students, and help them identify the inverse relationship between temperature changes in the sun's atmosphere and interior.

🔺 **Interpret Data** Explain that to answer Question 1 students need to interpret the temperature data in the chart by finding the highest temperature *(about 1,000,000 °C)* and using it to identify the hottest layer of the sun. *(The core)* Practice by having students identify the coolest layer in the sun's atmosphere. *(The inner chromosphere, at about 4,300 °C)*

See *Math Skill and Problem-Solving Activities* for support.

Lab Resource: Quick Lab 📖

L2 **LAYERS OF THE SUN** Students will investigate the layers of the sun.

Evaluate

Assess Your Understanding

After students answer the questions, have them evaluate their understanding by completing the appropriate sentence.

RTI Response to Intervention

1a. If students need help listing the layers of the sun's atmosphere and interior, **then** have them review **Figures 1 and 2.**

b. If students have trouble contrasting the radiation and convection zones, **then** suggest they use the different words in each compound, *radiation* and *convection*, as clues.

my science COACH Have students go online for help in understanding the structure of the sun.

Differentiated Instruction

L1 **Interpret Diagrams** Show students color photographs of the sun at various stages of an eclipse. Point out the photosphere, the chromosphere, and the corona. Have students use the photographs as a guide to draw their own diagrams and label them appropriately.

L3 **Make a Diagram** With their books closed, have students diagram the sun's interior and atmosphere. Students can decide whether to make one or two diagrams. Ask students to exchange diagram(s) with a partner, open their books, and check the work that they received.

Explain

Teach Key Concepts 🗝

Explain to students that you can see several features on or just above the sun's surface. Ask: **What are the three features called?** (Sunspots, prominences, and solar flares) **What is a sunspot?** (Sunspots are areas of gas on the sun's surface that are cooler than the gases around them.) **What are prominences?** (Huge loops of gas that link different parts of sunspot regions) **What are solar flares?** (Eruptions of gas from the sun into space) **How do they form?** (They form when prominences connect.)

🔄 **Relate Cause and Effect** Tell students that science involves many cause-and-effect relationships. A cause makes something happen. An effect is what happens. When you recognize that one event causes another, you are relating cause and effect.

Teach With Visuals

Tell students to look at **Figure 3.** Ask students to compare and contrast sunspots and prominences. *(Sample: Both are made of gas. Sunspots are regions of relatively cool gas that usually occur in groups, whereas prominences are huge loops of gas that often link different parts of sunspot regions.)* Point out that cycles of solar activity affect how much energy the sun emits, and these changes in energy can affect climates on Earth. Scientists have found that the number of sunspots correlates to solar output: More sunspots means increased solar output.

21st Century Learning 📖

INTERPERSONAL SKILLS Mirror, Mirror on the Building... Have students read *Solar Power* in the **Big Ideas of Science Reference Library.** Ask partners to debate the issue of installing heliostats in their town. One student should take the point of view of a town leader opposed to the idea and the other, the role of a solar engineer bidding on the project. Pairs should come up with a pro and con list as a result of their discussion.

What Features Can You See on the Sun?

For hundreds of years, scientists have used special telescopes to study the sun. They have spotted a variety of features on the sun's surface. 🗝 **Features on or just above the sun's surface include sunspots, prominences, and solar flares.**

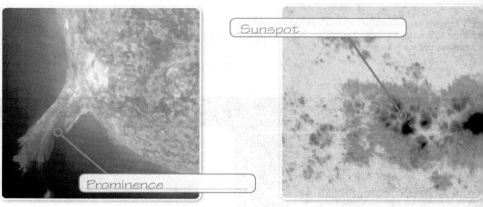

FIGURE 3 ·······

Sunspots and Prominences
Sunspots look dark in regular photographs. Some photos of the sun are taken with special filters that show the sun's structure. Sunspots may appear white in these photos. Sunspots are visible in both of the photos above. ✎ **Classify** Label a prominence and a sunspot in the photos.

🔄 **Relate Cause and Effect**
When prominences join, they cause (sunspots (solar flares))

Sunspots Photographs show dark areas on the sun's surface. These **sunspots** are areas of gas on the sun's surface that are cooler than the gases around them. Cooler gases don't give off as much light as hotter gases, which is why sunspots look dark. Sunspots look small, but in fact they can be larger than Earth. The number of sunspots varies in a regular cycle, with the most sunspots appearing about once every 11 years.

Prominences Sunspots usually occur in groups. Huge loops of gas called **prominences** often link different parts of sunspot regions. You can compare sunspots and prominences in **Figure 3.**

Solar Flares Sometimes the loops in sunspot regions suddenly connect, releasing large amounts of magnetic energy. The energy heats gas on the sun to millions of degrees Celsius, causing the gas to erupt into space. These eruptions are called **solar flares.**

92 The Solar System

Solar Wind The solar wind is made up of electrical particles from the sun. Solar flares can greatly increase the solar wind, which means that more particles reach Earth's upper atmosphere. Earth's atmosphere and magnetic field normally block these particles. But near the North and South poles, the particles can enter Earth's atmosphere. There, they create powerful electric currents that cause gas molecules in the atmosphere to glow. These particles cause auroras near the poles. They can also cause magnetic storms like the one that caused the blackout in Quebec in 1989. **Figure 4** shows how the solar wind interacts with Earth's magnetic field.

FIGURE 4 ....
Solar Wind
Particles from the solar wind spread through the solar system. When they reach Earth, they interact with Earth's magnetic field. (Note: The diagram is not to scale.)

✎ **Make Generalizations** The corona is the least dense layer of the sun's atmosphere. How do you think the density of the solar wind compares to the density of the corona?

The solar wind is even less
dense than the corona.
_____

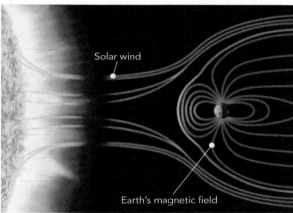
Solar wind
Earth's magnetic field

 Do the Quick Lab
Viewing Sunspots.

Assess Your Understanding

2a. Define (Prominences/sunspots) are loops of gas that extend from the sun's surface.

b. Explain Why do sunspots look darker than the rest of the sun's photosphere?
Sunspots are cooler than the
surrounding areas.
_____

c. ↻ Relate Cause and Effect How is the solar wind related to magnetic storms on Earth?
Particles in the solar wind
interact with Earth's mag-
netic field, leading to magnetic
storms.

got it? ....

○ I get it! Now I know that features on the sun include _sunspots, prominences, solar_
flares, and the solar wind.

○ I need extra help with _See TE note._

_Go to_ MY SCIENCE COACH _online for help with this subject._

93

Elaborate

Support the Big Q

AURORAS AND MAGNETIC STORMS Remind students that Earth is part of a system of objects that orbit the sun. Explain that all the parts of any system interact with one another. Ask: **What parts of the sun and Earth interact to create auroras and magnetic storms?** (The solar wind interacts with Earth's magnetic field.) **How do the solar wind and Earth's magnetic field interact to create auroras and magnetic storms?** (Electrical particles in the solar wind enter Earth's atmosphere, creating powerful electric currents that interact with Earth's magnetic field. The interaction of these fields causes auroras and magnetic storms.) **What do you think is the relationship between sunspot activity and magnetic storms on Earth?** (Sample: Because solar flares can increase the solar wind, you would expect to find more magnetic storms on Earth during period of high sunspot activity on the sun.) Tell students that auroras can occur on other planets, too.

Lab Resource: Quick Lab

L3 VIEWING SUNSPOTS Students will study sunspots each day and record on a data table the number of sunspots that they see. To safeguard students' vision, caution them *never to* look directly at the sun.

Assess Your Understanding

After students answer the questions, have them evaluate their understanding by completing the appropriate sentence.

RTI Response to Intervention

2a. If students have trouble differentiating prominences and sunspots, **then** have them reread the sentences in which the highlighted vocabulary terms appear.

b. If students need help explaining why sunspots look dark in the photosphere, **then** help them recall the relationship between the temperature of a gas and the amount of light that the gas emits.

c. If students have trouble identifying the cause-effect relationship between the solar wind and magnetic storms, **then** have them review **Figure 4.**

MY SCIENCE COACH Have students go online for help in understanding features on the sun

---

Differentiated Instruction

L1 Analyze Words The words used to describe the sun's features may be unfamiliar to some students. Point out that terms such as *sunspot* and *solar flare* are descriptive. Have students separate these terms into their parts. (sun + spot; solar + flare) Tell students to look up the words and word parts in a dictionary. Encourage students to explain how the terms help describe the

features of the sun. (A sunspot is a spot on the sun. A solar flare is a flare or an explosion on the sun.)

L3 Sunspots in Early Astronomy Have students research and report on how early astronomers used sunspots to measure the sun's rate of rotation. (By tracking sunspots as they move across the sun, the rotation rate can be determined.)

Lab zone **After the Inquiry Warm-Up**

The Sun

> **Inquiry Warm-Up,** *How Can You Safely Observe the Sun?*
> In the Inquiry Warm-Up, you investigated how to safely observe the sun. Using what you learned from that activity, answer the questions below.

1. **ANALYZE SOURCES OF ERROR** How might clouds affect your observation of the sun?

   _____

   _____

   _____

2. **EXPLAIN** Why shouldn't a person look directly at the sun?

   _____

   _____

   _____

3. **EXPLAIN** Why is it necessary to cover one lens of the binoculars?

   _____

   _____

   _____

4. **PREDICT** How would your drawing be different if the moon were between Earth and the sun?

   _____

   _____

   _____

   _____

Assess Your Understanding

The Sun

> ## What Is the Structure of the Sun?

1a. **LIST** List the layers of the sun's interior and atmosphere, starting from the center. _____

_____

b. **COMPARE AND CONTRAST** What is one key difference between the radiation and convection zones?

_____

_____

_____

gotit? ....

○ **I get it!** Now I know that the sun's structure includes _____

_____

○ **I need extra help with** _____

_____

> ## What Features Can You See on the Sun?

2a. **DEFINE** (Prominences/sunspots) are loops of gas that extend from the sun's surface.

b. **EXPLAIN** Why do sunspots look darker than the rest of the sun's photosphere?

_____

_____

c. **RELATE CAUSE AND EFFECT** How is the solar wind related to magnetic storms on Earth?

_____

_____

_____

gotit? ....

○ **I get it!** Now I know that features on the sun include _____

_____

○ **I need extra help with** _____

_____

The Sun

What Is the Structure of the Sun?

The sun has no solid surface. About three-fourths of its mass is hydrogen, and about one-fourth is helium. **The sun has an interior and an atmosphere. The interior includes the core, the radiation zone, and the convection zone.**

The sun produces a large amount of energy in its **core** though **nuclear fusion,** a process in which hydrogen atoms join together to form helium. The energy produced in the sun's core moves outward through the **radiation zone** mainly in the form of electromagnetic radiation. The outermost layer of the sun's interior is called the **convection zone.** In this zone, energy moves toward the sun's surface by convection.

Like the sun's interior, its atmosphere is composed mainly of hydrogen and helium. **The sun's atmosphere includes the photosphere, the chromosphere, and the corona. Each layer has unique properties.** The **photosphere** is the inner layer. The **chromosphere** is the middle layer. The **corona** is the outer layer. The corona extends far into space. It gradually thins into streams of electrically charged particles called the **solar wind.**

What Features Can You See on the Sun?

Features on or just above the sun's surface include sunspots, prominences, and solar flares.

Sunspots are areas of gas on the sun's surface that are cooler than the gases around them. Sunspots usually occur in groups. Huge loops of gas called **prominences** link different parts of sunspot regions.

When loops in sunspot regions suddenly connect, they release large amounts of magnetic energy. This energy heats the surrounding gas, causing it to erupt into space. These eruptions are called **solar flares.**

Earth's atmosphere and magnetic field normally block the **solar wind.** But near the North and South poles, the particles can enter Earth's atmosphere, where they cause auroras and magnetic storms.

On a separate sheet of paper, describe the structure of the sun, and identify three features of its surface.

Review and Reinforce

The Sun

Understanding Main Ideas
Label the diagram of the sun below.

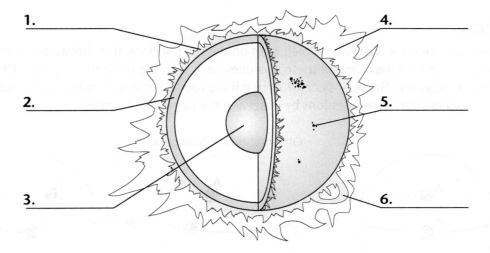

1.
2.
3.
4.
5.
6.

Building Vocabulary
Match each term with its definition by writing the letter of the correct definition in the right column on the line beside the term in the left column.

7. ___ solar flare

8. ___ core

9. ___ chromosphere

10. ___ sunspot

11. ___ corona

12. ___ nuclear fusion

13. ___ photosphere

14. ___ solar wind

15. ___ convection zone

a. layer of the sun's atmosphere that gives off visible light

b. layer of the sun's atmosphere that has a reddish glow

c. layer of the sun's atmosphere that looks like a halo during an eclipse

d. areas of gas on the sun's surface that are cooler than the areas around them

e. eruptions that occur when the loops in sunspot regions suddenly connect

f. stream of electrical particles from the sun

g. center of the sun

h. outermost layer of the sun's interior

i. joining of hydrogen atoms to form helium

The Sun

The diagrams below show how a series of sunspots behave over time. Read the passage and study the diagrams. Then use a separate sheet of paper to answer the questions that follow.

Sunspot Clues

Although sunspots were once unexplained blemishes on the sun's surface, their behavior has helped solve some of the sun's mysteries. One of these mysteries dealt with the rotation of the sun. Did it rotate, as did other objects in the solar system? And, if it did rotate, what was its period of rotation? Astronomers helped answer these questions by observing the behavior of sunspots.

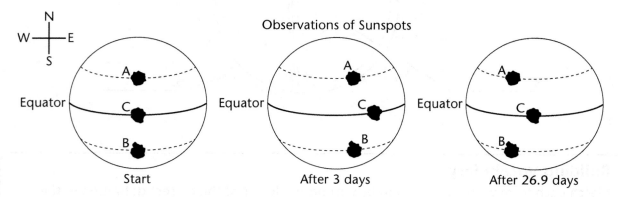

1. How have astronomers inferred that the sun rotates?
2. What direction does the sun rotate?
3. Sunspots at the equator take 26.9 days to move once around the sun. What can you infer about how long sunspots A and B take to move around the sun, compare to sunspot C, which is on the equator?
4. Why do astronomers say that the sun rotates once every 27 to 31 days, rather than give an exact number?

Lesson Quiz

The Sun

Write the letter of the correct answer on the line at the left.

1. ___ Areas of gas on the sun's surface that are cooler than the gases around them are called
   A solar flares
   B sunspots
   C solar wind
   D prominences

2. ___ Large eruptions of gas from the sun out into space are called
   A solar flares
   B sunspots
   C solar wind
   D prominences

3. ___ Huge loops of gas that link different parts of sunspot regions are called
   A solar flares
   B supra-sunspots
   C solar wind
   D prominences

4. ___ The sun produces energy through
   A fission
   B fusion
   C photovoltaic cells
   D photosynthesis

Fill in the blank to complete each statement.

5. The sun's layers, from innermost to outermost, are the core, _____, and convection zone.

6. You see the _____ when you look at an image of the sun.

7. You see the middle layer of the sun's atmosphere, the _____, at the start and end of a total eclipse.

8. The corona sends out a stream of charged particles called the _____ _____.

9. The solar wind can interact with Earth's magnetic field to create powerful electric currents that cause _____ near the poles.

10. About three fourth's of the sun's mass is _____.

The Sun

Answer Key

After the Inquiry Warm-Up

1. Clouds may obscure or block part of the sun.

2. The sun is too bright. Looking directly into the sun can harm a person's eyes.

3. If the other lens were not covered, it would produce a second image of the sun on the paper.

4. Answers will vary. Sample: The moon would block most or all of the sun. My drawing would look like a bright ring or crescent (the sun) around a dark circle (the moon).

Key Concept Summaries

Sample: The sun has an interior and an atmosphere. Both are made up mainly of hydrogen and helium. The interior includes three layers, the core, radiation zone, and convection zone. The atmosphere also has three main parts, the photosphere, chromosphere, and corona. Prominences, sunspots, and solar flares are features on or just above the sun's surface.

Review and Reinforce

1. chromosphere
2. photosphere
3. core
4. corona
5. sunspots
6. prominence
7. e
8. g
9. b
10. d
11. c
12. i
13. a
14. f
15. h

Enrich

1. Astronomers inferred that the sun rotates because the sunspots move in one direction over time.

2. The sun rotates from west to east.

3. Sunspots at points A and B take longer to move around the sun than does a sunspot on the equator.

4. Different parts of the sun's surface rotate at different rates, so scientists must give a range for the time of the sun's rotation.

Lesson Quiz

1. B
2. A
3. D
4. B
5. radiation zone
6. photosphere
7. chromosphere
8. solar wind
9. auroras
10. hydrogen

Place the outside corner, the corner away from the dotted line, in the corner of your copy machine to copy onto letter-size paper.

LESSON

4 Why are objects in the Solar System different from each other?

Lesson Pacing: 3–4 periods or 1–1½ blocks

SHORT ON TIME? To do this lesson in approximately half the time, do the Activate Prior Knowledge activity on page 94. A discussion of the Key Concepts on pages 95, 96, 97, 99 and 100 will familiarize students with the lesson content. Have students do the Quick Labs. The rest of the lesson can be completed by students independently.

Preference Navigator, in the online Planning tools, allows you to customize *Interactive Science* to your own teaching style. You can also edit lesson plans by selecting the Lesson Planner option.

Digital Teacher's Edition allows you to access your Teacher's Edition and Resource materials online.

Lesson Vocabulary

- terrestrial planet
- greenhouse effect

Content Refresher

Professional Development Note

Exploring Venus Because of Venus's extreme heat, high atmospheric pressure, and clouds of sulfuric acid, it is almost impossible for astronauts to go there. To gather information about Venus, scientists rely on uncrewed space probes. The Soviet Union was the first nation to attempt interplanetary exploration. In 1961, it launched *Venera I,* a probe which passed within 100,000 km of Venus but did not transmit information back to Earth. In 1966, the Soviets launched *Venera 3,* the first spacecraft to crash-land on another planet. In 1967, *Venera 4* parachuted a capsule of instruments to Venus's surface. *Venera 7* (1970) detected radioactive isotopes on its surface. In 1975, *Venera 9* sent back the first close-up photographs of Venus's surface.

In 1962, NASA launched *Mariner 2* to gather information about Venus. The data confirmed that Venus has a very hot surface and, unlike Earth, does not have a magnetic field. About sixteen years later, *The Pioneer Venus Orbiter* was launched to gather radar images, transmit data about the solar winds, and learn more about the outermost atmospheres around Venus. *Magellan* probed Venus from 1990 to 1994, taking images of nearly the entire surface. In November 2005, the European Space Agency (ESA) launched its first Venus exploration mission with *Venus Express.* It reached Venus in 2006 to study the planet's atmosphere and plasma environment and investigate the role of greenhouse effects in the creation of the atmosphere. The Venus Express mission, expected to continue into 2012, will help scientists understand climate change on Earth.

LESSON OBJECTIVES

- Describe the characteristics that the inner planets have in common.
- Identify the main characteristics that distinguish each of the inner planets.

Blended Path
Active learning using Student Edition, Inquiry Path, and Digital Path

ENGAGE AND EXPLORE

Teach this lesson using a variety of resources. Begin by reading **My Planet Diary** as a class. Have students share ideas about how their names were chosen. Then have students do the **Inquiry Warm-Up activity.** Students will investigate the orbits of the inner planets. Discuss the radius of Mercury. The **After the Inquiry Warm-Up worksheet** sets up a discussion about why some planets travel faster or slower around the sun than other planets. Have volunteers share their drawings of models of the inner planets for question 4.

EXPLAIN AND ELABORATE

Teach Key Concepts by explaining why the inner planets are called the terrestrial planets.

Teach Key Concepts by asking students to compare the characteristics of Mercury and Earth's moon. Use **Figure 2** to illustrate how Mercury's surface is different from Earth's surface. Continue to **Teach Key Concepts** by explaining that although Venus is often called "Earth's twin" there are three significant ways that Venus differs from Earth. **Lead a Discussion** about the temperature and atmospheric pressure of Venus. Discuss how scientists have been able to collect data about Venus. To **Support the Big Q,** discuss why there are differences in the greenhouse effect on Earth and on Venus. **Teach Key Concepts** by explaining the importance of Earth's atmosphere, Earth's temperature, and liquid water on Earth. Continue to **Teach Key Concepts** by asking students how Mars is similar to and different from other inner planets. Then have students practice the inquiry skill in the **Apply It activity.** Have students do the **Quick Lab** and then share their results. Hand out the **Key Concept Summaries** as a review of each part of the lesson. Students can also use the online **Vocab Flash Cards** to review key terms.

EVALUATE

Have students take the **Lesson Quiz.** For an alternate assessment, see the **EXAM**VIEW® Assessment Suite, Progress Monitoring Assessments, or SuccessTracker™.

1 Content and Language

Introduce the term *composition.* Students may be familiar with the term because of music or writing. Explain that this is also a term used by scientists to describe the parts or substances that combine to make a planet.

Lab zone Inquiry Path
Hands-on learning in the Lab zone

Digital Path
Online learning at **my science online**.com

ENGAGE AND EXPLORE

To teach this lesson with an emphasis on inquiry, begin with the **Inquiry Warm-Up activity.** Students will investigate the orbits of the inner planets. Discuss the radius of Mercury. Have students do the **After the Inquiry Warm-Up worksheet.** Talk about what impacts the amount of time it takes each planet to travel around the sun. Have volunteers share their diagrams of the inner planets' orbits from question 4.

EXPLAIN AND ELABORATE

Focus on the **Inquiry Skill** for the lesson. Point out that when you communicate, you share information with others in an organized manner. How did students communicate about the inner planets in the **Inquiry Warm-Up activity?** *(By drawing a diagram)* Have students do the **Quick Lab** to investigate the characteristics of the inner planets.

Assign the **Build Inquiry activity** to help students understand why it is difficult for scientists to observe features on Mercury. Do the **Teacher Demo** to compare and contrast Earth and Venus. To **Support the Big Q,** discuss why Earth's atmosphere traps much less heat than Venus's does. To **Build Inquiry,** have students draw flowcharts about the paths of light and heat energy in a greenhouse effect on Venus. Review the characteristics of Mercury, Venus, and Mars before beginning the **Apply It activity.** Ask volunteers to share their descriptions and drawings. Do the **Quick Lab** to reinforce understanding of how the greenhouse effect keeps Earth warm. Students can use the online **Vocab Flash Cards** to review key terms.

EVALUATE

Have students take the **Lesson Quiz.** For an alternate assessment, see the **EXAM**VIEW® Assessment Suite, Progress Monitoring Assessments, or SuccessTracker™.

ENGAGE AND EXPLORE

Teach this lesson using digital resources. Begin by having students explore real-world connections to the inner planets of the solar system at **My Planet Diary** online. Have them access the Chapter Resources to find the **Unlock the Big Question activity.** There they can answer the questions and refine their responses as they continue through the lesson. You can re-assign the activity and have students submit their work so you can track their progress.

EXPLAIN AND ELABORATE

Students reading above, at, or below the lexile measure of this lesson can access basic content readings at their level at **My Reading Web.** Have students use the online **Vocab Flash Cards** to preview key terms. Do the **Quick Lab** to investigate the distinguishing characteristics of the inner planets. Have students do the online **Interactive Art activity** to explore the inner planets of the solar system.

Support the Big Q by discussing the differences in the greenhouse effect on Earth and on Venus. Review the characteristics of Mercury, Venus, and Mars before assigning the online **Apply It activity.** Ask volunteers to share their descriptions and drawings. Have students submit their work to you. Students will infer how the greenhouse effect keeps Earth warm by observing a model in the **Quick Lab.** The **Key Concept Summaries** online allow students to read a summary and see an image associated with each part of the lesson. Online remediation is available at **My Science Coach.**

EVALUATE

Have students take the **Lesson Quiz.** For an alternate assessment, see the **EXAM**VIEW® Assessment Suite, Progress Monitoring Assessments, or SuccessTracker™.

2 Frontload the Lesson
Preview the lesson questions (blue heads). Ask students if there are any words they do not understand. Explain the specific meanings these words have in science.

3 Comprehensible Input
Have students compare and contrast the inner planets with one another using Venn Diagrams.

4 Language Production
Pair or group students with varied language abilities to complete labs collaboratively for language practice. Have each student copy the completed written lab for personal reference.

5 Assess Understanding
Have students keep a content area log for this lesson using a two-column format with the headings "What I Understand" and "What I Don't Understand." Follow up so that students can move items from the "Don't Understand" to the "Understand" column.

The Inner Planets

Establish Learning Objectives

After this lesson, students will be able to:

⚷ Describe the characteristics that the inner planets have in common.

⚷ Identify the main characteristics that distinguish each of the inner planets.

Engage

Activate Prior Knowledge

MY PLANET DIARY Read *What's in a Name?* with the class. Invite students to share the author, artist, or musician they would choose, if they discovered a feature on Mercury. Ask: **Suppose an astronomer in your grandparents' hometown discovered a crater on Mars. What might the crater's name be?** *(Sample: Sacramento, Sante Fe, Summit—whatever the grandparents' hometown is)*

BIG IDEAS OF SCIENCE REFERENCE LIBRARY 📖 Have students look up the following topics: Constellations, Earth, Mars, Mercury, Venus.

Explore

Lab Resource: Inquiry Warm-Up 🔬

L1 **RING AROUND THE SUN** Students will investigate the orbits of the inner planets around the sun.

LESSON
4 The Inner Planets

UNLOCK THE BIG ?

⚷ What Do the Inner Planets Have in Common?

⚷ What Are the Characteristics of the Inner Planets?

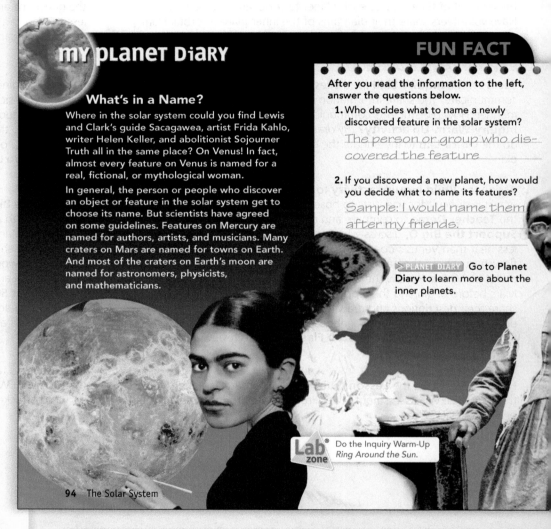

MY PLANET DIARY

What's in a Name?

Where in the solar system could you find Lewis and Clark's guide Sacagawea, artist Frida Kahlo, writer Helen Keller, and abolitionist Sojourner Truth all in the same place? On Venus! In fact, almost every feature on Venus is named for a real, fictional, or mythological woman.

In general, the person or people who discover an object or feature in the solar system get to choose its name. But scientists have agreed on some guidelines. Features on Mercury are named for authors, artists, and musicians. Many craters on Mars are named for towns on Earth. And most of the craters on Earth's moon are named for astronomers, physicists, and mathematicians.

FUN FACT

After you read the information to the left, answer the questions below.

1. Who decides what to name a newly discovered feature in the solar system?

   The person or group who discovered the feature

2. If you discovered a new planet, how would you decide what to name its features?

   Sample: I would name them after my friends.

▷ **PLANET DIARY** Go to Planet Diary to learn more about the inner planets.

🔬 Lab zone Do the Inquiry Warm-Up *Ring Around the Sun.*

94 The Solar System

SUPPORT ALL READERS

Lexile Measure = 920L   Lexile Word Count = 1845

Prior Exposure to Content: May be the first time students have encountered this topic

Academic Vocabulary: *communicate, compare, contrast*

Science Vocabulary: *terrestrial planet, greenhouse effect*

Concept Level: May be difficult for students who struggle with abstract ideas

Preteach With: My Planet Diary "What's in a Name?" and Figure 1 activity

Go to **My Reading Web** to access leveled readings that provide a foundation for the content.

my science online .com

Vocabulary
- terrestrial planet
- greenhouse effect

Skills
- Reading: Compare and Contrast
- Inquiry: Communicate

What Do the Inner Planets Have in Common?

Earth, Mercury, Venus, and Mars are more like each other than they are like the outer planets. **The inner planets are small and dense and have rocky surfaces.** The inner planets are often called the **terrestrial planets,** from the Latin word *terra,* which means "Earth." **Figure 1** summarizes data about the inner planets.

The terrestrial planets all have relatively high densities. They are rich in rocky and metallic materials, including iron and silicon. Each has a solid surface. All except Mercury have atmospheres.

FIGURE 1

INTERACTIVE ART

The Inner Planets

Interpret Data **Use the table to answer the questions below.**

1. Which planet is largest?
   Earth
2. Which planet has the most moons?
   Mars
3. Which planet is most similar to Earth in size?
   Venus

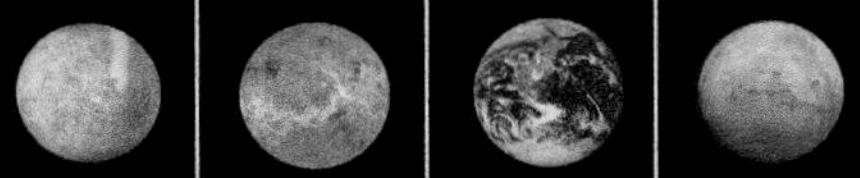

Planet	Mercury	Venus	Earth	Mars
Diameter (km)	4,879	12,104	12,756	6,794
Period of rotation (Earth days)	58.9	244	1.0	1.03
Average distance from sun (AU)	0.39	0.72	1.0	1.52
Period of revolution (Earth days)	88	224.7	365.2	687
Number of moons	0	0	1	2

Note: Planets are not shown to scale.

Lab zone: Do the Quick Lab *Characteristics of the Inner Planets.*

Assess Your Understanding

got it? ....

O I get it! Now I know that the inner planets are small and dense and have rocky surfaces. Most have atmospheres.

O I need extra help with See TE note.

Go to my science coach online for help with this subject.

Explain

Introduce Vocabulary

Explain to students that the term *planet* comes from the Greek word *planan,* meaning "to wander." Ancient Greek astronomers observed that some celestial bodies moved faster relative to the stars in the sky. They named these bodies the "wanderers."

Teach Key Concepts

Explain to students that the inner planets share three main characteristics. Ask: **How do the inner and outer planets compare in size?** *(The inner planets are all small compared to the outer planets.)* **What are two more shared characteristics of the inner planets?** *(They are dense and rocky.)* **What vocabulary term refers to the inner planets?** *(Terrestrial planets)* **What is the origin of that term?** *(The Latin word* terra, *which means "Earth")*

Elaborate

Lab Resource: Quick Lab

L2 **CHARACTERISTICS OF THE INNER PLANETS** Students will investigate the distinguishing characteristics of the inner planets.

Evaluate

Assess Your Understanding

Have students evaluate their understanding by completing the appropriate sentence.

RTI Response to Intervention

If students have trouble explaining how the inner, or terrestrial, planets are alike, **then** have them reread the Key Concept statement and the succeeding paragraph.

my science coach Have students go online for help in understanding the inner planets.

My Planet Diary provides an opportunity for students to explore real-world connections to the inner planets.

Interactive Art allows students to explore the inner planets of the solar system.

my science online.com | Terrestrial Planets

LESSON 3.4

ELL Support

1 Content and Language

Write the term *greenhouse effect* on the board. Next to it, draw a simple diagram of a greenhouse. Explain that this structure is designed to gather sunshine and retain heat.

2 Frontload the Lesson

Invite students to name planets near Earth. Once they name Mercury, Venus, and Mars, discuss what they know about each planet's size, location, and characteristics. Tell students they will learn similarities and differences among these planets.

3 Comprehensible Input

Ask small groups of students to make four cluster diagrams, one for each inner planet. Each group should identify defining characteristics of a planet's composition, temperature, and distance from the sun. Have groups share their work with the class.

Explain

Teach Key Concepts

Explain to students that Mercury is the smallest of the inner planets and the planet closest to the sun. It takes Mercury about 88 days to orbit the sun and it rotates on its axis three times for every two revolutions around the sun. Then show students images of Mercury and Earth's moon. Ask: **What features are similar on Mercury and Earth's moon?** *(Heavily cratered surfaces, little atmosphere, no liquid water, little erosion)* **What differences do you see between the surface of Earth's moon and the surface of Mercury?** *(Sample: Mercury's surface has no maria.)* Point out that, in some ways, Mercury has more features in common with Earth's moon than with Earth and the other inner planets.

Teach With Visuals

Tell students to look at **Figure 2.** Ask: **How is Mercury's surface different from Earth's?** *(Sample: Mercury's surface is heavily cratered and barren, unlike Earth's.)*

Elaborate

Build Inquiry **Lab** zone

L2 **OBSERVE MERCURY**

Materials coin, desk lamp, ruler

Time 20 minutes

Pair students. Explain that Mercury is a difficult planet to view from Earth because it always appears in the sky very close to the sun. Therefore, it can only be viewed in twilight. Have one student hold a coin about 10 cm in font of a dim desk lamp. The head side of the coin should face away from the bulb. Challenge the other student to determine the date on the coin. Caution the student not to look directly at the bulb.

Ask: **What do you observe about the coin?** *(The brightness of the bulb makes it impossible to see the date.)* **How is this similar to problems encountered by scientists who want to observe features on Mercury?** *(The brightness of the sun makes it hard to see Mercury's surface features.)*

What Are the Characteristics of the Inner Planets?

Though the four inner planets have many features in common, they differ in size and composition as well as distance from the sun.

Mercury Would you like to visit a place where the temperature can range from 430°C to below −170°C? **Mercury is the smallest terrestrial planet and the planet closest to the sun.** Mercury is not much larger than Earth's moon. The interior of Mercury is probably made up mainly of the dense metal iron.

Mercury's Surface As you can see in **Figure 2,** Mercury has flat plains and craters on its surface. Most of these craters formed early in the history of the solar system. Since Mercury has no water and not much atmosphere, the craters have not worn away over time.

Mercury's Atmosphere Mercury has virtually no atmosphere. Because Mercury's mass is small, its gravity is weak. Gas particles can easily escape into space. However, astronomers have detected small amounts of sodium and other gases around Mercury.

During the day, the side of Mercury facing the sun can reach temperatures of 430°C. Because there is so little atmosphere, the planet's heat escapes at night. Then the temperature drops below −170°C.

Exploring Mercury Much of what astronomers know about Mercury has come from space probes. *Mariner 10* flew by Mercury three times in 1974 and 1975. *Mercury MESSENGER* has passed Mercury several times, and will begin orbiting Mercury in 2011.

Size of Mercury compared to Earth

I'm visiting the planets! As you read this lesson and the next one, keep track of how far I've traveled.

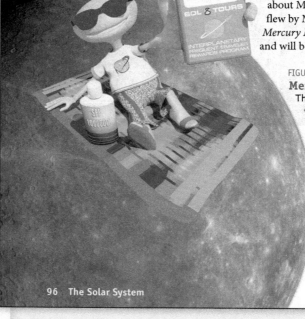

FIGURE 2 ·········
Mercury
The photo shows Mercury's cratered surface.

✏️ **Answer the questions below.**

1. **Solve Problems** List three things a visitor to Mercury would need to bring.

   Sample: oxygen, water, protection from heat and cold

2. **CHALLENGE** Refer to **Figure 1.** How many Mercury days are there in a Mercury year?

   About one and a half

TOTAL AU:
0.39
SOL 8 TOURS

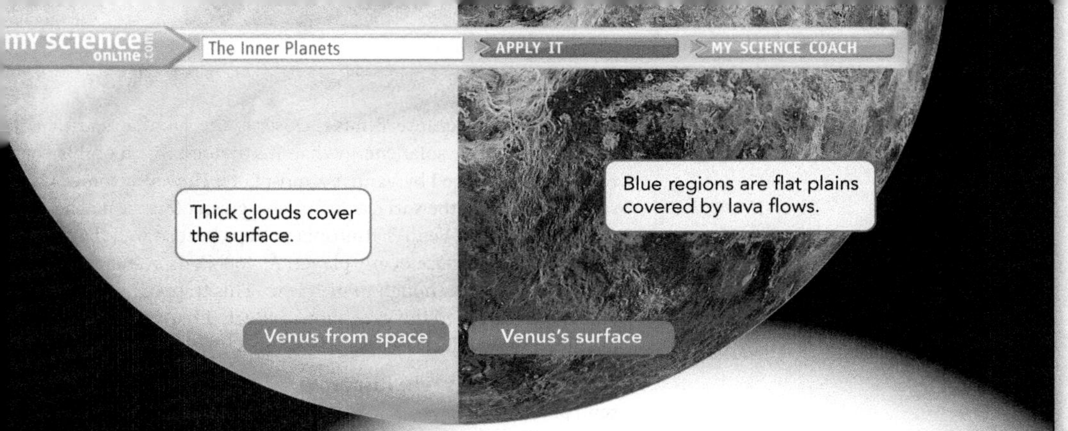

Thick clouds cover the surface.

Blue regions are flat plains covered by lava flows.

Venus from space

Venus's surface

FIGURE 3

Venus

This figure combines images of Venus taken from space with a camera (left) and radar (right). Radar is able to penetrate Venus's thick clouds to reveal the surface. The colors in both images are altered to show more details.

✏ **Infer** Why do scientists need to use radar to study Venus's surface?

Sample: The clouds are too thick to see through with normal cameras.

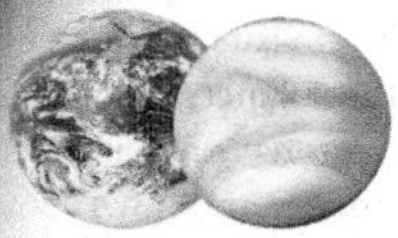

Size of Venus compared to Earth

Venus Venus is so similar in size and mass to Earth that it is sometimes called "Earth's twin." Venus's density and internal structure are similar to Earth's. But in other ways Venus and Earth are very different. ⚷ **Venus has a thick atmosphere, an unusual pattern of rotation, and the hottest surface of any planet.**

Venus's Atmosphere Venus's atmosphere is so thick that it is always cloudy. As you can see in **Figure 3**, astronomers can see only a smooth cloud cover over Venus. The thick clouds are made mostly of droplets of sulfuric acid.

At Venus's surface, you would quickly be crushed by the weight of its atmosphere. The pressure of Venus's atmosphere is 90 times greater than the pressure of Earth's atmosphere. You couldn't breathe on Venus because its atmosphere is mostly carbon dioxide.

Venus's Rotation Venus takes about 7.5 Earth months to revolve around the sun. It takes about 8 months for Venus to rotate once on its axis. Thus, Venus rotates so slowly that its day is longer than its year! Oddly, Venus rotates from east to west, the opposite direction from most other planets and moons. Astronomers hypothesize that this unusual rotation was caused by a very large object that struck Venus billions of years ago. Such a collision could have caused the planet to change its direction of rotation. Another hypothesis is that Venus's thick atmosphere could have somehow altered its rotation.

97

Explain

Teach Key Concepts ⚷

Explain to students that Venus differs from Earth in three main ways. Ask: **What are three very significant differences between Venus and Earth?** *(The pressure of Venus's atmosphere is 90 times greater than the pressure of Earth's atmosphere; Venus rotates from east to west and so slowly that its day is longer than its year; Venus's surface is much hotter than Earth's—hotter than any planet's surface.)*

21st Century Learning

L1 INTERPERSONAL SKILLS Have students close their books and listen while you read the paragraph about Venus's rotation. Ask students to describe how they visualize the cause of this unusual rotation. *(Sample: I imagined a larger, massive planet crashing into Venus.)* Ask students to work in pairs and discuss how they visualized the process by which a collision changed Venus's rotation. Ask: **What other possible cause have scientists identified to explain Venus's rotation?** *(Venus's thick atmosphere somehow changed its rotation.)*

Teacher Demo

L1 VENUS'S ROTATION

Materials 2 globes

Time 5 minutes

Place a globe on a table and spin it so that it turns from west to east. Place a second globe on the table and spin it very slowly so that it turns from east to west.

Ask: **Which globe represented Earth?** *(The first; Earth rotates from west to east.)* **What did the other globe represent?** *(Venus; it rotates very slowly from east to west.)* Ask students to compare Venus and Earth. *(They are similar in size and mass. They have different atmospheres and rotations.)*

Differentiated Instruction

L1 Compare and Contrast Inner Planets Suggest that students use Venn diagrams to compare and contrast each inner planet with Earth. Demonstrate how to use a Venn diagram to compare and contrast two subjects. First, have volunteers read aloud the information about Earth and Venus in the section. Then draw a Venn diagram on the chalkboard. As students name similarities between Venus and Earth, write these in the overlapping portion of the diagram. Then have students name differences and record these in the outer portions of the circles. Instruct students to complete additional Venn diagrams for the remaining inner planets and Earth.

Explain

Lead a Discussion

VENUS'S ATMOSPHERE Explain that the carbon dioxide in Venus's atmosphere traps heat so well that Venus has the hottest surface of any planet. Ask: **Could astronauts land on Venus? Why or why not?** *(Sample: Probably not. The surface is so hot and the atmospheric pressure so great that the first probe to land on Venus survived for only a few minutes.)* **How was the *Magellan* probe able to map Venus's hot surface?** *(By using radar, which works through clouds)* Inform students that *Magellan* was in orbit around Venus until the end of its mission, when scientists intentionally crash-landed it. The crash-landing enabled *Magellan* scientists to collect data on the behavior of molecules in Venus's upper atmosphere and gave engineers useful information for spacecraft design. Contact with the probe was lost one day after its landing.

Make Analogies

THE GREENHOUSE EFFECT Explain that a garden greenhouse traps part of the light absorbed by Earth's surface, with the result that the temperature in a greenhouse remains quite warm. Ask: **How is this like the greenhouse effect on Venus?** *(Sample: The carbon dioxide in Venus's atmosphere acts like a garden greenhouse, trapping heat so well that Venus's surface has an average temperature of 460°C.)*

Support the Big Q ❓

VENUS AND EARTH Remind students that both Venus and Earth experience a greenhouse effect. Ask: **What is different about the greenhouse effect on the two planets?** *(Earth's atmosphere traps much less heat that Venus's does.)* **What is the reason for this difference?** *(Venus' atmosphere has a much greater proportion of carbon dioxide than Earth's atmosphere.)* You may wish to mention that on Earth, water vapor is the major factor in the greenhouse effect but the accelerated addition of carbon dioxide to the atmosphere is now increasing it.

🔄 **Compare and Contrast** Explain that when you compare and contrast, you examine the similarities and differences between two things.

🔄 **Compare and Contrast**
List one feature Venus has in common with Earth and one feature that is different.

In common: *Sample: greenhouse effect*

Different: *Sample: high amount of carbon dioxide*

A Hot Planet Because Venus is closer to the sun than Earth is, it receives more solar energy than Earth does. Much of this radiation is reflected by Venus's atmosphere. However, some radiation reaches the surface and is later given off as heat. The carbon dioxide in Venus's atmosphere traps heat so well that Venus has the hottest surface of any planet. At 460°C, its average surface temperature is hot enough to melt lead. This trapping of heat by the atmosphere is called the **greenhouse effect**. **Figure 4** shows how the greenhouse effect occurs.

Exploring Venus The first probe to land on Venus's surface and send back data, *Venera 7*, landed in 1970. It survived for only a few minutes because of the high temperature and pressure. Later probes were more durable and sent images and data back to Earth.

The *Magellan* probe reached Venus in 1990, carrying radar instruments. Radar works through clouds, so *Magellan* was able to map nearly the entire surface. The *Magellan* data confirmed that Venus is covered with rock. Venus's surface has more than 10,000 volcanoes. Lava flows from these volcanoes have formed plains.

More recent probes have included *Venus Express*, from the European Space Agency, as well as brief visits by space probes headed for other planets. Images from *Venus Express* have helped scientists understand how Venus's clouds form and change.

FIGURE 4
Greenhouse Effect
Gases in the atmosphere trap some heat energy, while some is transmitted into space. More heat is trapped on Venus than on Earth.

✏️ **Apply Concepts** Look at what happens to heat energy on Venus. Then draw arrows to show what happens on Earth.

Radiation absorbed by greenhouse gases

Escaping radiation

Solar radiation

Earth There's only one planet in the solar system where you could live easily: Earth.  **Earth has liquid water and a suitable temperature range and atmosphere for living things to survive.**

The Water Planet Earth is unique in our solar system in having liquid water on its surface. In fact, most of Earth's surface, about 70 percent, is covered with water.

Earth's Temperature Scientists sometimes speak of Earth as having "Goldilocks" conditions—in other words, Earth is "just right" for life as we know it. Earth is not too hot and not too cold. If Earth were a little closer to the sun, it would be so hot that liquid water would evaporate. If it were a little farther away and colder, water would always be solid ice.

Earth's Atmosphere Earth has enough gravity to hold on to most gases. These gases make up Earth's atmosphere. Earth is the only planet with an atmosphere that is rich in oxygen. Oxygen makes up about 20 percent of Earth's atmosphere. Nearly all the rest is nitrogen, with small amounts of other gases such as argon, carbon dioxide, and water vapor.

Like Venus, Earth experiences a greenhouse effect. Earth's atmosphere traps heat, though less heat than Venus's atmosphere does. Without the atmosphere, Earth would be much colder.

FIGURE 5 ·····················
Earth's Structure
Earth has three main layers—a crust, a mantle, and a core. The crust includes the solid, rocky surface. Under the crust is the mantle, a layer of hot rock. Earth has a dense core made mainly of iron and nickel.

✎ **Relate Text and Visuals**
Label the layer of Earth with the highest density.

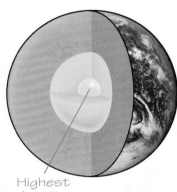

Highest density

Solar radiation

99

Differentiated Instruction

L1 Identify Earth's Layers Place a hard-boiled egg on a paper towel. Use a knife to slice the egg crosswise. Ask students to identify what each part of the egg represents. *(Shell—crust; white—mantle; yolk—core)*

L3 Create a Diagram Have students use a computer graphics program to create a scale diagram showing Earth's layers. Have students label the diagram and add pertinent information, such as the depth of each layer, gathered from independent research.

Teach Key Concepts

Explain to students that Earth is unique in the solar system in having ideal conditions to support life as we know it. Ask: **What characteristics does Earth have that enable living things to survive?** *(Liquid water and the right temperature range and atmosphere)* **How much liquid water does Earth have on its surface?** *(About 70 percent of Earth's surface is covered with water.)* **How would conditions on Earth be different if Earth were just a little farther from or closer to the sun?** *(If Earth were a little farther from the sun, it would be so much colder that its water would always be solid ice. If Earth were a little closer to the sun, Earth would be so hot that liquid water would evaporate.)* **What enables Earth to hold onto a mix of gases that support life?** *(Gravity)* **Does oxygen make up most of Earth's atmosphere?** *(No, the atmosphere is mostly made up of nitrogen.)*

Elaborate ————————

Build Inquiry [Lab zone]

L3 INTERPRET THE GREENHOUSE EFFECT

Materials photograph of a greenhouse

Time 20 minutes

Show students a photograph of a greenhouse with plants growing inside. Explain that a greenhouse lets in sunlight and prevents convection from carrying away heat. The plants stay warm inside. Have students work in pairs to create flowcharts or sketches that compare the path of light and heat energy in a greenhouse with the path of light and heat energy on Venus.

Ask students to discuss possible environmental problems caused by changes in Earth's greenhouse effect. *(Sample: The burning of fossil fuels and logging of forests, faster than they can grow back, increases the percentage of carbon dioxide in Earth's atmosphere beyond its ordinary fluctuations. Air pollution and accelerated climate change are two results.)*

Explain

Teach Key Concepts 🔑

Explain to students that Mars has water in the form of ice now and had more liquid water in the past than it does today. Inform students that people on Earth can view the surface of Mars with a telescope. Ask: **What does Mars have in common with the other inner planets?** *(Like Earth, Mars has seasons, volcanoes, polar caps, and water ice. Mars's moons are covered with craters, like Earth's moon. The composition of Mars's atmosphere is similar to Venus's. Like Mercury, Mars is barren.)* **What distinguishes Mars from the other inner planets?** *(Unlike Earth and Venus, Mars has a very thin atmosphere. Mars has two moons.)*

21st Century Learning

CRITICAL THINKING Tell students that no spacecraft with a human crew has visited Mars. Ask: **What challenges might astronauts face if they went to Mars?** *(Sample: Lack of oxygen in the atmosphere, distance from Earth, extreme temperatures, lack of liquid water)*

Address Misconceptions

SCIENCE OR SCIENCE FICTION? Students' ideas about the features and history of Mars may be partly based on science-fiction stories, television shows, and movies. Have each student prepare a Fact/Fiction sheet to distinguish scientific findings about Mars from science fiction. Ask: **Are there intelligent life forms known as "Martians" on Mars?** *(No, Martians are fictional.)* **Is Mars's nickname, the red planet, a creation of science fiction?** *(No, Mars is called the red planet because when you see it in the sky it looks red. The reddish color results from the breakdown of rocks that are rich in iron.)*

Size of Mars compared to Earth

Mars Mars is called the "red planet." **Figure 6** shows why. This reddish color is due to the breakdown of iron-rich rocks, leaving a rusty dust behind. 🔑 **Though Mars is mostly too cold for liquid water, it does have water ice now and shows evidence of intermittent seasonal flowing water today as well as liquid water in the past.**

Mars's Atmosphere The atmosphere of Mars is more than 95 percent carbon dioxide. You could walk around on Mars, but you would have to wear an airtight suit and carry your own oxygen. Mars has few clouds, and they are very thin compared to clouds on Earth. Temperatures on the surface range from −140°C to 20°C.

Water and Ice Images of Mars taken from space show a variety of features that look as if they were made by ancient streams, lakes, or floods. Scientists think that more liquid water flowed on Mars's surface in the distant past. Scientists infer that Mars must have been much warmer and had a thicker atmosphere at that time.

Today, Mars's atmosphere is so thin that most liquid water would quickly turn into a gas. Some water is located in the planet's two polar ice caps, which are almost entirely made of frozen water. Observations from the *Mars Reconnaissance Orbiter* in 2015 found evidence of flowing water in warmer areas today.

FIGURE 6 ··············

The Red Planet

Remote-controlled landers such as *Phoenix*, *Spirit*, and *Opportunity* have sent back pictures of the surface of Mars.

✏️ **Design a Solution** If you were designing a lander to work on Mars, where on Earth would you test it? Why?

Sample: in a desert area, because the dry conditions are similar to those on Mars

Digital Lesson: Assign the *Apply It* activity online and have students submit their work to you.

MY SCIENCE ONLINE.com | **The Inner Planets**

apply it!

Communicate Choose one of the inner planets other than Earth. Describe an alien that could live there. Include at least three features of your alien that make it well suited for the planet you chose. Draw your alien to the right.

Students' descriptions should reflect an understanding of the conditions on the chosen planet.

FIGURE 7 ....

Olympus Mons
This computer-generated image is based on data from the *Mars Global Surveyor* mission.

Volcanoes Some regions of Mars have giant volcanoes. There are signs that lava flowed from the volcanoes in the past, but the volcanoes are rarely active today. Olympus Mons, shown in **Figure 7,** is the largest volcano in the solar system. It is as large as Missouri and is nearly three times as tall as Mount Everest!

Mars's Moons Mars has two very small moons. Phobos, the larger moon, is about 22 kilometers across. Deimos is even smaller, about 13 kilometers across. Like Earth's moon, Phobos and Deimos are covered with craters.

Exploring Mars Many space probes have visited Mars, looking for signs of water and possible life. Rovers called *Spirit* and *Opportunity* found traces of salts and minerals that form in the presence of water. The *Phoenix* mission found frozen water near the north polar cap, and the *Mars Reconnaissance Orbiter* found evidence of flowing water in warmer areas. *Mars Express* detected methane gas in Mars's atmosphere. This gas might be a clue that microscopic life forms exist on Mars, even today!

Lab zone | Do the Quick Lab *Greenhouse Effect.*

Assess Your Understanding

1a. Name Which inner planet has the thickest atmosphere? *Venus*

b. Relate Cause and Effect Why is Venus hotter than Mercury? *Venus's atmosphere traps heat, while Mercury has little atmosphere to hold heat.*

got it?

○ I get it! Now I know that the inner planets differ in *size, atmosphere, and whether they have water.*

○ I need extra help with *See TE note.*

Go to **my science COACH** online for help with this subject.

101

Elaborate

Apply It!

L1 Before beginning the activity, review the information on Mercury, Venus, and Mars.

Communicate Explain that communicating effectively requires many skills, including writing, reading, and making models. To complete this activity they must combine the skills of writing and making a model in the form of a drawing.

Lab Resource: Quick Lab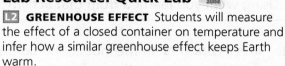

L2 **GREENHOUSE EFFECT** Students will measure the effect of a closed container on temperature and infer how a similar greenhouse effect keeps Earth warm.

Evaluate

Assess Your Understanding

After students answer the questions, have them evaluate their understanding by completing the appropriate sentence.

RTI Response to Intervention

1a. If students have trouble recalling which inner planet has the thickest atmosphere, **then** have help them review the material that describe each planet's atmosphere.

b. If students need help explaining why Venus is hotter **then** Mercury, then suggest they compare the two planets' atmospheres.

my science COACH Have students go online for help in understanding differences among the inner planets.

Differentiated Instruction

L1 **Oral Review** Have students work in groups of four. Assign each member of the group one inner planet. Have each student review the information about the assigned planet in the text and then teach the other members of the group what he or she has learned.

L3 **Musical Planets** The English composer Gustav Holst (1874–1934) composed a group of pieces for orchestra entitled *The Planets*. The seven pieces

describe musically the planets Mercury, Venus, Mars, Jupiter, Saturn, Uranus, and Neptune. Have interested students listen to one of the pieces. Ask each to write a paragraph describing how Holst used the music to represent the planet. Encourage students to research more about *The Planets* to find out why the planets are not in their correct order from the sun.

Lab zone **After the Inquiry Warm-Up**

The Inner Planets

Inquiry Warm-Up, *Ring Around the Sun*

In the Inquiry Warm-Up, you investigated the orbits of the inner planets around the sun. Using what you learned from that activity, answer the questions below.

1. **APPLY CONCEPTS** In the model, should the radius of Mercury's orbit be greater than or less than 3.5 meters?

   _____

2. **APPLY CONCEPTS** If Jupiter is farther away from the sun than Mars, will it take more or less time to travel around the sun than Mars does?

   _____

3. **APPLY CONCEPTS** Why does Earth take longer to travel around the sun than Venus?

   _____

   _____

4. **COMMUNICATE** Draw a diagram of your model of the inner planets.

Assess Your Understanding

The Inner Planets

What Do the Inner Planets Have in Common?

got it? ···

○ **I get it!** Now I know that the inner planets are _____

_____

_____

○ **I need extra help with** _____

_____

What Are the Characteristics of the Inner Planets?

1a. NAME Which inner planet has the thickest atmosphere? _____

b. RELATE CAUSE AND EFFECT Why is Venus hotter than Mercury? _____

_____

_____

got it? ···

○ **I get it!** Now I know that the inner planets differ in _____

_____

_____

○ **I need extra help with** _____

_____

Name _____ Date _____ Class _____

The Inner Planets

What Do the Inner Planets Have in Common?

The inner planets are small and dense and have rocky surfaces. They are often called the **terrestrial planets,** from the Latin word *terra*, which means "Earth."

What Are the Characteristics of the Inner Planets?

Although the four inner planets have many features in common, they differ in size and composition as well as distance from the sun.

Mercury is the smallest terrestrial planet and the planet closest to the sun. It has virtually no atmosphere because its gravity is too weak to hold gas particles. Much of what astronomers know about Mercury has come from space probes.

Venus has a thick atmosphere, an unusual pattern of rotation, and the hottest surface of any planet. It is so hot because its atmosphere traps heat in a process called the **greenhouse effect.** It rotates slowly, so its day is longer than its year! Oddly, Venus rotates from east to west, the opposite direction from most other planets and moons.

There is only one planet in the solar system where you could live easily. **Earth has liquid water and a suitable temperature range and atmosphere for living things to survive.** Earth has enough gravity to hold on to most gases, which make up Earth's atmosphere. Earth is the only planet with an oxygen-rich atmosphere. Like Venus, Earth experiences a greenhouse effect.

Mars appears reddish because of the breakdown of iron-rich rocks. **Although Mars is mostly too cold for liquid water, it does have water ice now and it shows evidence of intermittent flowing water today and more liquid water in the past.** Mars's atmosphere is more than 95 percent carbon dioxide. Some regions of the planet have giant volcanoes.

On a separate sheet of paper, explain how the four inner planets are alike and tell one distinctive thing about each.

Review and Reinforce

The Inner Planets

Understanding Main Ideas
Label the diagram with the names of the inner planets.

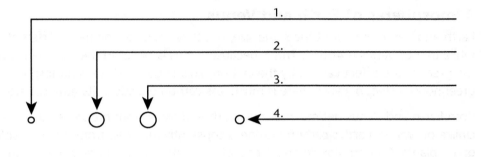

1. _____

2. _____

3. _____

4. _____

Write the name of the inner planet or planets that the statement describes.

5. _____ has a rocky surface

6. _____ 70 percent is covered with water

7. _____ rotates in the opposite direction of most other planets and moons

8. _____ called the "red planet"

9. _____ has at least one moon

10. _____ similar to each other in size and mass

11. _____ has almost no atmosphere

12. _____ atmosphere so heavy and thick that it would crush a human

13. _____ has enough gravity to hold on to most gases

14. _____ atmosphere is mostly carbon dioxide

Building Vocabulary
Write a definition for each of these terms on a separate sheet of paper.

15. terrestrial planets

16. greenhouse effect

The Inner Planets

> Read the passage and study the figures below. Then use a separate sheet of paper to answer the questions that follow.

Atmospheres of Earth and Venus

Earth and Venus are about the same size, but they could not be more different. Earth's surface is cool while that of Venus is 460°C. This is because Venus is closer to the sun than Earth and because of the greenhouse effect caused by the carbon dioxide gas in Venus's atmosphere. Earth has a smaller greenhouse effect because there is much less carbon dioxide in its atmosphere.

Both Earth and Venus get much of their carbon dioxide from the same source: erupting volcanoes. Unlike on Venus, Earth's carbon dioxide is constantly removed from the atmosphere by liquid water and green plants. Carbon dioxide dissolves easily in water. Once there, it joins with other chemicals to form solid substances that become part of sea-floor rocks. This carbon dioxide is "locked up" for long periods of time in these rocks. Plants also absorb carbon dioxide and lock up some of the gas. However on Venus, carbon dioxide simply builds up in the atmosphere.

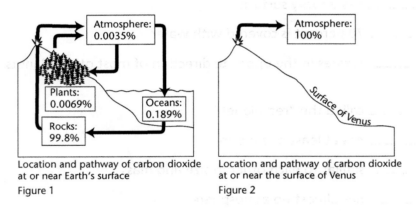

Location and pathway of carbon dioxide at or near Earth's surface
Figure 1

Location and pathway of carbon dioxide at or near the surface of Venus
Figure 2

1. Figure 1 shows, in very simple terms, the pathways taken by carbon dioxide on Earth. According to the diagram, where does carbon dioxide go when it leaves Earth's atmosphere?

2. On Earth, where is most of the carbon dioxide located at any one time? On Venus, where is most of the carbon dioxide located at any one time?

3. On Earth, how does carbon dioxide move from the atmosphere into rocks? Why does this movement not occur on Venus?

4. If all carbon dioxide coming out of volcanoes were to remain in the atmosphere, what further effect would this have on Earth's temperature?

Lesson Quiz

The Inner Planets

Write the letter of the correct answer on the line at the left.

1. ___ Mars's atmosphere is composed mostly of
   A nitrogen
   B hydrogen
   C oxygen
   D carbon dioxide

2. ___ Some regions of Mars have giant
   A lakes
   B volcanoes
   C forests
   D rivers

3. ___ All the inner planets have an atmosphere except
   A Mercury
   B Venus
   C Earth
   D Mars

4. ___ The inner planets that experience a greenhouse effect are
   A Mercury and Mars
   B Venus and Mars
   C Venus and Earth
   D Mercury and Earth

If the statement is true, write _true_. If the statement is false, change the underlined word or words to make the statement true.

5. _____ The inner planets are small and dense and have <u>smooth</u> surfaces.

6. _____ <u>Mercury</u> rotates so slowly that its day is longer than its year.

7. _____ The thick clouds on Venus are made up mostly of <u>carbonic</u> acid droplets.

8. _____ Earth is unique in our solar system for having liquid <u>mercury</u> on its surface.

9. _____ Oxygen makes up about <u>20</u> percent of Earth's atmosphere.

10. _____ Space <u>ships</u> have given scientists important information about Mercury, Venus, and Mars.

The Inner Planets

Answer Key

After the Inquiry Warm-Up

1. less than 3.5 meters

2. more

3. Venus is closer to the sun so it has a shorter distance to travel.

4. Students should draw a model of the inner solar system showing the sun, and four concentric circles representing the four inner planets.

Key Concept Summaries

Sample: The inner, or terrestrial, planets are small and dense and have rocky surfaces. Mercury has virtually no atmosphere. Venus rotates from east to west. Earth has liquid water and a suitable temperature range and atmosphere for living things to survive. Mars appears reddish because of the breakdown of iron-rich rocks.

Review and Reinforce

1. Mercury

2. Venus

3. Earth

4. Mars

5. Mercury, Venus, Earth, Mars

6. Earth

7. Venus

8. Mars

9. Earth, Mars

10. Venus, Earth

11. Mercury

12. Venus

13. Earth

14. Venus, Mars

15. Sample: The first four planets from the sun: Mercury, Venus, Earth, and Mars. They are the Earth-like planets with rocky surfaces.

16. the trapping of heat by the atmosphere

Enrich

1. Carbon dioxide is either dissolved in the oceans or absorbed by green plants.

2. On Earth, at any one time, most of the carbon dioxide is locked up in rocks. On Venus, it is in the atmosphere.

3. On Earth, carbon dioxide dissolves in ocean water. While there, it reacts with other chemicals to form rocks. On Venus, there are no oceans in which the carbon dioxide can dissolve.

4. The carbon dioxide would increase the greenhouse effect and would further warm Earth's surface.

Lesson Quiz

1. D

2. B

3. A

4. C

5. rocky

6. Venus

7. sulfuric

8. water

9. true

10. probes

Place the outside corner, the corner away from the dotted line, in the corner of your copy machine to copy onto letter-size paper.

The Outer Planets

? Why are objects in the Solar System different from each other?

Lesson Pacing: 3–4 periods or 1–1½ blocks

🕐 **SHORT ON TIME?** To do this lesson in approximately half the time, do the Activate Prior Knowledge activity on page 102. A discussion of the Key Concepts on pages 103, 104, 106, 108, and 109 will familiarize students with the lesson content. Have students do the Quick Labs. The rest of the lesson can be completed by students independently.

Preference Navigator, in the online Planning tools, allows you to customize *Interactive Science* to your own teaching style. You can also edit lesson plans by selecting the Lesson Planner option.

Digital Teacher's Edition allows you to access your Teacher's Edition and Resource materials online.

MY SCIENCE online.com

Lesson Vocabulary

- gas giant
- ring

Content Refresher

Professional Development Note

Gravity and the Discovery of Pluto The American astronomer Clyde Tombaugh discovered Pluto in 1930. He was only 25 years old. Soon after high school, Tombaugh built his first telescope. When he sent sketches of his observations of Jupiter and Mars to the Lowell Observatory, they offered him a job: finding Pluto.

Astronomers had predicted the existence of Pluto based on calculations that indicated that a distant object was disturbing the orbits of Uranus and Neptune. Scientists now know that Pluto's small mass could not have caused the disturbance. In fact, Pluto's lack of sufficient gravity to clear its orbital area ultimately led to its reclassification as a dwarf planet. Regardless, Tombaugh spent 10 months looking at hundreds of thousands of images and, despite all odds, found Pluto. In addition to discovering Pluto, Tombaugh made other discoveries as well. He found hundreds of other small objects in the solar system including fourteen asteroids that he named after his family members, small clusters of stars, and even a comet. After the discovery of Pluto, Tombaugh became an astronomer and later a professor of astronomy at New Mexico State University.

LESSON OBJECTIVES

 Describe characteristics that the gas giants have in common.

🔑 Identify characteristics that distinguish each outer planet.

Blended Path
Active learning using Student Edition, Inquiry Path, and Digital Path

ENGAGE AND EXPLORE

Teach this lesson using a variety of resources. Begin by reading **My Planet Diary** as a class. Have students share ideas about how astronomers worked together to discover Neptune. Then have students do the **Inquiry Warm-Up activity.** Students will explore the relative sizes of the outer planets. Discuss how they calculated the relative diameter of Jupiter in millimeters. The **After the Inquiry Warm-Up worksheet** sets up a comparison of diameters and masses of the outer planets. Have volunteers share their answers to question 4 about how best to precisely compare the sizes of the outer planets.

EXPLAIN AND ELABORATE

Teach Key Concepts by explaining the similarities and differences between the gas giants and Earth. **Lead a Discussion** about the atmospheres and surfaces of the gas giants.

Teach Key Concepts by telling students about Jupiter's size, atmosphere, structure, and moons. To **Support the Big Q,** discuss why hydrogen and helium are in a liquid, rather than gaseous state in Jupiter's core. Use **Figure 3** to identify the four largest moons of Jupiter and the characteristics that set them apart from the others. Continue to **Teach Key Concepts** by describing Saturn's rings. **Lead a Discussion** about how Saturn and Jupiter are similar and different. Look at **Figure 4** to determine why it would be difficult to see Saturn's rings when their edges are facing Earth. **Teach Key Concepts** by asking students why astronomers Uranus's axis is tilted so far from its orbit. **Teach Key Concepts** by identifying characteristics of Neptune and its moons. Then have students practice the inquiry skill in the **Apply It activities.** Hand out the **Key Concept Summaries** as a review of each part of the lesson. Students can also use the online **Vocab Flash Cards** to review key terms.

EVALUATE

Have students take the **Lesson Quiz.** For an alternate assessment, see the **EXAM**VIEW® Assessment Suite, Progress Monitoring Assessments, or SuccessTracker™.

E L L Support

1 Content and Language

The terms *invisible* and *visible* are use to describe Saturn's rings and Neptune's clouds. The word *invisible* contains the prefix *in-,* which means "not". *Visible* means "able to be seen." Therefore, *invisible* means "not able to be seen."

Lab zone Inquiry Path
Hands-on learning in the Lab zone

Digital Path
Online learning at my science online.com

ENGAGE AND EXPLORE

To teach this lesson with an emphasis on inquiry, begin with the **Inquiry Warm-Up activity.** Students will calculate the relative sizes of the outer planets. Discuss how they calculated the relative diameter of Jupiter in millimeters. Have students do the **After the Inquiry Warm-Up worksheet.** Talk about the mass and diameter of the outer planets. Have volunteers share their answers to question 4 about how best to precisely compare the sizes of the outer planets.

EXPLAIN AND ELABORATE

Focus on the **Inquiry Skill** for the lesson. Point out that when you pose questions, you inquire about a situation that requires the gathering of scientific evidence. Pose a question about the outer planets that could be answered based on the evidence gathered in the **Inquiry Warm-Up activity.** *(Questions will vary but should be able to be answered based on the information gathered in the Inquiry Warm-Up activity.)* Have students do the **Quick Lab** to explore the densities of the outer planets and then share their results.

To **Support the Big Q,** discuss the composition of Jupiter's core. Do the **Teacher Demo** to model Jupiter's Great Red Spot. The second **Teacher Demo** sets up a comparison between Jupiter and Saturn. Review the planets and their moons before beginning the **Apply It activity.** Ask volunteers to share where they would travel and what question they would pose. Do the **Quick Lab** to reinforce understanding of why Saturn's rings are occasionally invisible from Earth. Students can use the online **Vocab Flash Cards** to review key terms.

EVALUATE

Have students take the **Lesson Quiz.** For an alternate assessment, see the **EXAM**VIEW® Assessment Suite, Progress Monitoring Assessments, or SuccessTracker™.

ENGAGE AND EXPLORE

Teach this lesson using digital resources. Begin by having students explore real-world connections to the outer planets at **My Planet Diary** online. Have them access the Chapter Resources to find the **Unlock the Big Question activity.** There they can answer the questions and refine their responses as they continue through the lesson. You can re-assign the activity and have students submit their work so you can track their progress.

EXPLAIN AND ELABORATE

Students reading above, at, or below the lexile measure of this lesson can access basic content readings at their level at **My Reading Web.** Have students use the online **Vocab Flash Cards** to preview key terms. Have students do the online **Interactive Art activity** to explore the outer planets. Do the **Quick Lab** to explore the densities of the outer planets and then ask students to share their results.

Support the Big Q by discussing why Jupiter is not really a "gas" giant. Review the planets and their moons before assigning the online **Apply It activity.** Ask volunteers to share why they chose to travel to a specific planet and what question they would pose. Have students submit their work to you. Have students make a model of Saturn's rings in the **Quick Lab** in order to see why they are sometimes invisible from Earth. The **Key Concept Summaries** online allow students to read a summary and see an image associated with each part of the lesson. Online remediation is available at **My Science Coach.**

EVALUATE

Have students take the **Lesson Quiz.** For an alternate assessment, see the **EXAM**VIEW® Assessment Suite, Progress Monitoring Assessments, or SuccessTracker™.

2 Frontload the Lesson
Preview the lesson visuals, labels, and captions. Ask students what they know about the words *atmosphere, rings,* and *moon.* Explain the specific meanings these words have in science.

3 Comprehensible Input
Have students compare and contrast the outer planets with one another using Venn Diagrams.

4 Language Production
Pair or group students with varied language abilities to complete labs collaboratively for language practice. Have each student copy the completed written lab for personal reference.

5 Assess Understanding
Divide the class into small groups. Have each student identify a Key Concept from the lesson to discuss in his or her group. After the discussions, have students talk about the Key Concepts as a group.

The Outer Planets

Establish Learning Objectives

After this lesson, students will be able to:

🔑 Describe characteristics that the gas giants have in common.

🔑 Identify characteristics that distinguish each outer planet.

Engage

Activate Prior Knowledge

MY PLANET DIARY Read *Predicting a Planet* with the class. Remind students that gravity is a force of attraction. Ask: **What does the strength of gravity between two objects depend on?** *(The distance between them and their masses)* **What could Adams and Leverrier infer about why Uranus did not follow the expected path?** *(Uranus was being acted on by a strong gravitational force, like that exerted by a neighboring planet in the solar system.)*

BIG IDEAS OF SCIENCE REFERENCE LIBRARY 📖
Have students look up the following topics: Jupiter's Moons, Neptune, Saturn, Uranus.

Explore

Lab Resource: Inquiry Warm-Up 🔬

L2 **HOW BIG ARE THE PLANETS?** Students will calculate the relative sizes of the outer planets and list them in order from largest to smallest.

The Outer Planets

🔑 **What Do the Outer Planets Have in Common?**

🔑 **What Are the Characteristics of Each Outer Planet?**

MY PLANET DIARY

DISCOVERY

Predicting a Planet

In the 1840s, astronomers were puzzled. Uranus didn't move as expected, based on the theory of gravity. Astronomers John Couch Adams and Urbain Leverrier independently hypothesized that Uranus was being affected by another planet's gravity. They calculated where this planet should be. Another astronomer, Johann Galle, aimed his telescope at the place Leverrier predicted. On September 23, 1846, he discovered the new planet—Neptune.

✏️ **Communicate** Work with a partner to answer the question.

What science skills did the astronomers use when they discovered Neptune?

Sample: developing hypotheses, predicting, posing questions, observing

▶ **PLANET DIARY** Go to Planet Diary to learn more about the outer planets.

🔬 **Lab zone** Do the Inquiry Warm-Up *How Big Are the Planets?*

What Do the Outer Planets Have in Common?

If you could visit the outer planets, you wouldn't have a solid place to stand! 🔑 **The four outer planets are much larger and more massive than Earth, and they do not have solid surfaces.** Because these four planets are so large, they are often called **gas giants**. **Figure 1** summarizes some basic facts about the gas giants.

Composition Jupiter and Saturn are composed mainly of hydrogen and helium. Uranus and Neptune contain some of these gases, but also ices of ammonia and methane. Because they are so massive, the gas giants exert a very strong gravitational force. This gravity keeps gases from escaping, forming thick atmospheres.

SUPPORT ALL READERS
Lexile Measure = 960L   Lexile Word Count = 1647

Prior Exposure to Content: May be the first time students have encountered this topic

Academic Vocabulary: *outline, question, estimate, calculate*

Science Vocabulary: *gas giant, ring*

Concept Level: May be difficult for students who struggle with abstract ideas

Preteach With: My Planet Diary "Predicting a Planet" and Figure 1 activity

Go to **My Reading Web** to access leveled readings that provide a foundation for the content.

my science online

Vocabulary
- gas giant
- ring

Skills
- ↻ Reading: Outline
- △ Inquiry: Pose Questions

Despite the name "gas giant," much of the material in these planets is actually liquid because the pressure inside the planets is so high. The outer layers are extremely cold because they are far from the sun. Temperatures increase greatly within the planets.

Moons and Rings All the gas giants have many moons, ranging from 13 around Neptune to more than 60 around Jupiter! These moons vary from tiny balls of rock and ice barely a kilometer across to moons larger than Mercury. Some of these moons even have their own atmospheres!

In addition, each of the gas giants is surrounded by a set of rings. A **ring** is a thin disk of small particles of ice and rock. Saturn's rings are the largest and most complex.

Planet	Jupiter	Saturn	Uranus	Neptune
Diameter (km)	142,984	120,536	51,118	49,528
Period of rotation (Earth hours)	9.9	10.7	17.2	16.1
Average distance from sun (AU)	5.20	9.54	19.2	30.07
Period of revolution (Earth years)	11.9	29.5	83.8	163.8
Number of moons	at least 63	at least 61	at least 27	at least 13

Note: Planets are not shown to scale.

As you visit each planet, don't forget to keep track of how many AU you've collected!

TOTAL AU:

SOL TOURS
INTERPLANETARY
FREQUENT TRAVELER
REWARDS PROGRAM

FIGURE 1 ······
> INTERACTIVE ART
The Outer Planets
The table summarizes data about the outer planets.

✏ **Estimate** Earth's diameter is about 12,750 km. About how many times larger is Jupiter's diameter than Earth's?

About 11 times

Do the Quick Lab
Density Mystery.

⊂⊃ Assess Your Understanding

got it? ······

○ I get it! Now I know that the gas giants all *contain hydrogen and helium, have many moons, have rings, and do not have solid surfaces.*

○ I need extra help with *See TE note.*

Go to my science ⊙ coach online for help with this subject.

103

Explain

Introduce Vocabulary
Write the term *gas giant* on the board and explain that the outer planets are large and massive like giants and made out of gases.

Teach Key Concepts 🗝
Explain that the gas giants are much larger and more massive than Earth. Ask: **How else does the structure of the gas giants differ from Earth?** *(Gas giants do not have solid surfaces.)* **What are the main gases that make up gas giants?** *(Hydrogen and helium)* **What feature do gas giants have that Earth does not?** *(Rings of ice and rock)* **How do moons of gas giants and Earth's moon differ?** *(Earth has one moon, gas giants have many moons. Some of the moons of gas giants have their own atmospheres, unlike Earth's moon.)*

Lead a Discussion
GAS GIANTS Tell students to imagine a space probe exploring a gas giant. Ask: **What would the probe encounter approaching the visible surface?** *(A planet with an atmosphere that gets thicker)* **Could the probe penetrate the solid part of the planet?** *(Probably not)*

Elaborate

Lab Resource: Quick Lab 🧪
L2 DENSITY MYSTERY Students will explore the densities of the outer planets.

Evaluate

Assess Your Understanding
Have students evaluate their understanding by completing the appropriate sentence.

R T I Response to Intervention
If students need help explaining what all the gas giants have in common, **then** have them review the boldfaced Key Concept and the section subheads.

my science ⊙ coach Have students go online for help in understanding the gas giants.

My Planet Diary provides an opportunity for students to explore real-world connections to the outer planets.

Interactive Art allows students to explore the outer planets.

my science online.com | Gas Giants

Explain

Teach Key Concepts

Remind students that Jupiter is the largest planet in the solar system. It takes Jupiter about 12 years to orbit the sun and just under 10 hours to rotate on its axis (the fastest of any planet in the solar system). As a result, the planet appears to bulge at the equator when viewed through a telescope on Earth. Ask: **How massive is Jupiter?** *(Sample: About $2\frac{1}{2}$ times greater than that of all the other planets together)* **What is the only object in the solar system that is more massive than Jupiter?** *(The sun)* **What is one notable feature of Jupiter's atmosphere?** *(The Great Red Spot, a storm that is larger than Earth)* **How many moons does Jupiter have?** *(At least 63)*

Outline Explain to students that using an outline format can help them organize information by main topic, subtopic, and details.

Support the Big Q ❓

L3 JUPITER'S STRUCTURE Remind students that a thick mantle of liquid hydrogen and helium surround Jupiter's core. Ask: **Why is it somewhat misleading to call Jupiter a "gas" giant?** *(Much of the planet is liquid.)* **Why?** *(The force of gravity on Jupiter is immense because Jupiter is so massive. Therefore, the hydrogen and helium deep within the planet are under a great pressure, which causes them to be compressed into the liquid state as their molecules slow down and are forced into a smaller volume.)*

Teacher Demo 🔬

L2 MODEL THE GREAT RED SPOT

Materials water, pepper, funnel or spoon, clear plastic 1-L bottle with lid

Time 10 minutes

Point out the resemblance between the Great Red Spot and a hurricane on Earth. If needed, show students images of hurricanes taken by satellites orbiting above Earth. Then half fill a clear plastic bottle with water. Using a funnel or spoon, pour in a spoonful of pepper. Seal the bottle and swirl the water forcefully.

Ask: **What happens to the pepper grains?** *(They spin in a large swirl.)* **What forces are causing the Great Red Spot to swirl?** *(Sample: Differences in pressure in Jupiter's atmosphere)* **What kind of data would you need to test your inferences?** *(Sample: Data that show the pressure of the atmosphere around the Great Red Spot)*

What Are the Characteristics of Each Outer Planet?

Since telescopes were first invented, scientists have studied the features of the outer planets and their moons. Today, space-based telescopes and space probes including the *Voyager, Galileo,* and *Cassini* missions have revealed many details of these planets that are not visible from Earth. Scientists are constantly discovering new information about these planets and their moons.

Jupiter 🔒 **Jupiter is the largest and most massive planet.** Jupiter's enormous mass dwarfs the other planets. In fact, its mass is about $2\frac{1}{2}$ times that of all the other planets combined!

Jupiter's Atmosphere Like all of the gas giants, Jupiter has a thick atmosphere made up mainly of hydrogen and helium. One notable feature of Jupiter's atmosphere is its Great Red Spot, a storm that is larger than Earth! The storm's swirling winds are similar to a hurricane, as you can see in **Figure 2.** Unlike hurricanes on Earth, however, the Great Red Spot shows no signs of going away.

Jupiter's Structure Astronomers think that Jupiter probably has a dense core of rock and iron at its center. A thick mantle of liquid hydrogen and helium surrounds this core. Because of the weight of Jupiter's atmosphere, the pressure at Jupiter's core is estimated to be about 30 million times greater than the pressure at Earth's surface.

Size of Jupiter
compared to Earth

✏️ **Outline** As you read, make an outline about Jupiter.

I. Atmosphere

  A. <u>Thick atmosphere</u>

  B. <u>Mostly hydrogen</u>
    <u>and helium</u>

II. Structure

  A. <u>Dense core of</u>
    <u>rock and iron</u>

  B. <u>Mantle of liquid</u>
    <u>hydrogen, helium</u>

  C. <u>High pressure at</u>
    <u>the core</u>

FIGURE 2
The Great Red Spot
This storm is about 20,000 km long and 12,000 km wide. The largest tropical storm on Earth was 2,200 km across.

✏️ **Calculate** Think of the storm on Earth as a square and the Great Red Spot as a rectangle. About how many Earth storms would fit inside the Great Red Spot?

<u>About 50</u>

Jupiter's Moons The Italian astronomer Galileo Galilei discovered Jupiter's largest moons in 1610. These moons, shown in **Figure 3,** are named Io, Europa, Ganymede, and Callisto. Since Galileo's time, astronomers have discovered dozens of additional moons orbiting Jupiter. Many of these are small moons that have been found in the last few years thanks to improved technology.

FIGURE 3 ....

The Moons of Jupiter

Jupiter's four largest moons are larger than Earth's moon. Each has characteristics that set it apart from the others.

✎ **Relate Text and Visuals** Based on the photograph, match each description below to its moon.

❶ **Ganymede** is Jupiter's largest moon. It is larger than Mercury! Its surface is divided into dark and bright areas.

❷ **Callisto** is second to Ganymede in size, but has less ice. It has the most craters of any of Jupiter's moons.

❸ **Io** is not icy, unlike most of Jupiter's moons. It may have as many as 300 active volcanoes. The eruptions from those volcanoes constantly change the moon's surface.

❹ **Europa** is covered with ice. There may be liquid water below the ice—and if there's water, there might be life!

TOTAL AU: 5.2

SOL TOURS

INTERPLANETARY FREQUENT TRAVELER REWARDS PROGRAM

Io

Europa

Callisto

Ganymede

105

Teach With Visuals

L1 Tell students to look at **Figure 3**. Ask: **Which of these four moons is the largest?** *(Ganymede)* **If Ganymede is larger than Mercury, why is Ganymede not a planet?** *(It is not in its own orbit around the sun. It orbits Jupiter.)* **How is Io different from the other moons?** *(Io has active volcanoes and is not icy.)*

Address Misconceptions

L1 **LIFE ON EUROPA** The *Galileo* probe verified that Europa's surface is water in the form of ice. More surprisingly, the probe indicated liquid water beneath the ice. Some students may think that *extraterrestrial life* comprises only mammals. Ask: **Does "life" include only organisms such as rabbits, dogs, and chimpanzees?** *(Sample: No. "Life" includes plants, fungi, and microorganisms.)* **When scientists speculate that there might be life on Europa, what do they mean?** *(Sample: There might be simple organisms in liquid water below the ice.)*

Elaborate

21st Century Learning

CRITICAL THINKING Point out that Jupiter's thick atmosphere is made up mainly of hydrogen and helium. Ask: **Why doesn't the gas on a gas giant, such as Jupiter, escape into space, as it has from Mercury?** *(Most of the gas can't escape because the planet's gravity is so great.)* **What other object in the solar system has a composition similar to that of Jupiter and the other gas giants?** *(The sun)*

Differentiated Instruction

L3 **Photo Research** Have students find images that show Jupiter's moons, their relative sizes, and at least one distinguishing characteristic of each. If resources allow, encourage students to scan and print one of their images to share with the class.

L1 **Oral Presentation** Have students describe what they would see if they stood on the surfaces of Jupiter's four largest moons.

Explain

Teach Key Concepts 🔑

Explain to students that Saturn is distinguished by its rings. Ask: **What are Saturn's rings made of?** *(Chunks of rock and ice)* **What are Saturn's rings like?** *(There are many broad, thin rings.)* **What keeps some of Saturn's rings in place?** *(Gravity from tiny moons that orbit on either side of the rings.)*

Lead a Discussion

SATURN AND JUPITER Remind that is the only planet whose size comes close to that of Jupiter. Ask: **How are Saturn and Jupiter similar?** *(Both have atmospheres made up of hydrogen and helium. Both atmospheres have clouds and storms.)* **How are Saturn and Jupiter different?** *(In addition to being smaller than Jupiter, Saturn is also less dense.)* **How are Saturn's moons like those of Jupiter?** *(Both planets have many moons. The largest moon of each is bigger than the planet Mercury.)*

Teach With Visuals

Tell students to look at **Figure 4.** Ask: **Why would it be hard to see Saturn's rings when their edges are facing Earth?** *(The rings are so thin that when their edges face Earth they are nearly invisible.)*

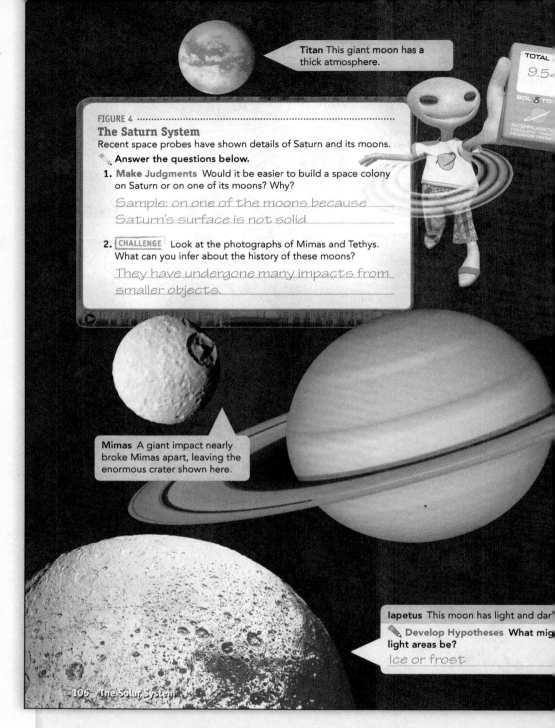

Titan This giant moon has a thick atmosphere.

FIGURE 4

The Saturn System

Recent space probes have shown details of Saturn and its moons.

✏️ **Answer the questions below.**

1. **Make Judgments** Would it be easier to build a space colony on Saturn or on one of its moons? Why?

   Sample: on one of the moons because Saturn's surface is not solid

2. **CHALLENGE** Look at the photographs of Mimas and Tethys. What can you infer about the history of these moons?

   They have undergone many impacts from smaller objects.

Mimas A giant impact nearly broke Mimas apart, leaving the enormous crater shown here.

Iapetus This moon has light and dar"

✏️ **Develop Hypotheses** What mig light areas be?

Ice or frost

106 The Solar System

106 The Solar System

Saturn The second-largest planet in the solar system is Saturn. Saturn, like Jupiter, has a thick atmosphere made up mainly of hydrogen and helium. Saturn's atmosphere also contains clouds and storms, but they are less dramatic than those on Jupiter. The *Cassini* space probe found unusual six-sided cloud patterns around Saturn's north pole. Scientists aren't sure what causes these patterns.

Saturn's Rings **Saturn has the most spectacular rings of any planet.** These rings are made of chunks of ice and rock, each traveling in its own orbit around Saturn. From Earth, it looks as though Saturn has only a few rings and that they are divided from each other by narrow, dark regions. Space probes have shown that each of these obvious rings is divided into many thinner rings. Saturn's rings are broad and thin, like a compact disc. Some rings are kept in place by gravity from tiny moons that orbit on either side of the ring.

Saturn's Moons Saturn's largest moon, Titan, is larger than the planet Mercury. It is also the only moon in the solar system that has a thick atmosphere. The atmosphere is composed mostly of nitrogen and methane. Some of these gases break down high in the atmosphere, forming a haze that is somewhat like smog on Earth. In 2005, the *Huygens* probe landed on Titan's surface. Photos from *Huygens* show features that may have been formed by flowing liquid. A few scientists think that Titan might support life.

Scientists have learned a great deal about Saturn's moons from the *Cassini* space probe. Giant craters and trenches cut cross Mimas (MY mus) and Tethys (TEE this). Ice and water erupt in geysers from the surface of Enceladus (en SEL uh dus), which was found in 2015 to have a warm ocean. In 2009, scientists discovered a ring of material that may come from the outermost moon, Phoebe (FEE bee). **Figure 4** shows some of the members of the Saturn system.

Size of Saturn compared to Earth

did you know?

Saturn has the lowest density of any planet. If you could build a bathtub big enough, Saturn would float!

Tethys In this photo, you can just see a group of canyons that circle this moon.

Enceladus This photo shows faint bluish plumes erupting from the surface of Enceladus.

✎ Make Generalizations Eruptions from Enceladus form one of Saturn's rings. What is that ring most likely made of?

Water ice

107

LESSON 3.5

Elaborate

21st Century Learning

CRITICAL THINKING Direct students' attention to the image of Mimas. Ask: **What is the huge circle visible on the surface of Mimas?** *(A crater)* Scientists do not know what hit Mimas, but the large cracks on the opposite side of the moon indicate that the impact was almost strong enough to break the moon apart. Ask: **What other effect might have resulted from such an impact?** *(Students may hypothesize that the impact might have caused changes in this moon's orbit.)*

Teacher Demo 🔬 Lab zone

L2 COMPARE AND CONTRAST PLANETS

Materials none

Time 15 minutes

Ask students to note similarities and differences between Saturn and Jupiter as they read about Saturn. After they finish reading, have students make a table comparing and contrasting Saturn and Jupiter. The table should include size, density, appearance, and composition.

Ask: **What is the biggest difference that you noticed?** *(Sample: The planets' unique features, Jupiter's Great Red Spot and Saturn's rings.)* **What are some similarities?** *(Sample: Both planets have a thick atmosphere made up mainly of hydrogen and helium; also, the atmospheres of both planets contain clouds and storms.)*

Differentiated Instruction

L3 Create Fact Sheets Have students create two fact sheets about Saturn and its moons. The first should include facts known about the planet and its moons before the *Huygens* and *Cassini* probes. The second should include facts learned since those missions. Encourage students to use the information in the text as a departure point for additional research.

L1 Make a Diagram Display an image of Saturn and its moons. Have students use the image and the information in this section to draw a diagram of Saturn and its moons. Tell students that their diagrams should show at least two distinguishing characteristics.

Explain

Teach Key Concepts 🔑

Explain to students that Uranus has a distinctive axis of rotation. Ask: **How is Uranus's rotation different from that of the other planets?** *(Uranus rotates from top to bottom instead of from side to side.)* **What do astronomers think caused Uranus's unusual rotation?** *(Astronomers think that Uranus was probably hit by a large object that knocked it on its side.)*

21st Century Learning

L3 **CRITICAL THINKING** Remind students that Uranus's axis of rotation is tilted at an angle of about 90 degrees from the vertical. Ask: **How must Uranus's seasons be unusual?** *(During spring and fall, all parts of the planet experience equal hours of sunlight and darkness. During winter and summer, one hemisphere is always in darkness while the other is always in sunlight.)* If students have difficulty visualizing the seasons on Uranus, use a ball or an orange on which you have placed stickers marked N and S for the North and South poles. Turn the ball to show vertical rotation. Keeping the N always to your left, move the ball in a circle around an object that represents the sun. Point out the times when the equator faces the sun and when the poles face the sun.

Size of Uranus
compared to Earth

Uranus Although the gas giant Uranus (YOOR uh nus) is about four times the diameter of Earth, it is still much smaller than Jupiter and Saturn. Uranus is twice as far from the sun as Saturn, so it is much colder. Uranus looks blue-green because of traces of methane in its atmosphere. Like the other gas giants, Uranus is surrounded by a group of thin, flat rings, although they are much darker than Saturn's rings.

Uranus's Moons Photographs from *Voyager 2* show that Uranus's five largest moons have icy, cratered surfaces. The craters show that rocks from space have hit the moons. Uranus's moons also have lava flows on their surfaces, suggesting that material has erupted from inside each moon. *Voyager 2* images revealed 10 moons that had never been seen before. Recently, astronomers discovered several more moons, for a total of at least 27.

A Tilted Planet 🔑 **Uranus's axis of rotation is tilted at an angle of about 90 degrees from the vertical.** Viewed from Earth, Uranus rotates from top to bottom instead of from side to side, as other planets do. You can see the tilt in **Figure 5**. Uranus's rings and moons rotate around this tilted axis. Astronomers think that billions of years ago, an object hit Uranus and knocked it on its side. Images from the *Voyager 2* space probe allowed scientists to determine that Uranus rotates in about 17 hours.

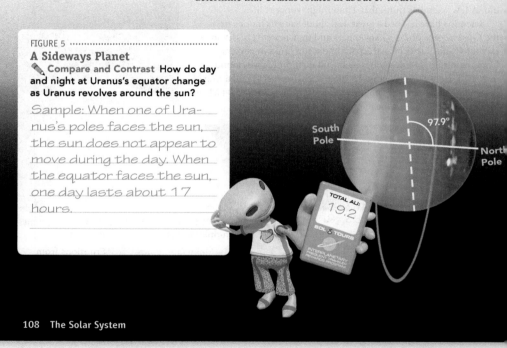

FIGURE 5 ·······················
A Sideways Planet
✏️ **Compare and Contrast** How do day and night at Uranus's equator change as Uranus revolves around the sun?

Sample: When one of Uranus's poles faces the sun, the sun does not appear to move during the day. When the equator faces the sun, one day lasts about 17 hours.

South Pole

97.9°

North Pole

TOTAL AU:
19.2

108 The Solar System

Digital Lesson: Assign the *Apply It* activity online and have students submit their work to you.

my science online · **The Outer Planets**

Neptune Neptune is similar in size and color to Uranus. **Neptune is a cold, blue planet. Its atmosphere contains visible clouds.** The color comes from methane in the atmosphere. Neptune's interior is hot due to energy left over from its formation. As this energy rises, it produces clouds and storms in the atmosphere.

Neptune's Atmosphere In 1989, *Voyager 2* flew by Neptune and photographed a Great Dark Spot about the size of Earth. Like the Great Red Spot on Jupiter, the Great Dark Spot was probably a giant storm. But it didn't last long. Images taken five years later showed that the spot was gone.

Neptune's Moons Astronomers have discovered at least 13 moons orbiting Neptune. The largest moon is Triton, which has a thin atmosphere. *Voyager 2* images show that the area of Triton's south pole is covered by nitrogen ice.

Size of Neptune compared to Earth

FIGURE 6 ....
Changing Neptune
The photograph above was taken in 1989. The photograph below was taken in 2002.

✎ **Interpret Photos** How did Neptune change?

Sample: The Great Dark spot disappeared and other storms developed.

apply it!

Congratulations! You've earned enough AU in your travels to qualify for a free mission to one planet or moon of your choice!

❶ **Make Judgments** Which planet or moon do you choose? List three reasons for your choice.

Students should justify their answers.

❷ ✎ **Pose Questions** What is one question you would want your mission to answer?

Sample: What is the planet made of?

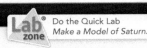

Lab zone Do the Quick Lab *Make a Model of Saturn.*

Assess Your Understanding

1. **Describe** Describe one feature of each outer planet that distinguishes it from the others.

Sample: Jupiter is the largest planet. Saturn has the most extensive rings. Uranus is tilted. Neptune is cold and blue.

got it?

○ I get it! Now I know that the outer planets differ in size, ring structure, and number of moons.

○ I need extra help with See TE note.

Go to **my science COACH** online for help with this subject.

109

Teach Key Concepts

Explain to students that Neptune is cold and blue, with visible clouds. Ask: **How many moons does Neptune have?** *(At least 13)* **What is the name of Neptune's largest moon?** *(Triton)* **What is unusual about a region near Triton's south pole?** *(It is covered by nitrogen ice.)*

Elaborate ——————
Apply It!

L1 Before beginning the activity, have students scan this and the previous lesson to review the planets and their moons.

⚠ **Pose Questions** Remind students that a scientific question is a question that can be answered by gathering evidence.

Lab Resource: Quick Lab **Lab** zone

L1 MAKE A MODEL OF SATURN Students will make a three-dimensional model of Saturn and use it to demonstrate why Saturn's rings are occasionally invisible from Earth.

Evaluate ——————
Assess Your Understanding

After students answer the questions, have them evaluate their understanding by completing the appropriate sentence.

RTI Response to Intervention

1. If students need help describing one distinctive feature of each outer planet, **then** have them review the Key Concept statements in this lesson.

my science COACH Have students go online for help in understanding the outer planets.

Differentiated Instruction

L3 Research Planet Names The ancient Romans named the planets they knew after the gods they worshipped. Mercury was the fast, winged messenger of the gods. Venus was the goddesses of beauty, and Mars was the god of war. Many of the planets, dwarf planets, and moons discovered in the last 200 years have also been named after ancient gods. Have students research the origin of the name of Jupiter, Saturn, Uranus, or Neptune. Students can give brief oral presentations on what they learned, while researching a planet's name, about Greek or Roman religion and/or make posters describing the character of the god. *(Jupiter was the king of the Roman gods, Saturn was the god of agriculture. Uranus, a Greek god, was the husband of Gaea (Earth), and Neptune was the Roman god of the sea.)*

The Outer Planets

Inquiry Warm-Up, *How Big Are the Planets?*

In the Inquiry Warm-Up, you investigated the relative sizes of the outer planets. Using what you learned from that activity, answer the questions below.

1. **EXPLAIN** Explain how in Step 2 you calculated the relative diameter of Jupiter in millimeters.

   _____

   _____

   _____

2. **CALCULATE** About how many Neptunes would you have to place side by side in order to equal the diameter of Jupiter?

   _____

   _____

3. **INFER** Based on their relative sizes, would you expect Saturn or Neptune to have the lesser mass? Explain.

   _____

   _____

   _____

4. **ANALYZE SOURCES OF ERROR** Explain whether a diagram, a data table, or a pie chart is better to use to precisely compare the sizes of the outer planets.

   _____

   _____

   _____

Assess Your Understanding

The Outer Planets

What Do the Outer Planets Have in Common?

got it? ....

○ **I get it!** Now I know that the gas giants all _____

_____

_____

○ **I need extra help with** _____

_____

What Are the Characteristics of Each Outer Planet?

1. **DESCRIBE** Describe one feature of each outer planet that distinguishes it from the others.

_____

_____

_____

_____

got it? ....

○ **I get it!** Now I know that the outer planets differ in _____

_____

_____

○ **I need extra help with** _____

_____

Key Concept Summaries

The Outer Planets

What Do the Outer Planets Have in Common?

The four outer planets are much larger and more massive than Earth, and they do not have solid surfaces. Because these four planets are so large, they are often called **gas giants.** The gas giants all contain hydrogen and helium. In addition, all have many moons and are surrounded by a set of rings. A **ring** is a thin disk of small particles of ice and rock. They do not have solid surfaces. If you could visit them, you wouldn't have a solid place to stand.

What Are the Characteristics of Each Outer Planet?

Jupiter is the largest and most massive planet. Its mass is about $2\frac{1}{2}$ times that of all the other planets combined. One notable feature of Jupiter's atmosphere is its Great Red Spot, a storm that is larger than Earth.

Saturn has the most spectacular rings of any planet. The rings are made of chunks of ice and rock, each traveling in its own orbit around Saturn. Saturn's largest moon, Titan, is larger than the planet Mercury, and has features that look as if they were formed by flowing liquid. A few scientists think that Titan might support life.

Uranus is twice as far from the sun as Saturn, so it is much colder. It looks blue-green because of methane traces in its atmosphere. Its five largest moons have icy, cratered surfaces. **Uranus's axis of rotation is tilted at an angle of about 90 degrees from the vertical.** Viewed from Earth, Uranus rotates from top to bottom—not side to side.

Neptune is a cold, blue planet. Its atmosphere contains visible clouds. Neptune's blue color comes from methane in the atmosphere. Its interior is hot from energy left from its formation. As the energy rises, it produces clouds and storms in the atmosphere.

On a separate sheet of paper, explain how the four outer planets are alike and tell one distinctive thing about each.

Name _____ Date _____ Class _____

The Outer Planets

Understanding Main Ideas
Answer the following questions in the spaces provided.

1. What are the outer planets?

_____

2. Which planets are the gas giants?

_____

3. Which planet is by far the most massive of all the planets that revolve around the sun?

_____

4. What are Saturn's rings made of?

_____

5. Describe the tilt of Uranus's axis, and explain how the tilt affects Uranus's rotation as viewed from Earth.

_____

_____

_____

_____

6. Name one feature of Neptune's atmosphere.

_____

_____

Building Vocabulary
Answer the following questions on a separate sheet of paper.

7. Define *gas giant*.
8. What is a *ring*?

The Outer Planets

> The diagram below shows the orbits of Neptune and Pluto. Read the passage and study the diagram. Then answer the questions that follow on a separate sheet of paper.

The Orbits of Neptune and Pluto

Pluto is a celestial body known as a dwarf planet. It orbits the sun and has a roundish shape, but has not cleared other objects out of the path of its orbit, a qualification for full planet status. Pluto was once thought of as a planet, but scientists downgraded it to a dwarf planet in 2006.

The orbit of Neptune is very close to circular. Pluto's orbit is more elliptical. The arrows on the diagram show Pluto's position at different times. The unit of distance used in the diagram is the *astronomical unit,* or a.u. An a.u. is the average distance from Earth to the sun, about 150 million kilometers. Neptune's distance from the sun is about 30 astronomical units, or 4,495 million kilometers.

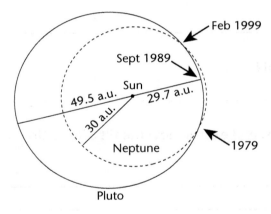

1. In September of 1989, Pluto was as close to the sun as it ever gets. How close was it?

2. What was Neptune's distance from the sun in September of 1989?

3. Pluto takes 248 years to complete one revolution around the sun. When will Pluto and Neptune next be an equal distance from the sun?

4. When will Pluto next be as far from the sun as it ever gets?

5. Which body is farther from the sun now, Neptune or Pluto?

Name _____ Date _____ Class _____

The Outer Planets

Fill in the blank to complete each statement.

1. All the outer planets have many _____, which range in number from 13 to greater than 60.

2. A(n) _____ is a thin disk of small particles of ice and rock.

3. Because the four outer planets are so large, they are often called _____ _____.

4. A few scientists believe that Saturn's largest moon, _____, may support life.

5. Uranus's axis is tilted at an angle of about _____ degrees from the vertical.

If the statement is true, write _true_. If the statement is false, change the underlined word or words to make the statement true.

6. _____ Temperatures <u>decrease</u> tremendously from the outer to inner layers of the gas giants.

7. _____ All the gas giants' atmospheres are made up primarily of helium and <u>oxygen</u>.

8. _____ Space <u>telescopes</u> such as _Cassini_ have revealed many details of the outer planets.

9. _____ Uranus is <u>three times</u> as far from the sun as Saturn, so it is much colder.

10. _____ Neptune's blue color comes from <u>methane</u> in its atmosphere.

The Outer Planets

Answer Key

After the Inquiry Warm-Up

1. I found the diameter of the quarter and then multiplied by 11.2.

2. about four

3. Ignoring all other factors, the smallest planet should have the least mass. Neptune should have less mass than Saturn.

4. A data table would provide more accurate data to use in precisely comparing the sizes of the outer planets.

Key Concept Summaries

Sample: The four outer planets, known as the "gas giants," all contain hydrogen and helium. They all have many moons and are surrounded by a set of rings. Jupiter has an enormous storm, larger than Earth, called the Great Red Spot. Saturn has the most spectacular rings. Viewed from Earth, Uranus rotates from top to bottom, because its axis of rotation is tilted at about 90 degrees from the vertical. Neptune's atmosphere has visible clouds.

Review and Reinforce

1. Jupiter, Saturn, Uranus, and Neptune

2. Jupiter, Saturn, Uranus, and Neptune

3. Jupiter

4. chunks of ice and rock

5. Uranus's axis is tilted at 90 degrees from the vertical. Viewed from Earth, Uranus rotates from top to bottom instead of from side to side.

6. Sample: Visible clouds

7. Sample: A planet that is very large and does not have a solid surface

8. a thin disk of small particles of ice and rock

Enrich

1. 29 a.u.

2. 30 a.u.

3. In 2227 (1979 + 248)

4. In 2113 (1989 + 124)

5. Pluto (after February 1999)

Lesson Quiz

1. moons
2. ring
3. gas giants
4. Titan
5. 90
6. increase
7. hydrogen
8. probes
9. twice
10. true

Place the outside corner, the corner away from the dotted line, in the corner of your copy machine to copy onto letter-size paper.

Small Solar System Objects

Lesson Pacing: 2–3 periods or 1–1$\frac{1}{2}$ blocks

🕐 **SHORT ON TIME?** To do this lesson in approximately half the time, do the Activate Prior Knowledge activity on page 110. A discussion of the Key Concept on page 111 will familiarize students with the lesson content. Have students do the Quick Lab. The rest of the lesson can be completed by students independently.

Preference Navigator, in the online Planning tools, allows you to customize *Interactive Science* to your own teaching style. You can also edit lesson plans by selecting the Lesson Planner option.

Digital Teacher's Edition allows you to access your Teacher's Edition and Resource materials online.

Lesson Vocabulary

- asteroid belt
- Kuiper belt
- Oort cloud
- comet
- coma
- nucleus
- asteroid
- meteoroid
- meteor
- meteorite

Content Refresher
Professional Development Note

Ceres Ceres has been reclassified twice since its discovery. Moreover, Ceres was discovered twice. Giuseppe Piazzi made the first sighting on January 1, 1801, in Palermo, Sicily. Piazzi named the object *Ceres* after the Roman goddess of grain and the patron saint of Sicily. Piazzi observed Ceres for roughly one month before it moved into the daytime sky. The German astronomer Franz von Zach rediscovered Ceres exactly one year later.

Ceres was originally classified as a planet. Then, because it resembles objects in the asteroid belt, Ceres was reclassified as an asteroid, a classification that it retained for 150 years. In 2006, Ceres was again reclassified as a dwarf planet.

Ceres has never been formally explored by NASA, but it will be probed in 2015 when the *Dawn* spacecraft orbits the dwarf planet and collects information from an altitude as close as 700 km. It is believed that Ceres has a rocky core, an ice mantle, and potentially a large body of liquid water under its surface. This characteristic has lead some scientists to think that extraterrestrial life could exist on Ceres.

LESSON OBJECTIVE

🔖 Explain how scientists classify small bodies in the solar system.

Blended Path
Active learning using Student Edition, Inquiry Path, and Digital Path

ENGAGE AND EXPLORE

Teach this lesson using a variety of resources. Begin by reading **My Planet Diary** as a class. Have students share ideas about what a shooting star is. Then have students do the **Inquiry Warm-Up activity.** Students will collect micrometeorites. Discuss why micrometeorites are round. The **After the Inquiry Warm-Up worksheet** sets up a discussion about how micrometeorites are affected by the atmosphere. Have volunteers share their diagrams of micrometeorites for question 4.

EXPLAIN AND ELABORATE

Teach Key Concepts by explaining the major categories of small objects in the solar system and how they are classified. Use **Figure 1** to illustrate the relative positions of the asteroid belt, the Kuiper belt, and the Oort cloud in the solar system. Use the **Support the Big Q** to illustrate the characteristics used to define dwarf planets. **Lead a Discussion** about where four of the five identified dwarf planets are located. Have students identify the parts of a comet by using **Figure 3. Lead a Discussion** about the shape of the orbit of a comet. **Lead a Discussion** identifying the small, irregular, rocky objects orbiting the sun as asteroids. Then have students practice the inquiry skill in the **Apply It activity.** Finally, **Lead a Discussion** about the differences between meteors, meteorites, and meteoroids. Hand out the **Key Concept Summaries** as a review of each part of the lesson. Students can also use the online **Vocab Flash Cards** to review key terms.

EVALUATE

Have students take the **Lesson Quiz.** For an alternate assessment, see the **EXAM**VIEW® Assessment Suite, Progress Monitoring Assessments, or SuccessTracker™.

ⓔⓛⓛ Support

1 Content and Language
The Greek suffix *-oid* meaning "similar to" is found in the words *asteroid* and *meteoroid*. Help students determine what *asteroids* and *meteoroids* are similar to. (*Stars and meteors*)

DIFFERENTIATED INSTRUCTION KEY
L1 Struggling Students or Special Needs
L2 On-Level Students **L3** Advanced Students

LESSON PLANNER 3.6

Lab Inquiry Path
Hands-on learning in the Lab zone

ENGAGE AND EXPLORE

To teach this lesson with an emphasis on inquiry, begin with the **Inquiry Warm-Up activity.** Students will collect micrometeorites. Discuss the shape of micrometeorites. Have students do the **After the Inquiry Warm-Up worksheet.** Talk about how micrometeorites are affected by the atmosphere. Have volunteers share the diagrams they drew for question 4.

EXPLAIN AND ELABORATE

Focus on the **Inquiry Skill** for the lesson. Point out that when you classify, you group objects with similar characteristics. How could the objects collected in the **Inquiry Warm-Up activity** be classified? *(As micrometeorites.)* To **Support the Big Q,** discuss the characteristics of dwarf planets. Review the names and definitions of the small objects in the solar system before beginning the **Apply It activity.** Ask volunteers how they classified the objects. Do the **Quick Lab** to explore the orbits of small solar system objects. Students can use the online **Vocab Flash Cards** to review key terms.

EVALUATE

Have students take the **Lesson Quiz.** For an alternate assessment, see the **EXAM**VIEW® Assessment Suite, Progress Monitoring Assessments, or SuccessTracker™.

Digital Path
Online learning at my science online.com

ENGAGE AND EXPLORE

Teach this lesson using digital resources. Begin by having students explore real-world connections to the small objects in the solar system at **My Planet Diary** online. Have them access the Chapter Resources to find the **Unlock the Big Question activity.** There they can answer the questions and refine their responses as they continue through the lesson. You can re-assign the activity and have students submit their work so you can track their progress.

EXPLAIN AND ELABORATE

Students reading above, at, or below the lexile measure of this lesson can access basic content readings at their level at **My Reading Web.** Have students use the online **Vocab Flash Cards** to preview key terms. Use the **Support the Big Q** to illustrate how dwarf planets are defined by their characteristics. Have students do the online **Virtual Lab** to explore Pluto's new status as a dwarf planet. Review the names and definitions of the small objects in the solar system before assigning the online **Apply It activity.** Ask volunteers to share how they classified the objects. Have students submit their work to you. Do the **Quick Lab** to explore the orbits of small solar system objects and then ask students to share their results. The **Key Concept Summaries** online allow students to read a summary and see an image associated with each part of the lesson. Online remediation is available at **My Science Coach.**

EVALUATE

Have students take the **Lesson Quiz.** For an alternate assessment, see the **EXAM**VIEW® Assessment Suite, Progress Monitoring Assessments, or SuccessTracker™.

2 Frontload the Lesson
Preview the lesson visuals, labels, and captions. Ask students what they know about the terms *meteor, meteorite,* and *meteoroid.* Explain the specific meanings these words have in science.

3 Comprehensible Input
Have students study the visuals and their captions on pages 111, 113, and 115 to support the Key Concepts of the lesson.

4 Language Production
Pair or group students with varied language abilities to complete labs collaboratively for language practice. Have each student copy the completed written lab for personal reference.

5 Assess Understanding
Make true or false statements using lesson content and have students indicate if they agree or disagree with a thumbs up or thumbs down gesture to check whole-class comprehension.

Small Solar System Objects

Establish Learning Objective

After this lesson, students will be able to:

🗝 Explain how scientists classify small bodies in the solar system.

Engage

Activate Prior Knowledge

MY PLANET DIARY Read *Haley's Blog* with the class. Invite students to describe times that they have seen shooting stars or a meteor storm in the night sky. Have students tell where they were. Ask: **Where is Haley blogging from?** *(Constantia, New York)* **Does it surprise you that she saw shooting stars in New York?** *(Sample: No, because Constantia is in the Finger Lakes Region—far away from city lights, which are bright enough to block the light from many of the stars in the night sky.)*

BIG IDEAS OF SCIENCE REFERENCE LIBRARY 📖 Have students look up the following topics: Asteroids, Comets, Meteorites, Pluto.

Explore

Lab Resource: Inquiry Warm-Up

L2 **COLLECTING MICROMETEORITES** Students will use two techniques to gather magnetic and nonmagnetic micrometeorites.

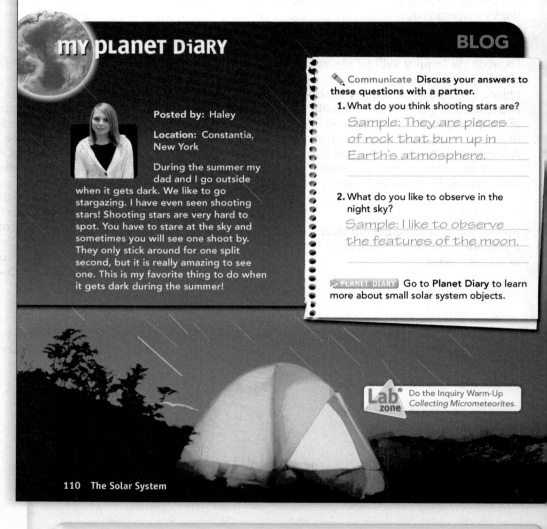

Small Solar System Objects

🗝 **How Do Scientists Classify Small Objects in the Solar System?**

my pLANeT DiaRY — BLOG

Posted by: Haley

Location: Constantia, New York

During the summer my dad and I go outside when it gets dark. We like to go stargazing. I have even seen shooting stars! Shooting stars are very hard to spot. You have to stare at the sky and sometimes you will see one shoot by. They only stick around for one split second, but it is really amazing to see one. This is my favorite thing to do when it gets dark during the summer!

✎ **Communicate** Discuss your answers to these questions with a partner.

1. What do you think shooting stars are?
   Sample: They are pieces of rock that burn up in Earth's atmosphere.

2. What do you like to observe in the night sky?
   Sample: I like to observe the features of the moon.

▶ **PLANET DIARY** Go to **Planet Diary** to learn more about small solar system objects.

Lab zone Do the Inquiry Warm-Up *Collecting Micrometeorites.*

110 The Solar System

SUPPORT ALL READERS

Lexile Measure = 880L   Lexile Word Count = 1252

Prior Exposure to Content: May be the first time students have encountered this topic

Academic Vocabulary: *classify, summarize, predict, compare, contrast*

Science Vocabulary: *comet, asteroid, meteoroid, meteor, meteorite*

Concept Level: May be difficult for students who struggle with abstract ideas

Preteach With: My Planet Diary "Haley's Blog" and Figure 1 activity

Go to **My Reading Web** to access leveled readings that provide a foundation for the content.

my science online .com

Vocabulary

- asteroid belt • Kuiper belt • Oort cloud
- comet • coma • nucleus • asteroid
- meteoroid • meteor • meteorite

Skills

- Reading: Summarize
- Inquiry: Classify

How Do Scientists Classify Small Objects in the Solar System?

The solar system contains many small objects that, like the planets, orbit the sun. **Scientists classify these objects based on their sizes, shapes, compositions, and orbits. The major categories include dwarf planets, comets, asteroids, and meteoroids.**

Areas of the Solar System Most of the small objects in the solar system are found in three areas: the asteroid belt, the Kuiper belt, and the Oort cloud. The **asteroid belt** is a region of the solar system between Mars and Jupiter. Beyond Neptune's orbit is a region called the **Kuiper belt** (KY per) which extends to about 100 times Earth's distance from the sun. Beyond the Kuiper belt, the **Oort cloud** (ort) stretches out more than 1,000 times the distance between the sun and Neptune. **Figure 1** shows these areas.

FIGURE 1 ·······

Areas of the Solar System

The diagram below shows the relative positions of the asteroid belt, the Kuiper belt, and the Oort cloud.

✎ **Relate Text and Visuals** As you read this lesson, write a C to show where a comet would most likely come from. Write a P to show where you would expect to find a plutoid. Write an A to show where you would expect to find an asteroid.

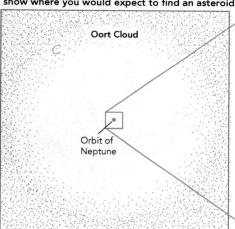

Oort Cloud

C

Orbit of Neptune

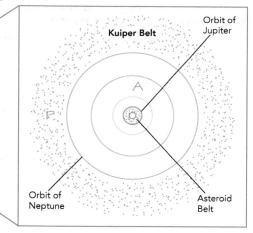

Kuiper Belt

Orbit of Jupiter

A

P

Orbit of Neptune

Asteroid Belt

111

ELL Support

1 Content and Language

Write *meteor*, *meteoroid*, and *meteorite* on the board. Review the meanings of *meteoroid* (a small chunk of rock or dust in the solar system) and *meteor* (a meteoroid that enters Earth's atmsphere). If a meteoroid lands on Earth's surface, it is a *meteorite*.

2 Frontload the Lesson

Invite volunteers to share experiences of seeing a meteor or a comet in a darkened sky. Tell students they will learn more about small objects in the solar system.

3 Comprehensible Input

Have students draw a compare/contrast table with column heads labeled: *dwarf planet*, *asteroid*, *comet*, and *meteoroid* and rows labeled *size*, *shape*, *composition*, *orbit*, and *other characteristics*. Students should complete the chart with facts and details.

Explain

Introduce Vocabulary

Tell students that the terms *meteor, meteorite,* and *meteoroid* come from the Greek root *meteōros,* which means "high in the air."

Teach Key Concepts

Explain to students that scientists use size, shape, composition, and orbit to classify small objects in the solar system. Ask: **What are the major categories of small objects in the solar system?** *(Dwarf planets, asteroids, comets, and meteoroids)* **What do all the objects in those four categories have in common?** *(They all orbit the sun.)* **In what areas are they found?** *(Asteroid belt, Kuiper belt, and Oort cloud)*

Teach With Visuals

L1 Tell students to look at **Figure 1.** Make sure that they understand the relationship between the two parts of the figure—the diagram on the right is "pulled out" from the diagram on the left. Ask: **What is the dot in the center of the diagram at the left?** *(Neptune's orbit)* **Where else is Neptune's orbit shown?** *(As a circle in the diagram at the right)* **What is between the asteroid belt and the Kuiper belt?** *(The orbits of Jupiter, Saturn, Uranus, and Neptune)* If students have trouble recognizing all four orbits, point out that the orbits of Saturn and Uranus are shown as unlabeled circles. Ask: **Where is the Oort cloud in relation to the things shown in the diagram at the right?** *(Very far away)* Point out that if the Oort cloud were shown to the scale of the diagram at the right, it would not be on the page!

21st Century Learning

CRITICAL THINKING Point out the three areas of the solar system that are highlighted vocabulary terms. Ask: **Who can order the Kuiper belt, the Oort cloud, and the asteroid belt in order from closest to farthest from the sun?** *(Asteroid belt, Kuiper belt, Oort cloud)* **Now order the three areas from closest to farthest from Neptune.** *(Kuiper belt, asteroid belt, Oort cloud)*

My Planet Diary provides an opportunity for students to explore real-world connections to small objects in the solar system.

my science online.com | Small Objects

Explain

Support the Big Q

DEFINE DWARF PLANETS Explain that dwarf planets are a relatively new category of objects in the solar system, having been developed in 2006. Ask: **Why would astronomers develop new categories?** *(Sample: As astronomers learn more about the solar system from space probes and other means of gathering data, the old categories no longer fit.)* **What solar system object prompted astronomers to define dwarf planets?** *(Pluto)* **How?** *(Sample: Scientists discovered other objects that were more like Pluto than like the other planets.)* **In what ways?** *(The other objects were at least Pluto's size and, while, like Pluto, they have enough gravity to pull themselves into spheres, they have other objects in the areas of their orbits. Unlike planets, Pluto and similar objects have not cleared those areas.)*

Lead a Discussion

LOCATE DWARF PLANETS Remind students to go back to **Figure 1** and complete the item for dwarf planets. Ask: **What are the five dwarf planets?** *(Pluto, Eris, Makemake, Haumea, and Ceres)* **Where are most dwarf planets located?** *(In the Kuiper belt)* **Which dwarf planet is not located in the Kuiper belt?** *(Ceres)*

Vocabulary Greek Word Origins The word *comet* comes from the Greek word *kometes*, meaning "long hair." Why do you think this word is used?

A comet's tail looks like long hair.

Dwarf Planets "What happened to Pluto?" You may have found yourself asking this question as you have learned about the solar system. For many years, Pluto was considered a planet. But then scientists discovered other objects that were at least Pluto's size. Some were even farther away than Pluto. Scientists began debating how to define a planet.

Defining Dwarf Planets In 2006, astronomers developed a new category of objects, called dwarf planets. These objects orbit the sun and have enough gravity to pull themselves into spheres, but they have other objects in the area of their orbits. As of 2009, scientists had identified five dwarf planets: Pluto, Eris, Makemake, Haumea, and Ceres. Eris is believed to be the largest dwarf planet so far. There are at least a dozen more objects that may turn out to be dwarf planets, once scientists are able to study them.

Like planets, dwarf planets can have moons. Pluto has three moons: Charon, Nix, and Hydra. Haumea has two and Eris has one.

Kuiper Belt Objects All the known dwarf planets except Ceres orbit beyond Neptune. (Ceres orbits in the asteroid belt.) A dwarf planet that orbits beyond Neptune is also called a plutoid. Most plutoids orbit the sun in the Kuiper belt, though Eris may be beyond it. The Kuiper belt also includes many other objects that are too small to be considered dwarf planets.

FIGURE 2 ·······

▷VIRTUAL LAB **Planet or Not?**
This figure shows one artist's idea of what the surface of Pluto looks like.

✎ **Make Judgments** Do you think Pluto should be considered a planet? Why or why not?

Sample: I think Pluto should be considered a planet, because it was discovered long ago and has been treated as a planet for many years.

112 The Solar System

Virtual Lab allows students to explore Pluto's new status as a dwarf planet.

my science online.com   Small Objects

Comets A comet is one of the most dramatic objects you can see in the night sky. On a dark night, you can see its fuzzy white head and long, streaming tails. **Comets** are loose collections of ice, dust, and small rocky particles whose orbits can be very long, narrow ellipses. Some comets have smaller orbits that bring them near Earth regularly. Most comets originate in the Oort cloud.

A Comet's Head When a comet gets close to the sun, the energy in sunlight turns the ice into gas, releasing gas and dust. Clouds of gas and dust form a fuzzy outer layer called a **coma**. **Figure 3** shows the coma and the **nucleus,** the solid inner core of a comet. The nucleus is usually only a few kilometers across.

A Comet's Tail As a comet approaches the sun, it heats up and starts to glow. Some of its gas and dust stream outward, forming a tail. Most comets have two tails—a gas tail and a dust tail. The gas tail points away from the sun and the dust tail points along the path the comet has taken. A comet's tail can be more than 100 million kilometers long and from Earth, appears to stretch across most of the sky. The material is stretched out very thinly, however.

✎ Summarize Write a few sentences to summarize the structure of a comet.

Sample: A comet has a head containing a solid nucleus and a coma made of gas and dust. It also has a gas tail and a dust tail as it approaches the sun.

FIGURE 3 ·············
A Comet's Orbit
Comets, as shown here, have long, narrow orbits. Their tails tend to grow longer as they approach the sun.
✎ **Apply Concepts Complete the diagram above by adding the comet's tails.**

Comet orbit

Sun

Gas tail

Dust tail

Nucleus

Coma

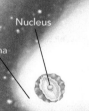

113

Explain

Lead a Discussion

ASTEROIDS Ask: **Where are most asteroids found in space?** *(In the asteroid belt, between the orbits of Mars and Jupiter)* **What are asteroids made of?** *(Rock)* **What is an asteroid's shape?** *(It varies. Asteroids are irregularly shaped.)* **What hypothesis suggests a reason for this shape?** *(They are leftover pieces of the early solar system that never came together to form a planet.)* **Why aren't asteroids classified as dwarf planets?** *(They are too small and too numerous at more than 100,000 and counting.)* Explain to students that scientists think that Jupiter's immense gravity prevented these asteroids from coalescing into another planet.

21st Century Learning

L3 **CRITICAL THINKING** Show the Yucatan Peninsula of Mexico on a world map. Explain to students that the asteroid strike described in their books happened there, about 65 million years ago. Ask: **What may have happened to the dust from the asteroid(s) that hit the Yucatan?** *(Sample: It fell into the ocean, settled on the ocean floor, was buried by layers of sediments, and eventually turned back into rock.)*

Apply It!

L1 Before beginning the activity, review the names and definitions of the small objects in the solar system.

▲ Classify Explain to students that when they classify, they group together objects that are alike in some way. They can classify items in many ways: by size, composition, or other important characteristics. Suggest that students use the highlighted vocabulary terms in this lesson to help them classify small solar system objects.

Asteroids Hundreds of small, irregular, rocky objects orbit the sun. These **asteroids** are rocky objects, most of which are too small and too numerous to be considered planets or dwarf planets. Astronomers have discovered more than 100,000 asteroids, and they are constantly finding more.

Small Bodies Most asteroids are small—less than a kilometer in diameter. Only Ceres, Pallas, Vesta, and Hygiea are more than 300 kilometers across. (Ceres is both a dwarf planet and the largest asteroid.) Most asteroids are not spherical. Scientists hypothesize that asteroids are leftover pieces of the early solar system that never came together to form a planet.

Asteroid Orbits Most asteroids orbit the sun in the asteroid belt. Some, however, have very elliptical orbits that bring them closer to the sun than Earth's orbit. Someday, an asteroid will hit Earth. One or more large asteroids did hit Earth about 65 million years ago, filling the atmosphere with dust and smoke and blocking out sunlight around the world. Scientists hypothesize that many species of organisms, including the dinosaurs, became extinct as a result.

apply it!

Classify For each description below, classify the object as a dwarf planet, comet, asteroid, or meteoroid.

1 This object is slightly smaller than Pluto. It orbits the sun beyond Neptune and is spherical. _Dwarf planet_

2 This object is irregularly shaped. It orbits the sun just outside the orbit of Mars. _Asteroid_

3 This object is a chunk of rock and metal. It was once part of another object that orbited the sun. _Meteoroid_

4 This object is composed of ice and rock. It orbits the sun in an elongated orbit, taking many years to complete one orbit.
Comet

5 **CHALLENGE** Which two types of objects are hardest to tell apart? Why? _Sample: asteroids and meteoroids, because they are made of similar materials_

Digital Lesson: Assign the *Apply It* activity online and have students submit their work to you.

MY SCIENCE online.com **Small Objects**

Meteoroids Chunks of rock or dust smaller than asteroids are called **meteoroids.** Meteoroids are generally less than 10 meters across. Some meteoroids form when asteroids collide. Others form when comets break up, creating dust clouds.

Meteors and Meteorites When a meteoroid enters Earth's atmosphere, friction with the air creates heat and produces a streak of light. This streak is a **meteor.** (People often call meteors shooting stars, but they are not stars.) Most meteors come from tiny bits of rock or dust that burn up completely. But some larger meteoroids do not burn up. Meteoroids that pass through the atmosphere and are found on Earth's surface are called **meteorites.** Meteorite impacts can leave craters, such as the one shown in **Figure 4.**

Meteor Showers Meteor showers occur when Earth passes through an area with many meteoroids. Some of these groups of meteoroids are bits of comets that broke up. These meteor showers occur every year as Earth passes through the same areas. Meteor showers are often named for the constellation from which they appear to come. The Perseids, Geminids, and Orionids are examples of meteor showers.

FIGURE 4 ....
Meteor Crater
Meteor Crater in Arizona formed about 50,000 years ago from the impact of a meteorite 50–100 meters wide. ✏ **Predict** How would a large meteorite impact affect Earth today?

<u>Sample: If it hit in a city, it could</u>
<u>kill many people.</u>

○ Approximate size of meteorite relative to crater

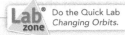 Do the Quick Lab *Changing Orbits.*

Assess Your Understanding

1a. Review (Comets/~~Asteroids~~) are rocky, while (~~comets~~/asteroids) are made of ice and dust.

b. Compare and Contrast What is the difference between a dwarf planet and an asteroid?

<u>Dwarf planets have enough</u>
<u>gravity to be spheres. Most</u>
<u>asteroids do not.</u>

c. Relate Cause and Effect How and why does a comet change as it approaches the sun?

<u>Energy from the sun causes</u>
<u>gas and dust to be released,</u>
<u>forming the coma and two</u>
<u>tails.</u>

got it? ....

○ I get it! Now I know that small solar system objects include <u>dwarf planets, comets,</u>
<u>asteroids, and meteoroids.</u>

○ I need extra help with <u>See TE note.</u>

Go to **my science COACH** online for help with this subject.

115

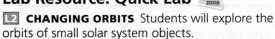

Explain

Lead a Discussion

METEORS Remind students of the difference between a meteoroid, a meteor, and a meteorite. Ask: **What do you see when a meteor burns up in Earth's atmosphere?** *(A bright streak of light)* **What causes the streak of light?** *(Friction with the air creates heat, and the air becomes white-hot.)*

Elaborate

Lab Resource: Quick Lab

L2 **CHANGING ORBITS** Students will explore the orbits of small solar system objects.

Evaluate

Assess Your Understanding

After students answer the questions, have them evaluate their understanding by completing the appropriate sentence.

RTI Response to Intervention

1a. If students have trouble differentiating comets and asteroids, **then** have them reread the sentences in which the highlighted vocabulary terms appear.

b. If students need help differentiating a dwarf planet and an asteroid, **then** have them review the subsection *Defining Dwarf Planets.*

c. If students need help explaining how and why a comet changes as it approaches the sun, **then** jog their memories by asking how the energy in sunlight affects the comet's ice.

my science COACH Have students go online for help in understanding small objects in the solar system.

Differentiated Instruction

L3 **Multimedia Presentation** Have interested students work in collaborative groups to make a multimedia presentation about small objects in the solar system. You might assign each group one object: dwarf planets, asteroids, comets, or meteoroids. If practicable, invite other science classes to the presentations.

L1 **Reinforce Content** Give students time to review **Figure 4** and the material on meteoroids. Then have students use the figure to review meteoroids, meteors, and meteorites in class discussion. Call on students at random to explain each term.

Name _____ Date _____ Class _____

Small Solar System Objects

> **Inquiry Warm-Up, *Collecting Micrometeorites***
> In the Inquiry Warm-Up, you investigated how to collect micrometeorites. Using what you learned from that activity, answer the questions below.

1. **USE PRIOR KNOWLEDGE** Why do you think the micrometeorites are round?

   _____

   _____

   _____

2. **INFER** How would a lack of an atmosphere affect the shape of the micrometeorites?

   _____

   _____

   _____

3. **DRAW CONCLUSIONS** Explain why micrometeorites don't usually produce craters in the ground.

   _____

   _____

4. **COMMUNICATE** Draw an illustration of the micrometeorite, and identify any distinguishing characteristics and features (such as color, shine, hardness, etc.) of the micrometeorite on your drawing.

Assess Your Understanding

Small Solar System Objects

How Do Scientists Classify Small Objects in the Solar System?

1a. **REVIEW** (Comets/asteroids) are rocky, while (comets/asteroids) are made of ice and dust.

b. **COMPARE AND CONTRAST** What is the difference between a dwarf planet and an asteroid?

_____

_____

_____

c. **RELATE CAUSE AND EFFECT** How and why does a comet change as it approaches the sun?

_____

_____

_____

gotit? ···

○ **I get it!** Now I know that small solar system objects include _____

_____

_____

○ **I need extra help with** _____

_____

Key Concept Summary

Small Solar System Objects

How Do Scientists Classify Small Objects in the Solar System?

The solar system contains many small objects that, like the planets, orbit the sun. **Scientists classify these objects based on their sizes, shapes, compositions, and orbits. The major categories include dwarf planets, comets, asteroids, and meteoroids.**

Most small solar system objects are found in three areas: the asteroid belt, the Kuiper belt, and the Oort cloud. The **asteroid belt** is a region between Mars and Jupiter. Beyond Neptune is a region called the **Kuiper belt,** which extends to about 100 a.u. Further out is the **Oort cloud,** extending more than 1,000 times the distance between the sun and Neptune.

Dwarf planets orbit the sun and have enough gravity to pull themselves into spheres, but they have other objects in the area of their orbits. There are five known dwarf planets, including Pluto. Like planets, dwarf planets can have moons. Except Cere, all dwarf planets orbit beyond Neptune.

Comets are loose collections of ice, dust, and small rocky particles whose orbits can be long, narrow ellipses. Most comets originate in the Oort cloud.

When a comet gets close to the sun, the ice melts, releasing gas and dust. Clouds of gas and dust form a comet's glowing, fuzzy outer layer, or **coma.** The **nucleus** is the solid inner core of a comet. Some of the gas and dust streams outward, forming two tails—a gas tail that points away from the sun, and a dust tail that points along the path the comet has taken.

Asteroids are rocky objects, most of which are too small and too numerous to be considered planets or dwarf planets. Asteroids are leftover pieces of the early solar system that never came together to form a planet.

Meteoroids are chunks of rock or dust smaller than asteroids. When a meteoroid enters Earth's atmosphere, friction with the air creates heat and produces a streak of light, called a **meteor.** Most meteoroids burn up completely. But those reaching the Earth's surface are known as **meteorites.** Meteorite impacts can leave craters. Meteor showers occur as Earth passes through areas with many meteoroids, and are often named for the constellations from where they appear to come.

On a separate sheet of paper, describe the orbits of dwarf planets, comets, and asteroids.

Name _____ Date _____ Class _____

Small Solar System Objects

Understanding Main Ideas

Answer the following questions in the spaces provided.

1. Describe dwarf planets and their orbits in the solar system.

_____

_____

_____

2. Describe asteroids and their orbits in the solar system.

_____

_____

_____

3. Describe comets and their orbits in the solar system.

_____

_____

_____

Building Vocabulary

Match each term with its definition by writing the letter of the correct definition in the right column on the line beside the term in the left column.

4. ___ meteoroid

5. ___ nucleus

6. ___ Kuiper belt

7. ___ coma

8. ___ Oort cloud

9. ___ meteorite

10. ___ asteroid belt

11. ___ meteor

a. region of the solar system between Mars and Jupiter

b. region where most comets originate

c. streak of light produced when a meteoroid enters Earth's atmosphere

d. region where most of the known dwarf planets orbit

e. solid inner core of a comet

f. meteoroid found on Earth's surface

g. fuzzy outer layer of a comet

h. chunk of rock or dust smaller than an asteroid

Enrich

Small Solar System Objects

> The graph below shows the amount of iridium present in rocks at a site in Italy. Read the passage and study the graph. Then use a separate sheet of paper to answer the questions that follow.

Evidence of a Large Meteorite

Meteorites frequently hit Earth. If Earth did not have an atmosphere, its surface would probably look like the moon. Earth's atmosphere not only prevents many meteoroids from hitting the surface, but also erases craters over time through the action of wind and rain. Scientists must look for other evidence that large meteorites have hit Earth. One place they look is in rocks.

When a large meteorite hits Earth, the result is similar to a huge bomb exploding. Some of the meteorite's material turns to dust and is blown high into the atmosphere, where winds carry it over the surface of Earth. Over millions of years, mud, sand, and dust (including the dust from meteors) can build up and eventually turn into layers of rock.

Iridium is an element that is very rare in rocks on Earth, except those rocks that are very deep below the surface. Iridium is much more common in rocks from space.

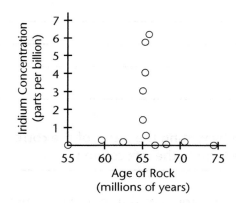

1. Why is evidence of meteorite impact rare on Earth, despite the fact that meteoroids often pass into Earth's atmosphere?
2. About what age are the rocks that show the highest level of iridium?
3. What are two possible sources for the high iridium level shown in the graph?
4. In several other parts of the world, rocks of the same age have similar levels of iridium. What can you infer from this information?

Lesson Quiz

Small Solar System Objects

Write the letter of the correct answer on the line at the left.

1. ___ Between Mars and Jupiter is a region of the solar system called the
   A asteroid belt
   B Milky Way
   C Kuiper belt
   D Oort cloud

2. ___ All the known dwarf planets except Ceres orbit in the
   A asteroid belt
   B Milky Way
   C Kuiper belt
   D Oort cloud

3. ___ Most comets originate in the
   A asteroid belt
   B Milky Way
   C Kuiper belt
   D Oort cloud

4. ___ Most asteroids orbit the sun in the
   A asteroid belt
   B Milky Way
   C Kuiper belt
   D Oort cloud

Fill in the blank to complete each statement.

5. When a meteoroid enters Earth's atmosphere, friction causes it to burn up and produce a streak of light called a(n) _____.

6. A chunk of ice and dust whose orbit is usually a long, narrow ellipse is a(n) _____.

7. If a meteoroid hits Earth's surface, it is called a(n) _____.

8. A chunk of rock or dust in space that usually comes from a comet or an asteroid is called a(n) _____.

9. Clouds of gas and dust on a comet form a fuzzy outer layer called a(n) _____.

10. Pluto was recently reclassified as a(n) _____

Small Solar System Objects

Answer Key

After the Inquiry Warm-Up

1. Answers will vary. Sample: Friction with the atmosphere heats, melts, and smoothes the outer layers of the meteoroid as it passes through Earth's atmosphere.

2. Without an atmosphere there would be little to no friction produced as the meteoroid passes through the atmosphere, producing little heat to melt and smooth the micrometeorite's outer layers.

3. Micrometeorites are too small to produce a crater.

4. Students should draw an illustration of their micrometeorite, identifying and labeling any characteristics or distinguishing features.

Key Concept Summary

Sample: All three types of objects orbit the sun. Most dwarf planets orbit the sun in the Kuiper Belt. Ceres is the only known exception. Comets have long narrow elliptical orbits. They usually originate in the Oort Cloud. Most asteroids orbit the sun in the asteroid belt between Mars and Jupiter.

Review and Reinforce

1. Dwarf planets have enough gravity to pull themselves into spheres, but they have other objects in the area of their orbit. All known dwarf planets but one (Ceres) orbit beyond Neptune, in the Kuiper belt.

2. Asteroids are rocky objects that are too small and numerous to be considered a planet or dwarf planet. Most orbit in the asteroid belt between the orbits of Mars and Jupiter.

3. Comets are loose collections of ice, dust, and small rocky particles that begins to glow and stream outward, forming a tail as they approach the sun. Most orbit the sun in a very long, narrow ellipse.

4. h
5. e
6. d
7. g
8. b
9. f
10. a
11. c

Enrich

1. Many meteoroids never hit Earth's surface because they burn up in Earth's atmosphere. When a meteoroid does hit the surface, wind and rain often erase the crater over time.

2. about 65 million years old

3. rocks from deep below Earth's surface, rocks from space

4. A large meteoroid might have hit Earth 65 million years ago, causing meteor dust to be spread around Earth. This is one possible explanation of the mass extinction of dinosaurs and other creatures at that time.

Lesson Quiz

1. A
2. C
3. D
4. A
5. meteor
6. comet
7. meteorite
8. meteoroid
9. coma
10. dwarf planet

Place the outside corner, the corner away from the dotted line, in the corner of your copy machine to copy onto letter-size paper.

Study Guide

Review the Big Q

Have students complete the statement at the top of the page. These Key Concepts support their understanding of the chapter's Big Question. Have students return to the chapter opener pages. What is different about how students view the image of Saturn's rings now that they have completed the chapter? Thinking about this will help them prepare for the *Apply the Big Q* activity in the Review and Assessment.

Partner Review

Have partners review definitions of vocabulary terms by using the Study Guide to quiz each other. Students could read the Key Concept statements and leave out words for their partner to fill in, or change a statement so that it is false and then ask their partner to correct it.

Class Activity: Solar System Trading Cards

Have students work in small groups to make "trading cards" of the sun and other objects in the solar system. Give each group at least six 4 x 6 index cards. Completed cards should indicate students' understanding of the details of individual objects and the chapter's big idea. Each card should have more than 5 facts about the object. Students can use the following questions to help them:
- What is the position of the sun in our solar system?
- What is the position of Earth in our solar system?
- What types of objects make up our solar system?
- Consider the solar system as a whole: how and when was it formed?

My Science Coach allows students to complete the *Practice Test* online.

The Big Question allows students to complete the *Apply the Big Q* activity about why objects in the solar system are different from each other.

Vocab Flash Cards offer a way to review the chapter vocabulary words.

 The Solar System

---

REVIEW THE BIG Q

Objects in the solar system are different because they formed <u>in different places and from different materials.</u>

LESSON 1 Models of the Solar System

🔑 In a geocentric model, Earth is at the center.

🔑 Copernicus worked out the arrangement of the known planets and how they orbit the sun.

🔑 Kepler found that planets' orbits are ellipses.

🔑 Evidence from Galileo Galilei convinced others that the heliocentric model was correct.

Vocabulary
- geocentric • heliocentric • ellipse

LESSON 2 Introducing the Solar System

🔑 Our solar system consists of the sun, the planets, their moons, and smaller objects.

🔑 The solar system formed about 4.6 billion years ago from a cloud of hydrogen, helium, rock, ice, and other materials pulled together by gravity.

Vocabulary
- solar system • astronomical unit • planet
- dwarf planet • planetesimal

LESSON 3 The Sun

🔑 The sun's interior consists of the core, the radiation zone, and the convection zone. The sun's atmosphere includes the photosphere, the chromosphere, and the corona.

🔑 Features on or just above the sun's surface include sunspots, prominences, and solar flares.

Vocabulary
- core • nuclear fusion • radiation zone
- convection zone • photosphere
- chromosphere • corona • solar wind
- sunspot • prominence • solar flare

LESSON 4 The Inner Planets

🔑 The inner planets are small and dense and have rocky surfaces.

🔑 Mercury is the smallest terrestrial planet and the planet closest to the sun. Venus has a thick atmosphere and the hottest surface of any planet. Earth has a suitable temperature range and atmosphere for living things to survive. Mars has ice and evidence of flowing liquid water.

Vocabulary
- terrestrial planet • greenhouse effect

LESSON 5 The Outer Planets

🔑 The outer planets are much larger than Earth and do not have solid surfaces.

🔑 Jupiter is the largest and most massive planet. Saturn has the most spectacular rings of any planet. Uranus's axis of rotation is tilted at an angle of about 90 degrees from the vertical. Neptune is a cold, blue planet with visible clouds.

Vocabulary
- gas giant • ring

LESSON 6 Small Solar System Objects

🔑 Scientists classify small objects based on their sizes, shapes, compositions, and orbits. The major categories include dwarf planets, comets, asteroids, and meteoroids.

Vocabulary
- asteroid belt • Kuiper belt • Oort cloud
- comet • coma • nucleus • asteroid
- meteoroid • meteor • meteorite

(E)(L)(L) Support

4 Language Production

Divide the students into teams of four. Each member is given numbers of 1, 2, 3, or 4. Ask questions based on the essential questions from the lessons in the chapter. Groups should work together to answer the question so that all can agree on the answer. Call out a number and the corresponding member in each group answers.

Beginning
LOW/HIGH Allow students to answer with single words or short phrases.

Intermediate
LOW/HIGH Have students work cooperatively to answer the question aloud.

Advanced
LOW/HIGH Have students assist by acting as a coach for each team.

Review and Assessment

LESSON 1   Models of the Solar System

1. What object is at the center of a geocentric system?

   (**a.**) Earth   **b.** the moon

   c. a star   **d.** the sun

2. Kepler discovered that planets move in
elliptical orbits.

3. Relate Cause and Effect How did Tycho Brahe's work contribute to the development of the heliocentric model?

His observations allowed Kepler to determine planets' orbits accurately.

4. **Write About It** Suppose you lived at the time of Copernicus. Write a letter to a scientific journal supporting the heliocentric model.

See TE rubric.

LESSON 2   Introducing the Solar System

5. Pluto is an example of a(n)

   (**a.**) dwarf planet.   **b.** inner planet.

   c. outer planet.   **d.** planetesimal.

6. An astronomical unit is equal to *the dis-tance from Earth to the sun.*

7. Compare and Contrast Compare the conditions that led to the formation of the inner planets with those that led to the formation of the outer planets.

The inner planets formed in a hot area, where ice could not form. The outer planets formed in an area where ice and light gases could accumulate.

LESSON 3   The Sun

8. In which part of the sun does nuclear fusion take place?

   a. chromosphere   **b.** convection layer

   (**c.**) core   **d.** corona

9. Relatively cool areas on the sun's surface are called *sunspots.*

10. Explain How can the solar wind affect life on Earth? *By causing auroras and magnetic storms on Earth*

11. math! The density of the sun's core is about 160 g/cm^3. The density of Earth's core is about 13.0 g/cm^3. About how many times denser is the sun's core than Earth's?

About 12.3 times

LESSON 4   The Inner Planets

12. What feature is shared by all the inner planets?

   a. thick atmosphere   (**b.**) rocky surface

   c. ring system   **d.** liquid water

13. The inner planets are also called *terres-trial planets.*

14. Apply Concepts Explain why Venus has the hottest surface of any planet.

Venus's thick atmosphere causes a strong greenhouse effect, trapping heat.

15. **Write About It** Choose one inner planet. Write a news article describing a visit to that planet's surface. Include descriptive details.

See TE rubric.

117

Review and Assessment

Assess Understanding

Have students complete the answers to the Review and Assessment questions. Have a class discussion about what students find confusing. Write Key Concepts on the board to reinforce knowledge.

R T I   Response to Intervention

3. If students have trouble identifying Tycho Brahe's contribution to the development of the heliocentric model, **then** remind them that Brahe's assistant, Johannes Kepler, made excellent use of Brahe's observations.

7. If students have trouble comparing conditions that led to the formation of the inner and outer planets, **then** have them recall the relative distances of the inner and outer planets from the sun.

10. If students have trouble describing the affects of solar wind, **then** have them review **Figure 4** in Lesson 3.

14. If students cannot explain why Venus has the hottest surface, **then** have them review **Figure 4** in Lesson 4.

Alternate Assessment

L1 **MAKE A MODEL** Have students create a model of the solar system showing the sun and the planets. Tell students that their models should show the relative distances from the sun to each planet, so they will need to determine an appropriate scale to use for their models. Students do not need to worry about creating models for each planet that show their relative sizes. Provide a wide variety of materials that students can use such as tennis balls, marbles, Styrofoam, and so on. Encourage students to write a fact sheet for the sun and each planet that describes the major characteristics of each celestial body.

Write About It   Assess student's writing using this rubric.

SCORING RUBRIC	SCORE 4	SCORE 3	SCORE 2	SCORE 1
Describe the heliocentric model of the solar system	Student thoroughly describes the heliocentric solar system model.	Student adequately describes the heliocentric solar system model.	Student inaccurately describes the heliocentric solar system model.	Student does not describe the heliocentric solar system model.

Write About It   Assess student's writing using this rubric.

SCORING RUBRIC	SCORE 4	SCORE 3	SCORE 2	SCORE 1
Visit to an inner planet's surface	Student accurately describes the surface of an inner planet in the style of a news article.	Student adequately describes the surface of an inner planet.	Student imprecisely describes the surface of an inner planet.	Student does not describe the surface of an inner planet.

Review and Assessment, Cont.

Response to Intervention

18. If students cannot identify and describe the planet in the diagram, **then** have them review **Figure 5** in Lesson 5.

22. If students have trouble comparing and contrasting small solar system objects, **then** remind them to think about each object's size, composition, and orbit.

Apply the Big Q

TRANSFER Students should be able to demonstrate understanding of why objects in the solar system are different from each other by answering this question. See the scoring rubric below.

Connect to the Big Idea

BIG IDEA: Earth is part of a system of objects that orbit the sun.

Send students back to the Big Ideas of Science at the beginning of their student edition. Have them read what they wrote before they started the chapter. Lead a class discussion about how their thoughts have changed. If all chapters have been completed, have students fill in the bottom section for the Big Idea.

L3 WRITING IN SCIENCE Ask students to write an article for a science magazine that explains to readers why the objects in the solar system are different from each other.

LESSON 5 **The Outer Planets**

16. Which planet's orbit is farthest from Earth's?
 a. Jupiter
 b. Neptune
 c. Saturn
 d. Uranus

17. All the gas giants are surrounded by _____ systems of rings.

Use the illustration to answer Question 18.

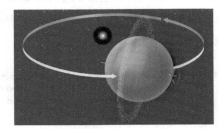

18. **Interpret Diagrams** What planet is shown above? What is unusual about it? What do scientists think caused that unusual feature?
 Uranus; it is unusual because its axis is tilted about 90 degrees. Scientists think it collided with a large body.

19. **Predict** Do you think astronomers have found all the moons of the outer planets? Explain.
 No; many new moons have been discovered through improved technology, so more moons will likely be discovered in the future.

LESSON 6 **Small Solar System Objects**

20. Where are most dwarf planets found?
 a. asteroid belt
 b. Kuiper belt
 c. Oort cloud
 d. plutoid belt

21. A ___meteorite___ is a meteoroid that reaches Earth's surface.

22. **Compare and Contrast** Compare and contrast asteroids, comets, and meteoroids.
 Sample: Asteroids are rocky, irregular bodies. Comets are icy bodies that develop tails as they orbit the sun. Meteoroids are small rocky bodies.

23. **Write About It** Suppose you could witness a large meteorite or asteroid striking Earth. Write a news report explaining the event.
 See TE rubric.

APPLY **Why are objects in the solar system different from each other?**

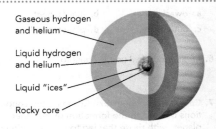

Gaseous hydrogen and helium

Liquid hydrogen and helium

Liquid "ices"

Rocky core

24. What type of planet is shown? Under what conditions would it most likely have formed?
 A gas giant; it most likely formed in an area that was relatively cool and contained light gases that it could capture. See TE rubric.

| **Write About It** | Assess student's writing using this rubric. |

SCORING RUBRIC	SCORE 4	SCORE 3	SCORE 2	SCORE 1
Describe meteorite or asteroid striking Earth	Student gives a clear and plausible description of a large asteroid or meteorite strike in the form of a news report.	Student gives an adequate description of a large asteroid or meteorite strike.	Student gives an incorrect description of an asteroid or meteorite strike.	Student does not describe an asteroid or meteorite strike.

 Why are objects in the solar system different from each other?

SCORING RUBRIC	SCORE 4	SCORE 3	SCORE 2	SCORE 1
Interpret a diagram	Identifies and describes planet type correctly; explains conditions under which planet formed.	Identifies planet type and explains conditions under which planet formed.	Identifies planet type imprecisely and inaccurately explains conditions under which planet formed.	Neither identifies planet type nor explains conditions under which planet formed.

Standardized Test Prep

Multiple Choice

Circle the letter of the best answer.

1. The table below shows data for five planets.

Planet	Period of Rotation (Earth days)	Period of Revolution (Earth years)	Average Distance from the Sun (million km)
Mars	1.03	1.9	228
Jupiter	0.41	12	779
Saturn	0.45	29	1,434
Uranus	0.72	84	2,873
Neptune	0.67	164	4,495

According to the table, which planet has a "day" that is most similar in length to a day on Earth?

Ⓐ Mars   B Jupiter
C Neptune   D Uranus

2. What characteristic do all of the outer planets share?

A They have rocky surfaces.
B They are larger than the sun.
Ⓒ They have many moons.
D They have thin atmospheres.

3. Which layer of the sun has the highest density?

Ⓐ core
B corona
C photosphere
D radiation zone

4. Mercury has a daytime temperature of about 430°C and a nighttime temperature below –170°C. What is the *best* explanation for this?

A Mercury has a greenhouse effect.
B Mercury is the closest planet to the sun.
Ⓒ Mercury has little to no atmosphere.
D Mercury has no liquid water.

5. From what region do *most* comets come?

A asteroid belt
B inner solar system
C Kuiper belt
Ⓓ Oort cloud

Constructed Response

Use the diagram below to answer Question 6.

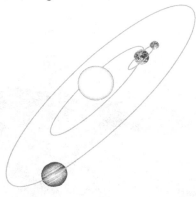

6. What model of the solar system is shown above? Give at least two pieces of evidence that support the model.

See TE note.

119

Standardized Test Prep

Test-Taking Skills

INTERPRETING DATA Tell students that when they are asked to interpret a data table, as in Question 1, they should read carefully to tell which data answers the question. The only relevant column in Question 1's data table is column 1, which shows the period of rotation (1 day) on Mars, Jupiter, Saturn, Uranus, and Neptune in Earth days.

Constructed Response

6. The model is a heliocentric model. Evidence for the model includes the fact that Venus has phases, the fact that there are moons orbiting Jupiter, and the fact that predictions made with the heliocentric model match observations better than predictions made with a geocentric model.

Additional Assessment Resources

Chapter Test
EXAMVIEW® Assessment Suite
Performance Assessment
Progress Monitoring Assessments
SuccessTracker™

ⒺⓁⓁ Support

5 Assess Understanding

Have ELLs complete the Alternate Assessment. Provide guidelines on the information it must cover, and a rubric for assessment. You may wish to have students work in small groups to complete the activity.

Beginning

LOW/HIGH Students can use single words and short phrases in their fact sheets.

Intermediate

LOW/HIGH Allow students extra time to complete their fact sheets.

Advanced

LOW/HIGH Challenge students to use as many vocabulary terms as possible in their fact sheets.

Remediate If students have trouble with...

QUESTION	SEE LESSON	STANDARDS
1	2	
2	5	
3	3	
4	4	
5	6	
6	1	

Science Matters

Frontiers of Technology

Have students read *Mars Rovers.* Point out to students that, not only does Mars's distance from Earth make it difficult to explore, but also that its surface temperature would be difficult to survive. The average temperature on the surface of Mars is about –60°C (–80°F). The atmosphere is much thinner on Mars than it is on Earth. These same reasons that make it difficult for humans to explore Mars are the same reasons that water in its liquid state is rare on the surface of Mars.

Tell students that the Mars rovers have a lot of equipment on them that we can use to help us learn more about Mars. They have cameras that send pictures back to Earth, magnets that can collect dust with metallic particles in it, and instruments that can analyze the composition of the rocks, soil, and atmosphere. The cameras provide a 360-degree view and the robotic arm can move similar to a human arm. Using the Mars rovers is as close to putting a human geologist on Mars as possible.

As students gather their information, ask them to find the purpose of the mission and have them tell whether they think the purpose was accomplished. Then have them propose a new mission for the rovers.

Ask: **What is an advantage of using rovers to explore the surface of Mars?** *(Rovers can explore the surface directly in the same way a human geologist could but without being damaged.)* **What problems could occur using rovers for remote exploration?** *(If a rover breaks, it would be difficult to fix it in a remote location.)*

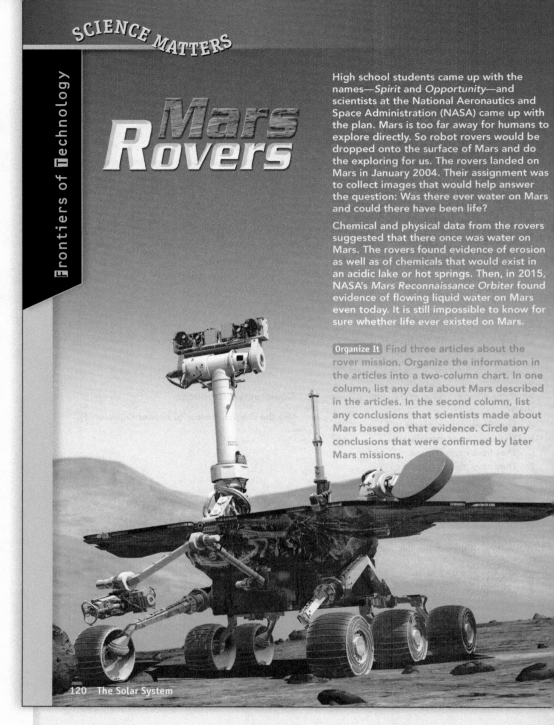

Frontiers of Technology

Mars Rovers

High school students came up with the names—*Spirit* and *Opportunity*—and scientists at the National Aeronautics and Space Administration (NASA) came up with the plan. Mars is too far away for humans to explore directly. So robot rovers would be dropped onto the surface of Mars and do the exploring for us. The rovers landed on Mars in January 2004. Their assignment was to collect images that would help answer the question: Was there ever water on Mars and could there have been life?

Chemical and physical data from the rovers suggested that there once was water on Mars. The rovers found evidence of erosion as well as of chemicals that would exist in an acidic lake or hot springs. Then, in 2015, NASA's *Mars Reconnaissance Orbiter* found evidence of flowing liquid water on Mars even today. It is still impossible to know for sure whether life ever existed on Mars.

Organize It Find three articles about the rover mission. Organize the information in the articles into a two-column chart. In one column, list any data about Mars described in the articles. In the second column, list any conclusions that scientists made about Mars based on that evidence. Circle any conclusions that were confirmed by later Mars missions.

120   The Solar System

Quick Facts

Maria Mitchell blazed a trail to the stars that many women would follow. More than 100 years after she became the first female professional astronomer, the world saw the first female astronauts. Sally Ride was the first American woman to go into space in 1963. Since her historic flight, NASA has trained several female astronauts to command missions and fly the space shuttle. In 2007, Peggy Whitson became the first woman to command the International Space Station. She has completed six spacewalks and her total time spent on spacewalks is the most of any woman. Suggest students research female astronauts and choose one to write a profile about. Have them include the astronaut's mission experience and any first she may have achieved.

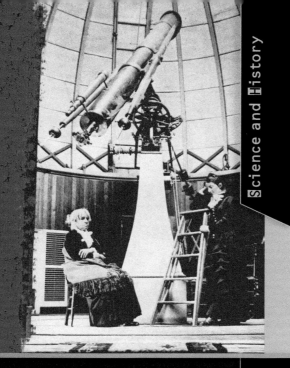

Maria Mitchell

In the mid-1800s, the idea of a woman astronomer seemed far-fetched. But then Maria Mitchell changed everything. In 1847, Mitchell was the first American woman astronomer to use a telescope to find a comet. Later, she taught astronomy at Vassar College, and inspired other young women to follow in her footsteps. She was a true astronomical pioneer.

Write About It Research more about Maria Mitchell's career. Write a biographical essay about her life and work.

Maria Mitchell (left) and Mary Whitney in the observatory at Vassar. Mary Whitney studied with Maria Mitchell, and later taught with her. ▶

GOODBYE, PLUTO!

What is a planet? That question was hotly debated by astronomers in 2006. Everyone agreed that a planet must be round and orbit the sun. But some said that a planet must also be dominant in its area of space. And then, the astronomers voted. The result: Pluto was demoted to a dwarf planet.

Research It Find out more about the Pluto decision. Participate in a debate and vote on the definition of *planet*. Write a newspaper article about the result of your debate. Be sure to include information from both sides of the argument.

121

Science and History

Have students read *Maria Mitchell*. Point out to students that during this period in history, women were not considered equals in many things. When Maria Mitchell discovered her comet, she did not have the right to vote. However, her discovery led her to become the first female professional astronomer. She was also the first astronomy professor at Vassar College.

As students research for their essay, ask them to focus on what made Maria Mitchell a pioneer and how she was an inspiration to her students.

Ask: **How did Maria Mitchell find her comet?** *(She discovered a blurry object she was not familiar with while looking at the stars through her telescope.)* **How was her discovery important?** *(It was a milestone for women in science and opened the door for women to study astronomy.)*

Hot Science

Have students read *Goodbye, Pluto!* Point out that, when their parents were in school, students were taught that Pluto was the ninth planet in the solar system. This is an example of how scientific facts can be changed based on new information.

Tell students that Pluto was discovered in 1930 by an American astronomer named Clyde Tombaugh who searched for a planet that many thought existed beyond Neptune. This planet was nicknamed Planet X. Tombaugh patiently spent many months looking for and finding the planet.

As students research the Pluto decision, make sure they cite the criteria an object must meet in order to be considered a planet.

Ask: **How long was Pluto considered a planet?** *(76 years)* **How many planets are in our solar system?** *(8)*

CHAPTER 4

Stars, Galaxies, and the Universe

Introduce the Big Q

Have students look at the image and read the Engaging Question and description. Ask students to infer how astronomers can see so far into space. Have volunteers explain their inferences. Point out that the image shows objects that are incredibly far away from Earth. Ask: **Have you seen astronomical photos before? If so, where?** *(Many students will have seen photos in magazines or newspapers, or on Web sites.)* **How do you think astronomers obtain these photos?** *(With telescopes and big, expensive cameras)*

Untamed Science Video

REACHING INTO DEEP SPACE Before viewing, invite students to discuss what they know about deep space. Then play the video. Lead a class discussion and make a list of questions that this video raises. You may wish to have students view the video again after they have completed the chapter to see if their questions have been answered.

> **To access the online resources for this chapter, search on or navigate to Stars, Galaxies, and the Universe.**
>
> **Untamed Science Video** shows the work of an aerospace manufacturer involved in a number of important space missions.
>
> **The Big Question** allows students to answer the Engaging Question about gazing deep into space.

mY science online | Stars, Galaxies, and the Universe

HOW CAN YOU GAZE DEEP INTO SPACE?

How do astronomers learn about distant objects in the universe?

Two galaxies are colliding! It all started 40 million years ago and will take millions more for these two spiral galaxies to actually combine. Astronomers know that the galaxy on the left, NGC 2207, and the galaxy on the right, IC 2163, are 140 million light-years from Earth. A light-year is the distance light travels in one year, or 9.46 trillion kilometers. That makes these galaxies about 1,320,000,000,000,000,000,000 kilometers away. **Infer** How can astronomers see so far into space?

Astronomers use large, powerful telescopes.

> **UNTAMED SCIENCE** Watch the **Untamed Science** video to learn more about the universe.

Professional Development Note **From the Author**

If you live in an urban area, it can be hard to see the stars and galaxies due to light pollution. You can access high-quality telescopes at dark-sky sites worldwide online and request that they take photos for you, free! The Bradford Robotic Telescope on the Canary Islands has a 36-cm telescope with a view from the north celestial pole to 52 degrees south. At the Micro-Observatory run by Harvard you can use a 15-cm diameter telescope; its field of view is the northern celestial hemisphere to 48 degrees south. With a similar field of view, Seeing in the Dark (through PBS) uses a 36-cm diameter telescope. Or you can research already published photos in a number of sources.

✏ *Don Buckley*

Stars, Galaxies, and the Universe

CHAPTER 4

Chapter at a Glance

CHAPTER PACING: 11–17 periods or $5\frac{1}{2}$–$8\frac{1}{2}$ blocks

INTRODUCE THE CHAPTER: Use the Engaging Question and the opening image to get students thinking about stars, galaxies, and the universe. Activate prior knowledge and preteach vocabulary using the Getting Started pages.

Lesson 1: Telescopes

Lesson 2: The Scale of the Universe

Lesson 3: Characteristics of Stars

Lesson 4: Lives of Stars

Lesson 5: Star Systems and Galaxies

Lesson 6: The Expanding Universe

ASSESSMENT OPTIONS: Chapter Test, **EXAM**VIEW® Assessment Suite, Performance Assessment, Progress Monitoring Assessments, SuccessTracker™

Preference Navigator, in the online Planning tools, allows you to customize *Interactive Science* to your own teaching style. You can also edit lesson plans by selecting the Lesson Planner option.

Digital Teacher's Edition allows you to access your Teacher's Edition and Resource online.

my science online.com

Differentiated Instruction

L1 Telescopes Let students use a small, hand-held telescope to look at different objects, both close and farther away. Having a second, similar telescope opened would let students see the optics.

L3 Telescopes and Binoculars Invite students to investigate the differences between small, hand-held telescopes and binoculars.

Getting Started

Check Your Understanding

This activity assesses students' understanding of wave energy. By shaking the parachute fabric, the children are transferring energy to the fabric and creating mechanical waves. Explain to students that the distance between the tops of the waves is referred to as *wavelength*.

Preteach Vocabulary Skills

Explain to students that a suffix is a word part added to the end of a word that changes the meaning of the word. Write the suffixes *-tion/-ion* and *-ory* on the board. Have students identify words that contain these suffixes and offer definitions for these words.

In the *Quick Check* section, the sample answers given for the terms *observatory* and *scientific notation* are not actual definitions, but sample guesses that students might make.

Check Your Understanding

1. **Background** Read the paragraph below and then answer the question.

> The children all held onto the edge of the giant parachute and shook it. The fabric moved up and down as a **wave** moved across it. "There's **energy** traveling across the fabric," their teacher said. "If we shake the edge quickly, the **distance** between the tops of the waves will get smaller."

> A **wave** is a disturbance that transfers energy from place to place.
>
> **Energy** is the ability to do work or cause change.
>
> **Distance** is the length of a path between two points.

- What will happen if the students shake the parachute more slowly?

  The distance between the tops of the waves will get longer.

> **MY READING WEB** If you had trouble completing the question above, visit **My Reading Web** and type in **Stars, Galaxies, and the Universe**.

Vocabulary Skill

Suffixes A suffix is a letter or group of letters added to the end of a word to form a new word with a slightly different meaning. Adding a suffix to a word often changes its part of speech.

Suffix	Meaning	Part of Speech	Example
-tion/-ion	Process of, action of	Noun	scientific nota*tion*
-ory	Place or thing connected with or used for	Noun	observat*ory*

2. **Quick Check** Use the information in the chart to suggest a meaning for each vocabulary term below.

- observatory: *Sample: a place where you can watch something carefully*

- scientific notation: *Sample: writing used in science*

My Reading Web offers leveled readings that offer a foundation for the chapter content.

Vocab Flash Cards offer extra practice with the chapter vocabulary words.

Digital Lesson
- Assign the *Check Your Understanding* activity online and have students submit their work to you.
- Assign the *Vocabulary Skill* activity online and have students submit their work to you.

my science online.com | **Stars, Galaxies, and the Universe**

radio telescope

supernova

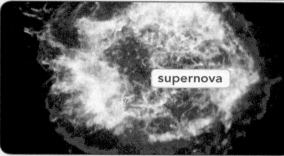

spiral galaxy

big bang

Chapter Preview

LESSON 1
- electromagnetic radiation
- visible light • wavelength
- spectrum • telescope
- optical telescope
- refracting telescope • convex lens
- reflecting telescope • observatory
- radio telescope

  ⟳ Ask Questions
  △ Infer

LESSON 2
- parallax • universe
- light-year • scientific notation

  ⟳ Summarize
  △ Calculate

LESSON 3
- spectrograph
- apparent brightness
- absolute brightness
- Hertzsprung-Russell diagram
- main sequence

  ⟳ Identify the Main Idea
  △ Interpret Data

LESSON 4
- nebula • protostar • white dwarf
- supernova • neutron star
- pulsar • black hole

  ⟳ Compare and Contrast
  △ Predict

LESSON 5
- binary star • eclipsing binary
- open cluster • globular cluster
- galaxy • spiral galaxy
- elliptical galaxy • irregular galaxy
- quasar

  ⟳ Relate Cause and Effect
  △ Draw Conclusions

LESSON 6
- big bang • Hubble's law
- cosmic background radiation
- dark matter • dark energy

  ⟳ Identify Supporting Evidence
  △ Make Models

125

Preview Vocabulary Terms

Have students create a word map graphic organizer for the vocabulary terms in this chapter. This organizer helps students learn vocabulary by associating the terms with related words and images. To fill in a word map, have students write the vocabulary terms in the top box. They should fill in the bottom boxes with terms, phrases, or images that are associated with the vocabulary term. As the class progresses through the chapter, have students continue adding to or refining their word maps. A list of Academic Vocabulary for each lesson can be found in the Support All Readers box at the start of the lesson.

L1 Have students look at the images on this page as you pronounce the vocabulary word. Have students repeat the word after you. Then read the definition. Use the sample sentence in italics to clarify the meaning of the term.

radio telescope *(RAY dee oh TEL uh skop)* Radio telescopes detect radio waves from objects in space. *The search for extraterrestrial life uses radio telescopes.*

supernova *(soo pur NOH vuh)* The explosion of a supergiant star when it runs out of fuel. *Supernovas are so bright that they can sometimes be seen during the day.*

spiral galaxy *(SPY rul GAL uk see)* a huge group of stars bound together by gravity into a pinwheel shape. *A spiral galaxy contains gas, dust, and bright young stars.*

big bang *(big bang)* the explosion of a tiny, unimaginably dense glob of matter which formed the universe in an instant. *The big bang formed the universe almost 14 billion years ago.*

CHAPTER 4

E L L Support

Have students work in small groups to complete their maps cooperatively for the Preview Vocabulary Terms activity. Introduce each term to students by writing it on the board and reading it aloud. You may wish to have students with different language proficiencies work together.

Beginning
LOW/HIGH Complete the map using images and some terms in the native language.

Intermediate
LOW/HIGH Complete the map using single words and short phrases.

Advanced
LOW/HIGH Include an example sentence using each of the vocabulary terms in the word map.

Telescopes

1 How do astronomers learn about distant objects in the universe?

Lesson Pacing: 2–3 periods or 1–1½ blocks

🕐 **SHORT ON TIME?** To do this lesson in approximately half the time, do the Activate Prior Knowledge activity on page 126. A discussion of the Key Concepts on pages 127 and 128 will familiarize students with the lesson content. Have students do the Quick Lab. The rest of the lesson can be completed by students independently.

> **Preference Navigator,** in the online Planning tools, allows you to customize *Interactive Science* to your own teaching style. You can also edit lesson plans by selecting the Lesson Planner option.
>
> **Digital Teacher's Edition** allows you to access your Teacher's Edition and Resource materials online.

my science online.com

Lesson Vocabulary

- electromagnetic radiation
- visible light
- wavelength
- spectrum
- telescope
- optical telescope
- refracting telescope
- convex lens
- reflecting telescope
- observatory
- radio telescope

Content Refresher

Light Pollution and Telescopes Many areas on Earth glow in the dark. Light streams upward from all of the street lamps, buildings, and airports, as can be seen from an airplane at night or in photos of Earth taken at night. Scattered by air molecules and dust particles in the air, this light becomes a haze that washes out the night sky for viewers at ground level on the planet. Our night sky is not the amazing night sky that our ancestors saw. Even in the 1800s, telescopes were built in fairly unpopulated areas to take advantage of the darkness around them. As the ground lights at night get brighter, the usefulness of these telescopes is decreasing.

Now astronomers are trying to overcome this problem by designing telescopes with narrow-band "nebula filters" or broad-band "light pollution filters." These telescopes allow astronomers to better view galaxies and nebula by generating a more pronounced contrast. While these telescopes may allow astronomers to see dim objects in the night sky, they also distort color, making it difficult to determine the brightness of objects using just the eye. Viewing stars is not as dramatically impacted by light pollution because they have a brighter surface than galaxies and nebulae.

LESSON OBJECTIVES

🔑 State the regions of the electromagnetic spectrum.

🔑 Explain what telescopes are and how they work.

Blended Path
Active learning using Student Edition, Inquiry Path, and Digital Path

ENGAGE AND EXPLORE

Teach this lesson using a variety of resources. Begin by reading **My Planet Diary** as a class. Have students share ideas about when infrared goggles would be useful. Then have students do the **Inquiry Warm-Up activity.** Students will investigate how distance affects an image. Discuss what they saw with and without the lens. The **After the Inquiry Warm-Up worksheet** sets up a discussion about how an image changes when viewed through a lens. Have volunteers share their answers to question 4 comparing the views of the printed page in Step 3.

EXPLAIN AND ELABORATE

Teach Key Concepts by explaining the types of wavelengths on the electromagnetic spectrum.

Teach Key Concepts by explaining that an optical telescope collects visible light in order to make distant objects appear closer and larger. **Support the Big Q** by comparing and contrasting how refracting and reflecting telescopes work. **Lead a Discussion** about the benefits of using a large telescope, especially for astronomy; however, also discuss the disadvantages of large telescopes. Use **Figure 3** to illustrate the size of the Hubble telescope. **Lead a Discussion** about why optical telescopes are located on mountaintops and in space. **Lead a Discussion** about the benefits of radio telescopes. Then have students practice the inquiry skill in the **Apply It activity.** Hand out the **Key Concept Summaries** as a review of each part of the lesson. Students can also use the online **Vocab Flash Cards** to review key terms.

EVALUATE

Have students take the **Lesson Quiz.** For an alternate assessment, see the **EXAM**VIEW® Assessment Suite, Progress Monitoring Assessments, or SuccessTracker™.

ELL Support

1 Content and Language
Telescope consists of two word parts, the prefix *tele-* meaning "from a distance" and *-scope* meaning "a tool used to see objects."

Lab zone Inquiry Path
Hands-on learning in the Lab zone

Digital Path
Online learning at my science online.com

ENGAGE AND EXPLORE

To teach this lesson with an emphasis on inquiry, begin with the **Inquiry Warm-Up activity.** Students will see how distance affects an image. Discuss how the image looked at each stage of the investigation. Have students do the **After the Inquiry Warm-Up worksheet.** Talk about how viewing an image through a lens changes it. Have volunteers share their answers to question 4 about what happened to the image of the printed page in Step 3.

EXPLAIN AND ELABORATE

Focus on the **Inquiry Skill** for the lesson. Point out that when you infer, you interpret a situation based on evidence and information. Based on the **Inquiry Warm-Up activity,** when could students infer that it would be useful to use a lens? *(When wanting to see something small in a larger form)* Have students do the **Quick Lab** to explore the different wavelengths of light and then share their results.

To **Support the Big Q,** explain the similarities and differences between reflecting and refracting telescopes. Do the **Teacher Demo** to show students how light pollution can make objects difficult to view in the night sky. The second **Teacher Demo** shows students how radio waves can be located. Review light pollution and how various type of telescopes work before beginning the **Apply It activity.** Ask volunteers to share their inferences. Give students a chance to build and construct simple telescopes during the **Lab Investigation.** Students can use the online **Vocab Flash Cards** to review key terms.

EVALUATE

Have students take the **Lesson Quiz.** For an alternate assessment, see the **EXAM**VIEW® Assessment Suite, Progress Monitoring Assessments, or SuccessTracker™.

ENGAGE AND EXPLORE

Teach this lesson using digital resources. Begin by having students explore real-world connections to the electromagnetic spectrum at **My Planet Diary** online. Have them access the Chapter Resources to find the **Unlock the Big Question activity.** There they can answer the questions and refine their responses as they continue through the lesson. You can re-assign the activity and have students submit their work so you can track their progress.

EXPLAIN AND ELABORATE

Students reading above, at, or below the lexile measure of this lesson can access basic content readings at their level at **My Reading Web.** Have students use the online **Vocab Flash Cards** to preview key terms. Do the **Quick Lab** and then ask students to share their results.

To **Support the Big Q,** discuss how refracting and reflecting telescopes work. Have students do the online **Interactive Art activity** to explore refracting and reflecting telescopes. Review light pollution and how the various types of telescopes work before assigning the online **Apply It activity.** Ask volunteers to share their inferences. Have students submit their work to you. The **Key Concept Summaries** online allow students to read a summary and see an image associated with each part of the lesson. Online remediation is available at **My Science Coach.**

EVALUATE

Have students take the **Lesson Quiz.** For an alternate assessment, see the **EXAM**VIEW® Assessment Suite, Progress Monitoring Assessments, or SuccessTracker™.

2 Frontload the Lesson
Preview the lesson visuals, labels, and captions. Ask students what they know about the terms *telescope* and *observatory.* Explain the specific meanings these words have in science.

3 Comprehensible Input
Have students study the visuals and their captions on pages 127–130 to support the Key Concepts of the lesson.

4 Language Production
Pair or group students with varied language abilities to complete labs collaboratively for language practice. Have each student copy the completed written lab for personal reference.

5 Assess Understanding
Have students keep a content area log for this lesson using a two-column format with the headings "What I Understand" and "What I Don't Understand." Follow up so that students can move items from the "Don't Understand" to the "Understand" column.

LESSON 4.1

Telescopes

Establish Learning Objectives

After this lesson, students will be able to:

 State the regions of the electromagnetic spectrum.

 Explain what telescopes are and how they work.

Engage

Activate Prior Knowledge

MY PLANET DIARY Read *Infrared Goggles* with the class. Ask students if they have seen infrared goggles, commonly called night vision goggles. Many will have seen them on movies or TV shows or know that the military uses them. Explain that 'light' comes in many wavelengths. Ask: **What kind of 'light' do you see using infrared goggles?** *(Infrared)* **Can humans see that kind of light without special equipment?** *(No.)*

BIG IDEAS OF SCIENCE REFERENCE LIBRARY 📖
Have students look up the following topic: Hubble Space Telescope.

Explore

Lab Resource: Inquiry Warm-Up 🔬

L2 **HOW DOES DISTANCE AFFECT AN IMAGE?**
Students will use a hand lens to investigate the inversion of images.

LESSON

1 Telescopes

 What Are the Regions of the Electromagnetic Spectrum?

 What Are Telescopes and How Do They Work?

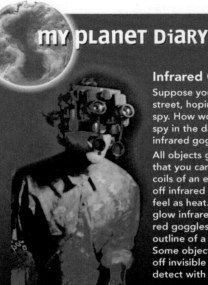

MY PLANET DIARY

TECHNOLOGY

Infrared Goggles

Suppose you're a spy on a dark street, hoping to spot another spy. How would you see the other spy in the dark? Wear a pair of infrared goggles.

All objects give off radiation that you can't see. The glowing coils of an electric heater give off infrared radiation, which you feel as heat. Human beings also glow infrared, and with the infra-red goggles you can see a green outline of a person in the dark. Some objects in space also give off invisible radiation that we can detect with special telescopes.

Communicate Answer the following question. Then discuss your answer with a partner.

In what other situations might you want to use infrared goggles?

Sample: at night in the woods on a hike or in a dark room without a flashlight

▶ **PLANET DIARY** Go to **Planet Diary** to learn more about telescopes.

🔬 **Lab zone** Do the Inquiry Warm-Up *How Does Distance Affect an Image?*

What Are the Regions of the Electromagnetic Spectrum?

To understand how telescopes work, it's useful to understand **electromagnetic radiation** (ih LEK troh mag NET ik), or energy that can travel through space in the form of waves.

Scientists call the light you can see **visible light.** Visible light is just one of many types of electromagnetic radiation. Many objects give off radiation that you can't see. Objects in space give off all types of electromagnetic radiation.

126 Stars, Galaxies, and the Universe

Vocabulary

- electromagnetic radiation • visible light • wavelength • spectrum
- telescope • optical telescope • refracting telescope • convex lens
- reflecting telescope • observatory • radio telescope

Skills

- Reading: Ask Questions
- Inquiry: Infer

The distance between the crest of one wave and the crest of the next wave is called the **wavelength**. Visible light has very short wavelengths, less than one millionth of a meter. There are some electromagnetic waves that have even shorter wavelengths. Other waves have much longer wavelengths, even several meters long.

If you shine white light through a prism, the light spreads out to make a range of different colors with different wavelengths, called a **spectrum.** The spectrum of visible light is made of the colors red, orange, yellow, green, blue, and violet. **The electromagnetic spectrum includes the entire range of radio waves, infrared radiation, visible light, ultraviolet radiation, X-rays, and gamma rays.** Look at **Figure 1** to see the spectrum.

Flower seen in visible light

FIGURE 1 ·······························

The Electromagnetic Spectrum
Humans see visible light, but bees can see ultra-violet light, so flowers look different to a bee.

✏️ CHALLENGE **What advantage does having ultraviolet vision give bees?**

The bee can see the center of
the flower better, leading it to
the pollen.

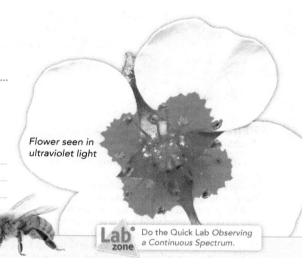

Flower seen in ultraviolet light

Lab zone · Do the Quick Lab _Observing a Continuous Spectrum._

Assess Your Understanding

got it? ·······················

O I get it! Now I know that the electromagnetic spectrum includes _radio waves, infrared_ _radiation, visible light, ultraviolet radiation, X-rays, and gamma rays._

O I need extra help with _See TE note._

Go to **my science COACH** _online for help with this subject._

127

Explain ─────────

Introduce Vocabulary

Tell students that _optical_ means relating to or involving sight. Optical telescopes are telescopes that use visible light. Reflecting and refracting telescopes are kinds of optical telescopes.

Teach Key Concepts 📖

Explain to students that what they think of as light is just a small portion of the electromagnetic spectrum, which also includes radio waves, microwaves, infrared radiation, ultraviolet radiation, X-rays, and gamma rays. Ask: **Which electromagnetic waves have the longest wavelength?** (_Radio waves_) **Shortest?** (_Gamma rays_) **What waves are on either side of visible light?** (_Infrared waves and ultraviolet waves_) Tell students that microwaves are between radio waves and infrared radiation.

Address Misconceptions

[L1] **HEARING RADIO WAVES** Students may mistakenly think they can hear radio waves. Point out that we hear sound waves, which are compression waves—areas of higher and lower density in the air.

Elaborate ─────────

Lab Resource: Quick Lab 🧪

[L2] **OBSERVING A CONTINUOUS SPECTRUM**
Students will use a prism to explore the different wavelengths of light.

Evaluate ─────────

Assess Your Understanding

Have students evaluate their understanding by completing the appropriate sentence.

[RTI] Response to Intervention

If students cannot explain what makes up the electromagnetic spectrum, **then** have them reread the Key Concept statement.

my science COACH Have students go online for help in understanding the electromagnetic spectrum.

My Planet Diary provides an opportunity for students to explore real-world connections to the electromagnetic spectrum.

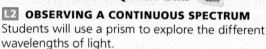

my science online.com | Regions of the EM Spectrum

Explain

Teach Key Concepts 🔑

Explain to students that telescopes collect and focus many forms of electromagnetic radiation. Ask: **Which part of the electromagnetic spectrum does an optical telescope collect?** *(Visible light)* Ask students if they have ever looked through a telescope or a pair of binoculars. Many of them will have done so. Ask: **How did these instruments change the view of the object you were looking at?** *(They made the object look bigger and closer than it really was.)*

Support the Big Q ❓

HOW TELESCOPES WORK Tell students that refracting is the bending of light rays that occurs when light moves from one material to another material. Reflection occurs when light waves bounce off a surface. Ask: **What is used in refracting telescopes to collect light and magnify images?** *(Lenses)* **Where in these telescopes does refraction occur?** *(Where light passes through the lenses)* **What does refraction in the telescope do to light?** *(Refraction brings it together, focusing an image.)* **What is used in reflecting telescopes to collect and focus light?** *(A mirror)* **What can be changed to help a telescope collect more light?** *(Make the lens or mirror bigger.)* **Which is easier to make larger, a lens or a mirror?** *(A mirror)* Explain to students that there is another type of optical telescope called a catadioptric telescope. These telescopes combine elements of refracting and reflecting telescopes. Catadioptric telescopes, such as the Schmidt-Cassegrain telescope, are very popular with amateur astronomers because they allow for more light-gathering capabilities in smaller form factors.

Lead a Discussion

LARGE TELESCOPES Tell students that larger telescopes can gather more light and view more distant objects than smaller telescopes. However, large mirrors can be distorted by gravity. The wavelength of light is a thousand times smaller than the diameter of a human hair. A very small distortion in a mirror can distort the image. Some modern optical telescopes have mirrors that are made up of sections. A computer fine-tunes the shape of each part of the mirror. The largest such telescope in the United States is in Hawaii. The mirror has a diameter of nearly 10 meters. Ask: **Why are telescopes that astronomers use so large?** *(To gather a large amount of light so that they can see objects that are very far away)*

What Are Telescopes and How Do They Work?

On a clear night, your eyes can see at most a few thousand stars. But with a telescope, you can see many millions. Why? The light from stars spreads out as it moves through space and your eyes are too small to gather much light.

🔑 **Telescopes are instruments that collect and focus light and other forms of electromagnetic radiation.** Telescopes make distant objects appear larger and brighter. A telescope that uses lenses or mirrors to collect and focus visible light is called an **optical telescope.** There are also nonoptical telescopes. These telescopes collect and focus different types of electromagnetic radiation, just as optical telescopes collect visible light.

Optical Telescopes The two major types of optical telescopes are refracting telescopes and reflecting telescopes.

> **Vocabulary** Suffixes Complete the sentence by circling the correct words. An (optics/**optical**) device may use many different kinds of (**optics**/optical) including mirrors and lenses.

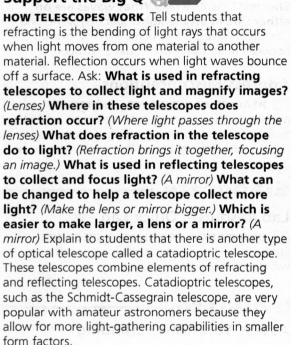

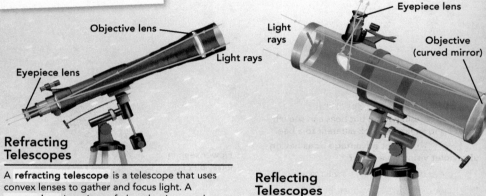

Refracting Telescopes

A **refracting telescope** is a telescope that uses convex lenses to gather and focus light. A **convex lens** is a piece of glass that is curved, so the middle is thicker than the edges.

A simple refracting telescope has two convex lenses, one at each end of a long tube. Light enters the telescope through the large objective lens at the top. The objective lens focuses the light at a certain distance from the lens. This distance is the focal length of the lens. A larger objective lens means that the telescope can collect more light. This makes it easier for astronomers to see faint objects, or objects that are far away.

The smaller lens at the lower end of a refracting telescope is the eyepiece lens. The eyepiece lens magnifies the image produced by the objective lens. A magnified image can be easier to study.

Reflecting Telescopes

In 1668, Isaac Newton built the first reflecting telescope. A **reflecting telescope** uses a curved mirror to collect and focus light. Like the objective lens in a refracting telescope, the curved mirror in a reflecting telescope focuses a large amount of light onto a small area. A larger mirror means that the telescope can collect more light. The largest optical telescopes today are all reflecting telescopes.

Why are the largest optical telescopes reflecting telescopes? Because the mirror can be supported from below. But the lens of a refracting telescope must be supported from the edges, so light can pass through it.

128 Stars, Galaxies, and the Universe

Interactive Art:

my science online.com ▶ **Telescopes**

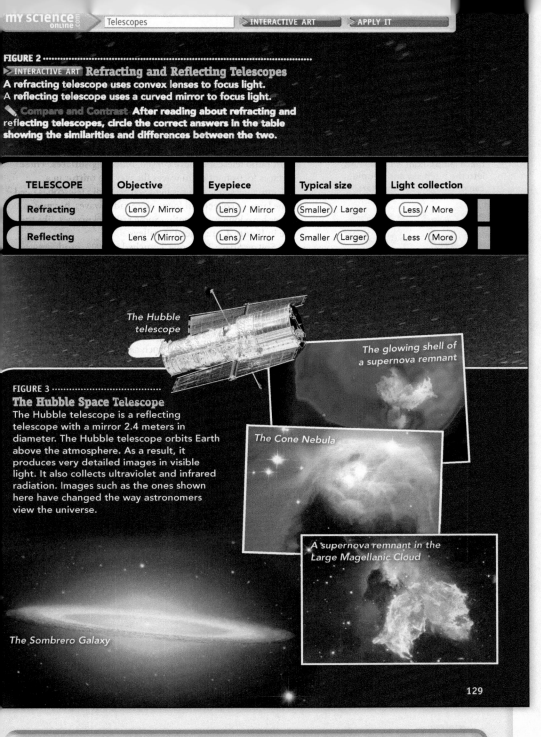

FIGURE 2 ············
> INTERACTIVE ART **Refracting and Reflecting Telescopes**
A refracting telescope uses convex lenses to focus light.
A reflecting telescope uses a curved mirror to focus light.

Compare and Contrast After reading about refracting and reflecting telescopes, circle the correct answers in the table showing the similarities and differences between the two.

TELESCOPE	Objective	Eyepiece	Typical size	Light collection
Refracting	(Lens) / Mirror	(Lens) / Mirror	(Smaller) / Larger	(Less) / More
Reflecting	Lens / (Mirror)	(Lens) / Mirror	Smaller / (Larger)	Less / (More)

The Hubble telescope

The glowing shell of a supernova remnant

FIGURE 3 ·······························
The Hubble Space Telescope
The Hubble telescope is a reflecting telescope with a mirror 2.4 meters in diameter. The Hubble telescope orbits Earth above the atmosphere. As a result, it produces very detailed images in visible light. It also collects ultraviolet and infrared radiation. Images such as the ones shown here have changed the way astronomers view the universe.

The Cone Nebula

A supernova remnant in the Large Magellanic Cloud

The Sombrero Galaxy

129

Differentiated Instruction

L1 Lenses and Mirrors Explain to students that optical telescopes are made of lenses and mirrors. Let students investigate some lenses and mirrors (curved, if available), both individually and in combination. They should observe objects through the lenses and observe reflections from the mirrors.

L3 History of the Telescope Invite students to investigate the invention and development of the telescope, through the Hubble telescope. They can present their findings in a multimedia presentation or as a written report.

Teach With Visuals

Tell students to look at **Figure 3.** To give them a sense of the size of the telescope, tell them that it is about the size of a school bus. Ask: **What is the diameter of Hubble's mirror?** *(2.4 meters)* Draw a line 2.4 meters long on the board and ask students to visualize a mirror that large and about 30 centimeters thick. Tell students that there are many larger telescopes on Earth. Ask: **What might have limited the size of the Hubble Space Telescope?** *(It was launched from the Space Shuttle, so it had to be able to fit into the payload area. It had to be light enough that it would be possible for a rocket to launch it and the shuttle into orbit.)*

Elaborate ————————

21st Century Learning

INFORMATION LITERACY Have students use the Internet to find images of the Crab Nebula. They should locate images made optically, from radio waves, from infrared waves, and from X-rays. NASA has a large catalog of images. Students should compare and contrast the photos. Ask students to keep track of the sites they used and consider the quality of the information available at each source. Remind students to follow prescribed guidelines for Internet use.

Address Misconceptions

GALILEO Many students may think that Galileo invented the telescope. Explain that Galileo made significant improvements to the refracting telescope, and that he was the first person to use a telescope to view the night sky. Galileo was also the first to view the four largest moons of Jupiter, to observe the phases of Venus, and to see the rings of Saturn. Galileo's observations helped to develop and confirm the heliocentric model of the solar system.

21st Century Learning

COMMUNICATION Have students read *Hubble Space Telescope* in the **Big Ideas of Science Reference Library** and create a crossword puzzle based on the facts learned from the reading. Students can work with partners for this activity and exchange their puzzle with another pair.

Explain

Lead a Discussion

USING TELESCOPES Tell students that many large optical telescopes are located on mountaintops. As technology has improved, telescopes have been placed in space, too. Ask: **What is the advantage of placing telescopes on satellites and in space?** *(They can detect parts of the electromagnetic spectrum blocked by the atmosphere. They also provide clearer pictures using visible light.)*

 Ask Questions Tell students that asking questions as they read will help them remember new information. Questions might be about what might be coming next, or why this information is important to the topic.

Lead a Discussion

RADIO TELESCOPES Explain to students that astronomers can gain different information about objects in the universe by examining different parts of the electromagnetic spectrum. Ask: **Why do radio telescopes not have to be placed on mountaintops?** *(The atmosphere does not interfere much with radio waves.)*

Elaborate

Teacher Demo

L1 MODELING LIGHT POLLUTION

Materials large poster board, adhesive, glow-in-the-dark decals of stars and planets, several small penlights

Time 20 minutes

Before the demonstrations, place decals of different sizes on a large poster board. Then place the poster board under the light to charge the decals. Explain to students that light from streetlights, businesses, and signs makes it difficult to view objects in the night sky. This is called light pollution. Place the poster board in a prominent position, close the shades, and turn off the room lights. Give students a few moments to observe the brightness of the decals. Ask volunteers to help you shine penlights on the poster board. Tell students to note the difference in the brightness of the decals.

Ask: **Did the decals look dimmer in the penlights?** *(Yes)* **Were the decals actually putting out less light when the penlights were in use?** *(No)* **Why did they look dimmer?** *(The light from the penlights was "competing" with the light from the decals.)* **What does this simulate?** *(Light pollution makes it difficult for users of telescopes to see distant stars and objects.)*

---

did you know?

Astronomers are concerned about "light pollution," artificial lighting that makes it hard to see the skies at night. Some cities have replaced their street lamps with ones that point down. With these lamps, light isn't beamed into the night sky and people can once again see the stars.

 **Ask Questions** Write a question you would like answered about telescopes.

Sample: Which is the most powerful kind of telescope?

Other Telescopes Telescopes are usually located in observatories. An **observatory** is a building that contains one or more telescopes. Many large observatories are located on the tops of mountains or in space. Why? Earth's atmosphere makes objects in space look blurry. The sky on some mountaintops is clearer than at sea level and is not brightened by city lights.

- **Radio telescopes** detect radio waves from objects in space. Most radio telescopes have curved, reflecting surfaces. These surfaces focus faint radio waves the way the mirror in a reflecting telescope focuses light waves. Radio telescopes need to be large to collect and focus more radio waves, because radio waves have long wavelengths. Some radio telescopes, like the one in **Figure 4**, are placed in valleys.
- The Spitzer Space Telescope, launched in 2003, produces images in the infrared portion of the spectrum.
- Very hot objects in space give off X-rays. The Chandra X-ray Observatory produces images in the X-ray portion of the spectrum. X-rays are blocked by Earth's atmosphere, so this telescope is located in outer space.

Some new telescopes are equipped with computer systems that correct images for problems such as telescope movement and changes in air temperature or mirror shape.

FIGURE 4

Arecibo Radio Telescope
The Arecibo telescope in Puerto Rico is 305 meters in diameter.

Evaluate the Design Why are radio telescopes so large?

To collect more radio waves, which have long wavelengths

130 Stars, Galaxies, and the Universe

Professional Development Note — Teacher to Teacher

A Different Way of "Looking" at Stars Most students have had the opportunity to look up into the nighttime sky and see the stars. Through participation in NASA's Radio Jove project, students have the opportunity to "see" stars as emitters of energy from other regions of the electromagnetic spectrum. Radio Jove antennas and receivers make observing the radio emissions of the sun a relatively simple exercise. Attaching speakers to the receiver allows students to listen to the Sun's emissions. As Solar Cycle 24 gets underway, we will record the increasing activity of the Sun as it moves toward solar maximum.

✎ *James Kuhl*
Central Square Middle School
Central Square, New York

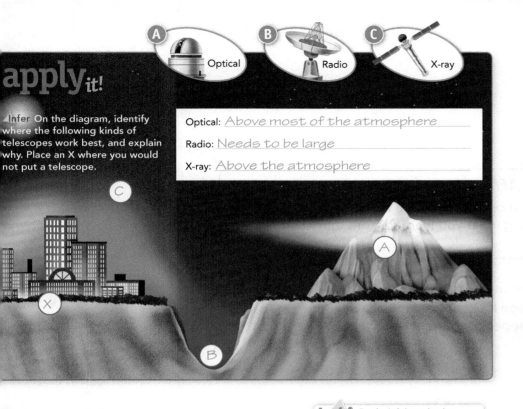

A Optical

B Radio

C X-ray

apply it!

Infer On the diagram, identify where the following kinds of telescopes work best, and explain why. Place an X where you would not put a telescope.

Optical: *Above most of the atmosphere*

Radio: *Needs to be large*

X-ray: *Above the atmosphere*

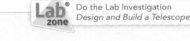

Lab zone Do the Lab Investigation *Design and Build a Telescope.*

🔑 Assess Your Understanding

1a. Sequence List the electromagnetic waves, from longest to shortest wavelength.

Radio, infrared, visible light, ultraviolet, X-rays, and gamma rays

b. Identify Faulty Reasoning A student of astronomy suggests locating a radio telescope near a radio station. Is this a good idea? Why or why not?

It is not a good idea, as the station's radio waves would drown out the radio waves from space.

got it? ....

O **I get it!** Now I know that telescopes are *instruments that collect and focus light and other forms of electromagnetic radiation.*

O **I need extra help with** *See TE note.*

Go to MY SCIENCE COACH *online for help with this subject.*

131

Differentiated Instruction

L1 Use a Telescope Choose several objects outside that are difficult to see because of their distance. Have students use telescopes of various sizes to view the objects. They should record their findings including notes on how large the images appear in the telescopes.

L3 Galileo Versus Newton Form small groups of students; some groups will represent Galileo and others will represent Newton. The groups that represent Galileo should investigate, sketch, and learn the benefits and disadvantages of refracting telescopes. The Newton groups will do the same with reflecting telescopes. The different groups can debate each other about the pros and cons of their telescope designs.

Teacher Demo Lab zone

L3 LOCATING RADIO WAVES

Materials umbrella, aluminum foil, radio

Time 20 minutes

Tell students that waves with wavelengths between 0.5 m and 1 m are radio waves (UHF). So an umbrella is a reasonable size to try to 'capture' radio waves. Have students line the inside of an open umbrella with aluminum foil. Turn on a small radio and tune it to a station. Move the radio up and down along the umbrella handle. Find the position where the station is the clearest. Tape the radio to the handle. Hold the umbrella at different angles, finding the one where the reception is best.

Ask: **What is occurring at the location where you taped the radio?** *(The radio waves are focused at this point.)* **In which direction do you think the radio transmitter is located?** *(The angle where reception was the clearest)*

Apply It!

L1 Review light pollution and how the various types of telescopes work before beginning the activity.

▲ **Infer** Tell students that when they interpret an observation, they are inferring. An inference is not a fact.

Lab Resource: Lab Investigation Lab zone

L2 DESIGN AND BUILD A TELESCOPE Students will construct and use a simple telescope.

Evaluate

Assess Your Understanding

After students answer the questions, have them evaluate their understanding by completing the appropriate sentence.

R T I Response to Intervention

1a. If students cannot sequence electromagnetic waves, **then** have them review **Figure 1.**

b. If students need help with understanding radio telescopes, **then** have them first think about optical telescopes and the effects of light pollution.

MY SCIENCE COACH Have students go online for help in understanding telescopes.

Digital Lesson: Assign the *Apply It* activity online and have students submit their work to you.

MY SCIENCE online.com > Telescopes

Lab zone **After the Inquiry Warm-Up**

Telescopes

Inquiry Warm-Up, *How Does Distance Affect an Image?*
In the Inquiry Warm-Up, you investigated how an object's distance from a lens affects the object's image as seen through the lens. Using what you learned from that activity, answer the questions below.

1. **COMMUNICATE** Draw a three-part diagram showing what the letter looked like with the unaided eye, what its image looked like through the lens once you had it in focus, and what happened to the image when you moved the page far from the lens.

2. **RELATE CAUSE AND EFFECT** Look at the first and second parts of the diagram you made in question 1. In Step 2, what effect did looking through the hand lens have on your view of the letter?

_____

_____

3. **OBSERVE** Turn the hand lens you used, and look at it from the side. What is the shape of the lens?

_____

4. **COMPARE AND CONTRAST** Consider what happened to the image of the printed page in Step 3. Compare what you saw through the lens as the printed page became more distant with what you normally see with your unaided eyes as an object becomes more distant.

_____

_____

_____

_____

Assess Your Understanding

Telescopes

What Are the Regions of the Electromagnetic Spectrum?

gotit? ···

○ **I get it!** Now I know that the electromagnetic spectrum includes _____
_____
_____

○ **I need extra help with** _____
_____

What Are Telescopes and How Do They Work?

1a. **SEQUENCE** List the electromagnetic waves, from longest to shortest
wavelength. _____
_____
_____

b. **IDENTIFY FAULTY REASONING** A student of astronomy suggests locating
a radio telescope near a radio station. Is this a good idea? Why or why
not? _____
_____
_____

gotit? ···

○ **I get it!** Now I know that telescopes are _____
_____
_____

○ **I need extra help with** _____
_____

Key Concept Summaries

Telescopes

What Are the Regions of the Electromagnetic Spectrum?

Electromagnetic radiation is energy that can travel through space in the form of waves. **Visible light,** the light you can see, is just one of many types of electromagnetic radiation. Many objects give off radiation that you cannot see.

The distance between the crest of one wave and the crest of the next wave is called the **wavelength.** Visible light has very short wavelengths, less than one millionth of a meter. Other types of radiation have much longer wavelengths, even several meters long. If you shine white light through a prism, the light spreads out to make a range of different colors with different wavelengths, called a **spectrum.** **The electromagnetic spectrum includes the entire range of radio waves, infrared radiation, visible light, ultraviolet radiation, X-rays, and gamma rays.**

What Are Telescopes and How Do They Work?

Telescopes are instruments that collect and focus light and other forms of electromagnetic radiation. Telescopes make distant objects appear larger and brighter. A telescope that uses lenses or mirrors to collect and focus visible light is called an **optical telescope.** The two major types of optical telescopes are refracting telescopes and reflecting telescopes. **Refracting telescopes** use convex lenses to gather and focus light. A **convex lens** is a piece of glass that is curved, so the middle is thicker than the edges. A **reflecting telescope** uses a curved mirror to collect and focus light. The largest optical telescopes today are all reflecting telescopes because, while a mirror can be supported from below, a lens must be supported from the sides so that light can pass through it.

An **observatory** is a building that contains one or more telescopes. Because Earth's atmosphere makes objects in space look blurry, many large observatories are located on the tops of mountains or in space. Just as optical telescopes collect visible light, nonoptical telescopes collect and focus different types of electromagnetic radiation. **Radio telescopes** detect radio waves from objects in space. Other telescopes produce images in the infrared or X-ray portions of the spectrum.

On a separate sheet of paper, explain the difference between optical and nonoptical telescopes, and give examples of each.

Review and Reinforce

Telescopes

Understanding Main Ideas

Answer the following questions on a separate sheet of paper.

1. What is electromagnetic radiation?
2. List the types of radiation in the electromagnetic spectrum.
3. Describe how telescopes work and explain why professional astronomers use large telescopes.
4. Explain the placement of optical telescopes.

Building Vocabulary

Match each term with its definition by writing the letter of the correct definition in the right column on the line beside the term in the left column.

5. ___ visible light

6. ___ telescope

7. ___ refracting telescope

8. ___ observatory

9. ___ convex lens

10. ___ wavelength

11. ___ radio telescope

12. ___ optical telescope

13. ___ reflecting telescope

a. building that houses telescopes

b. the crest-to-crest distance on a wave

c. instrument that collects and focuses electromagnetic radiation

d. an optical telescope that uses convex lenses to gather and focus light

e. an optical telescope that uses a curved mirror to gather and focus light

f. a telescope that collects radio waves

g. a piece of glass that is curved so the middle is thicker than the edges

h. electromagnetic radiation visible to the human eye

i. a telescope that collects and focuses visible light

Enrich

Telescopes

> Read the passage and study the table below. Then use a separate sheet of paper to answer the questions that follow.

Seeing Without Light

Many interesting objects in the sky, such as new stars, are hidden behind the huge clouds of gas and dust.

Astronomers can now "see" through these barriers by using parts of the electromagnetic spectrum that have wavelengths longer than those of visible light. An astronomer deciding which part of the electromagnetic spectrum to use must deal with at least two problems:

- **Some wavelengths don't pass through the atmosphere:** Earth's atmosphere stops X-rays, gamma rays, and most ultraviolet light. Astronomers who want to use wavelengths other than visible light, infrared, and radio waves must obtain their observations from telescopes in space.

- **Some wavelengths produce images with low resolution:** *Resolution* is the ability to distinguish objects that are close together. Low-resolution images are fuzzy. High-resolution images are sharp. Generally, the larger the diameter of the telescope's collecting surface, the higher the resolution of the image produced. And the shorter the wavelength of radiation used, the higher the resolution of the image that can be produced. Radio telescopes, despite their large diameter, produce very low-resolution images because of the long wavelengths of radio waves. Infrared, on the other hand, has wavelengths closer to those of visible light.

Radiation Type	Passes Through Atmosphere?	Wavelength
Radio	Yes	> 1 mm
Infrared	Some	0.0007 mm–1 mm
Visible light	Yes	0.0004 mm–0.0007 mm
Ultraviolet	Small amount	0.00002 mm–0.0004 mm
X-ray	No	0.00000001 mm–0.00002 mm
Gamma	No	< 0.00000001 mm

1. Which form of radiation gives the highest resolution image? Why?
2. What are some disadvantages of using a space telescope?
3. Suppose astronomers are interested in obtaining an image of a large area in the sky. Which radiation should astronomers observe if they want to get images 24 hours a day, quickly and cheaply? Why?
4. If astronomers want a very detailed image of an image of an object behind a dust cloud, which radiation should they observe? Why?

Lesson Quiz

Telescopes

If the statement is true, write *true*. If the statement is false, change the underlined word or words to make the statement true.

1. _____ Telescopes that collect <u>radio waves</u> must be placed in orbit around Earth.

2. _____ The <u>electromagnetic spectrum</u> includes radio waves, infrared radiation, and X-rays.

3. _____ Humans can see the <u>infrared</u> part of the electromagnetic spectrum.

4. _____ Large optical telescopes gather <u>more</u> light than the human eye, so stars that are much farther away can be seen.

Fill in the blank to complete each statement.

5. A(n) _____ is a building that contains one or more telescopes.

6. Energy that can travel through space in the form of waves is _____ radiation.

7. _____ telescopes are optical telescopes that use lenses to collect and focus light.

8. The distance between the crest of one wave and the crest of the next is the _____.

9. Prisms make a rainbow out of white light. The rainbow is called a(n) _____.

10. _____ are instruments that collect and focus electromagnetic radiation from space.

Telescopes

Answer Key

After the Inquiry Warm-Up

1. Students' diagrams should show a small letter on the page, a larger image of the letter seen through the lens, and an inverted image of the letter when the page was moved far from the lens.

2. Looking through the hand lens magnified or enlarged the image of the letter.

3. The lens is thicker in the middle than it is at its edges.

4. Looking through the hand lens, an object moving farther away becomes harder and harder to see, and then suddenly the image flips upside down. With my unaided eyes, as an object is moved away, it becomes harder and harder to see, but it never flips upside down.

Key Concept Summaries

Telescopes are instruments that collect and focus light and other forms of electromagnetic radiation. An optical telescope uses lenses or mirrors to collect and focus visible light. The two major types of optical telescopes are refracting telescopes, which use convex lenses to gather and focus light, and reflecting telescopes, which use a curved mirror. Nonoptical telescopes collect and focus types of electromagnetic radiation besides visible light. Radio telescopes collect and focus radio waves from space. Other telescopes produce images in the infrared or X-ray portions of the spectrum.

Review and Reinforce

1. Electromagnetic radiation is energy that can travel through space in the form of waves.

2. radio waves, infrared radiation, visible light, ultraviolet radiation, X-rays, and gamma rays

3. Telescopes collect and focus electromagnetic radiation. Larger telescopes can collect more radiation, allowing astronomers to see farther.

4. Optical telescopes are placed on mountaintops or in space to avoid light pollution and minimize distortion by Earth's atmosphere.

5. h	**6.** c	**7.** d
8. a	**9.** g	**10.** b
11. f	**12.** i	**13.** e

Enrich

1. Gamma radiation should give the highest resolution image because it has the shortest wavelength.

2. Answers will vary. Sample: Space telescopes are expensive to build and launch. A large telescope, with high resolution, would be especially expensive to launch. A telescope in space that breaks is harder to fix than one that is on the ground.

3. Radio waves could be observed more cheaply and easily from ground-based radio telescopes. The low-resolution images are acceptable because the astronomers are looking at broad areas of the sky, not tiny details.

4. Infrared radiation because this kind of radiation can pass through the clouds of gas and dust in space and because its wavelength is short enough to create a higher resolution image.

Lesson Quiz

1. X-rays	**2.** true
3. visible	**4.** true
5. observatory	**6.** electromagnetic
7. Refracting	**8.** wavelength
9. spectrum	**10.** Telescopes

Place the outside corner, the corner away from the dotted line, in the corner of your copy machine to copy onto letter-size paper.

LESSON

2

How do astronomers learn about distant objects in the universe?

Blended Path Active learning using Student Edition, Inquiry Path, and Digital Path

Lesson Pacing: 1–2 periods or $\frac{1}{2}$–1 block

🕐 **SHORT ON TIME?** To do this lesson in approximately half the time, do the Activate Prior Knowledge activity on page 132. A discussion of the Key Concepts on pages 133 and 134 will familiarize students with the lesson content. Have students do the Quick Labs. The rest of the lesson can be completed by students independently.

Preference Navigator, in the online Planning tools, allows you to customize *Interactive Science* to your own teaching style. You can also edit lesson plans by selecting the Lesson Planner option.

Digital Teacher's Edition allows you to access your Teacher's Edition and Resource materials online.

my science online.com

Lesson Vocabulary

- parallax
- universe
- light-year
- scientific notation

 Content Refresher

Parsecs Just as kilometers become unwieldy as a unit to measure distances to the sun and farther, light-years become unwieldy for even greater astronomical distances such as between other galaxies and galaxy clusters. So, professional astronomers use the unit *parsecs* for these enormous distances. It was in 1913 that this unit of distance was recognized by astronomers and needed a formal name. Astronomer Royal Frank Watson Dyson recommended calling this unit of distance an *astron,* while Carl Charlier proposed calling it a *siriometer.* However Herbert Hall Turner coined the name *parsec,* which is a combination of the terms *parallax* and *second.* Parsecs are related to parallax; an object one parsec from Earth has a parallax of one second of arc ($\frac{1}{3,600}$ of a degree). One parsec is equal to 3.26 light-years.

Astronomers often use kiloparsecs (1 kiloparsec = 1,000 parsecs) to measure distance to stars in the Milky Way, and they use megaparsecs (1 megaparsec = 1 million parsecs) to measure distances to other galaxies or clusters of galaxies. So, the sun is 8.5 kiloparsecs from the center of the Milky Way. Some galaxies are 3,000 to 4,000 megaparsecs from Earth, which is 9 to 13 billion light-years away.

In general, parsec is the unit of distance regularly referred to in professional journals concerning astronomy. However, the light-year is most commonly used when addressing the general public.

LESSON OBJECTIVES

📖 Describe how astronomers measure distances to the stars.

📖 Explain how astronomers describe the scale of the universe.

ENGAGE AND EXPLORE

Teach this lesson using a variety of resources. Begin by reading **My Planet Diary** as a class. Have students share ideas about why astronomers would want to share information about Earth with aliens. Then have students do the **Inquiry Warm-Up activity.** Students will investigate scientific notation. Discuss why their measurements varied. The **After the Inquiry Warm-Up worksheet** sets up a discussion about how to make the most precise measurements. Have volunteers share their answers to question 4 about how to record a part of a string length.

EXPLAIN AND ELABORATE

Teach Key Concepts by explaining the term *parallax* and how it is useful to astronomers. To **Support the Big Q,** describe why parallax is only useful for stars up to a few hundred light-years away. Use **Figure 1** to illustrate how astronomers measure the movement of a star using parallax.

Teach Key Concepts by explaining to students how to write numbers using scientific notation. Continue to **Teach Key Concepts** by explaining that light-year is a unit of distance, not time. Hand out the **Key Concept Summaries** as a review of each part of the lesson. Students can also use the online **Vocab Flash Cards** to review key terms.

EVALUATE

Have students take the **Lesson Quiz.** For an alternate assessment, see the **EXAM**VIEW® Assessment Suite, Progress Monitoring Assessments, or SuccessTracker™.

ELL Support

1 Content and Language

The word *parallax* comes from the Greek word *parallaxis* meaning "tendency of two lines to connect at an angle."

Lab zone Inquiry Path
Hands-on learning in the Lab zone

Digital Path
Online learning at my science online.com

ENGAGE AND EXPLORE

To teach this lesson with an emphasis on inquiry, begin with the **Inquiry Warm-Up activity.** Students will investigate scientific notation. Discuss why their measurements varied. Have students do the **After the Inquiry Warm-Up worksheet.** Talk about which string they should use to get the most precise measurements. Have volunteers share their answers to question 4 about how to record the measurement of a part of a string.

EXPLAIN AND ELABORATE

Focus on the **Inquiry Skill** for the lesson. Point out that when you calculate, you use mathematical operations to describe a situation. What did students calculate in the **Inquiry Warm-Up activity?** *(The lengths of the short string needed to cover the length of a long string.)* **Support the Big Q** by explaining why scientists use parallax to measure distances up to a few hundred light-years away. Have students do the **Quick Lab** to see how parallax can be used to measure distance and then share their results.

Have students do the **Quick Lab** to explore the scale of the universe. Students can use the online **Vocab Flash Cards** to review key terms.

EVALUATE

Have students take the **Lesson Quiz.** For an alternate assessment, see the **EXAM**VIEW® Assessment Suite, Progress Monitoring Assessments, or SuccessTracker™.

ENGAGE AND EXPLORE

Teach this lesson using digital resources. Begin by having students explore real-world connections to the distances to stars at **My Planet Diary** online. Have them access the Chapter Resources to find the **Unlock the Big Question activity.** There they can answer the questions and refine their responses as they continue through the lesson. You can re-assign the activity and have students submit their work so you can track their progress.

EXPLAIN AND ELABORATE

Students reading above, at, or below the lexile measure of this lesson can access basic content readings at their level at **My Reading Web.** Have students use the online **Vocab Flash Cards** to preview key terms. **Support the Big Q** by explaining why astronomers use parallax and at what distances it is useful. Do the **Quick Lab** and then ask students to share their results.

Assign the **Do the Math activity** online and have students submit their work to you. Have students do the online **Interactive Art activity** to explore the scale of the universe. Have students do the **Quick Lab** to explore the scale of the universe and then submit their work to you. The **Key Concept Summaries** online allow students to read a summary and see an image associated with each part of the lesson. Online remediation is available at **My Science Coach.**

EVALUATE

Have students take the **Lesson Quiz.** For an alternate assessment, see the **EXAM**VIEW® Assessment Suite, Progress Monitoring Assessments, or SuccessTracker™.

2 Frontload the Lesson
Preview the lesson visuals, labels, and captions. Ask students what they know about the terms *light-year* and *scientific notation*. Explain the specific meanings these words have in science.

3 Comprehensible Input
Have students study the visuals and their captions on pages 133 and 135 to support the Key Concepts of the lesson.

4 Language Production
Pair or group students with varied language abilities to complete labs collaboratively for language practice. Have each student copy the completed written lab for personal reference.

5 Assess Understanding
Have students develop a portfolio of their notes and then do oral presentations of lesson content.

The Scale of the Universe

LESSON 4.2

Establish Learning Objectives

After this lesson, students will be able to:

🔑 Describe how astronomers measure distances to the stars.

🔑 Explain how astronomers describe the scale of the universe.

Engage

Activate Prior Knowledge

MY PLANET DIARY Read *Voyager Golden Record* with the class. Help students realize that *Voyager* is acting as an ambassador from Earth. Ask: **Have you ever listened to a phonograph record? How does it work?** *(The record is turned, and the shape of the groove in the record makes the needle vibrate, producing sound waves.)* Explain to students that the images on the surface of the record are instructions on how to play it. If students wonder how aliens will be able to play the record, tell them that it has a needle cartridge packed with it.

BIG IDEAS OF SCIENCE REFERENCE LIBRARY 📖 Have students look up the following topic: Universe.

Explore

Lab Resource: Inquiry Warm-Up 🧪

L2 STRINGING ALONG Students will create their own form of scientific notation.

LESSON 2

The Scale of the Universe

🔑 **How Do Astronomers Measure Distances to the Stars?**

🔑 **How Do Astronomers Describe the Scale of the Universe?**

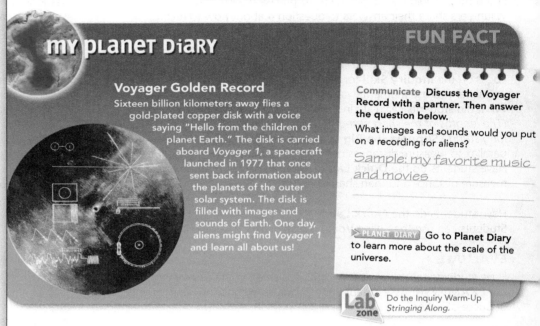

my PLANET DiARY

FUN FACT

Voyager Golden Record

Sixteen billion kilometers away flies a gold-plated copper disk with a voice saying "Hello from the children of planet Earth." The disk is carried aboard *Voyager 1*, a spacecraft launched in 1977 that once sent back information about the planets of the outer solar system. The disk is filled with images and sounds of Earth. One day, aliens might find *Voyager 1* and learn all about us!

Communicate Discuss the Voyager Record with a partner. Then answer the question below.

What images and sounds would you put on a recording for aliens?

Sample: my favorite music and movies

▶ PLANET DIARY Go to **Planet Diary** to learn more about the scale of the universe.

🧪 **Lab zone** Do the Inquiry Warm-Up *Stringing Along.*

How Do Astronomers Measure Distances to the Stars?

Standing on Earth looking up at the sky, it may seem as if there is no way to tell how far away the stars are. However, astronomers have found ways to measure those distances. 🔑 **Astronomers often use parallax to measure distances to nearby stars.**

Parallax is the apparent change in position of an object when you look at it from different places. Astronomers can measure the parallax of nearby stars to determine their distances.

SUPPORT ALL READERS
Lexile Measure = 910L   Lexile Word Count = 933

Prior Exposure to Content: May be the first time students have encountered this topic

Academic Vocabulary: *calculate, summarize*

Science Vocabulary: *parallax, universe, light year, scientific notation*

Concept Level: May be difficult for students who struggle with abstract ideas

Preteach With: My Planet Diary "Voyager Golden Records" and Figure 2 activity

Go to **My Reading Web** to access leveled readings that provide a foundation for the content.

my science online.com

Vocabulary
- parallax
- light-year
- universe
- scientific notation

Skills
- ⟳ Reading: Summarize
- △ Inquiry: Calculate

FIGURE 1 ....

Parallax of Stars

The apparent movement of a star when seen from a different position is called parallax. Note that the diagram is not to scale.

✏️ **CHALLENGE** Hold a finger about half an arm's length away from your face, as shown in the picture below. Switch back and forth between closing your left and right eye and watch how your finger appears to move against the background. Why does your finger seem to move? How is this related to the parallax of stars?

The position of your finger seems to move because your eyes are a few centimeters apart. In the same way, the position of a star appears to move when viewed from different places in Earth's orbit.

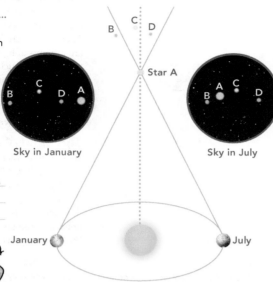

Sky in January

Star A

Sky in July

January · · · · · · · · July

As shown in **Figure 1**, astronomers look at a nearby star when Earth is on one side of the sun. Then they look at the same star again six months later, when Earth is on the opposite side of the sun. Astronomers measure how much the nearby star appears to move against a background of stars that are much farther away. They can then use this measurement to calculate the distance to the nearby star. The less the nearby star appears to move, the farther away it is.

Astronomers can use parallax to measure distances up to a few hundred light-years from Earth. The parallax of any star that is farther away is too small to measure accurately.

Lab zone Do the Quick Lab
How Far Is That Star?

🔑 **Assess Your Understanding**

got it? ....

○ I get it! Now I know that astronomers often measure the distances to nearby stars using __parallax__, which is *the apparent change in position of an object when you look at it from different places.*

○ I need extra help with *See TE note.*

Go to **MY SCIENCE COACH** *online for help with this subject.*

133

Explain

Introduce Vocabulary

Students who watch or read science fiction may be familiar with the term *light-year.* Tell students that a light-year is a measure of distance. It is the distance that light travels in one year.

Teach Key Concepts 🗝️

Explain to students that astronomers can measure distances to nearby stars by using parallax. Ask: **What is parallax?** *(The apparent change in position of an object when looked at from different places.)* **What different places do astronomers use?** *(Different points along Earth's orbit)* Point out that using parallax to find distance is not a direct measurement. It provides information astronomers use to calculate distance.

Support the Big Q ❓▸

USING PARALLAX Students may ask why there isn't another method, such as radar, to measure distances in space. Point out that the distances are too large for any method of direct measurement that works on Earth. **Over what distance is parallax useful?** *(For stars up to a few hundred light-years away)* **Why?** *(The farther away an object is, the smaller its parallax. The parallax of an object more than a few hundred light-years away is too small to measure.)*

Elaborate

Lab Resource: Quick Lab 🧪

L3 **HOW FAR IS THAT STAR?** Students will explore how parallax can be used to measure distance.

Evaluate

Assess Your Understanding

Have students evaluate their understanding by completing the appropriate sentence.

RTI Response to Intervention

If students cannot explain the use of parallax to measure distances, **then** have them reread the Key Concept and the definition of *parallax.*

MY SCIENCE ⑤ **COACH** Have students go online for help in understanding how astronomers use distance to measure parallax.

My Planet Diary provides an opportunity for students to explore real-world connections to the distances to stars.

Explain

Teach Key Concepts 🔑

Explain to students that distances in astronomy are often very, very large. Instead of writing out a number with many zeros, scientists use scientific notation. Ask: **How are numbers written in scientific notation?** *(A number between 1 and 10 is multiplied by a power of 10.)* Tell students that the power of ten tells how many decimal places there should be after the number. Give students some examples, such as $9,000,000 = 9 \times 10^6$. and $730,000,000 = 7.3 \times 10^8$. If students have difficulty converting standard notation to scientific notation, have them write out the standard form. Starting at the right of the digit in the ones column, students can use a pencil to mark decimal places to the left until there is only one digit to the left of the pencil. The pencil is where the decimal point is placed. The number of decimal places moved is the power of ten.

🔄 **Summarize** Tell students that when they summarize, they restate the main points of the passage and eliminate details and examples.

Teach Key Concepts 🔑

Tell students that astronomers developed a unit of distance to measure distances in space. This unit is called a light-year. Ask: **What is a light-year based on?** *(The distance light travels in one year)* **How many kilometers are equal to a light-year?** *(9.46 trillion kilometers)* **How would you write this in scientific notation?** *(9.46×10^{12} km or 9.46×10^{15} m)*

Elaborate

Do the Math!

L1 Assist students in converting the first number to scientific notation. Emphasize that they should count decimal places, not zeroes.

🔺 **Calculate** Tell students that calculating involves performing mathematical operations like multiplication, division, addition, and subtraction. Scientists perform calculations on data to help them analyze the data.

See *Math Skill and Problem-Solving Activities* for support.

🖊 ....

🔄 **Summarize** Explain why astronomers use scientific notation to describe sizes.

Because the numbers they use are very large or very small

do the
math!
....
Scientific Notation

To express a number in scientific notation, first insert a decimal point in the original number so you have a number between one and ten. Then count the number of places that the decimal point moved. That gives you the power of ten.

1 🔺 **Calculate** The sun takes about 220,000,000 years to revolve once around the center of the galaxy. Express this length of time in scientific notation.

2.2×10^8 years

2 🔺 **Calculate** The distant star Deneb is thought by some astronomers to be 3,230 light-years away. Write this distance in scientific notation.

3.23×10^3 light-years

How Do Astronomers Describe the Scale of the Universe?

Astronomers define the **universe** as all of space and everything in it. The universe is enormous, almost beyond imagination. Astronomers study objects as close as the moon and as far away as quasars. They study incredibly large objects, such as clusters of galaxies that are millions of light-years across. They also study the behavior of tiny particles, such as the atoms within the stars. 🔑 **Since the numbers astronomers use are often very large or very small, they frequently use scientific notation to describe sizes and distances in the universe. They use a unit called the light-year to measure distances between the stars.**

The Light-Year Distances to the stars are so large that meters are not very practical units. In space, light travels at a speed of about 300,000,000 meters per second. A **light-year** is the distance that light travels in one year, about 9.46 trillion kilometers.

The light-year is a unit of distance, not time. To understand this better, consider an example. If you bicycle at 10 kilometers per hour, it would take you 1 hour to go to a mall 10 kilometers away. You could say that the mall is "1 bicycle-hour" away.

Scientific Notation **Scientific notation** uses powers of ten to write very large or very small numbers in shorter form. Each number is written as the product of a number between 1 and 10 and a power of 10. For example: 1,200 is written as 1.2×10^3.

One light-year is about 9,460,000,000,000,000 meters. To express this number in scientific notation, first insert a decimal point in the original number so that you have a number between one and ten. In this case, the rounded number is 9.5. To determine the power of ten, count the number of places that the decimal point moved. Since there are 15 digits after the first digit, in scientific notation this number can now be written as 9.5×10^{15} meters.

The Immensity of Space The objects in the universe vary greatly in their distance from Earth. To understand the scale of these distances, imagine that you are going on a journey through the universe. Refer to **Figure 2** as you take your imaginary trip. Start on Earth. Now shift to the right and change the scale by 100,000,000,000, or 10^{11}. You're now close to the sun, which is located 1.5×10^{11} meters away. As you move from left to right across **Figure 2**, the distance increases. The nearest star to our sun, Alpha Centauri, is 4.2×10^{16} meters or 4.3 light-years away. The nearest galaxy to the Milky Way, the Andromeda galaxy, is about 2.4×10^{22} meters away.

Digital Lesson: Assign the *Do the Math* activity online and have students submit their work to you.

Interactive Art: allows students to explore the scale of the universe.

my science online.com ▸ **Scale of the Universe**

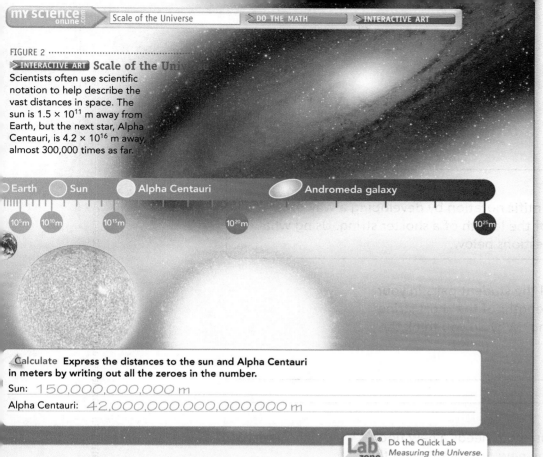

FIGURE 2 ....

INTERACTIVE ART Scale of the Universe
Scientists often use scientific notation to help describe the vast distances in space. The sun is 1.5×10^{11} m away from Earth, but the next star, Alpha Centauri, is 4.2×10^{16} m away, almost 300,000 times as far.

Earth | Sun | Alpha Centauri | Andromeda galaxy

10^5 m | 10^{10} m | 10^{15} m | 10^{20} m | 10^{25} m

Calculate Express the distances to the sun and Alpha Centauri in meters by writing out all the zeroes in the number.

Sun: 150,000,000,000 m

Alpha Centauri: 42,000,000,000,000,000 m

 Do the Quick Lab
Measuring the Universe.

Assess Your Understanding

1a. Review What is scientific notation?

A system that uses powers of ten to write very large or very small numbers in shorter form.

b. Explain How is scientific notation useful to astronomers?

Astronomers use scientific notation to help describe the vast distances and sizes found in space.

c. Calculate The Andromeda galaxy is 2,200,000 light-years away. Write that measurement using scientific notation.

2.2×10^6 light-years

got it? ....

O **I get it!** Now I know that to describe the scale of the universe, astronomers use scientific notation and light-years.

O **I need extra help with** See TE note.

Go to my science COACH *online for help with this subject.*

135

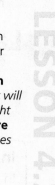
LESSON 4.2

Make Analogies

L1 MEASURING DISTANCE TO SCHOOL Explain to students that they choose appropriate units for measurements, just as astronomers use units like light-years. Ask: **What is the distance between your home and school?** (*Answers will vary, but will probably be given in miles. Shorter distances might be measured in city blocks.*) **Would you measure that distance using inches? Explain.** (*No, inches are too small to measure a distance that large.*)

Lab Resource: Quick Lab

L3 MEASURING THE UNIVERSE Students will explore the scale of the universe.

Evaluate

Assess Your Understanding

After students answer the questions, have them evaluate their understanding by completing the appropriate sentence.

RTI Response to Intervention

1a. If students cannot define *scientific notation*, **then** have them locate the highlighted term and review the definition.

b. If students need help with explaining how scientific notation is useful to astronomers, **then** have them reread the information for the read head *The Immensity of Space.*

c. If students have trouble using scientific notation, **then** have them review the *Do the Math* activity.

my science COACH Have students go online for help in understanding scientific notation.

Differentiated Instruction

L1 Scientific Notation and Abbreviations Have students explain how using scientific notation is similar to using abbreviations. They can write out a very large number, like 8 trillion, and then write the number using scientific notation as an example.

L3 Scientific Notation for Very Small Numbers Tell students that scientific notation is used for very big numbers, and for very small numbers (such as measurements having to do with atoms and with cells). Challenge students to learn how scientific notation is used to write numbers much smaller than one.

Lab zone — After the Inquiry Warm-Up

The Scale of the Universe

Inquiry Warm-Up, *Stringing Along*

In the Inquiry Warm-Up, you investigated scientific notation by developing a way to describe the length of a long string in terms of the length of a shorter string. Using what you learned from that activity, answer the questions below.

---

1. **ANALYZE SOURCES OF ERROR** In Step 2, did all the student pairs in your classroom arrive at an identical number of lengths of the short string needed to cover the length of the long string? Why do you think the measurements varied?

   _____

   _____

2. **MAKE JUDGMENTS** Suppose your school gymnasium needs a new floor. Would you rather take measurements for the new gym floor using the long string or the short string? Explain.

   _____

   _____

   _____

3. **MAKE JUDGMENTS** When construction workers saw the wood to make the new gym floor, they need to be very precise so that the floor fits in place. Which would be more precise, measurements given in terms of the long string or measurements given in terms of the short string? Explain.

   _____

   _____

4. **SOLVE PROBLEMS** As you measure the gymnasium floor with the long string, you find that the first side you measure does not divide evenly into lengths of the long string. It measures a certain number of whole string lengths plus one last portion of the string length. How can you record the measurement?

   _____

   _____

Assess Your Understanding

The Scale of the Universe

How Do Astronomers Measure Distances to the Stars?

gotit? ···

○ **I get it!** Now I know that astronomers measure the distances to nearby stars using
_____, which is _____
_____
_____

○ **I need extra help with** _____
_____

How Do Astronomers Describe the Scale of the Universe?

1a. REVIEW What is scientific notation? _____
_____
_____

b. EXPLAIN How is scientific notation useful to astronomers? _____
_____
_____

c. CALCULATE The Andromeda galaxy is 2,200,000 light-years away.
Write that measurement using scientific notation. _____

gotit? ···

○ **I get it!** Now I know that to measure the scale of the universe, astronomers use _____
_____

○ **I need extra help with** _____
_____

Key Concept Summaries

The Scale of the Universe

How Do Astronomers Measure Distances to Stars?

Astronomers often use parallax to measure the distances to nearby stars. Parallax is the apparent change in position of an object when you look at it from different places. Astronomers note the position of a star, then they note its position six months later. They measure how much the star appears to move against a background of stars much farther away. The less the nearby star appears to move, the farther away it is. Parallax works as a measuring tool for distances up to a few hundred light-years from Earth.

How Do Astronomers Describe the Scale of the Universe?

Astronomers define the **universe** as all of space and everything in it. The universe is enormous, almost beyond imagination. Astronomers study objects as close as the moon and as far away as quasars. They study incredibly large objects, such as clusters of galaxies that are millions of light-years across. They also study the behavior of tiny particles, such as atoms within the stars.

Since the numbers astronomers use are often very large or very small, they frequently use scientific notation to describe sizes and distances in the universe. **Scientific notation** uses powers of ten to write very large or very small numbers in shorter form. Each number is written as the product of a number between 1 and 10 and a power of 10. For example, 1,200 is written as 1.2×10^3.

Astronomers use a unit called a light-year to measure distances between stars. A light-year is the distance light travels in one year, about 9,460,000,000,000,000 meters (9.46×10^{15} meters in scientific notation).

On a separate sheet of paper, describe how astronomers can use parallax to measure distances to nearby stars. The nearest star to the sun, Proxima Centauri, is about 39,700,000,000,000,000 meters away. Rewrite this distance using scientific notation.

Review and Reinforce

The Scale of the Universe

Understanding Main Ideas

If the statement is true, write *true*. If the statement is false, change the underlined word or words to make the statement true.

1. _____ The spacecraft *Voyager* is 16,000,000,000 km away from Earth. That is the same as 1.6×10^{10} km.

2. _____ An astronomer says that his house cost 2.9×10^5. That is $2,900,000.

3. _____ A light-year is a measure of time on an astronomical scale.

4. _____ Astronomers often use parallax to measure distances to stars.

5. _____ Refraction makes nearby stars look like they shift position against the background of stars between winter and summer viewings from Earth.

6. _____ The solar system is all of space and everything in it.

Building Vocabulary

Write a definition for each of these terms on the lines below.

7. light-year

_____

_____

8. parallax

_____

_____

9. universe

_____

_____

10. scientific notation

_____

_____

The Scale of the Universe

Read the passage and study the table below. Then use a separate sheet of paper to answer the questions that follow.

The Apparent Magnitude Scale

The apparent magnitude of stars was first recorded by the Greek astronomer Hipparchus about 160 B.C. Hipparchus grouped stars according to their brightness or *magnitude*. He called the twenty brightest stars *first magnitude* stars. Stars half that bright were *second magnitude*. *Third magnitude* stars were half as bright as second magnitude stars, and so on. Modern astronomers have changed Hipparchus's system a little. In the modern system, an object of magnitude 1 appears 100 times as bright as one of magnitude of 6. This means that if two objects are separated by one unit of magnitude, the brighter object appears about 2.5 times as bright as the dimmer one. A star of magnitude 1 is about 2.5 times as bright as a star of magnitude 2. Using this scale, the *dimmer* the object, the *larger* the magnitude number.

What about very bright objects? Remember, the brighter an object appears, the lower the magnitude number. Very bright objects have negative magnitudes. Sirius, the brightest star in the sky (except for the sun), has a magnitude of –1.5. Venus is the brightest planet. Its brightness varies, but at its brightest, its magnitude is –4. The suns magnitude is –26.5.

Object	Apparent Magnitude
Sun	–26.50
Venus (maximum brightness)	–4.00
Mars (maximum brightness)	–2.00
Procyon	0.36
Regulus	1.36
Dimmest visible to the naked eye	6.00
Dimmest visible with binoculars	10.00

1. What is the difference between the magnitudes of the bright stars Regulus and Procyon? Which is brighter? How much brighter is it than the dimmer one?
2. How much brighter is Venus than Mars?
3. What is the difference between the magnitude of the dimmest star that is visible with the naked eye and the magnitude of the dimmest star that can be seen with binoculars? How much brighter is the former than the latter?

Name _____ Date _____ Class _____

The Scale of the Universe

Write the letter of the correct answer on the line at the left.

1. ___ In space, light travels at a speed of about 300,000,000 m/s. Which expresses that speed correctly in scientific notation?

   A 300,000 km/s

   B 3×10^9 m/s

   C 3×10^8 m/s

   D 3×10^7 m/s

2. ___ A star is 9×10^{12} meters from Earth. What is that number in expanded form?

   A 900,000,000,000 meters

   B 9,000,000,000,000 meters

   C 90,000,000,000,000 meters

   D 9.0×10^{12} meters

3. ___ After six months, an astronomer notices that star A moves a greater distance than star B. Which conclusion is correct?

   A Star A is closer than star B.

   B Star A and star B are equally far away.

   C Star A is farther away than star B.

   D More observations are necessary to determine which star is farther away.

4. ___ A star looks like it's located one place in the sky in January and a different place in June. What is this phenomenon called?

   A a light-year

   B parallax

   C refraction

   D scientific notation

Fill in the blank to complete each statement.

5. _____ uses powers of ten to write very large or very small numbers in shorter form.

6. The _____ is made up of all of space and everything in it.

7. A light-year is a measure of _____.

8. Astronomers use _____ to measure the distance to stars that are within several hundred light-years of Earth.

9. The distance light travels through space in a year is one _____.

10. Parallax is the apparent change of _____ of an object when you look at it from different places.

The Scale of the Universe

Answer Key

After the Inquiry Warm-Up

1. No. The measurements varied because flipping the short string end over end more than 100 times introduced some error.

2. Answers will vary. Sample: I would rather measure the gym floor using the long string. Using the short string would take a long time, and flipping it end over end would introduce error to my measurements.

3. Measurements written in terms of the short string will be more precise because the increments are smaller.

4. Use a fraction or decimal to indicate the last portion of string length.

Key Concept Summaries

To use parallax to calculate a star's distance from earth, astronomers first note the position of the star against a background of more distant stars. Then, six months later, when Earth has moved to the other side of the sun, they note the new position of the star. By measuring the change in position relative to the background stars, astronomers can calculate the nearby star's distance from Earth. Proxima Centauri is about 3.97×10^{16} meters away.

Review and Reinforce

1. true

2. $290,000

3. distance

4. true

5. Parallax

6. universe

7. the distance light travels in one year

8. the apparent change of position of an object when you look at it from different places

9. all of space and everything in it

10. uses powers of ten to write very large or very small numbers in shorter form

Enrich

1. The difference in magnitude is 1. Procyon is about 2.5 times brighter than Regulus.

2. The magnitude of Venus is 2 less than that of Mars, so Venus is about 2.5 × 2.5, or about 6.3 times brighter than Mars.

3. The difference in magnitude between the dimmest star that can be seen with the naked eye and the dimmest one that can be seen with binoculars is 4. This means that the dimmest naked-eye star is about 2.5 × 2.5 × 2.5 × 2.5 = about 39 times brighter than the dimmest binocular star.

Lesson Quiz

1. C
2. B
3. A
4. B
5. Scientific notation
6. universe
7. distance
8. parallax
9. light-year
10. position

Place the outside corner, the corner away from the dotted line, in the corner of your copy machine to copy onto letter-size paper.

LESSON 3

How do astronomers learn about distant objects in the universe?

Lesson Pacing: 2–3 periods or 1–1½ blocks

🕐 **SHORT ON TIME?** To do this lesson in approximately half the time, do the Activate Prior Knowledge activity on page 136. A discussion of the Key Concepts on pages 137, 139, and 140 will familiarize students with the lesson content. Have students do the Quick Labs. The rest of the lesson can be completed by students independently.

Preference Navigator, in the online Planning tools, allows you to customize *Interactive Science* to your own teaching style. You can also edit lesson plans by selecting the Lesson Planner option.

Digital Teacher's Edition allows you to access your Teacher's Edition and Resource materials online.

my science online.com

Lesson Vocabulary

- spectrograph
- apparent brightness
- absolute brightness
- Hertzsprung-Russell diagram
- main sequence

Content Refresher

Hertzsprung-Russell Diagrams The realization that the color of stars could be related to their brightness came independently to Ejnar Hertzsprung and to Henry Norris Russell. The result was the Hertzsprung-Russell diagram, or H-R diagram, which was published in 1914.

There are several versions of the Hertzsprung-Russell diagram. Initially, the diagram plotted the spectral type of stars on the horizontal axis and displayed the absolute magnitude on the vertical axis. Now, more often the horizontal axis identifies the B-V (blue-violet) color index and is commonly called the color-magnitude diagram.

Another version of the H-R diagram shows the relationship between absolute brightness and temperature. Color and temperature of a star are related. The energy of light depends inversely on its wavelength. The wavelength of light is inversely related to its frequency; a long wavelength corresponds to a low frequency. Consequently, the energy is directly related to the frequency; a low frequency corresponds to a low energy. Since blue light is high frequency (short wavelength), it is high energy. Students often associate red with hot and blue with cold; that is not the case here. Blue stars are hotter than red stars. This is evident on the H-R diagrams.

LESSON OBJECTIVES

- Explain how stars are classified.
- Explain the H-R diagram, and explain how astronomers use it.

Blended Path
Active learning using Student Edition, Inquiry Path, and Digital Path

ENGAGE AND EXPLORE

Teach this lesson using a variety of resources. Begin by reading **My Planet Diary** as a class. Have students share ideas about black holes. Then have students do the **Inquiry Warm-Up activity.** Students will investigate how stars differ from each other. Discuss how the stars, Jupiter, and Earth's moon appear from Earth. The **After the Inquiry Warm-Up worksheet** sets up a discussion about why some objects in the sky appear to be brighter or larger than they really are. Have volunteers share their answers to question 4 about whether it is possible to determine the brightness of stars using photos taken on Earth.

EXPLAIN AND ELABORATE

Teach Key Concepts by describing how scientists classify stars. To **Support the Big Q,** explain how scientists use spectrographs to determine the elements found in stars. Then have students practice the inquiry skill in the **Apply It activity. Teach Key Concepts** by explaining the terms apparent brightness and absolute brightness.

Continue to **Teach Key Concepts** by telling students how astronomers use the H-R diagram to classify stars. Interpret information about stars using the H-R diagram in **Figure 3. Lead a Discussion** about the size of supergiants such as Betelgeuse. Hand out the **Key Concept Summaries** as a review of each part of the lesson. Students can also use the online **Vocab Flash Cards** to review key terms.

EVALUATE

Have students take the **Lesson Quiz.** For an alternate assessment, see the **EXAM**VIEW® Assessment Suite, Progress Monitoring Assessments, or SuccessTracker™.

ELL Support

1 Content and Language

The terms *absolute brightness* and *apparent brightness* both contain the word *brightness.* The suffix *-ness* means "quality, condition, or degree." What other words contain the suffix *-ness? (Darkness, goodness, kindness)*

Lab zone Inquiry Path
Hands-on learning in the Lab zone

Digital Path
Online learning at **my science online**.com

ENGAGE AND EXPLORE

To teach this lesson with an emphasis on inquiry, begin with the **Inquiry Warm-Up activity.** Students will investigate how stars differ. Discuss how Earth's moon, the stars, and Jupiter appear from Earth. Have students do the **After the Inquiry Warm-Up worksheet.** Talk about why the size and brightness of objects is sometimes difficult to accurately describe. Have volunteers share their answers to question 4 about whether it is possible to determine the brightness of stars using photos taken on Earth.

EXPLAIN AND ELABORATE

Focus on the **Inquiry Skill** for the lesson. Point out that when you interpret data, you scrutinize data to look for patterns. Where did students get the data to interpret the size and brightness of the objects in the **Inquiry Warm-Up activity?** *(From a photograph taken on Earth)* To **Support the Big Q,** describe how astronomers use a spectrograph to determine the elements found in stars. Review the spectrums on page 138 and record characteristics of each element before beginning the **Apply It activity.** Ask volunteers to share their interpretations of the data. Do the **Teacher Demo** to model a spectrograph. Have students do the **Quick Lab** to see how distance affects apparent brightness of light and then share their results.

Do the **Quick Lab** to explore the creation and use of an H-R Diagram. Students can use the online **Vocab Flash Cards** to review key terms.

EVALUATE

Have students take the **Lesson Quiz.** For an alternate assessment, see the **EXAM**VIEW® Assessment Suite, Progress Monitoring Assessments, or SuccessTracker™.

ENGAGE AND EXPLORE

Teach this lesson using digital resources. Begin by having students explore real-world connections to the classifications of stars at **My Planet Diary** online. Have them access the Chapter Resources to find the **Unlock the Big Question activity.** There they can answer the questions and refine their responses as they continue through the lesson. You can re-assign the activity and have students submit their work so you can track their progress.

EXPLAIN AND ELABORATE

Students reading above, at, or below the lexile measure of this lesson can access basic content readings at their level at **My Reading Web.** Have students use the online **Vocab Flash Cards** to preview key terms. **Support the Big Q** by describing how the spectrograph is used to determine the elements found in stars. Review the spectrums on page 138 and discuss defining characteristics of the elements before assigning the online **Apply It activity.** Ask volunteers to share their interpretations. Have students submit their work to you. Do the **Quick Lab** and then ask students to share their results.

Have students do the **Quick Lab** to explore the development and use of an H-R diagram. The **Key Concept Summaries** online allow students to read a summary and see an image associated with each part of the lesson. Online remediation is available at **My Science Coach.**

EVALUATE

Have students take the **Lesson Quiz.** For an alternate assessment, see the **EXAM**VIEW® Assessment Suite, Progress Monitoring Assessments, or SuccessTracker™.

2 Frontload the Lesson
Preview the lesson visuals, labels, and captions. Ask students what they know about the terms *absolute brightness* and *apparent brightness.* Explain the specific meanings these words have in science.

3 Comprehensible Input
Have students study the visuals and their captions on pages 137–140 to support the Key Concepts of the lesson.

4 Language Production
Pair or group students with varied language abilities to complete labs collaboratively for language practice. Have each student copy the completed written lab for personal reference.

5 Assess Understanding
Have students keep a content area log for this lesson using a two-column format with the headings "What I Understand" and "What I Don't Understand." Follow up so that students can move items from the "Don't Understand" to the "Understand" column.

LESSON 4.3

Characteristics of Stars

Establish Learning Objectives

After this lesson, students will be able to:

 Explain how stars are classified.

 Explain the H-R diagram, and explain how astronomers use it.

Engage

Activate Prior Knowledge

MY PLANET DIARY Read *Black Holes* with the class. Tell students that black holes have so much gravity that they even drag light inside, not letting it escape. Ask: **If light cannot come out of a black hole, how can we see it?** *(We can look for evidence of the immense gravity. Matter being pulled into black holes gets so hot that it gives off X-rays while it is approaching the black hole. We can detect the X-rays.)*

BIG IDEAS OF SCIENCE REFERENCE LIBRARY
Have students look up the following topic: Constellations.

Explore

Lab Resource: Inquiry Warm-Up

L1 HOW STARS DIFFER Students will explore how stars differ from each other.

Characteristics of Stars

 How Are Stars Classified?

 What Is an H-R Diagram and How Do Astronomers Use It?

MY PLANET DIARY

CAREERS

Black Holes

If you were an astronomer, you might study some of the strangest objects in the universe. For almost 100 years, scientists believed that some stars became black holes when they died. But a black hole is an object with gravity so strong that not even light can escape. So scientists couldn't prove that black holes existed because they couldn't see them. Eventually, astronomers discovered a way to prove black holes exist. They realized that they could detect the matter being pulled into the black hole. That matter reaches such high temperatures that it releases X-rays. In the 1960s, astronomers launched a rocket to record X-rays from outer space. On this first mission, they found evidence for black holes!

Communicate Answer the questions below. Then discuss your answers with a partner.

1. Why was it so hard to prove that black holes exist?

   Sample: because you can't see them

2. What subjects, other than astronomy, would astronomers have to study in order to discover black holes?

   Sample: math and physics

> **PLANET DIARY** Go to Planet Diary to learn more about characteristics of stars.

Lab zone — Do the Inquiry Warm-Up *How Stars Differ.*

SUPPORT ALL READERS

Lexile Measure = 930L   Lexile Word Count = 1133

Prior Exposure to Content: Many students may have misconceptions on this topic

Academic Vocabulary: *data, identify, interpret, main idea*

Science Vocabulary: *spectrograph, main sequence*

Concept Level: May be difficult for students who struggle with abstract ideas

Preteach With: My Planet Diary "Black Holes" and Figure 3 activity

Go to **My Reading Web** to access leveled readings that provide a foundation for the content.

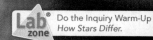

Vocabulary
- spectrograph
- apparent brightness
- absolute brightness
- Hertzsprung-Russell diagram
- main sequence

Skills
- Reading: Identify the Main Idea
- Inquiry: Interpret Data

How Are Stars Classified?

All stars are huge spheres of glowing gas. Made up mostly of hydrogen, stars produce energy through the process of nuclear fusion. Astronomers classify stars according to their physical characteristics. **Characteristics used to classify stars include color, temperature, size, composition, and brightness.**

Color and Temperature If you look at the night sky, you can see slight differences in the colors of the stars. Some stars look reddish. Others are yellow or blue-white, as shown in **Figure 1**.

A star's color reveals its surface temperature. The coolest stars—with a surface temperature of about 3,200°C—appear red. Our yellow sun has a surface temperature of about 5,500°C. The hottest stars, with surface temperatures of over 20,000°C, appear bluish.

Size When you look at stars in the sky, they all appear to be points of light of the same size. Many stars are actually about the size of the sun. However, some stars are much larger than the sun. Very large stars are called giant stars or supergiant stars.

Most stars are smaller than the sun. White dwarf stars are about the size of Earth. Neutron stars are even smaller, about 20 kilometers in diameter.

✎ **Identify the Main Idea**
Write a sentence that says what the color of a star indicates.

The color of a star indicates the star's temperature.

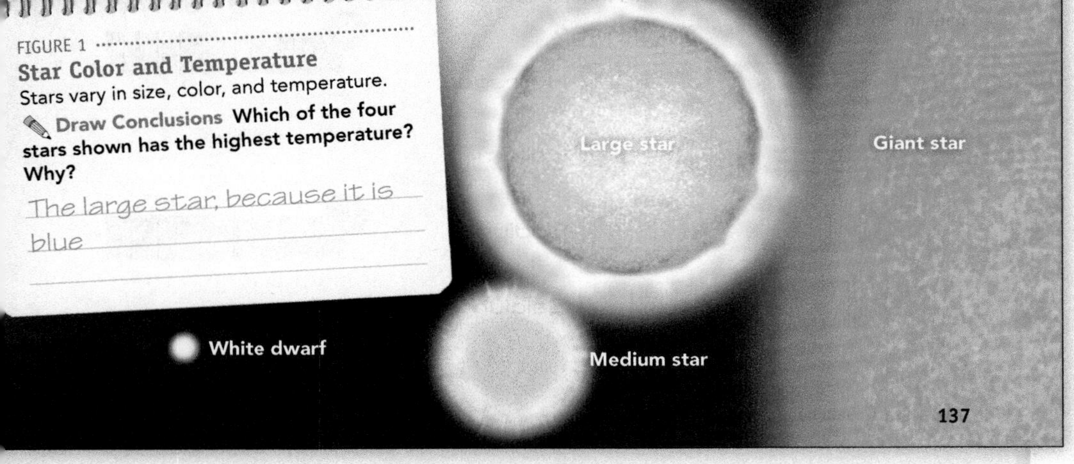

FIGURE 1 ....
Star Color and Temperature
Stars vary in size, color, and temperature.
✎ **Draw Conclusions** Which of the four stars shown has the highest temperature? Why?

The large star, because it is blue

Large star

Giant star

White dwarf

Medium star

137

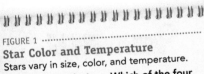

ELL Support

1 Content and Language
Write *absolute brightness* and *apparent brightness* on the board. Contrast the descriptions by explaining that *absolute* means "complete" or "definite," whereas *apparent* means "seeming to be, but perhaps not so."

2 Frontload the Lesson
Invite students to reflect on times they have looked at a night sky full of stars. Encourage them to share whether all of

the visible stars are about the same size and color. Tell students they will learn how scientists classify stars.

3 Comprehensible Input
Have students demonstrate the principle underlying *apparent brightness*. In a darkened room, students should observe the levels of brightness when a flashlight is a few meters away and very close to them.

Explain

Introduce Vocabulary
Students have probably heard someone preface a statement with the word *apparently,* indicating that the speaker is basing the statement on how a situation appears, not on the facts. Write the term *apparent brightness* on the board. Tell students that this describes how bright a star appears to be from our vantage point on Earth. It does not describe how bright the star actually is.

Teach Key Concepts 🔑
Explain to students that astronomers classify stars based on their color, temperature, size, composition, and brightness. This is similar to the way biologists classify plants or geologists classify rocks. Ask: **What does a star's color indicate?** *(Surface temperature)* **What are some colors of stars?** *(Yellow, blue-white or reddish)* **What color are the hottest stars?** *(Bluish)* **Why is it difficult to tell how large a star is?** *(Stars appear to all be small because they are very far away. Really, some are much larger than our sun.)* Point out that most stars are about 70% hydrogen and 28% helium, with the remaining 2% made up of other elements.

Identify the Main Idea Tell students that the main idea is the most important, or biggest, idea in every paragraph or section. The other information supports or further explains the main idea.

Address Misconceptions
L1 ENERGY AND THE ELECTROMAGNETIC SPECTRUM Students may mistakenly think that red stars are hotter than blue stars, since we tend to represent hot with red (like on a hot water faucet) and cold with blue (like snow and ice). Instead, blue light comes from higher temperature stars than red light. If students think of a gas flame, they should be able to remember correctly. Ask: **What is the hottest part of the fame of a gas stove?** *(The blue flame)*

My Planet Diary provides an opportunity for students to explore real-world connections to the classification of stars.

my science online | Star Classification

Explain

Support the Big Q

SPECTROGRAPHS Explain to students that, like a prism, a spectrograph separates light into the individual colors of which it is made. Ask: **How can chemical elements be identified using spectrums?** *(Each element has its own signature spectrum. Just like each person has a unique set of fingerprints.)* **What are the dark lines in a spectrum?** *(Wavelengths of light is absorbed by the element.)* **What happens to some of the light as it passes through the gases in the outer layers of a star?** *(The gases absorb certain wavelengths of light, leaving dark lines in the spectrum.)*

Elaborate

Apply It!

L1 Before beginning the activity, have students study the spectrums for the four elements. Spectrums shown from a spectrograph are often shown from violet to red. In the *Apply It!* activity, they are shown from red to violet to be consistent with the way the color spectrum is usually presented. The spectrums in the book are simplified to help students have a better understanding.

△ **Interpret Data** Tell students that scientists analyze data to look for any patterns or trends.

Teacher Demo

L2 MODEL COLOR SEPARATION

Materials projector; prism; red, green, and blue cellophane

Time 15 minutes
In a dark room, shine the light from the projector through the prism so the spectrum is visible on a white surface. Use a double thickness of red cellophane to reduce light leaks. Ask students to predict what will happen when the red cellophane is held between the prism and the spectrum. Students will observe that only the red part of the spectrum remains visible.

Ask: **Why did the other colors disappear?** *(The cellophane allowed only the red light to pass through.)*

Repeat the process with green and then blue cellophane. Ask students what will happen when both red and blue cellophane sheets are held in front of the projector. *(No light will pass.)*

Ask: **How does this demonstration relate to a spectrograph?** *(Like a spectrograph, the prism breaks light into a spectrum. Different colors are absorbed by the different pieces of cellophane.)*

Chemical Composition Stars vary in their chemical composition. The chemical composition of most stars is about 73 percent hydrogen, 25 percent helium, and 2 percent other elements by mass. This is close to the composition of the sun.

Astronomers use spectrographs to determine the elements found in stars. A **spectrograph** (SPEK truh graf) is a device that breaks light into colors and produces an image of the resulting spectrum. Today, most large telescopes have spectrographs to analyze light.

The gases in a star's atmosphere absorb some wavelengths of light produced within the star. When the star's light is seen through a spectrograph, each absorbed wavelength is shown as a dark line on a spectrum. Each chemical element absorbs light at particular wavelengths. Just as each person has a unique set of fingerprints, each element has a unique set of spectral lines for a given temperature.

Alnitak approximately **800** light-years away

Alnilam approximately **1,300** light-years away

apply it!

The lines on the spectrums below are from four different elements. By comparing a star's spectrum with the spectrums of known elements, astronomers can infer each element found in the star. Each star's spectrum is an overlap of the spectrums from the individual elements.

△ **Interpret Data** Identify the elements with the strongest lines in Stars A, B, and C.

Hydrogen

Helium

Sodium

Calcium

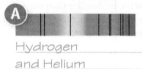
A

Hydrogen and Helium

B

Helium and Calcium

C

Hydrogen and Sodium

138 Stars, Galaxies, and the Universe

Digital Lesson: Assign the *Apply It* activity online and have students submit their work to you.

my science online.com | **Star Classification**

Brightness of Stars Stars also differ in brightness, the amount of light they give off. **The brightness of a star depends upon both its size and temperature.** A larger star tends to be brighter than a smaller star. A hotter star tends to be brighter than a cooler star.

How bright a star appears depends on both its distance from Earth and how bright the star truly is. Because of these two factors, the brightness of a star is described in two ways: apparent brightness and absolute brightness.

Apparent Brightness A star's **apparent brightness** is its brightness as seen from Earth. Astronomers can measure apparent brightness fairly easily using electronic devices. However, astronomers can't tell how much light a star gives off just from the star's apparent brightness. Just as a flashlight looks brighter the closer it is to you, a star looks brighter the closer it is to Earth. For example, the sun looks very bright. This does not mean that the sun gives off more light than all other stars. The sun looks so bright simply because it is so close.

Absolute Brightness A star's **absolute brightness** is the brightness the star would have if it were at a standard distance from Earth. Finding absolute brightness is more complex than finding its apparent brightness. An astronomer must first find out both the star's apparent brightness and its distance from Earth. The astronomer can then calculate the star's absolute brightness.

Astronomers have found that the absolute brightness of stars can vary tremendously. The brightest stars are more than a billion times brighter than the dimmest stars!

FIGURE 2 ....

Apparent and Absolute Brightness
The three stars Alnitak, Alnilam, and Mintaka in the constellation Orion all seem to have the same apparent brightness from Earth. But Alnilam is actually farther away than the other two stars.

CHALLENGE Which star has the greatest absolute brightness? How do you know?

Alnilam; because if it were closer it would appear brighter

Mintaka
approximately
900
light-years away

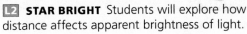 Do the Quick Lab
Star Bright.

Assess Your Understanding

got it? ....

O I get it! Now I know that stars are classified by _color, temperature, size, composition, and brightness._

O I need extra help with _See TE note._

Go to MY SCIENCE COACH online for help with this subject.

139

Differentiated Instruction

L1 Color and Surface Temperature
Have students prepare a display sequencing different colors by their energy levels. They should include blue, yellow, orange, and red at a minimum. This is a good activity to complete in pairs.

L3 Apparent Magnitude and Absolute Magnitude Magnitude is the scale for the measure of a star's brightness as well as the brightness of any object in space. Challenge students to investigate the terms _apparent magnitude_ and _absolute magnitude_.

Explain

Teach Key Concepts

Explain to students that the brightness of a star depends on it size and also its temperature. Ask: **What are the two ways to describe a star's brightness?** (Apparent brightness and absolute brightness) **What is apparent brightness?** (How bright a star looks from Earth) **What is absolute brightness?** (How bright a star would look if it were at a standard distance from Earth) **What information is needed to determine a star's absolute brightness?** (Apparent brightness and distance from Earth)

Make Analogies

L1 HEADLIGHTS Tell students to imagine that they are riding in a car at night, and two cars are approaching from the opposite direction. Ask: **Which car appears to have brighter headlights?** (The car that is closer) **Does that mean the headlights are actually brighter?** (Not necessarily; the headlights on the other car may be the same brightness but appear dimmer because they are farther away.) Tell students that the brightness of the headlights was like apparent brightness of stars. It was how bright the headlights appeared to be as seen from the car they were in.

Elaborate

Lab Resource: Quick Lab

L2 STAR BRIGHT Students will explore how distance affects apparent brightness of light.

Evaluate

Assess Your Understanding

Have students evaluate their understanding by completing the appropriate sentence.

RTI Response to Intervention

If students cannot explain how stars are classified, **then** have them review the read headings for this section.

MY SCIENCE COACH Have students go online for help in understanding the criteria that are used to classify stars.

Explain

Teach Key Concepts 🔑

Explain to students that scientists made graphs to see if the temperature and the absolute brightness of stars are related. They recorded information for many stars and developed a diagram called a Hertzsprung-Russell (or H-R) diagram. They saw that types of stars grouped together, so now the H-R diagram is a tool to classify stars and understand how they change over their lifetimes. Ask: **Where do most stars fall on the H-R diagram?** *(Most stars are main sequence stars.)* **What kind of star is our sun?** *(It is a main sequence star.)* **Do all main sequence stars look like our sun?** *(No, some can be blue or blue-white instead of yellow. Others are orange or red.)* **What else do you need to know to classify a star as a main sequence star?** *(Its absolute brightness)*

Teach With Visuals

Tell students to look at **Figure 3**. Ask: **What are the values on the *x*-axis?** *(Temperature)* **Is there anything unusual about this *x*-axis?** *(The larger numbers are at the left and decrease moving toward the right.)* Have students locate Betelgeuse on the diagram. Ask: **What color is Betelgeuse?** *(Red)* **What is its surface temperature?** *(About 3,500°C)* **What is the absolute brightness of Betelgeuse?** *(It is high, so the star is very bright.)* **What type of star is Betelgeuse?** *(It is a supergiant.)*

21st Century Learning 📖

INFORMATION LITERACY Have students read *Constellations* in the **Big Ideas of Science Reference Library.** Six constellations are mentioned in the pages. Have students research four more and create information cards for each one. Each card should include: 1) any alternate name for the constellation, 2) the names of any named stars in the constellation, 3) a description of mythology associated with the constellation, and 4) a drawing of the constellation.

What Is an H-R Diagram and How Do Astronomers Use It?

About 100 years ago, two scientists working independently made the same discovery. Both Ejnar Hertzsprung (EYE nahr HURT sprung) in Denmark and Henry Norris Russell in the United States made graphs to find out if the temperature and the absolute brightness of stars are related. They plotted the surface temperatures of stars on the *x*-axis and their absolute brightness on the *y*-axis. The points formed a pattern. The graph they made is still used by astronomers today. It is called the **Hertzsprung-Russell diagram,** or H-R diagram.

FIGURE 3 ···

Hertzsprung-Russell Diagram
The H-R diagram shows the relationship between surface temperature and absolute brightness of stars.

✎ **Interpret Diagrams** Place the stars listed in the table on the diagram, and note on the table the classification of each star.

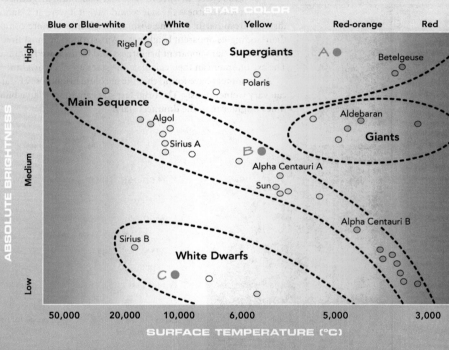

Astronomers use H-R diagrams to classify stars and to understand how stars change over time. As shown in **Figure 3,** most of the stars in the H-R diagram form a diagonal area called the **main sequence.** More than 90 percent of all stars, including the sun, are main-sequence stars. Within the main sequence, the surface temperature increases as absolute brightness increases. Thus, hot bluish stars are located at the left of an H-R diagram and cooler reddish stars are located at the right of the diagram.

The brightest stars are located near the top of an H-R diagram, while the dimmest stars are located at the bottom. Giant and supergiant stars are very bright. They can be found near the top center and right of the diagram. White dwarfs are hot, but not very bright, so they appear at either the bottom left or bottom center of the diagram.

STAR A

Color	Red-orange
Temperature	5,000°C
Brightness	High
Type	*Supergiant*

STAR B

Color	Yellow
Temperature	6,000°C
Brightness	Medium
Type	*Main sequence*

STAR C

Color	White
Temperature	10,000°C
Brightness	Low
Type	*White dwarf*

Lab zone Do the Quick Lab *Interpreting the H-R Diagram.*

Assess Your Understanding

1a. Review What two characteristics of stars are shown in an H-R diagram?

Surface temperature and absolute brightness

b. Explain What is the relationship between brightness and temperature shown within the main sequence?

Surface temperature increases as absolute brightness increases.

c. Interpret Diagrams The star Procyon B has a surface temperature of 7,500°C and a low absolute brightness. What type of star is it?

It is a white dwarf.

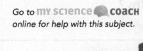

O I get it! Now I know that astronomers use H-R diagrams to *classify stars and to understand how stars change over time.*

O I need extra help with *See TE note.*

Go to **my science COACH** online for help with this subject.

141

Lead a Discussion

HOW BIG IS A GIANT? Tell students that supergiants are much larger than our sun. If Betelgeuse were at the center of our solar system its surface might extend out to between the orbits of Mars and Jupiter. Ask: **If this was the case, which planets in our solar system would be inside Betelgeuse?** *(Mercury, Venus, Earth, and Mars)* Encourage students to think about how far away the sun is, and how incredibly large a supergiant can be.

Elaborate

Lab Resource: Quick Lab

L2 **INTERPRETING THE H-R DIAGRAM** Students will explore the creation and use of an H-R diagram.

Evaluate

Assess Your Understanding

After students answer the questions, have them evaluate their understanding by completing the appropriate sentence.

RTI Response to Intervention

1a. If students have trouble understanding what an H-R diagram shows, **then** have them review **Figure 3.**

b. If students cannot describe the relationship between brightness and temperature, **then** have them review the Key Concept statement for the brightness of stars.

c. If students need help with interpreting the H-R diagram, **then** have them locate the temperature and absolute brightness on the H-R diagram in **Figure 3.**

my science COACH Have students go online for help in understanding H-R diagrams.

Differentiated Instruction

L1 **Our Sun** Have students use the H-R diagram to list characteristics of our sun. Include color, absolute brightness, and surface temperature. Ask them if these characteristics fit with their own observations.

L3 **Supernovas** Invite students to investigate supernovas and what types of stars will create supernovas. Have them identify the area of the H-R diagram that contains future supernovas.

Lab zone After the Inquiry Warm-Up

Characteristics of Stars

Inquiry Warm-Up, *How Stars Differ*

In the Inquiry Warm-Up, you investigated a few of the ways in which stars differ from each other. Using what you learned from that activity, answer the questions below.

1. **USE PRIOR KNOWLEDGE** Which is larger, Earth's moon or Jupiter? From Earth, which looks larger? Why?

_____

_____

2. **ANALYZE SOURCES OF ERROR** Consider your answer to question 1. Is there a problem in describing stars' sizes by using photos taken on Earth? Explain.

_____

_____

_____

3. **USE PRIOR KNOWLEDGE** Which is brighter, a flashlight shone on you by a friend across a darkened room or the beam projected by a lighthouse several miles away? Which looks brighter to you? Why?

_____

_____

_____

4. **ANALYZE SOURCES OF ERROR** Consider your answer to question 3. Is there a problem in describing stars' brightness by using photos taken on Earth? Explain.

_____

_____

_____

Assess Your Understanding

Characteristics of Stars

How Are Stars Classified?

gotit? ....

○ **I get it!** Now I know that stars are classified by _____

_____

○ **I need extra help with** _____

_____

What Is an H-R Diagram and How Do Astronomers Use It?

1a. REVIEW What two characteristics of stars are shown on an

H-R diagram? _____

_____

b. EXPLAIN What is the relationship between brightness and

temperature shown within the main sequence? _____

_____

_____

c. INTERPRET DIAGRAMS The star Procyon B has a surface temperature
of 7,500 degrees Celsius and a low absolute brightness. What type

of star is it? _____

_____

gotit? ....

○ **I get it!** Now I know that astronomers use H-R diagrams to _____

_____

_____

○ **I need extra help with** _____

_____

Key Concept Summaries

Characteristics of Stars

How Are Stars Classified?

Stars are huge spheres of glowing gas. Made up mostly of hydrogen, stars produce energy through the process of nuclear fusion. **Astronomers classify stars according to color, temperature, size, composition, and brightness.**

A star's color reveals its surface temperature. Blue stars are the hottest and red stars are coolest. Because they are so far away, all stars look about the same size, but they are not. Some, such as giant stars and supergiant stars, are much larger than our sun. Most stars are smaller than the sun. White dwarf stars are about the size of Earth, while tiny neutron stars are only about 20 kilometers in diameter.

The chemical composition of most stars is about 73 percent hydrogen, 25 percent helium, and 2 percent other elements by mass. But each star contains different amounts of various elements. Astronomers use a spectrograph to determine the elements found in a particular star. A **spectrograph** is a device that breaks light into colors and produces an image of the resulting spectrum. The gases in a star's atmosphere absorb some wavelengths of light produced within a star. On a spectrograph, each absorbed wavelength is shown as a dark line on the spectrum. Every chemical element has its own unique "fingerprint" of lines.

The brightness of a star depends upon both its size and temperature. A star's **apparent brightness** is the brightness as seen from Earth. Its **absolute brightness** is the brightness the star would have if it were at a standard distance from Earth.

What Is an H-R Diagram and How Do Astronomers Use It?

A **Hertzsprung-Russell diagram** is a graph of stars' surface temperature versus their absolute brightness. The points form a pattern. **Astronomers use H-R diagrams to classify stars and to understand how stars change over time.** Most stars fall in a diagonal area of the diagram called the **main sequence.** The brightest stars are located near the top of an H-R diagram while the dimmest stars are located at the bottom.

Look at the H-R diagram on page 140 in your book, and locate the star Rigel. On a separate sheet of paper, describe Rigel's color, surface temperature, absolute brightness, and type.

Characteristics of Stars

Understanding Main Ideas
Fill in the blank to complete each statement.

Use the H-R diagram on the right to answer questions 1–5. Write your answers in the spaces provided.

1. Star _____ has the greatest absolute brightness.

2. Star _____ has the greatest surface temperature.

3. Stars B, C, D, and E are probably _____ _____ stars.

4. Star F is probably a(n) _____ _____ star.

5. The three other characteristics used to classify stars are _____

_____

Building Vocabulary
Write a definition for each of these terms on a separate piece of paper.

6. apparent brightness
7. spectrograph
8. Hertzsprung-Russell diagram
9. absolute brightness
10. main sequence

Enrich

Characteristics of Stars

> Read the passage and study the calculation. Then use a separate sheet of paper to answer the questions that follow.

Units and Scientific Notation

You have seen that scientists use a unit called a light-year (l-y) to measure distances in space. One light-year is equal to the distance light travels in one year. This distance is about 9.5×10^{15} m.

Another unit, called an astronomical unit (AU), is used for smaller distances, such as distances to planets in our solar system. One astronomical unit is equal to the distance between Earth and the sun. This distance is about 1.5×10^{11} m.

A third unit, called a parsec (pc), is used for distances to stars. The term *parsec* is based on *parallax* and *seconds*. The seconds in parsec are not units of time. They are measurements of the angle used in parallax to calculate the distance to a star. One parsec is equal to about 3.1×10^{16} m.

The star Deneb has been estimated to be 1,500 l-y away from Earth. If you wanted to find out how many meters away Deneb is, you would multiply the distance in light years by the number of meters in a light year. To do this calculation in scientific notation, you must convert 1,500 to scientific notation.

1,500 l-y = 1.5×10^3 l-y	Convert 1,500 to scientific notation.
$(1.5 \times 10^3$ l-y$) \times (9.5 \times 10^{15}$ m/l-y$)$	Multiply that number by the number of meters in a light year.

Next, analyze the units. Multiplying light years by meters per light year gives the unit meters, which is the unit you are looking for.

$(1.5 \times 9.5) \times (10^3 \times 10^{15})$ m	Rearrange the numbers so that like numbers are grouped together.
$(14) \times (10^{18})$ m	Multiply within the parentheses.
1.4×10^{19} m	Rewrite in scientific notation.

1. Which of the three units described is the largest? How can you tell?

2. The nearest star to Earth is about 4.1×10^{16} meters. Why is the light-year a better unit than the astronomical unit for expressing this distance?

3. Beta Centauris is 161 pc from Earth. How many meters is this?

Lesson Quiz

Characteristics of Stars

Fill in the blank to complete each statement.

1. On a Hertzsprung-Russell diagram, the star in the _____ left corner will have the highest absolute brightness and surface temperature.

2. A star is closer to Earth than the standard distance to measure absolute brightness. Its apparent brightness is _____ its absolute brightness.

3. Stars A and B have the same absolute brightness and are far from Earth. Star A is twice as far away as Star B. Star A's apparent brightness is _____ _____ Star B's apparent brightness.

4. A star's surface temperature and its _____ are directly related.

5. Larger stars usually appear _____ than smaller stars.

If the statement is true, write *true*. If the statement is false, change the underlined word or words to make the statement true.

6. _____ A star's brightness if it were a standard distance from Earth is its <u>apparent</u> brightness.

7. _____ A device that breaks light into colors and produces an image of the spectrum is a(n) <u>electromagnetic spectrum</u>.

8. _____ The region of the H-R diagram that most stars fall within is the <u>stellar</u> sequence.

9. _____ The brightness of a star as seen from Earth is its <u>apparent</u> brightness.

10. _____ A graph of stars showing surface temperature on the *x*-axis and <u>color</u> on the *y*-axis is a Hertzsprung-Russell diagram.

Characteristics of Stars

Answer Key

After the Inquiry Warm-Up

1. Jupiter is much larger than Earth's moon, but when both are seen from Earth, Earth's moon looks much larger than Jupiter because it is much closer.

2. Yes. How large a star appears to be when seen from Earth depends on how far from Earth the star is. A small nearby star may appear much larger than a large star that is much farther away.

3. The beam from a lighthouse is much brighter than the beam from a flashlight. But when the flashlight is in the same room and the lighthouse is miles away, the flashlight beam looks much brighter because it is much closer.

4. Yes. How bright a star appears to be when seen from Earth depends on how far from Earth the star is. A dim nearby star may appear much brighter than a bright star that is much farther away.

Key Concept Summaries

Rigel is blue-white. Its surface temperature is about 15,000°C, and its absolute brightness is high. It is a supergiant.

Review and Reinforce

1. A
2. B
3. main sequence
4. white dwarf
5. size, color, and chemical composition
6. a star's brightness as seen from Earth
7. a device that breaks light into colors and produces an image of the resulting spectrum

8. a graph of stars showing surface temperature on the *x*-axis and absolute brightness on the *y*-axis

9. the brightness a star would have if it were a standard distance from Earth

10. the diagonal region of the H-R diagram that most stars fall within

Enrich

1. The parsec is the largest unit. The number of meters in a parsec has a greater power of 10 than the other units have.

2. The value of the light-year is close to this distance, so the distance can be expressed with a small number.

3. 5×10^{18} m

Lesson Quiz

1. upper
2. greater than
3. less than
4. color
5. brighter
6. absolute
7. spectrograph
8. main
9. true
10. absolute brightness

Place the outside corner, the corner away from the dotted line, in the corner of your copy machine to copy onto letter-size paper.

Lives of Stars

How do astronomers learn about distant objects in the universe?

Lesson Pacing: 2–3 periods or 1–1½ blocks

🕐 **SHORT ON TIME?** To do this lesson in approximately half the time, do the Activate Prior Knowledge activity on page 142. A discussion of the Key Concepts on pages 143 and 145 will familiarize students with the lesson content. Have students do the Quick Labs. The rest of the lesson can be completed by students independently.

Preference Navigator, in the online Planning tools, allows you to customize *Interactive Science* to your own teaching style. You can also edit lesson plans by selecting the Lesson Planner option.

Digital Teacher's Edition allows you to access your Teacher's Edition and Resource materials online.

Lesson Vocabulary

- nebula
- protostar
- white dwarf
- supernova
- neutron star
- pulsar
- black hole

Content Refresher

Supernovas Supernovas that are visible from Earth without a telescope are very rare. Only seven were recorded before the 17th century and the use of the telescope. They were seen in 185, 393, 1006, 1054, 1181, 1572, and 1604.

Rock paintings discovered in Arizona and New Mexico suggest that the supernova of 1054 may have been seen and recorded by Native Americans. The supernova of 1604 was first observed by Kepler's assistant. Kepler watched it until 1606 when it was no longer visible to the unaided eye. At its brightest, this supernova was brighter than Jupiter. It was not realized until nearly 1980 that another supernova explosion had occurred in the Milky Way in 1680. While this rare event was recorded in astronomical studies, it was considered a normal star until much later studies of supporting evidence prompted the occurrence to be classified it as a supernova—Cassiopeia A.

More recently, in 1987 there was a supernova explosion. This explosion did not occur in the Milky Way but in a neighboring galaxy known as Large Magellanic Cloud. Because this galaxy is relatively near to ours, astronomers were able to closely watch Supernova 1987A, saw how it evolved over time, and were able to gather more information about these rare events.

LESSON OBJECTIVES

🔑 Summarize the life cycle of stars.

🔑 Describe what happens to a star when it runs out of fuel.

Blended Path
Active learning using Student Edition, Inquiry Path, and Digital Path

ENGAGE AND EXPLORE

Teach this lesson using a variety of resources. Begin by reading **My Planet Diary** as a class. Have students share ideas about what the Supernova of 1054 might have looked like to astronomers and people on Earth. Then have students do the **Inquiry Warm-Up activity.** Students will investigate what determines how long stars live. Discuss the amount of mass the sun would burn through in 1 billion years. The **After the Inquiry Warm-Up worksheet** sets up a discussion about whether all stars burn at the same rate. Have volunteers share their answers to question 4 about the rates at which stars of different masses burn.

EXPLAIN AND ELABORATE

Teach Key Concepts by explaining the term *nebula* and discussing the major difference between a nebula and a star. **Lead a Discussion** about the changes that take place from nebula to protostar. **Lead a Discussion** about how long stars of different mass sizes are expected to live.

Continue to **Teach Key Concepts** by explaining what happens when a low-mass star becomes a white dwarf and then a black dwarf. **Lead a Discussion** about how and why stars change over the course of their lives. **Lead a Discussion** about how neutron stars compare to our sun and to a white dwarf. Then have students practice the inquiry skill in the **Apply It activity.** Use the **Support the Big Q** to explain the characteristics of black holes and to describe how astronomers know they exist. Hand out the **Key Concept Summaries** as a review of each part of the lesson. Students can also use the online **Vocab Flash Cards** to review key terms.

EVALUATE

Have students take the **Lesson Quiz.** For an alternate assessment, see the **EXAM**VIEW® Assessment Suite, Progress Monitoring Assessments, or SuccessTracker™.

ELL Support

1 Content and Language

The word *supernova* contains the prefix *super-* which means "larger than others of its kind." Help students see that a *supernova* is an explosion of a high-mass star whose luminosity increases much more dramatically than that of a nova.

Lab zone Inquiry Path
Hands-on learning in the Lab zone

Digital Path
Online learning at **my science online.com**

ENGAGE AND EXPLORE

To teach this lesson with an emphasis on inquiry, begin with the **Inquiry Warm-Up activity.** Students will determine how long stars live. Discuss how much of the sun's mass would be burned through in 1 billion years. Have students do the **After the Inquiry Warm-Up worksheet.** Talk about the connection between star mass and star lifetime. Have volunteers share their answers to question 4 about the rates at which stars of different masses burn.

EXPLAIN AND ELABORATE

Focus on the **Inquiry Skill** for the lesson. Point out that when you predict, you use evidence to make inferences about a future event. About what did students make predictions in the **Inquiry Warm-Up activity?** *(Life expectancy of stars)* Do the **Teacher Demo** to model the formation of a white dwarf or neutron star. Have students do the **Quick Lab** to explore the life cycles of stars and then share their results.

Review the stages in a star's life in **Figure 4** before beginning the **Apply It activity.** Ask volunteers to share their predictions. To **Support the Big Q,** discuss how black holes are formed and how astronomers know they exist. Have students do the **Quick Lab** to model a star's death. Students can use the online **Vocab Flash Cards** to review key terms.

EVALUATE

Have students take the **Lesson Quiz.** For an alternate assessment, see the **EXAM**VIEW® Assessment Suite, Progress Monitoring Assessments, or SuccessTracker™.

ENGAGE AND EXPLORE

Teach this lesson using digital resources. Begin by having students explore real-world connections to stars at **My Planet Diary** online. Have them access the Chapter Resources to find the **Unlock the Big Question activity.** There they can answer the questions and refine their responses as they continue through the lesson. You can re-assign the activity and have students submit their work so you can track their progress.

EXPLAIN AND ELABORATE

Students reading above, at, or below the lexile measure of this lesson can access basic content readings at their level at **My Reading Web.** Have students use the online **Vocab Flash Cards** to preview key terms. Do the **Quick Lab** to explore the life cycles of stars and then ask students to share their results.

Review the stages of a star's life in **Figure 4** before assigning the online **Apply It activity.** Ask volunteers to share their predictions. Have students submit their work to you. Have students do the online **Interactive Art activity** to explore the lives of stars. To **Support the Big Q,** explain how black holes are formed and how astronomers know they exist. Do the **Quick Lab** to reinforce understanding of the death of a star. The **Key Concept Summaries** online allow students to read a summary and see an image associated with each part of the lesson. Online remediation is available at **My Science Coach.**

EVALUATE

Have students take the **Lesson Quiz.** For an alternate assessment, see the **EXAM**VIEW® Assessment Suite, Progress Monitoring Assessments, or SuccessTracker™.

2 Frontload the Lesson
Preview the lesson visuals, labels, and captions. Ask students what they know about the words *white dwarf, neutron star,* and *nebula.* Explain the specific meanings these words have in science.

3 Comprehensible Input
Have students draw a flowchart to show the stages of either a white dwarf or a neutron star's life.

4 Language Production
Pair or group students with varied language abilities to complete labs collaboratively for language practice. Have each student copy the completed written lab for personal reference.

5 Assess Understanding
Divide the class into small groups. Have each student identify a Key Concept from the lesson to discuss in his or her group. After the discussions, have students talk about the Key Concepts as a group.

LESSON 4.4

Lives of Stars

Establish Learning Objectives

After this lesson, students will be able to:

🔑 Summarize the life cycle of stars.

🔑 Describe what happens to a star when it runs out of fuel.

Engage

Activate Prior Knowledge

MY PLANET DIARY Read *The Supernova of 1054* with the class. Explain to students that in ancient times people used stars to navigate, to tell when the seasons would change, and, sometimes, to portend major events. Ask: **What can modern astronomers use to help them interpret these events?** *(Astronomers now have optical telescopes, radio telescopes, and other means of gathering electromagnetic radiation to help them understand what is happening in stars.)*

BIG IDEAS OF SCIENCE REFERENCE LIBRARY 📖 Have students look up the following topic: Black Holes.

Explore

Lab Resource: Inquiry Warm-Up 🔬

L1 **WHAT DETERMINES HOW LONG STARS LIVE?** Students will explore the connection between star mass and star lifetime.

LESSON

4 Lives of Stars

UNLOCK THE BIG ?

🔑 **How Does a Star Form and What Determines Its Life Span?**

🔑 **What Happens to a Star When It Runs Out of Fuel?**

MY PLANET DIARY

DISCOVERY

The Supernova of 1054

In the summer of 1054, some Chinese astronomers noticed a "guest star" in the night sky. The star was so bright people could see it during the day! The star remained visible for almost two years. How did these ancient astronomers interpret it? Was it a sign that the emperor would be visited by an important guest? People from around the world recorded and interpreted the event differently. Almost 1,000 years later, scientists realized the "guest star" was the explosion of a giant star 4,000 light-years away. So powerful was the explosion that all life within about 50 light-years would have been wiped out. Now called Supernova 1054, its remains are known as the Crab Nebula.

Communicate Discuss the supernova with a partner and answer the questions below.

1. Why was Supernova 1054 so notable?

   It was so bright that it could be seen during the day, and it was visible for two years.

2. How do you think ancient astronomers might have interpreted the event differently than astronomers today?

   Sample: People might have seen it as a good or bad omen.

🔬 **Lab zone** Do the Inquiry Warm-Up What Determines How Long Stars Live?

▶ PLANET DIARY Go to **Planet Diary** to learn more about stars.

142 Stars, Galaxies, and the Universe

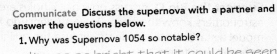

SUPPORT ALL READERS

Lexile Measure = 950L   **Lexile Word Count = 1382**

Prior Exposure to Content: Many students may have misconceptions on this topic

Academic Vocabulary: *compare, contrast, predict*

Science Vocabulary: *nebula, protostar, supernova, pulsar, black hole*

Concept Level: May be difficult for students who struggle with abstract ideas

Preteach With: My Planet Diary "The Supernova of 1054" and Figure 4 activity

Go to **My Reading Web** to access leveled readings that provide a foundation for the content.

MY SCIENCE online.com

Vocabulary
- nebula • protostar • white dwarf • supernova
- neutron star • pulsar • black hole

Skills
↻ Reading: Compare and Contrast
△ Inquiry: Predict

How Does a Star Form and What Determines Its Life Span?

Stars do not last forever. Each star is born, goes through its life cycle, and eventually dies. (Of course, stars are not really alive. The words *born*, *live*, and *die* are just helpful comparisons.) 🗩 **A star is born when the contracting gas and dust from a nebula become so dense and hot that nuclear fusion starts. How long a star lives depends on its mass.**

A Star Is Born All stars begin their lives as parts of nebulas, such as the one in **Figure 1**. A **nebula** is a large cloud of gas and dust spread out in an immense volume. A star, on the other hand, is made up of a large amount of gas in a relatively small volume.

In the densest part of a nebula, gravity pulls gas and dust together. A contracting cloud of gas and dust with enough mass to form a star is called a **protostar**. *Proto-* means "earliest" in Greek, so a protostar is the earliest stage of a star's life.

Recall that nuclear fusion is the process by which atoms combine to form heavier atoms. In the sun, for example, hydrogen atoms combine to form helium. During nuclear fusion, enormous amounts of energy are released. Nuclear fusion begins in a protostar.

FIGURE 1 ·······

A Stellar Nursery
New stars are forming in the nebula.

✎ **Summarize** Describe the process of star formation.

Sample: In a dense part of a
nebula, gravity pulls gas and
dust together into a protostar. Then nuclear fusion
starts. The protostar eventually becomes a star.

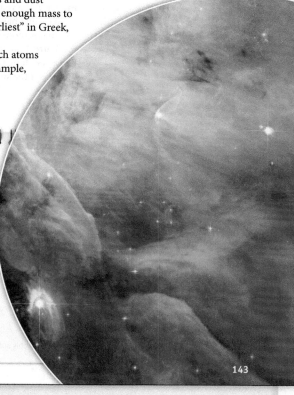

143

Explain

Introduce Vocabulary
Tell students that the terms for this lesson refer to stages of the lifespan of a star, from its formation to its end. The prefix *proto-* means "first or earliest," so a protostar is an early stage in the formation of a star.

Teach Key Concepts 🗩
Explain to students that stars go through different phases. Often these phases are spoken of in terms of a lifetime; a star is born when the contracting gas and dust from a nebula become so dense and hot that nuclear fusion starts. The length of time a star lives depends on its mass. Ask: **What is a nebula?** *(A large cloud of dust and gas)* **What causes the gas and dust in a nebula to contract?** *(Gravity)* **What is the major difference between a nebula and a star?** *(The amount of space they take up; in a star, the gas is packed into a relatively small volume; in a nebula, the gas is spread out over a large volume. The tightly packed gas in a star undergoes fusion, which produces energy; that in a nebula does not.)*

Lead a Discussion
FUSION Review with students the parts of an atom and how they take part in fusion. Show students that two hydrogen atoms, each of which has one proton in the nucleus, can join to form an atom with two protons in the nucleus. Ask: **What element has two protons in the nuclei of its atoms?** *(Helium)* Make sure that students understand that this is not a chemical reaction. It is a nuclear reaction that takes place only under conditions of great pressure and high temperature. Ask: **What change in the lifespan of a star is marked by the beginning of fusion?** *(The change from nebula to protostar)*

My Planet Diary provides an opportunity for students to explore real-world connections to stars.

my science online.com ⟩ Star Formation and Life Span

Explain

Lead a Discussion

STAR STAGES Tell students that the mass of a star determines how long the star will live. Ask: **How long can a small star that uses its fuel slowly be expected to live?** *(Up to 200 billion years)* **How long can a medium-mass star like our sun be expected to live?** *(About 10 billion years)* **How long can the most massive stars be expected to live?** *(About 10 million years)*

Elaborate

Teacher Demo

L1 SQUEEZING MATTER INTO A SMALLER SPACE

Materials plastic cup, marbles, sand, scale

Time 5 minutes

Remind students that all matter is mostly empty space; even atoms are mostly empty space. Fill a plastic cup with marbles and weigh it. Empty the cup, and refill it with sand. Weigh it.

Ask: **Glass and sand have nearly the same density; why does the cup weigh more when filled with sand than it does when filled with marbles?** *(There is less empty space when the cup is filled with sand.)* **How is this a model for the formation of a white dwarf or neutron star?** *(As these objects form, the matter squeezes into all of the empty space, increasing the density.)*

Lab Resource: Quick Lab

L1 LIFE CYCLE OF STARS Students will explore the life cycles of typical stars.

Evaluate

Assess Your Understanding

After students answer the questions, have them evaluate their understanding by completing the appropriate sentence.

RTI Response to Intervention

1a. If students have trouble explaining star formation, **then** have them review the summaries they created for **Figure 1.**

b. If students cannot state the factor that determines star life, **then** have them review the Key Concept statement.

c. If students need help with applying information to star lifetimes, **then** have them review information for the red heading *Lifetimes of Stars.*

MY SCIENCE COACH Have students go online for help in understanding star life cycles.

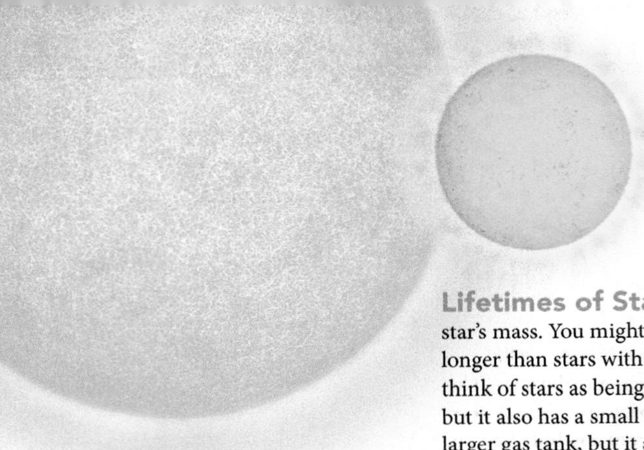

144 Stars, Galaxies, and the Universe

FIGURE 2 ·····················
Life of a Star
A star's lifetime depends on its mass.

✏ **Explain** The yellow star has much less mass than the blue star and so will live longer. Explain why.

<u>The yellow star will live</u>
<u>longer because stars</u>
<u>with less mass use up</u>
<u>fuel more slowly.</u>

Lifetimes of Stars How long a star lives depends on the star's mass. You might think that stars with more mass would last longer than stars with less mass. But the reverse is true. You can think of stars as being like cars. A small car has a small gas tank, but it also has a small engine that burns gas slowly. A large car has a larger gas tank, but it also has a larger engine that burns gas rapidly. So the small car can travel farther on a tank of gas than the larger car. Small-mass stars use up their fuel more slowly than large-mass stars, so they have much longer lives.

Generally, stars that have less mass than the sun use their fuel slowly, and can live for up to 200 billion years. A medium-mass star like the sun will live for about 10 billion years. The sun is about 4.6 billion years old, so it is about halfway through its lifetime. In **Figure 2**, the yellow star is similar to the sun.

Stars that have more mass than the sun have shorter lifetimes. A star that is more massive than the sun, such as the blue star shown in **Figure 2,** may live only about 10 million years. That may seem like a very long time, but it is only one tenth of one percent of the lifetime of the sun.

Do the Quick Lab
Life Cycle of Stars.

🗩 Assess Your Understanding

1a. Review How does a star form from a nebula?

<u>Gravity pulls some of the</u>
<u>gas and dust of the nebula</u>
<u>together, forming a protostar.</u>
<u>When nuclear fusion begins, a</u>
<u>star is born.</u>

b. Summarize What factor determines how long a star lives?

<u>Its mass</u>

c. Predict A star is twice as massive as the sun. How will its lifespan compare?

<u>Its lifespan will be shorter.</u>

got it? ·····················

○ **I get it!** Now I know that stars are born when <u>the contracting gas and dust from a</u> <u>nebula become so dense and hot that nuclear fusion starts,</u>

and how long a star lives depends on <u>its mass.</u>

○ **I need extra help with** <u>See TE note.</u>

Go to **MY SCIENCE COACH** online for help with this subject.

144 Stars, Galaxies, and the Universe

What Happens to a Star When It Runs Out of Fuel?

When a star begins to run out of fuel, its core shrinks and its outer portion expands. Depending on its mass, the star becomes either a red giant or a supergiant. Red giants and supergiants evolve in very different ways. **After a star runs out of fuel, it becomes a white dwarf, a neutron star, or a black hole.**

White Dwarfs Low-mass stars and medium-mass stars like the sun take billions of years to use up their nuclear fuel. As they start to run out of fuel, their outer layers expand, and they become red giants. Eventually, the outer parts grow larger still and drift out into space, forming a glowing cloud of gas called a planetary nebula. The blue-white core of the star that is left behind cools and becomes a **white dwarf.**

White dwarfs are about the size of Earth, but they have about as much mass as the sun. A white dwarf is about one million times as dense as the sun. White dwarfs have no fuel, but they glow faintly from leftover energy. After billions of years, a white dwarf stops glowing. Then it is called a black dwarf.

Supernovas The life cycle of a high-mass star is quite different. These stars quickly evolve into brilliant supergiants. When a supergiant runs out of fuel, it can explode suddenly. Within hours, the star blazes millions of times brighter. The explosion is called a **supernova.** After a supernova, some of the material from the star expands into space. This material may become part of a nebula. This nebula can then contract to form a new, partly recycled star. Recall that nuclear fusion creates heavy elements. A supernova provides enough energy to create the heaviest elements. Astronomers think that the matter in the sun and the planets around it came from a gigantic supernova. If so, this means that the matter all around you was created in a star, and all matter on Earth is a form of stardust.

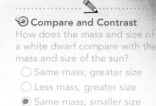

Compare and Contrast
How does the mass and size of a white dwarf compare with the mass and size of the sun?

- ○ Same mass; greater size
- ○ Less mass; greater size
- ● Same mass; smaller size
- ○ Less mass; smaller size

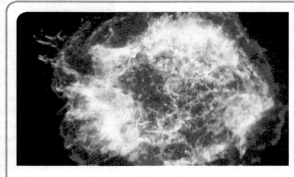

FIGURE 3

Supernova Remnant Cassiopeia A
Cassiopeia A is the remnant of a once-massive star that died in a supernova explosion seen 325 years ago.

✎ CHALLENGE **Explain the connection between your body and a supernova.**

Sample: All the matter in our solar system, including that in your body, came from a supernova.

145

Explain

Teach Key Concepts

Explain to students that stars eventually run out of fuel. After a star runs out of fuel, it becomes a white dwarf, a neutron star, or a black hole. Ask: **What happens to a low-mass star as it begins to run out of fuel?** *(Its outer layers expand, and the star becomes a red giant.)* **What happens to the outer layers?** *(They form a cloud of gas called a nebula.)* **What happens to the core?** *(It becomes a white dwarf.)* **How does a white dwarf compare to Earth?** *(It is about the same size as Earth but has much more mass, as much mass as the sun.)* **Does fusion occur in a white dwarf? Explain.** *(No; it has run out of fuel, so fusion cannot occur. The star glows because of leftover energy.)* **What does a white dwarf become when it stops glowing?** *(A black dwarf.)* **What happens to a high-mass star as it begins to run out of fuel?** *(It becomes a supergiant.)* **What happens to the supergiant?** *(It explodes.)* **What is this explosion called?** *(A supernova)*

Compare and Contrast Comparing and contrasting is examining the similarities and differences between things.

Lead a Discussion

CHANGES IN STARS Remind students that all stars begin as protostars and become main-sequence stars. Ask: **How do stars vary?** *(They vary in mass, temperature, and brightness.)* **What process begins when a protostar forms?** *(Nuclear fusion)* **What is the fuel for fusion?** *(Hydrogen)* **What change leads to the end of a star's life?** *(It runs out of fuel.)* **What characteristic of a star determines what happens to a star that runs out of fuel?** *(The mass of the star)*

Differentiated Instruction

L1 **Campfires and Stars** Ask students to explain the stages of a burning campfire. Help them come to the conclusion that when the wood has been consumed, the flame goes out. Assist students in building an analogy to the life cycle of a star. Help them understand that, unlike a campfire, a star does not just fade out when its fuel is exhausted; it goes through a series of changes. Refer them to **Figure 4** for the changes.

L3 **Our Sun a Red Giant?** Invite students to research the predictions for what will happen as our sun begins to exhaust its fuel. Be sure they include a timeline.

Explain

Lead a Disussion 🔑

NEUTRON STARS Remind students that after a supernova occurs, matter from the star still exists. Some of the matter may form a nebula. Matter from a supernova may also form a neutron star. Ask: **What is a neutron star?** (The remains of a high-mass star) **What do the remains of a low-mass star form?** (A white dwarf) **How does a neutron star compare to a white dwarf?** (A neutron star is much smaller and denser than a white dwarf.) **How does a neutron star compare to our sun?** (It has more mass than the sun but is much smaller, so it is much denser than that sun.) **What is the name for a neutron star that spins?** (Pulsar)

Address Misconceptions

L1 **DO PULSARS PULSE?** Many students may think that pulsars actually pulse since they appear to give off pulses of radio waves. Actually, neutron stars emit steady beams of radio waves in narrow cones. As the neutron star spins, these beams of radiation appear to turn on and off at regular intervals, like the spinning beacon of a lighthouse. Ask: **Pulsars are a subset of what kind of star?** (Neutron stars) **Do pulsars really turn on and off?** (No, they appear to because they spin.) You may wish to Invite students to research the speeds at which pulsars rotate. (Some can rotate hundreds of times per second, although once per second is more common.)

Elaborate

21st Century Learning

INFORMATION LITERACY Tell students that while he did research on radio waves coming from quasars, Antony Hewish designed a large radio telescope to receive radio signals from distant galaxies. In 1967, he noticed a significant observation made by Jocelyn Bell, a graduate assistant. With the aid of a radio telescope, Bell had detected radio signals at regular intervals, or pulses. Hewish recognized that these patterned signals were energy emitted from certain stars. For identifying pulsars, a new class of stars, Hewish was given a Nobel Prize for Physics.

Apply It!

L1 Tell students to review the stages of a star's life in **Figure 4** before beginning the activity.

Predict Remind students that predicting is making an inference about a future event based on current evidence. Ask: **What is the current evidence?** (The star is a high-mass supergiant.)

FIGURE 4 ·····················
▷ INTERACTIVE ART Lives of Stars
✎ **Relate Text and Visuals** Fill in the missing stages on the diagram. Now, think about where the sun fits on the diagram. On the lines below, describe what will happen to the sun when it runs out of fuel.

The sun's outer layers will expand and it will become a red giant. Eventually, the outer layers of the red giant will drift into space and the remaining hot core will become a white dwarf.

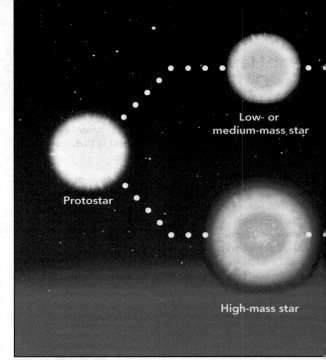

Protostar

Low- or medium-mass star

High-mass star

apply it!

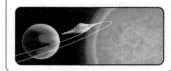

Predict An alien civilization is in orbit around a high-mass supergiant star. Should they stay or should they go elsewhere? Why?

They should leave because the star will explode as a supernova.

Neutron Stars After a supergiant explodes, some of the material from the star is left behind. This material may form a neutron star. **Neutron stars** are the remains of high-mass stars. They are even smaller and denser than white dwarfs. A neutron star may contain as much as three times the mass of the sun but be only about 25 kilometers in diameter, the size of a city.

In 1967, Jocelyn Bell, a British astronomy student working with Antony Hewish, detected an object in space that appeared to give off regular pulses of radio waves. Some astronomers thought the pulses might be signals from an extraterrestrial civilization. At first, astronomers even named the source LGM, for the "Little Green Men" in early science-fiction stories. Soon, however, astronomers concluded that the source of the radio waves was really a rapidly spinning neutron star. Spinning neutron stars are called **pulsars**, short for pulsating radio sources. Some pulsars spin hundreds of times per second!

Interactive Art allows students to explore the lives of stars.

Digital Lesson: Assign the *Apply It* activity online and have students submit their work to you.

my science online.com ▷ Aging Stars

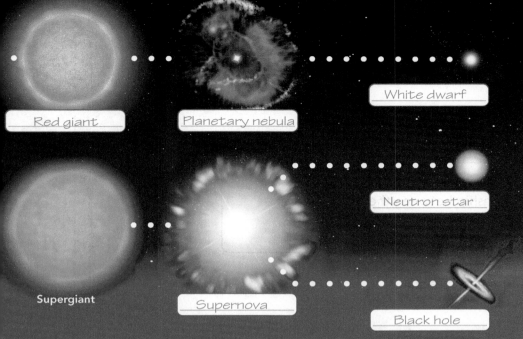

Red giant

Planetary nebula

White dwarf

Neutron star

Supergiant

Supernova

Black hole

Black Holes

The most massive stars—those that have more than 10 times the mass of the sun—may become black holes when they die. A **black hole** is an object with gravity so strong that nothing, not even light, can escape. After a very massive star dies in a supernova explosion, more than five times the mass of the sun may be left. The gravity of this mass is so strong that the gas is pulled inward, packing the gas into a smaller and smaller space. The star's gas becomes squeezed so hard that the star converts into a black hole, and its intense gravity will not allow even light to escape.

No light, radio waves, or any other form of radiation can ever get out of a black hole, so it is not possible to detect directly. But astronomers can detect black holes indirectly. For example, gas near a black hole is pulled so strongly that it revolves faster and faster around the black hole. Friction heats the gas up. Astronomers can detect X-rays coming from the hot gas and infer that a black hole is present.

> **Lab zone** Do the Quick Lab *Death of a Star.*

Assess Your Understanding

2a. Review What determines if a star becomes a white dwarf, neutron star, or black hole?

Its mass

b. Predict Which will the sun become: a white dwarf, neutron star, or a black hole? Why?

A white dwarf, because of its
mass

got it?

○ I get it! Now I know that after a star runs out of fuel, it becomes _a white_
dwarf, neutron star, or
black hole.

○ I need extra help with _See TE note._

Go to **MY SCIENCE COACH** online for help with this subject.

147

Differentiated Instruction

L1 Where Is the Sun? Tell students to use **Figure 4** to identify the image that represents the sun. Using the information on the diagram, students should forecast the stages the sun will go through. Help them comprehend the time scale of these changes (billions of years).

L3 Science Fiction Invite students to research black holes, white dwarfs, or neutron stars. Then students should write a short, creative story about life and civilization near one of these old stars. They should work as much science in as possible—true "science fiction."

Explain

Support the Big Q

BLACK HOLES Tell students a black hole forms when the remains of a supernova collapse. After it explodes, the mass is spread out, but there is so much mass that its gravity pulls it back together. *The term black hole was coined in the 1960s, although scientists had considered the possibility of a collapsed star before then.* Ask: **What is the most significant property of a black hole?** (*Very strong gravity*) **What is the result of this strong gravity?** (*Nothing escapes from a black hole, not even light. Matter can be pulled into the black hole.*) **If a black hole cannot be seen, how do astronomers know they exist?** (*Astronomers have detected X-rays coming from hot gas that swirls as it is pulled into a black hole.*) Tell students that, if a star is near a black hole, astronomers can calculate the mass of the black hole from the effect of its gravity on the star.

Make Analogies

KNOWING WITHOUT SEEING Explain to students that they frequently use senses other than seeing to gather information and then make inferences about what has happened. For example, if they are talking with a friend on the phone, and they hear a brief pause, then their friend says, "Hold on a minute," they infer that the friend is answering another call. Ask: **How does this compare to black holes and how astronomers can verify their existence?** (*Black holes cannot be seen, but their effects can be. So astronomers infer that they are there.*)

Elaborate

Lab Resource: Quick Lab

L1 DEATH OF A STAR Students will model a star's death.

Evaluate

Assess Your Understanding

After students answer the questions, have them evaluate their understanding by completing the appropriate sentence.

RTI Response to Intervention

2. If students cannot explain the stages in the lives of stars, **then** have them review **Figure 4**.

MY SCIENCE COACH Have students go online for help in understanding what happens as a star dies.

Lab zone — **After the Inquiry Warm-Up**

Lives of Stars

Inquiry Warm-Up, *What Determines How Long Stars Live?*

In the Inquiry Warm-Up, you investigated the relationship between the mass of a star and the length of its lifetime. Using what you learned from that activity, answer the questions below.

---

1. **CALCULATE** Assume for now that almost the entire mass of a star is usable fuel, and that it burns fuel at a constant rate. How much of its mass does the sun burn through in 1 billion years?

   _____

2. **CALCULATE** Follow the same assumptions you followed in question 1. How much of its mass does a star with twice the mass of the sun burn through in 1 billion years?

   _____

3. **DRAW CONCLUSIONS** Do all stars burn fuel at the same rate?

   _____

   _____

4. **COMPARE AND CONTRAST** Compare the rate at which less massive stars burn fuel to the rate at which more massive stars burn fuel.

   _____

   _____

Assess Your Understanding

Lives of Stars

How Does a Star Form and What Determines Its Life Span?

1a. REVIEW How does a star form from a nebula? _____
_____
_____

b. SUMMARIZE What factor determines how long a star lives? _____
_____

c. PREDICT A star is twice as massive as the sun. How will its lifespan
compare? _____
_____

got it? ···

○ **I get it!** Now I know that stars are born when _____
_____

and how long a star lives depends on _____

○ **I need extra help with** _____
_____

What Happens to a Star When It Runs Out of Fuel?

2a. REVIEW What determines if a star becomes a white dwarf, neutron
star, or black hole? _____
_____

b. PREDICT Which will the sun become: a white dwarf, neutron star, or
black hole? _____
_____

got it? ···

○ **I get it!** Now I know that after a star runs out of fuel, it becomes _____
_____

○ **I need extra help with** _____
_____

Key Concept Summaries

Lives of Stars

How Does a Star Form and What Determines Its Life Span?

Stars do not last forever. Each star is born, goes through its life cycle, and eventually dies. **A star is born when the contracting gas and dust from a nebula become so dense and hot that nuclear fusion starts.** A **nebula** is a large cloud of gas and dust spread out in an immense volume. In the densest part of a nebula, gravity pulls gas and dust together. A **protostar** is a contracting cloud of gas and dust with enough mass to form a star; it's like a "pre-star." Nuclear fusion begins in a protostar.

How long a star lives depends on its mass. Small-mass stars use up their fuel more slowly than large-mass stars, so they have much longer lives. While small-mass stars may live for as long as 200 billion years, a large mass star may live only about ten million years.

What Happens to a Star When It Runs Out of Fuel?

When a star begins to run out if fuel, it becomes either a red giant or a supergiant, depending on its mass. **After a star runs out of fuel, it becomes a white dwarf, a neutron star, or a black hole.**

As low-mass and medium-mass stars begin to run out of fuel, their outer layers expand and they become red giants. Eventually, their outer layers drift off into space, forming a glowing cloud of gas called a planetary nebula. The blue-white core of the star that is left behind cools and becomes a **white dwarf.** White dwarfs have about the mass of the sun but are only the size of Earth.

As high-mass stars begin to run out of fuel they become supergiants. When a supergiant runs out of fuel, it can explode suddenly. The explosion, a **supernova,** blazes millions of times brighter. The remains of the high-mass star may form a **neutron star.** A neutron star may be only 25 kilometers in diameter yet contain as much as three times the mass of the sun. Rapidly spinning neutron stars are called **pulsars,** which give off regular pulses of radio waves. If the original star was extremely massive, what remains after a supernova may be a black hole. A **black hole** is an object with gravity so strong that nothing, not even light, can escape.

On a separate sheet of paper, compare and contrast red giants to supergiants. Include information about mass, how the star formed, and what the next stages in its life will be.

Review and Reinforce

Lives of Stars

Understanding Main Ideas

Fill in each blank with the correct letter from the diagram.

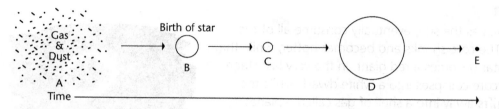

1. ____ Red giant or supergiant

2. ____ Where nuclear fusion begins

3. ____ Part of a nebula

4. ____ White dwarf, neutron star, or black hole

5. ____ The stage the sun is in

Building Vocabulary

On a separate sheet of paper, write a definition for each of these terms.

6. pulsar
7. white dwarf
8. nebula
9. protostar
10. supernova
11. neutron star
12. black hole

Enrich

Lives of Stars

Read the passage and study the figures. Then use a separate sheet of paper to answer the questions that follow.

Planetary Nebula

Medium-sized stars, such as the sun, eventually consume all of the nuclear fuel available. The core shrinks and becomes hotter, while the surface expands. The star becomes a red giant. In the very last stage of its life as a star, the core collapses into a white dwarf, while the remaining hydrogen drifts away into a shell of gas called a planetary nebula. Planetary nebulas are considered by many astronomers and photographers to be the most beautiful astronomical objects that can be seen with a telescope. They are called planetary nebulas because the astronomers who first saw them thought they resembled planets in size and color. One of the most attractive planetary nebulas is found in the constellation Lyra. It is called the Ring Nebula.

Figure 1

The gas surrounds the white dwarf in a three-dimensional sphere. Why does a three-dimensional spherical shell of gas appear to be a two-dimensional ring? Figure 2 shows the cross section of a shell of gas around a white dwarf. If you look at the shell from the right along line 1 or line 3, it appears bright. But if you look at the shell along line 2, it is less bright.

Figure 2

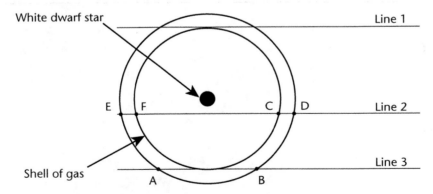

White dwarf star

Line 1

E F   C D   Line 2

Shell of gas   A   B   Line 3

1. How far is it from A to B in millimeters?
2. How far is it from C to D in millimeters, plus from E to F?
3. Are you looking through more of the shell along line 2 or along line 3?
4. Would the shell appear to be thicker and brighter along line 2 or along line 3?
5. Why does the Ring Nebula appear to us as a ring?

Name _____ Date _____ Class _____

Lives of Stars

Write the letter of the correct answer on the line at the left.

1. ___ A pulsar is a spinning
   A   black hole
   B   neutron star
   C   supernova
   D   white dwarf

2. ___ Which progression do astronomers expect our sun to follow as it runs out of fuel?
   A   red giant, white dwarf
   B   red giant, neutron star
   C   supergiant, supernova, white dwarf
   D   supergiant, supernova, black hole

3. ___ What determines the life cycle of a star?
   A   gravity
   B   the type of protostar
   C   its mass
   D   its temperature

4. ___ When is a star born?
   A   when the nebula starts spinning
   B   when gas and dust start to contract
   C   when X-rays get emitted
   D   when nuclear fusion starts

Fill in the blank to complete each statement.

5. Since no electromagnetic radiation escapes from a(n) _____ _____, astronomers locate them by looking for X-rays from gas accelerating toward them.

6. An explosion that occurs at the end of a massive star's life is a(n) _____.

7. A(n) _____ is a large cloud of gas and dust in space.

8. A low- or medium-mass star becomes a(n) _____ at the end of its life.

9. A(n) _____ appears to emit regular bursts of radio waves.

10. A(n) _____ forms from the leftover material from a supernova; it may contain as much as three times the mass of the sun.

Lives of Stars

Answer Key

After the Inquiry Warm-Up

1. $\frac{1}{10}$ of its mass

2. All of its mass

3. No, some stars burn fuel at a much faster rate than others.

4. Less massive stars burn fuel more slowly than more massive stars.

Key Concept Summaries

Red giants and supergiants both form as stars begin to run out of fuel. Red giants form from medium- to low-mass stars. They will eventually become white dwarfs. Supergiants form from high-mass stars. They will explode as supernovas and become either neutron stars or black holes.

Review and Reinforce

1. D

2. B

3. A

4. E

5. C

6. a spinning neutron star that emits pulses of radio waves

7. what a low- or medium-mass star becomes at the end of its life

8. a large cloud of gas and dust in space

9. a contracting cloud of gas and dust with enough mass to form a star

10. an explosion that occurs at the end of a high mass star's life

11. the small, dense remains of a high-mass star after it explodes

12. an object with gravity so strong that nothing, not even light, can escape

Enrich

1. 26 mm

2. 8 mm (4 mm + 4 mm)

3. You are looking through more of the shell along line 3.

4. The shell would appear thicker and brighter along line 3.

5. The shell must be glowing, since it shows up as light color. When you look through the outer part of the shell, your line of sight includes more of the glowing shell of gas than when you look nearer the center, so you can see the ring.

Lesson Quiz

1. B

2. A

3. C

4. D

5. black hole

6. supernova

7. nebula

8. white dwarf

9. pulsar

10. neutron star

Place the outside corner, the corner away from the dotted line, in the corner of your copy machine to copy onto letter-size paper.

Star Systems and Galaxies

5 How do astronomers learn about distant objects in the universe?

Lesson Pacing: 2–3 periods or 1–1½ blocks

🕐 **SHORT ON TIME?** To do this lesson in approximately half the time, do the Activate Prior Knowledge activity on page 148. A discussion of the Key Concepts on pages 149 and 152 will familiarize students with the lesson content. Use the Explore the Big Q to help students see how astronomers learn about distant objects in the universe. Do the Quick Labs and have students do the Real-World Inquiry online. The rest of the lesson can be completed by students independently.

Preference Navigator, in the online Planning tools, allows you to customize *Interactive Science* to your own teaching style. You can also edit lesson plans by selecting the Lesson Planner option.

Digital Teacher's Edition allows you to access your Teacher's Edition and Resource materials online.

my science online.com

Lesson Vocabulary

- binary star
- eclipsing binary
- open cluster
- globular cluster
- galaxy
- spiral galaxy
- elliptical galaxy
- irregular galaxy
- quasar

Content Refresher

Searching for Extraterrestrial Life Astronomers first started monitoring radio waves for signs of extraterrestrial life in 1960. Scientists at SETI (Search for Extraterrestrial Intelligence) Institute in Berkley, CA are using radio telescopes all over the world to search areas near sun-like stars for artificially produced signals. Because of interference from radio sources on Earth, SETI scientists use computers to screen out Earth-based signals.

In 1992 NASA used a High Resolution Microwave Survey to attempt to identify short radio waves coming from stars like the sun. In addition, they attempted to detect strong microwave signals by scanning the sky. These projects were concluded the following year for budget reasons.

Five years later, astronomers began to look for signals of intelligent life on other planets. They hoped to detect powerful pulses of laser light being emitted by intelligent beings on another planet. However, to date no artificial extraterrestrial signals have been detected.

LESSON OBJECTIVES

⊂▭ Define a star system.
⊂▭ Identify the major types of galaxies.

Blended Path
Active learning using Student Edition, Inquiry Path, and Digital Path

ENGAGE AND EXPLORE

Teach this lesson using a variety of resources. Begin by reading **My Planet Diary** as a class. Have students share ideas about the unique objects they have seen in the night sky. Then have students do the **Inquiry Warm-Up activity.** Students will investigate why the Milky Way looks hazy. Discuss the appearance of the holes up close and far away. The **After the Inquiry Warm-Up worksheet** sets up a discussion about how far apart the stars in the Milky Way really are. Have volunteers share their answers to question 4 about how the holes in the paper look similar to the stars in the Milky Way.

EXPLAIN AND ELABORATE

Teach Key Concepts by explaining how scientists can tell that there is a dim star in a binary system. **Lead a Discussion** about eclipsing binaries. **Lead a Discussion** about the characteristics of global and open clusters. To **Explore the Big Q,** discuss the diagrams and what the arrows at the bottom of the boxes represent. Talk about the information we can get from light and what it tells us about far away things. Help students **Answer the Big Q** by discussing ways in which astronomers learn about distant objects in the universe.

Continue to **Teach Key Concepts** by describing spiral, elliptical, and irregular galaxies, and quasars. Then have students practice the inquiry skill in the **Apply It activity.** Hand out the **Key Concept Summaries** as a review of each part of the lesson. Students can also use the online **Vocab Flash Cards** to review key terms.

EVALUATE

Have students take the **Lesson Quiz.** For an alternate assessment, see the **EXAM**VIEW® Assessment Suite, Progress Monitoring Assessments, or SuccessTracker™.

ⒺⓁⓁ Support

1 Content and Language
The Greek origin of the word *galaxy is galaxías kýklos,* which means "Milky Way."

Lab zone Inquiry Path
Hands-on learning in the Lab zone

Digital Path
Online learning at **my science online**.com

ENGAGE AND EXPLORE

To teach this lesson with an emphasis on inquiry, begin with the **Inquiry Warm-Up activity.** Students will investigate why the Milk Way looks hazy. Discuss the appearance of the holes close up and from across the room. Have students do the **After the Inquiry Warm-Up worksheet.** Talk about the distance between the stars and the distance between the holes on the paper. Have volunteers share their answers to question 4 about how the distances on their paper and in space can look similar.

EXPLAIN AND ELABORATE

Focus on the **Inquiry Skill** for the lesson. Point out that when you draw conclusions, you sum up what you have learned. What conclusion were students able to draw based on the **Inquiry Warm-Up activity?** *(The holes in the paper and the stars in the Milky Way both look blurry because their distances from the viewers are hundreds of thousands of times the distance between the objects themselves.)* Have students do the **Real-World Inquiry** to search for intelligent life in the universe. **Explore the Big Q** by using the diagrams and electromagnetic spectrums to explain what information can be derived from light and what it tells us about distant things. Have students do the **Quick Lab** to explore the difficulties involved in finding extrasolar planets and then share their results. **Answer the Big Q** by discussing how astronomers learn about objects in the universe.

Review the descriptions of the different types of galaxies before beginning the **Apply It activity.** Ask volunteers to share the conclusions they drew and their diagrams. Do the **Quick Lab** to reinforce understanding of a spiral galaxy. Students can use the online **Vocab Flash Cards** to review key terms.

EVALUATE

Have students take the **Lesson Quiz.** For an alternate assessment, see the **EXAM**VIEW® Assessment Suite, Progress Monitoring Assessments, or SuccessTracker™.

ENGAGE AND EXPLORE

Teach this lesson using digital resources. Begin by having students explore real-world connections to galaxies at **My Planet Diary** online. Have them access the Chapter Resources to find the **Unlock the Big Question activity.** There they can answer the questions and refine their responses as they continue through the lesson. You can re-assign the activity and have students submit their work so you can track their progress.

EXPLAIN AND ELABORATE

Students reading above, at, or below the lexile measure of this lesson can access basic content readings at their level at **My Reading Web.** Have students use the online **Vocab Flash Cards** to preview key terms. Do the **Real-World Inquiry** to search for intelligent life in the universe. **Explore the Big Q** by analyzing the diagrams and corresponding electromagnetic spectrums to determine what astronomers can learn about far away objects. Do the **Quick Lab** to explore the difficulties involved in finding extrasolar planets and then ask students to share their results. Have students **Answer the Big Q** and then share their responses.

Review the descriptions of the galaxies before assigning the online **Apply It activity.** Ask volunteers to share their diagrams and the conclusions they were able to draw. Have students submit their work to you. Have students do the **Quick Lab** to reinforce understanding of a spiral galaxy. The **Key Concept Summaries** online allow students to read a summary and see an image associated with each part of the lesson. Online remediation is available at **My Science Coach.**

EVALUATE

Have students take the **Lesson Quiz.** For an alternate assessment, see the **EXAM**VIEW® Assessment Suite, Progress Monitoring Assessments, or SuccessTracker™.

2 Frontload the Lesson
Preview the lesson visuals, labels, and captions. Ask students what they know about the term *galaxy.* Explain the specific meaning this word has in science.

3 Comprehensible Input
Have students study the visuals and their captions on pages 149, 152, and 153 to support the Key Concepts of the lesson.

4 Language Production
Pair or group students with varied language abilities to complete labs collaboratively for language practice. Have each student copy the completed written lab for personal reference.

5 Assess Understanding
Have students keep a content area log for this lesson using a two-column format with the headings "What I Understand" and "What I Don't Understand." Follow up so that students can move items from the "Don't Understand" to the "Understand" column.

LESSON 4.5

Star Systems and Galaxies

Establish Learning Objectives

After this lesson, students will be able to:

- Define a star system.
- Identify the major types of galaxies.

Engage

Activate Prior Knowledge

MY PLANET DIARY Read *Mike's Blog* with the class. Students who live in cities might not have had an opportunity to get a clear view of the night sky. Ask: **Who has seen the Milky Way at night?** *(Some students will raise their hands.)* **Ask students who have seen the Milky Way to describe it.** *(Students should describe a big, filmy, white swath in the sky that is full of stars.)* Tell students that the Milky Way is a galaxy. In fact, it is the galaxy that our solar system is in.

BIG IDEAS OF SCIENCE REFERENCE LIBRARY
Have students look up the following topics: Milky Way, Quasars.

Explore

Lab Resource: Inquiry Warm-Up

L1 WHY DOES THE MILKY WAY LOOK HAZY? Students will use a visual model to investigate why the Milky Way looks hazy.

LESSON

5 Star Systems and Galaxies

- What Is a Star System?

- What Are the Major Types of Galaxies?

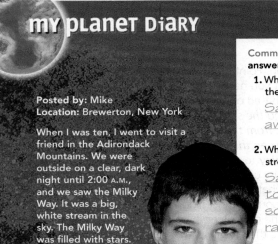

my planet diary

BLOG

Posted by: Mike
Location: Brewerton, New York

When I was ten, I went to visit a friend in the Adirondack Mountains. We were outside on a clear, dark night until 2:00 A.M., and we saw the Milky Way. It was a big, white stream in the sky. The Milky Way was filled with stars.

Communicate **Answer these questions. Discuss your answers with a partner.**

1. Why would it be easier to see the Milky Way from the mountains?

   Sample: In the mountains, you're away from bright city lights.

2. Why does the Milky Way appear more like a white stream than separate stars?

   Sample: The stars appear close together and are very far away, so they look like a white stream rather than individual stars.

▶ PLANET DIARY Go to **Planet Diary** to learn more about galaxies.

 Do the Inquiry Warm-Up *Why Does the Milky Way Look Hazy?*

What Is a Star System?

Our solar system has only one star: the sun. But this is not a common situation for stars. **Most stars are members of groups of two or more stars, called star systems.** If you were on a planet in one of these star systems, at times you might see two or more suns in the sky! At other times, one or more of these suns might be below the horizon.

148 Stars, Galaxies, and the Universe

SUPPORT ALL READERS

Lexile Measure = 930L   Lexile Word Count = 1186

Prior Exposure to Content: May be the first time students have encountered this topic

Academic Vocabulary: *cause, conclusions, effect*

Science Vocabulary: *binary star, globular cluster, galaxy, quasar*

Concept Level: May be difficult for students who struggle with abstract ideas

Preteach With: My Planet Diary "Mike's Blog" and Figure 4 activity

Go to **My Reading Web** to access leveled readings that provide a foundation for the content.

my science online.com

Vocabulary

- binary star • eclipsing binary • open cluster
- globular cluster • galaxy • spiral galaxy
- elliptical galaxy • irregular galaxy • quasar

Skills

- ⤸ Reading: Relate Cause and Effect
- △ Inquiry: Draw Conclusions

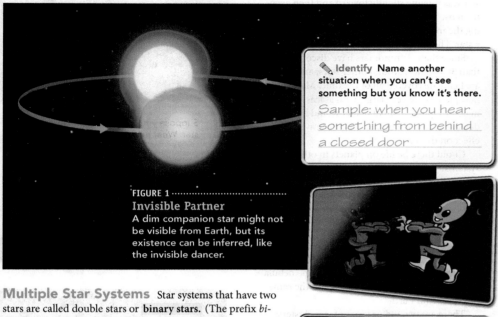

✎ **Identify** Name another situation when you can't see something but you know it's there.

Sample: when you hear
something from behind
a closed door

FIGURE 1 ....
Invisible Partner
A dim companion star might not be visible from Earth, but its existence can be inferred, like the invisible dancer.

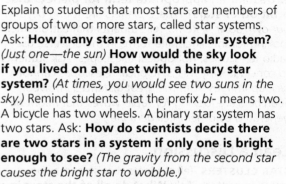

Multiple Star Systems Star systems that have two stars are called double stars or **binary stars.** (The prefix *bi-* means "two.") Those with three stars are called triple stars.

Often one star in a binary star is much brighter and more massive than the other. Astronomers can sometimes detect a binary star even if only one of the stars can be seen from Earth. Astronomers can often tell that there is a dim star in a binary system by observing the effects of its gravity. As the dim companion star revolves around a bright star, the dim star's gravity causes the bright star to wobble. Imagine watching a pair of dancers who are twirling each other around, as shown in **Figure 1**. Even if one dancer were invisible, you could tell the invisible dancer was there from the motion of the visible dancer.

Eclipsing Binaries A wobble is not the only clue that a star has a dim companion. A dim star in a binary star may pass in front of a brighter star and eclipse it. From Earth, the bright star would suddenly look much dimmer. A system in which one star blocks the light from another periodically is called an **eclipsing binary.**

⤸ **Relate Cause and Effect**
What causes a binary star to wobble back and forth?

- ⦿ Gravity of another star
- ○ Eclipsing by another star

149

Explain

Introduce Vocabulary

Tell students that clusters of stars can be either open or globular clusters. Globular clusters are packed with stars while open clusters are loose and disorganized. Students can remember which type is which by noting that open clusters have lots of open space.

Teach Key Concepts 🔑

Explain to students that most stars are members of groups of two or more stars, called star systems. Ask: **How many stars are in our solar system?** *(Just one—the sun)* **How would the sky look if you lived on a planet with a binary star system?** *(At times, you would see two suns in the sky.)* Remind students that the prefix *bi-* means two. A bicycle has two wheels. A binary star system has two stars. Ask: **How do scientists decide there are two stars in a system if only one is bright enough to see?** *(The gravity from the second star causes the bright star to wobble.)*

⤸ **Relate Cause and Effect** Tell students that a cause makes something happen. The effect is what happens. Science is all about relating cause and effect.

Lead a Discussion

ECLIPSING BINARIES Many students will be aware of eclipses, even if they have not observed one. Ask: **What happens in a solar eclipse?** *(During a solar eclipse, the moon moves between Earth and the sun, blocking our view of the sun.)* **How is this like an eclipsing binary?** *(In an eclipsing binary, one star temporarily blocks the light from the other because of their positions.)*

My Planet Diary provides an opportunity for students to explore real-world connections to galaxies.

ⒺⓁⓁ Support

1 Content and Language

Write *elliptical galaxy* on the board. Remind students *ellipse* means "oval shape." Point out the adjective form *elliptical* includes the suffix *-ical*, meaning "dealing with" or "pertaining to."

2 Frontload the Lesson

Invite students to offer ideas about the name of our galaxy and how many stars exist in it. In this lesson, they will learn terms scientists use to describe different types of star systems and galaxies.

3 Comprehensible Input

Ask student pairs or groups to make a poster that includes three cluster diagrams on the topics: *star system, star cluster,* and *galaxy*. Students should include two smaller circles for the star systems *binary star* and *triple star,* for *open cluster* and *globular cluster,* and four types of galaxies.

149

Explain

21st Century Learning

COMMUNICATION Have pairs of students use a dictionary to look up words that contain the prefix *extra-*. Students will likely think of extraordinary, extracurricular, or extraterrestrial. Ask: **What is the meaning of the prefix *extra-?*** *(Beyond)* Then have them describe how this prefix relates to the definition of each word they listed. Then ask: **Why is *extrasolar* an appropriate term for planets that orbit other stars?** *(These planets are found beyond our own solar system.)* Tell students that astronomers looking for intelligent life forms in the universe use radio telescopes, not optical telescopes. Ask students to conclude why this is. *(Optical telescopes cannot pick up images from the great distances involved. Searchers are looking for radio waves that might be generated by other intelligent life.)*

Lead a Discussion

STAR CLUSTERS Tell students that stars may be found in clusters. Ask: **What do all of the stars in a cluster have in common?** *(They formed from the same nebula, and they are about the same distance from Earth.)* **What are the two types of clusters?** *(Open clusters and globular clusters)* **Which type of cluster contains more stars?** *(Globular cluster)*

Planets Around Other Stars In 1995, astronomers first discovered a planet revolving around another ordinary star. They used a method similar to the one used in studying binary stars. The astronomers observed that the star was moving slightly toward and then away from us. They knew that the invisible object causing the movement didn't have enough mass to be a star. They inferred that it must be a planet.

Since then, astronomers have discovered more than 300 planets around other stars, and new ones are being discovered all of the time. Most of these new planets are very large, with at least half of the mass of Jupiter. A small planet would be hard to detect because it would have little gravitational effect on the star it orbited.

Could there be life on planets in other solar systems? Some scientists think it is possible. A few astronomers are using radio telescopes to search for signals that could not have come from natural sources. Such signals might be evidence that an alien civilization was sending out radio waves.

Star Clusters Many stars belong to larger groupings called star clusters. All of the stars in a particular cluster formed from the same nebula at about the same time and are about the same distance from Earth.

There are two major types of star clusters: open clusters and globular clusters. **Open clusters** have a loose, disorganized appearance as shown in **Figure 3** and contain up to a few thousand stars. They often contain many bright supergiants and much gas and dust. In contrast, **globular clusters** are large groupings of older stars. Globular clusters are round and packed with stars. Some may contain more than a million stars.

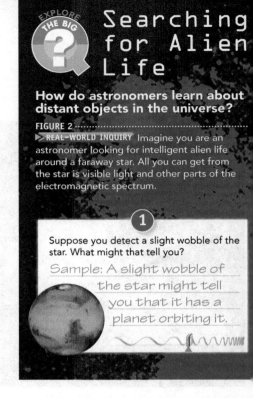

EXPLORE THE BIG ? Searching for Alien Life

How do astronomers learn about distant objects in the universe?

FIGURE 2 ....

▶ **REAL-WORLD INQUIRY** Imagine you are an astronomer looking for intelligent alien life around a faraway star. All you can get from the star is visible light and other parts of the electromagnetic spectrum.

1

Suppose you detect a slight wobble of the star. What might that tell you?

Sample: A slight wobble of the star might tell you that it has a planet orbiting it.

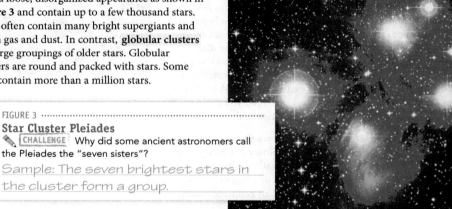

FIGURE 3 ....
Star Cluster Pleiades
✏ **CHALLENGE** Why did some ancient astronomers call the Pleiades the "seven sisters"?
Sample: The seven brightest stars in the cluster form a group.

Real-World Inquiry allows students to search for intelligent life in the universe.

my science online.com ▸ **Star Systems**

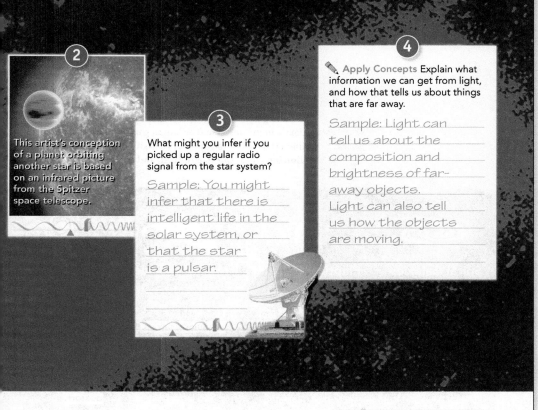

This artist's conception of a planet orbiting another star is based on an infrared picture from the Spitzer space telescope.

2

3

What might you infer if you picked up a regular radio signal from the star system?

Sample: You might infer that there is intelligent life in the solar system, or that the star is a pulsar.

4

✎ **Apply Concepts** Explain what information we can get from light, and how that tells us about things that are far away.

Sample: Light can tell us about the composition and brightness of far-away objects. Light can also tell us how the objects are moving.

Do the Quick Lab *Planets Around Other Stars.*

⊂⊃ Assess Your Understanding

1a. Define What is a binary star?

A star system with two stars

b. Apply Concepts In what two ways can we tell if a star is a binary star?

1. One of the stars periodically blocks light from the other star. 2. The star appears to wobble back and forth.

c. 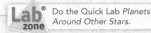 How do astronomers learn about distant objects in the universe?

Sample: Astronomers collect and analyze data in the form of visible light and other electromagnetic radiation from faraway objects.

got it?

○ **I get it!** Now I know that star systems are *groups of two or more stars.*

○ **I need extra help with** *See TE note.*

Go to **my science** **coach** *online for help with this subject.*

151

Elaborate

Explore the Big Q ❓▶

Direct students' attention to the four boxes in **Figure 2.** Ask: **What do the little diagrams at the bottom of the first three boxes represent?** *(They represent the electromagnetic spectrum.)* **What does the arrow indicate in the first box?** *(The visible portion of the spectrum)* **What does the arrow indicate in the second box?** *(The infrared portion of the spectrum)* **What does the arrow indicate in the third box?** *(The radio wave portion of the spectrum)* Tell students that this gives them a hint about the rest of the information in the box.

Lab Resource: Quick Lab

L1 PLANETS AROUND OTHER STARS Students will explore the difficulties involved in finding extrasolar planets.

Evaluate

Assess Your Understanding

After students answer the questions, have them evaluate their understanding by completing the appropriate sentence.

Answer the Big Q ❓▶

To help students focus on the Big Question, lead a class discussion about the ways in which astronomers learn about distant objects in the universe.

RTI Response to Intervention

1a., b. If students need help with understanding binary stars, **then** have them review the information for the red heading *Multiple Star Systems.*

c. If students cannot explain how astronomers gather information, **then** have them review **Figure 2.**

my science ⑤ coach Have students go online for help in understanding star systems.

Differentiated Instruction

L1 More Planets More extrasolar planets are being discovered all the time. Invite interested students to do research to learn about recent discoveries. Suggest that the NASA Web site might be a resourceful place to begin. If students do their research on the Internet, remind them to follow prescribed guidelines for Internet use.

L3 Binary Stars Challenge students to use their visualization and artistic skills to draw the view of the sky from a planet circling one of a pair of stars. Choosing the brighter star to base the definition of day on, they should draw the view in the morning, at midday, in the evening, and at night.

Explain

Teach Key Concepts

Explain to students that galaxies are large groups of stars, individual stars, star systems, and star clusters. Most galaxies can be classified into the following types: spiral, elliptical, and irregular. Ask: **What holds galaxies together?** *(Gravity)* **Which type of galaxy has many stars packed into a ball shape, but little gas and dust?** *(Elliptical)* **Which type of galaxy has many bright, young stars and lots of gas and dust?** *(Irregular)* **What is a quasar?** *(An active, young galaxy with a huge black hole at its center)*

Make Analogies

L1 **THE GLUE THAT HOLDS IT TOGETHER** Gravity is very important in understanding how the universe works. Gravity is what causes the gas in a nebula to pull together and form a star. It is also what holds Earth in orbit about the sun, and the moon in orbit about Earth. Ask: **What holds a galaxy together, causing it to maintain its shape?** *(Gravity)*

Elaborate

21st Century Learning

CRITICAL THINKING Tell students to read about spiral, elliptical, and irregular galaxies, noting information on the ages of stars in each type of galaxy. Then tell students to list the galaxies from the ones with the youngest stars to the ones with the oldest. *(Irregular, spiral, elliptical)*

What Are the Major Types of Galaxies?

A **galaxy** is a huge group of single stars, star systems, star clusters, dust, and gas bound together by gravity. There are billions of galaxies in the universe. The largest galaxies have more than a trillion stars. **Astronomers classify most galaxies into the following types: spiral, elliptical, and irregular.**

1 **2** **3** **4**

Spiral Galaxies

Some galaxies appear to have a bulge in the middle and arms that spiral outward, like pinwheels. These galaxies are **spiral galaxies.** The arms contain gas, dust, and many bright, young stars. Most new stars in spiral galaxies form in these arms. Barred-spiral galaxies have a bar-shaped area of stars and gas that passes through the center.

Elliptical Galaxies

Not all galaxies have spiral arms. **Elliptical galaxies** look like round or flattened balls. These galaxies contain billions of stars but have little gas and dust between the stars. Because there is little gas or dust, stars are no longer forming. Most elliptical galaxies contain only old stars.

Irregular Galaxies

Some galaxies do not have regular shapes. These are known as **irregular galaxies.** Irregular galaxies are typically smaller than other types of galaxies. They generally have many bright, young stars and lots of gas and dust to form new stars.

Quasars

Astronomers in the 1960s discovered distant, extremely bright objects that looked like stars. Since *quasi* means "something like" in Latin, these objects were called quasi-stellar objects, or **quasars.** Quasars are active young galaxies with huge black holes at their centers. Gas spins around the black hole, heats up, and glows.

FIGURE 4 ·····

Types of Galaxies

✏ Relate Text and Visuals **Identify the four galaxies shown on these pages and explain.**

A Spiral; it has a spiral shape and lots of bright stars.

B Elliptical; it looks like a round ball.

C Quasar; it has gas revolving around a black hole.

D Irregular; it does not have a regular shape.

A
- ⦿ Spiral   ◯ Elliptical
- ◯ Irregular   ◯ Quasar

152 Stars, Galaxies, and the Universe

Digital Lesson: Assign the *Apply It* activity online and have students submit their work to you.

my science ONLINE.com ▸ Types of Galaxies

apply it!

Our solar system is located in a galaxy called the Milky Way. From the side, the Milky Way would look like a narrow disk with a large bulge in the middle. But from the top or bottom, the Milky Way would have a pinwheel shape. You can't see the shape of the Milky Way from Earth because our solar system is inside one of the arms.

When you see the Milky Way at night during the summer, you are looking toward the center of our galaxy. The center of the galaxy is about 25,000 light-years away, but it is hidden from view by large clouds of dust and gas. But astronomers can study the center using X-rays, infrared radiation, and radio waves.

Draw Conclusions What kind of galaxy is the Milky Way? Explain why and draw a sketch of what the Milky Way might look like from outside.

Spiral; because of the pinwheel
shape and the arms

Sample:

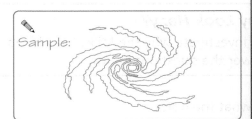

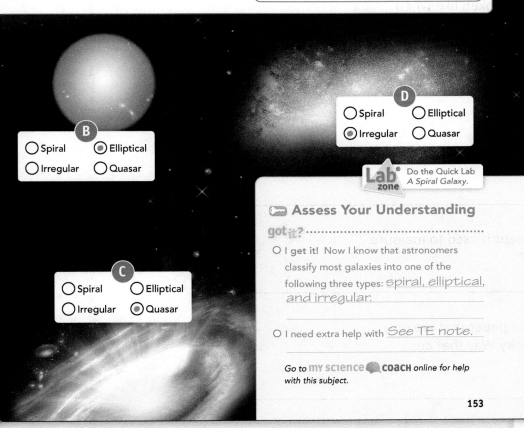

B
○ Spiral   ● Elliptical
○ Irregular   ○ Quasar

D
○ Spiral   ○ Elliptical
● Irregular   ○ Quasar

C
○ Spiral   ○ Elliptical
○ Irregular   ● Quasar

 Lab zone Do the Quick Lab *A Spiral Galaxy.*

Assess Your Understanding

got it?..

○ **I get it!** Now I know that astronomers classify most galaxies into one of the following three types: spiral, elliptical, and irregular.

○ **I need extra help with** See TE note.

Go to my science **COACH** *online for help with this subject.*

153

Apply It!

L1 Before beginning the activity, review the descriptions of the different types of galaxies. After students have completed the activity, explain to them that the Milky Way is a barred spiral galaxy.

Draw Conclusions Explain to students that a conclusion is a statement that sums up what they have learned.

Lab Resource: Quick Lab **Lab zone**

L1 A SPIRAL GALAXY Students will construct a model of a spiral galaxy.

Evaluate

Assess Your Understanding

Have students evaluate their understanding by completing the appropriate sentence.

RTI Response to Intervention

If students cannot classify galaxies, **then** have them review **Figure 4.**

my science COACH Have students go online for help in understanding the types of galaxies.

Differentiated Instruction

L1 Where in the Milky Way Are We? Have students construct a simple model of the Milky Way using small candies or markers as stars. They should indicate the approximate location of our solar system.

L3 How Many Stars Are in the Universe? Challenge students to use the numbers given just above the Key Concept Statement to make an estimate of how many stars are in the universe. They should use scientific notation to express their answer.

LESSON 4.5

Name _____ Date _____ Class _____

Star Systems and Galaxies

Inquiry Warm-Up, *Why Does the Milky Way Look Hazy?*
In the Inquiry Warm-Up, you used a simple model to investigate why the Milky Way looks hazy. Using what you learned from that activity, answer the questions below.

1. **COMMUNICATE** Draw a two-part diagram showing what the holes in the paper looked like up close and what they looked like when viewed from across the room.

2. **MEASURE** About how much distance is there between holes that are next to one another on the paper?

   _____

3. **USE PRIOR KNOWLEDGE** What unit of measurement is used to measure the distances between stars in the Milky Way?

   _____

4. **DRAW CONCLUSIONS** How can holes in a piece of paper that are only millimeters apart look similar to stars in the Milky Way that are light-years apart?

   _____

   _____

   _____

   _____

   _____

Name _____ Date _____ Class _____

Star Systems and Galaxies

What Is a Star System?

1a. **DEFINE** What is a binary star? _____
_____

b. **APPLY CONCEPTS** In what two ways can we tell if a star is a binary star? _____
_____
_____

c. **ANSWER** How do astronomers learn about distant objects in the
universe? _____
_____
_____

got it?..

○ **I get it!** Now I know that star systems are _____
_____

○ **I need extra help with** _____
_____

What Are the Major Types of Galaxies?

got it?..

○ **I get it!** Now I know that astronomers classify most galaxies into one of the following three
types: _____
_____

○ **I need extra help with** _____
_____

Star Systems and Galaxies

What Is a Star System?

Most stars are members of groups of two or more stars, called star systems. Star systems that have two stars are called double stars or **binary stars.** Often one star in a binary star is much brighter and more massive than the other. Even if only one star can be seen from Earth, astronomers can often detect its dimmer partner by observing the effects of its gravity. As a dim companion star revolves around a bright star, its gravity can cause the bright star to wobble. A dim star may also pass in front of a brighter star and eclipse it. A system in which one dim star blocks the light from another periodically is called an **eclipsing binary.** In 1995, astronomers first discovered a planet revolving around another star. Again, they detected the planet by observing the effect the planet's gravity had on the star. Since then, astronomers have discovered more than 200 more.

Many stars belong to larger groupings called clusters. All of the stars in a particular cluster formed from the same nebula at about the same time. An **open cluster** has a loose, disorganized appearance. Open clusters may contain up to a few thousand stars including many bright supergiants and a lot of gas and dust. **Globular clusters** are large groupings of older stars. They are round and can be packed with more than a million stars.

What Are the Major Types of Galaxies?

A **galaxy** is a huge group of single stars, star systems, star clusters, dust, and gas bound together by gravity. There are billions of galaxies in the universe. **Astronomers classify most galaxies into the following types: spiral, elliptical, and irregular.** From above, a **spiral galaxy** looks like a pinwheel. Its arms are full of young stars, and new ones form there. **Elliptical galaxies** look like round flattened balls. They contain billions of stars but have little gas or dust between the stars. Stars are no longer forming inside them, so they contain only old stars. **Irregular galaxies** do not have regular shapes. They are smaller than spiral or elliptical galaxies. They contain young, bright stars and include a lot of gas and dust to form new ones. **Quasars** are active, young galaxies with black holes at their center. Gas spins around the black hole, heats up, and glows.

On a separate sheet of paper, make a table that compares and contrasts the four types of galaxies. Include galaxy shape, types of stars, amount of gas and dust, whether new stars form in them, and any special attributes in your table.

Review and Reinforce

Star Systems and Galaxies

Understanding Main Ideas
Answer the following questions in the spaces provided.

1. How can astronomers detect a binary star if only one of the two stars is visible from Earth?

_____

_____

2. What holds a galaxy together?

_____

3. What type of galaxy is the Milky Way? _____

4. Which type of galaxy includes little gas and dust and no longer produces stars? _____

Building Vocabulary
Write a definition for each of these terms on a separate sheet of paper.

5. binary star
6. eclipsing binary
7. open cluster
8. globular cluster
9. spiral galaxy
10. elliptical galaxy
11. irregular galaxy
12. quasar

Name _____ Date _____ Class _____

Star Systems and Galaxies

Read the passage and study the graphs. Then fill in the table that follows.

Distances to the Galaxies

For nearly 100 years after galaxies were first seen with telescopes, astronomers didn't know what they were. At first, they were thought to be small nearby objects. Astronomers can use parallax to measure the distance to objects up to a few hundred light-years away. Galaxies were too far away to be measured by parallax. In 1923, the astronomer Edwin Hubble solved the problem by using a class of stars called variable stars. These unusual stars become brighter and dimmer in repeating cycles of 1 to 100 days.

By examining variable stars whose distance from the sun was determined by parallax, astronomers had discovered a useful relationship between the length of their brightness/dimness cycles and their average absolute brightness. Usually, to figure out a star's absolute brightness, you have to know both its apparent brightness and its distance from Earth. With a variable star, if you know the time period of its brightness/dimness cycle, you can calculate its absolute brightness. Then, comparing its absolute brightness with its apparent brightness, you can calculate its distance, even if it is much farther than 1,000 light-years away.

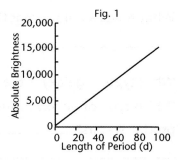

Fig. 1

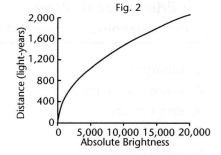

Fig. 2

Hubble identified some faint variable stars in photographs of the Andromeda galaxy. Using these, he calculated that the Andromeda galaxy and other galaxies were millions of light-years away and very large. Suppose astronomers discover the five variable stars in the table. Use the graph in Figure 1 to estimate their absolute brightness. All five have an average apparent brightness of 5. For variable stars with this apparent brightness, you can use the graph in Figure 2 to determine each star's distance from Earth.

	Length of bright/ dim cycle (days)	Absolute brightness (sun = 1)	Distance in light-years
Variable star A	5		
Variable star B	20		
Variable star C	35		
Variable star D	50		
Variable star E	90		

Name _____ Date _____ Class _____

Lesson Quiz

Star Systems and Galaxies

Fill in the blank to complete each statement.

1. Galaxies are held together by _____.

2. Astronomers can often identify a binary system that includes only one visible star by observing the effects of the dim star's _____ on its brighter companion.

3. _____ galaxies are small with many bright young stars and lots of gas and dust for star formation.

4. New stars tend to form in the _____ of a spiral galaxy.

If the statement is true, write *true*. If the statement is false, change the underlined word or words to make the statement true.

5. _____ A(n) <u>eclipsing binary</u> is an active, young galaxy with a giant black hole at its center.

6. _____ A(n) <u>globular cluster</u> is a galaxy shaped like a flattened ball.

7. _____ <u>Elliptical galaxies</u> have mostly old stars, without a lot of active star formation.

8. _____ The Milky Way galaxy is a(n) <u>spiral</u> galaxy.

9. _____ <u>Fewer</u> new stars are found in open clusters than globular clusters.

10. _____ Most stars are members of groups of two or more stars, called <u>star systems</u>.

Star Systems and Galaxies

Answer Key

After the Inquiry Warm-Up

1. Students should show a close-up view where the individual holes are clearly visible, and a distant view where the individual holes blur together.

2. Answers will vary. Answers should be given in millimeters or fractions of centimeters.

3. The stars in the Milky Way are light-years apart.

4. The holes in the piece of paper that are only millimeters apart and the stars in the Milky Way that are light-years apart both look blurry because of the distance from the viewer. In both cases the distance from the viewer is hundreds or thousands of times the distance between the objects themselves.

Key Concept Summaries

Students' tables should include the following information. Spiral galaxy: pinwheel shape; many bright, young stars; gas and dust in arms; new stars forming in arms. Elliptical: flattened ball; old stars; little gas and dust; stars no longer forming. Irregular: not regular; many bright, young stars; lots of gas and dust; new stars forming; smaller than other galaxies. Quasar: elliptical with bar through it; young stars; lots of gas and dust; new stars forming; huge black hole at center.

Review and Reinforce

1. The position of the visible star might wobble slightly due to the gravitational pull of the unseen star as it revolves around it.

2. gravity

3. spiral galaxy

4. elliptical galaxy

5. a star system that has two stars

6. a binary star in which one star periodically blocks the light from the other

7. a loose, disorganized group of stars

8. a large grouping of tightly-packed older stars

9. a pinwheel-shaped galaxy with new stars forming in its arms

10. a galaxy shaped like a round, flattened ball that contains old stars

11. a galaxy without a regular shape where many new stars form

12. an active, young galaxy with a black hole at its center

Enrich

A: 1,250; 500

B: 3,000; 700

C: 5,000; 1,000

D: 7,500; 1,200

E: 12,500; 1,600

Lesson Quiz

1. gravity

2. gravity

3. Irregular

4. arms

5. quasar

6. elliptical galaxy

7. true

8. true

9. More

10. true

Place the outside corner, the corner away from the dotted line, in the corner of your copy machine to copy onto letter-size paper.

...stronomers learn about distant ...the universe?

...riods or $\frac{1}{2}$–1 block

...To do this lesson in approximately half the time, ...Knowledge activity on page 154. A discussion of ...n page 155 will familiarize students with the lesson ...students do the Quick Lab. The rest of the lesson can be ...by students independently.

...rence Navigator, in the online Planning tools, allows you to ...tomize *Interactive Science* to your own teaching style. You can ...also edit lesson plans by selecting the Lesson Planner option.

Digital Teacher's Edition allows you to access your Teacher's Edition and Resource materials online.

Lesson Vocabulary

- big bang
- Hubble's Law
- cosmic background radiation
- dark matter
- dark energy

Content Refresher

Dark Matter Observations of the movement of stars and galaxies and theories about how the universe formed indicate that much more mass exists in the universe than can be seen with modern technology. The missing mass is called dark matter. Although little is known about this mysterious missing mass, it is possible that dark matter consists of some combination of normal matter and as-yet-unknown types of subatomic particles. The normal matter might include nonluminous objects such as brown dwarfs (failed stars that are not massive enough to produce nuclear fusion, which causes stars to shine), neutron stars, black holes, and cooled white dwarfs.

It is theorized that most dark matter may consist of exotic, unknown particles. These particles could be types of neutrinos or a group of particles called weakly interacting massive particles (WIMPS). Neutrinos are generated by our sun during nuclear processes. They are transmitted by the solar wind and light. Since these teensy particles have no electric charge and a smaller mass than electrons, humans are not even aware that neutrinos constantly flow through their bodies.

LESSON OBJECTIVE

State what the big bang theory says about the universe.

Blended Path Active learning using Student Edition, Inquiry Path, and Digital Path

ENGAGE AND EXPLORE

Teach this lesson using a variety of resources. Begin by reading **My Planet Diary** as a class. Have students share ideas about what they know about previous space shuttle missions. Then have students do the **Inquiry Warm-Up activity.** Students will explore how the universe expands. Discuss what the students observed about the dots as the balloon expanded. The **After the Inquiry Warm-Up worksheet** sets up a discussion about the direction in which a universe expands. Have volunteers share the questions they posed about the universe in question 4.

EXPLAIN AND ELABORATE

Teach Key Concepts by explaining how the universe formed and why some scientists believe that it will expand forever. Then have students practice the inquiry skill in the **Apply It activity.** Use **Figure 2** to illustrate how the universe is likely to continue to expand in the future. To **Support the Big Q,** discuss what scientists think is most likely to happen to the universe in the future and what supporting evidence they have for this theory. Hand out the **Key Concept Summaries** as a review of each part of the lesson. Students can also use the online **Vocab Flash Cards** to review key terms.

EVALUATE

Have students take the **Lesson Quiz.** For an alternate assessment, see the **EXAM**VIEW® Assessment Suite, Progress Monitoring Assessments, or SuccessTracker™.

ELL Support

1 Content and Language
The word *cosmic* originates from the Greek word *kosmikós* meaning "universe."

Lab zone Inquiry Path
Hands-on learning in the Lab zone

Digital Path
Online learning at **my science online**.com

ENGAGE AND EXPLORE

To teach this lesson with an emphasis on inquiry, begin with the **Inquiry Warm-Up activity.** Students will investigate how the universe expands. Discuss how the dots on the balloon moved. Have students do the **After the Inquiry Warm-Up worksheet.** Discuss what the students observed about the dots as the balloon expanded. Have volunteers share the questions they posed about the universe in question 4.

EXPLAIN AND ELABORATE

Focus on the **Inquiry Skill** for the lesson. Point out that when you make models, you create a representation of a complex object or process in order to analyze its parts more closely. What did students model in the **Inquiry Warm-Up activity?** *(The expansion of the galaxy.)* Review what the gridlines on the dough represent before beginning the **Apply It activity.** Ask volunteers to share their diagrams and explanations. To **Support the Big Q,** ask students what scientists think is most likely to happen to the universe and discuss the supporting evidence for their theory. Have students do the **Quick Lab** to explore the possible futures of the universe and then share their results. Students can use the online **Vocab Flash Cards** to review key terms.

EVALUATE

Have students take the **Lesson Quiz.** For an alternate assessment, see the **EXAM**VIEW® Assessment Suite, Progress Monitoring Assessments, or SuccessTracker™.

ENGAGE AND EXPLORE

Teach this lesson using digital resources. Begin by having students explore real-world connections to the universe at **My Planet Diary** online. Have them access the Chapter Resources to find the **Unlock the Big Question activity.** There they can answer the questions and refine their responses as they continue through the lesson. You can re-assign the activity and have students submit their work so you can track their progress.

EXPLAIN AND ELABORATE

Students reading above, at, or below the lexile measure of this lesson can access basic content readings at their level at **My Reading Web.** Have students use the online **Vocab Flash Cards** to preview key terms. Review what the gridlines on the dough represent before assigning the online **Apply It activity.** Ask volunteers to share their diagrams and explanations. Have students submit their work to you. To **Support the Big Q,** explain why scientists think it is most likely that the universe will continue to expand. Have students do the online **Art in Motion activity** to explore the big bang theory and the expanding universe. Do the **Quick Lab** to explore the possible futures of the universe and then ask students to share their results. The **Key Concept Summaries** online allow students to read a summary and see an image associated with each part of the lesson. Online remediation is available at **My Science Coach.**

EVALUATE

Have students take the **Lesson Quiz.** For an alternate assessment, see the **EXAM**VIEW® Assessment Suite, Progress Monitoring Assessments, or SuccessTracker™.

2 Frontload the Lesson
Preview the lesson visuals, labels, and captions. Ask students what they know about the terms *big bang* and *cosmic background radiation.* Explain the specific meanings these words have in science.

3 Comprehensible Input
Have students study the visuals and their captions on pages 156 and 157 to support the Key Concepts of the lesson.

4 Language Production
Pair or group students with varied language abilities to complete labs collaboratively for language practice. Have each student copy the completed written lab for personal reference.

5 Assess Understanding
Divide the class into small groups. Have each student identify a Key Concept from the lesson to discuss in his or her group. After the discussions, have students talk about the Key Concepts as a group.

The Expanding Universe

Establish Learning Objective

After this lesson, students will be able to:

 State what the big bang theory says about the universe.

Engage

Activate Prior Knowledge

MY PLANET DIARY Read *David's Blog* with the class. Explain that space shuttles often carry experiments onboard. They also carry instruments to assist scientists with their research. Ask students if they have watched a shuttle launch on television. Ask: **Where were the engines David described?** *(The engines used to launch the shuttle are on the rocket, not on the shuttle itself.)* Point out that March 2009 mission of the space shuttle *Discovery* was the first mission with the new class of Educator Astronauts going into space.

BIG IDEAS OF SCIENCE REFERENCE LIBRARY 📖
Have students look up the following topic: Big Bang Theory.

Explore

Lab Resource: Inquiry Warm-Up 🔬

L1 **HOW DOES THE UNIVERSE EXPAND?** Students will use a balloon to model the expansion of the universe.

The Expanding Universe

 What Does the Big Bang Theory Say About the Universe?

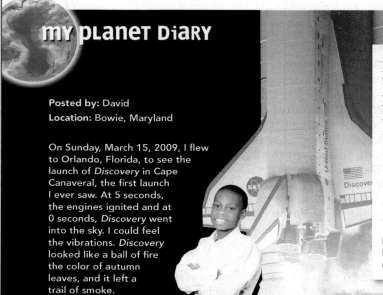

my pLaneT DiaRY

BLOG

Posted by: David
Location: Bowie, Maryland

On Sunday, March 15, 2009, I flew to Orlando, Florida, to see the launch of *Discovery* in Cape Canaveral, the first launch I ever saw. At 5 seconds, the engines ignited and at 0 seconds, *Discovery* went into the sky. I could feel the vibrations. *Discovery* looked like a ball of fire the color of autumn leaves, and it left a trail of smoke.

Communicate Write your answer to the question below. Then discuss your answer with a partner.

What would you want scientists to learn about the universe from a space shuttle mission?

Sample: New information about living in space

> **PLANET DIARY** Go to Planet Diary to learn more about the universe.

🔬 *Do the Inquiry Warm-Up How Does the Universe Expand?*

What Does the Big Bang Theory Say About the Universe?

Astronomers have learned a lot about the universe. They theorize that the universe began 13.7 billion years ago. At that time, the part of the universe we can see was no larger than the period at the end of this sentence. This tiny universe was incredibly hot and dense. The universe then exploded in what astronomers call the **big bang**.

154 Stars, Galaxies, and the Universe

SUPPORT ALL READERS

Lexile Measure = 920L   Lexile Word Count = 830

Prior Exposure to Content: May be the first time students have encountered this topic

Academic Vocabulary: *evidence, identify, models*

Science Vocabulary: *big bang, cosmic background radiation, dark matter*

Concept Level: May be difficult for students who struggle with abstract ideas

Preteach With: My Planet Diary "David's Blog" and Figure 2 activity

Go to **My Reading Web** to access leveled readings that provide a foundation for the content.

my science online.com

Vocabulary
- big bang
- cosmic background radiation
- dark matter
- Hubble's law
- dark energy

Skills
- Reading: Identify Supporting Evidence
- Inquiry: Make Models

🔑 **According to the big bang theory, the universe formed in an instant, billions of years ago, in an enormous explosion. New observations lead many astronomers to conclude that the universe will likely expand forever.** Since the big bang, the size of the universe has been increasing. The universe is immensely larger now than it once was.

As the universe expanded, it gradually cooled. After a few hundred thousand years, atoms formed. Within about the first 500 million years after the big bang, the first stars and galaxies formed.

Moving Galaxies In the 1920s, an American astronomer, Edwin Hubble, discovered important evidence that led to the big bang theory. Hubble studied the spectrums of many galaxies at various distances from Earth. By examining a galaxy's spectrum, Hubble could tell how fast the galaxy was moving and whether it was moving toward our galaxy or away from it.

Hubble discovered that almost all galaxies are moving away from us and from each other. Hubble found the relationship between the distance to a galaxy and its speed. **Hubble's law** states that the farther away a galaxy is, the faster it is moving away from us. Hubble's law strongly supports the big bang theory.

Cosmic Background Radiation Another piece of evidence for the big bang was discovered by accident. In 1965, two American physicists, Arno Penzias and Robert Wilson, detected faint radiation on their radio telescope coming from all directions. Scientists later concluded that this **cosmic background radiation** is the leftover thermal energy from the big bang. This energy was distributed in every direction as the universe expanded.

✏️ 🔍 **Identify Supporting Evidence** Underline the main evidence Hubble found that the universe is expanding.

apply it!

The galaxies in the universe are like raisins in rising bread dough.

🔺 **Make Models** Draw the raisins in their new positions on the bottom picture. Explain why the raisins are like galaxies.

The dough carries the raisins apart just as the universe carries the galaxies apart.

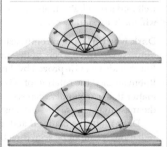

FIGURE 1 ·········
Age of the Universe
By measuring how fast the universe is expanding, astronomers can infer how long it has been expanding. The COBE satellite shown measured the cosmic background radiation, which also gave clues to the age of the universe.

155

Explain

Introduce Vocabulary
Tell students that *dark matter* and *dark energy* both refer to things we cannot see, which is why they earned the label *dark*.

Teach Key Concepts 🔑
Explain that scientists have a theory about the formation of the universe. They have evidence supporting the big bang theory, which says that the universe formed in an instant, billion of years ago, in an enormous explosion. Ask: **Before the big bang, what was the universe like?** (*Incredibly small, dense, and hot.*) **As the universe expanded, what happened to its temperature?** (*It cooled.*) **How long did it take until the first stars and galaxies formed?** (*About 500 million years*) Tell students many astronomers say the universe will expand forever. Ask: **What evidence supports this conclusion?** (*Hubble discovered almost all galaxies are moving away from us and each other.*) **What is Hubble's law?** (*The farther away a galaxy is, the faster it is moving away.*) **What is another piece of supporting evidence?** (*Cosmic radiation, which is leftover energy from the big bang. It causes static on TVs.*) Explain that the cosmic background radiation falls in the microwave part of the electromagnetic spectrum.

🔍 **Identify Supporting Evidence** Tell students that evidence consists of facts—information whose accuracy can be confirmed by testing or by observation. Supporting evidence can help students understand the theory or hypothesis.

Elaborate

Apply It!
L1 Before beginning the activity, tell students that the gridlines on the bread dough are like latitude and longitude lines on a map. Students can use them to locate the positions of the raisins.

🔺 **Make Models** Tell students that a model is a diagram, computer image, or other representation of a complex object or process. Models help people understand very small and very large things they cannot observe directly. The bread dough is being used as a model of the universe.

My Planet Diary provides an opportunity for students to explore real-world connections to the universe.

Digital Lesson: Assign the *Apply It* activity online and have students submit their work to you.

Explain

Teach With Visuals

Tell students to look at **Figure 2**. Ask: **How is time represented on the big green funnel?** *(Time goes up and down; it is on the vertical axis.)* **Where is the big bang on the image?** *(At the very bottom—the pouring part of the funnel shape.)* **Where is today on the funnel?** *(It is marked with a dark ring.)* **What does the visual show the universe will do in the future?** *(It shows it continuing to expand at an increasing rate.)*

Support the Big Q

EVIDENCE FOR FUTURE EXPANSION Tell students that one of two things could happen to the universe: It could keep expanding or it could complete its expansion and then start shrinking. Ask: **Which possibility do scientists think is most likely?** *(Scientists think that it is most likely the universe will continue to expand.)* **What is their supporting evidence for this theory?** *(Dark matter; its presence is inferred by observing the effect of gravity on visible objects. Dark matter makes up 90% of the matter in the universe. Scientists have noticed that the universe seems to be expanding faster and faster. They postulate that there is a force caused by dark energy, which is making this happen.)*

The Big Bang and the Future of the Universe What will happen to the universe in the future? One possibility is that the universe will continue to expand. All of the stars will eventually run out of fuel and burn out, and the universe will be cold and dark. Another possibility is that the force of gravity will begin to pull the galaxies back together, as shown in **Figure 2**. The result would be a reverse big bang, or "big crunch." The universe would be crushed in an enormous black hole.

FIGURE 2 ....

The Big Crunch

The small diagram represents the expansion of the universe until now. The big bang is at the bottom.

[CHALLENGE] On the top part of the diagram, draw a sketch of the universe collapsing to a big crunch. Explain your drawing.

Sample: The drawing comes to a point at the top because the universe would collapse to a point in a big crunch.

Big bang

Which of these possibilities is more likely? Recent discoveries have produced a surprising new view of the universe that is still not well understood. But many astronomers conclude that the universe will likely expand forever.

Dark Matter Until recently, astronomers assumed that the universe consisted solely of the matter they could observe directly. But this idea was disproved by American astronomer Vera Rubin. Rubin studied the rotation of spiral galaxies. She discovered that the matter that astronomers can see makes up as little as ten percent of the mass in galaxies. The rest exists in the form of dark matter.

Dark matter is matter that does not give off electromagnetic radiation. It cannot be seen directly. However, its presence can be inferred by observing the effect of its gravity on visible objects.

An Accelerating Expansion In the late 1990s, astronomers observed that the expansion of the universe appeared to be accelerating. That is, galaxies seemed to be moving apart at a faster rate than in the past. This observation was puzzling, as no known force could account for it. Astronomers infer that a mysterious new force, which they call **dark energy**, is causing the expansion of the universe to accelerate, as shown in **Figure 3**.

The static on your TV screen includes radiation left over from the big bang.

156 Stars, Galaxies, and the Universe

Art in Motion allows students to explore the big bang and the expanding universe.

my science online.com | **The Expanding Universe**

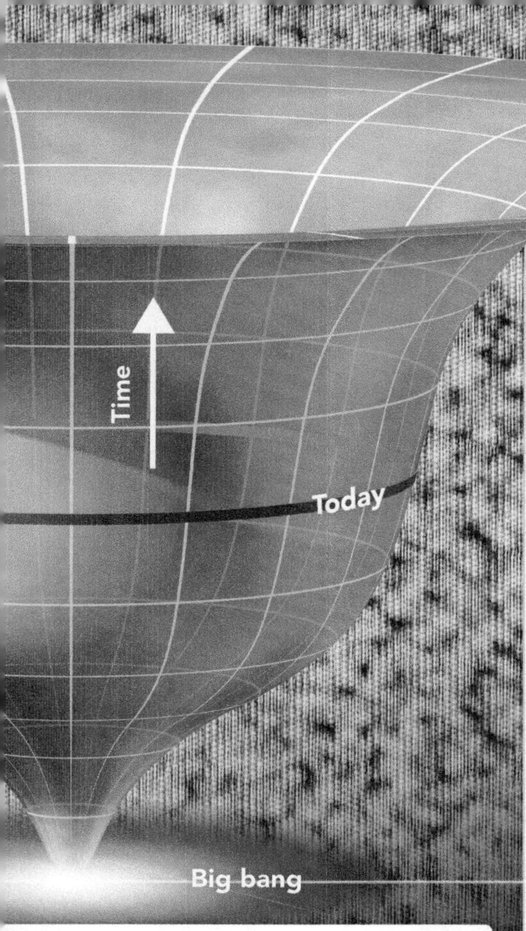

Do the Quick Lab *The Future of the Universe.*

Assess Your Understanding

1a. Define What was the big bang?

The big bang was a giant explosion after which all of the energy and matter in the universe began moving apart.

b. Summarize When did the big bang occur?

About 13.7 billion years ago

c. Relate Evidence and Explanation Describe two pieces of evidence that support the big bang theory.

Hubble's law: the observation that the farther away a galaxy is, the faster it is moving away from Earth; cosmic background radiation: radiation left over from the big bang

got it?

○ I get it! Now I know that the big bang theory says that *the universe formed in an instant, billions of years ago, and will expand forever.*

○ I need extra help with *See TE note.*

Go to **my science COACH** online for help with this subject.

157

FIGURE 3

ART IN MOTION **Expansion of the Universe**
Interpret Diagrams The diagram represents a universe that is expanding forever. Explain why scientists think this might happen.

Dark energy is making the expansion accelerate, which suggests that the universe will expand forever.

Time

Today

Big bang

Differentiated Instruction

L1 **Firecrackers and the Big Bang**
Ask students to describe what a fireworks display looks like. Show pictures or have the students find pictures. Then have them relate the fireworks explosion to the big bang.

L3 **How Can We Tell Stars and Galaxies Are Moving?** Invite students to investigate red shifts and blue shifts in

light. Tell them that these are ways that scientists can tell if stars are moving toward or away from us. You might suggest that they investigate the Doppler effect (sound) and relate it to red and blue shifts. Also they should include spectral analysis of stars in their research. This is a great group activity for a multimedia presentation.

Explain

Address Misconceptions

L1 **ACCELERATING UNIVERSE** From observations of objects moving by a frictional force, students may think objects in motion require a force to maintain that motion. In reality, only accelerating objects require a force be present. Ask: **Would a force be required to keep the universe expanding at a constant speed?** *(No)* **Is a force required to increase the speed of the universe expanding?** *(Yes)* **What have scientists named the source of this force?** *(Dark energy)*

Elaborate

21st Century Learning

INFORMATION LITERACY Fritz Zwicky was first to infer that unseen matter exists. In 1933, while observing the brightness of the Coma galaxy cluster, he estimated its mass. When he calculated the same cluster's mass, the computation was 400 times his estimation. This discrepancy between the observed and computed masses is known as "missing mass." In the 1970s, other scientists began to realize that the existence of unseen mass, or dark matter, could support theories about the structure of the universe. Have students do research about why astronomers think dark matter exists and ways to confirm its existence. Assist students in writing a bibliography of their sources.

Lab Resource: Quick Lab

L1 **THE FUTURE OF THE UNIVERSE** Students will explore the possible futures of the universe.

Evaluate

Assess Your Understanding

After students answer the questions, have them evaluate their understanding by completing the appropriate sentence.

R T I Response to Intervention

1a. If students cannot explain the big bang, **then** have them review the Key Concept statement for the lesson.

b. If students have trouble identifying the age of the universe, **then** have them reread the first paragraph of the lesson.

c. If students need help with describing supporting evidence for the big bang, **then** have them review the information for the red headings *Moving Galaxies* and *Cosmic Background Radiation.*

my science COACH Have students go online for help in understanding the big bang theory.

157

Name _____ Date _____ Class _____

The Expanding Universe

Inquiry Warm-Up, *How Does the Universe Expand?*
In the Inquiry Warm-Up, you used a simple model to investigate how galaxies move in an expanding universe. Using what you learned from that activity, answer the questions below.

1. **OBSERVE** In what directions do the 10 dots move as the balloon expands?

   _____

2. **EXPLAIN** As the balloon expands, is the motion of the dots random? How can you describe the direction in which all the dots move?

   _____

   _____

3. **DEVELOP HYPOTHESIS** Based on your answer to question 2, what might you say about a point at the center of the universe and how galaxies move?

   _____

   _____

4. **POSE QUESTIONS** If the hypothesis you developed in question 3 is accurate, what is one question it raises about the universe?

   _____

   _____

Assess Your Understanding

The Expanding Universe

What Does the Big Bang Theory Say About the Universe?

1a. **DEFINE** What was the big bang? _____

_____

_____

b. **SUMMARIZE** When did the big bang occur? _____

_____

c. **RELATE EVIDENCE AND EXPLANATION** Describe two pieces of evidence

that support the big bang theory. _____

_____

_____

_____

_____

gotit? ....

○ **I get it!** Now I know that the big bang theory says that _____

_____

_____

○ **I need extra help with** _____

_____

Name _____ Date _____ Class _____

The Expanding Universe

What Does the Big Bang Theory Say About the Universe?

Astronomers theorize that the universe began 13.7 billion years ago. At that time, the part of the universe we can see was no larger than the period at the end of this sentence. The universe then exploded in what astronomers call the **big bang. According to the big bang theory, the universe formed in an instant, billions of years ago, in an enormous explosion. New observations lead many astronomers to conclude that the universe will likely expand forever.**

Since the big bang, the universe has been expanding. In the 1920s, American astronomer Edwin Hubble discovered that almost all galaxies are moving away from us and from each other. **Hubble's law** states that the farther away a galaxy is, the faster it is moving away from us.

What will happen to the universe in the future? One possibility is that the universe will continue to expand. Another possibility is that the force of gravity will begin to pull the galaxies back together into a reverse big bang. The universe would be crushed in an enormous black hole. However, many astronomers believe the universe will likely expand forever.

Until recently, astronomers assumed that the universe consisted solely of the matter they could observe directly. But astronomer Vera Rubin discovered that the matter astronomers can see may make up as little as ten percent of the mass in the galaxies. The rest exists in the form of dark matter. **Dark matter** is matter that does not give off electromagnetic radiation. It cannot be seen directly. However, its presence can be inferred by observing the effect of its gravity on visible objects. In the late 1990s, astronomers observed that the expansion of the universe appeared to be accelerating. Astronomers infer that a mysterious new force, which they call **dark energy,** is causing the expansion of the universe to accelerate.

On a separate sheet of paper, describe the big bang theory. Then relate two theories about the future of the universe.

Review and Reinforce

The Expanding Universe

Understanding Main Ideas

Answer the following questions in the spaces provided.

1. What is Hubble's law?

_____

_____

2. What did astronomer Edwin Hubble discover that led to the formulation of his law?

_____

_____

3. Give two pieces of evidence that support the big bang theory.

_____

_____

_____

4. Why do scientists postulate that dark matter exists? Include an explanation of its name.

_____

_____

Building Vocabulary

Match each term with its definition by writing the letter of the correct definition in the right column on the line beside the term in the left column.

5. ___ big bang

6. ___ cosmic background radiation

7. ___ dark energy

8. ___ dark matter

9. ___ Hubble's law

a. a force that is causing the expansion of the universe to accelerate

b. leftover thermal energy from the formation of the universe

c. matter that does not give off electromagnetic radiation

d. the farther away a galaxy is, the faster it is moving away from us

e. the huge explosion that astronomers think was the birth of the universe

Enrich

The Expanding Universe

> Read the passage and study the figure. Based on the spectrums in the figure, use the table to rank the four galaxies in order of speed at which they are moving away from Earth, from slowest (1) to fastest (4).

How Far and How Fast?

You know that electromagnetic radiation is energy in the form of waves. Planets, stars, and galaxies emit electromagnetic radiation. As one of these objects moves through space toward an observer, the waves of electromagnetic radiation between the object and the observer move closer together. That is, the distance between the crests of the waves decreases, causing the wavelength to shorten. If that same object moved away from the observer, the waves between the object and the observer would move farther apart from each other. The distance between the crests of the waves would increase, and the wavelength would lengthen.

When a star is moving toward Earth very fast, the wavelength of its light shortens, causing it to appear slightly more blue than usual. If a star is moving away from Earth very fast, the wavelength of its light lengthens, causing it to appear slightly more red. By measuring this *blue shift* or *red shift* of light, astronomers can determine whether the star is moving toward or away from Earth, and how fast. To do this, astronomers use the shift of spectral lines produced by chemicals in the star's atmosphere. Astronomers can also use the spectrum of a galaxy to tell how fast the galaxy is moving toward or away from Earth.

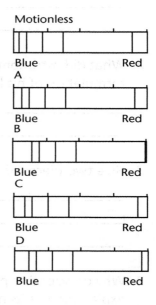

Using the principle of red shift, Edwin Hubble studied the relationship between a galaxy's distance and the speed at which it moves away from Earth. He found that the farther away a galaxy is, the faster it moves away from Earth. This relationship is called *Hubble's Law*.

	Rank (1 = slowest, 4 = fastest)
Galaxy A	
Galaxy B	
Galaxy C	
Galaxy D	

Answer the questions below on a separate sheet of paper.

1. Based on Hubble's Law, which of the galaxies is farthest from Earth?
2. Are any of the galaxies moving toward Earth? Explain.

Lesson Quiz

The Expanding Universe

Write the letter of the correct answer on the line at the left.

1. ___ Which are two pieces of evidence supporting the big bang theory?

   A   black holes and pulsars

   B   dark matter and dark energy

   C   eclipsing binaries and quasars

   D   cosmic background radiation and Hubble's law

2. ___ In the future, the universe will most likely

   A   continue to expand

   B   stay the same size

   C   start to shrink

   D   pulse in size

3. ___ What led astronomers to believe in the existence of dark matter?

   A   the fact that space is black

   B   the big bang theory

   C   the apparent effects of the gravity of unseen matter on visible objects

   D   the existence of black holes

4. ___ Which supports the presence of dark energy?

   A   The universe formed in a big bang.

   B   Galaxies are moving away from us and from each other.

   C   Galaxies that are farther away from us are moving away from us at a faster rate.

   D   The speed at which galaxies are moving apart is accelerating.

Fill in the blank to complete each statement.

5. Radiation leftover from the big bang is called _____.

6. _____ is causing the expansion of the universe to accelerate.

7. _____ does not give off electromagnetic radiation.

8. According to the _____ theory, the universe formed in a huge explosion.

9. Hubble's law states that the farther away from us that a galaxy is, the _____ it is moving away from us.

10. According to the big bang theory, the universe formed about 13.7 _____ years ago.

The Expanding Universe

Answer Key

After the Inquiry Warm-Up

1. The dots move in all directions.

2. No, the motion is not random. All the dots move away from the center of the balloon.

3. All the galaxies in the universe began at a point at the center of the universe and are moving outward away from that point.

4. Accept all reasonable answers. Sample: Will the universe expand forever?

Key Concept Summary

According to the big bang theory, the universe began 13.7 billion years ago in an enormous explosion. Since the big bang, the universe has been expanding, as galaxies continue to move away from the point where the big bang occurred. In the future, some believe that the force of gravity may begin to pull the galaxies back together into a reverse big bang, crushing the universe in an enormous black hole. However, many astronomers believe the universe will likely expand forever.

Review and Reinforce

1. The farther away a galaxy is, the faster it is moving away from us.

2. Hubble discovered that almost all galaxies are moving away from us and from each other.

3. Galaxies are moving away from us and from each other. Cosmic background radiation, first observed in the 1960s, is believed to be leftover thermal energy from the big bang.

4. Astronomers determined that something they couldn't see was exerting gravity on visible objects. Because it cannot be seen astronomers named it dark matter.

5. e

6. b

7. a

8. c

9. d

Enrich

A: 1

B: 4

C: 2

D: 3

1. Galaxy B is farthest from Earth, as it has the greatest red shift.

2. No, because none of the spectrums is blue shifted.

Lesson Quiz

1. D

2. A

3. C

4. D

5. cosmic background radiation

6. Dark energy

7. Dark matter

8. big bang

9. faster

10. billion

Place the outside corner, the corner away from the dotted line, in the corner of your copy machine to copy onto letter-size paper.

Study Guide

Review the Big Q

Have students complete the statement at the top of the page. These Key Concepts support their understanding of the chapter's Big Question. Have students return to the chapter opener pages. What is different about how students view the image of the colliding galaxies now that they have completed the chapter? Thinking about this will help them prepare for the *Apply the Big Q* activity in the Review and Assessment.

Partner Review

Have partners review definitions of vocabulary terms by using the Study Guide to quiz each other. Students could read the Key Concept statements and leave out words for their partner to fill in, or change a statement so that it is false and then ask their partner to correct it.

Class Activity: Concept Map

Have students develop a concept map to show how the information in this chapter is related. Have students brainstorm to identify the Key Concepts, vocabulary, details, and examples. Write each response on a sticky note and attach it at random on chart paper or on the board. Tell students that this concept map will be organized in hierarchal order—with Key Concepts at the top. Ask students to use the following questions to help them organize the information on the self-sticking notes:

- What are the regions of the electromagnetic spectrum?
- What are telescopes and how do they work?
- How do astronomers measure and describe the scale of the universe?
- How are stars classified?
- How do stars form and what happens at the end of a star's life span?
- What are the major types of galaxies?
- What is the big bang theory?

My Science Coach allows students to complete the *Practice Test* online.

The Big Question allows students to complete the *Apply the Big Q* activity about why objects in the solar system are different from each other.

Vocab Flash Cards offer a way to review the chapter vocabulary words.

my science online.com   Stars, Galaxies, and the Universe

Astronomers learn about distant objects in the universe by studying *electromagnetic radiation, such as visible light.*

LESSON 1 Telescopes

🔧 The electromagnetic spectrum includes radio waves, infrared radiation, visible light, ultraviolet radiation, X-rays, and gamma rays.

🔧 Telescopes collect and focus light and other forms of electromagnetic radiation.

Vocabulary
- electromagnetic radiation • visible light
- wavelength • spectrum • telescope
- optical telescope • refracting telescope
- convex lens • reflecting telescope
- observatory • radio telescope

LESSON 2 The Scale of the Universe

🔧 Astronomers often use parallax to measure distances to nearby stars.

🔧 Since the numbers astronomers use are often very large or very small, they frequently use scientific notation to describe sizes and distances in the universe. They use a unit called the light-year to measure distances between the stars.

Vocabulary
- parallax • universe
- light-year • scientific notation

LESSON 3 Characteristics of Stars

🔧 Characteristics used to classify stars include color, temperature, size, composition, and brightness.

🔧 The brightness of a star depends upon both its size and temperature.

🔧 Scientists use H-R diagrams to classify stars.

Vocabulary
- spectrograph • apparent brightness
- absolute brightness • Hertzsprung-Russell diagram
- main sequence

LESSON 4 Lives of Stars

🔧 A star is born when the contracting gas and dust from a nebula becomes so dense and hot that nuclear fusion starts. How long a star lives depends on its mass.

🔧 After a star runs out of fuel, it becomes a white dwarf, a neutron star, or a black hole.

Vocabulary
- nebula • protostar • white dwarf
- supernova • neutron star • pulsar
- black hole

LESSON 5 Star Systems and Galaxies

🔧 Most stars are members of groups of two or more stars, called star systems.

🔧 Astronomers classify most galaxies into the following types: spiral, elliptical, and irregular.

Vocabulary
- binary star • eclipsing binary
- open cluster • globular cluster
- galaxy • spiral galaxy • elliptical galaxy
- irregular galaxy • quasar

LESSON 6 The Expanding Universe

🔧 According to the big bang theory, the universe formed in an instant, billions of years ago, in an enormous explosion. New observations lead many astronomers to conclude that the universe will expand forever.

Vocabulary
- big bang • Hubble's law
- cosmic background radiation
- dark matter • dark energy

E L L Support

4 Language Production

Have students play a game of "20 Questions" using the vocabulary terms from the chapter. Tell students they can ask you 20 questions in order to identify the vocabulary term you are thinking of. Encourage students to incorporate information from the chapter in their questions.

Beginning
LOW/HIGH Allow students to use words and short phrases as questions.

Intermediate
LOW/HIGH Allow students extra time to formulate their questions.

Advanced
LOW/HIGH Allow students to act as coaches for students with less language proficiency.

Review and Assessment

LESSON 1 Telescopes

1. What is visible light?

a. gamma rays and X-rays

b. the spectrum of rays

c. a particular wavelength

d. a form of electromagnetic radiation

2. Explain An optical telescope works by
collecting and focusing visible
light.

3. Draw Conclusions What advantage might
there be in placing a telescope on the moon?
The moon has no atmosphere
to interfere with the collection
of light.

LESSON 2 The Scale of the Universe

4. Which type of numbers does scientific notation
best describe?

a. very small or very large

b. very large only

c. very small only

d. large and small combined

5. Develop Hypotheses Why can't astronomers
measure the parallax of a star that is a million
light-years away?
The distance the star appears
to move is too small to measure accurately.

6. math! The star Antares is about 604 light-
years from Earth. Write this distance in
scientific notation.
6.04×10^2 light-years

LESSON 3 Characteristics of Stars

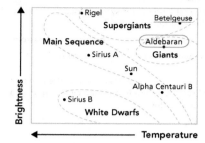

Use the diagram to answer the questions below.

7. Interpret Diagrams On the diagram, circle
the star that has a greater absolute brightness:
Aldebaran or Sirius B.

8. Apply Concepts On the diagram, underline
the star that is most likely to be red:
Rigel, Sirius B, or Betelgeuse.

LESSON 4 Lives of Stars

9. Relate Cause and Effect How does a star's
mass affect its lifetime?
Low-mass stars have longer
lifetimes because they use up
their fuel much more slowly
than high-mass stars.

10. Sequence Explain how a black hole forms.
A very massive star explodes
and dies. The gravity of the
resulting mass is very strong.
It pulls everything inward
into a very dense condition
from which not even light can
escape.

159

Review and Assessment

Assess Understanding

Have students complete the answers to the Review
and Assessment questions. Have a class discussion
about what students find confusing. Write Key
Concepts on the board to reinforce knowledge.

RTI Response to Intervention

2. If students cannot explain what an optical
telescope is, **then** have them locate the highlighted
term and restate the definition in their own words.

6. If students need help using scientific notation,
then remind them that scientific notation involves
writing the distance as a number between 1 and 10
and then multiplying it by multiples of 10. It is a form
of shorthand.

8. If students have trouble understanding the
diagram, **then** have them review **Figure 3**.

9. If students cannot relate a star's mass to its life
span, **then** have them reread the information for the
red heading *Lifetimes of Stars*.

Alternate Assessment

L1 DESIGN A GAME Have students work in pairs
or small groups to design a game about matter.
Students can design a board game that requires
players to answer trivia questions in order to
advance. Remind students to create rules, spinners,
game pieces, and questions for their games. The
questions for the game should include vocabulary
terms and Key Concepts from the chapter. Students
can exchange games with or play their own game
against other groups or pairs.

Review and Assessment, Cont.

R T I Response to Intervention

12. If students cannot contrast open clusters and globular clusters, **then** have them reread the information for the red heading *Star Clusters*.
15. If students need help explaining cosmic background radiation, **then** have them locate the highlighted term and review the definition.

Apply the Big Q

TRANSFER Students should be able to demonstrate understanding of the various ways in which astronomers learn about distant objects in the universe by answering this question. See the scoring rubric below.

Connect to the Big Idea

BIG IDEA The universe is very old, very large, and constantly changing.

Send students back to the Big Ideas of Science at the beginning of their student edition. Have them read what they wrote before they started the chapter. Lead a class discussion about how their thoughts have changed. If all chapters have been completed, have students fill in the bottom section for the Big Idea.

L3 WRITING IN SCIENCE Have students write a blog entry about at least three different types of objects (for example, a main sequence star, an elliptical galaxy, and a pulsar) from this chapter. They should write as an astronomer making observations, explaining the instruments they are using, what part of the electromagnetic spectrum they are examining, and what their observations are about the objects.

LESSON 5 Star Systems and Galaxies

11. In what kind of star system does one star block the light from another?

a. open cluster   b. binary star system
c. quasar system   **d.** eclipsing binary

12. Compare and Contrast How is the number of stars different in an open cluster than in a globular cluster?

Open clusters contain far fewer stars than do globular clusters.

13. Write About It Describe the "life story" of a star in a spiral galaxy. Explain where it was born and what it was like there.

See TE rubric.

LESSON 6 The Expanding Universe

14. What is the name of the explosion that began the universe?

a. solar nebula   **b.** big bang
c. dark matter   d. supernova

15. Classify Radio telescopes are able to detect cosmic background radiation, which is

leftover thermal energy from the big bang.

16. Compare and Contrast Explain the difference between a big crunch and an ever-expanding universe.

In a big crunch, gravity will crush the universe into a black hole. In an ever-expanding universe, the universe will become cold and dark.

How do astronomers learn about distant objects in the universe?

17. Write the introduction of a manual for young astronomers. Briefly describe different tools astronomers have for learning about distant objects in the universe. Tell what kind of information each tool can provide.

Sample: Astronomers learn about distant objects from light. They use optical telescopes to see distant objects. They can break up the light of an object into a spectrum and figure out what that object is made of. They use radio telescopes to collect radio waves from space. They can use parallax to determine a star's distance from Earth.
See TE rubric.

| **Write About It** | Assess student's writing using this rubric. |

SCORING RUBRIC	SCORE 4	SCORE 3	SCORE 2	SCORE 1
Describe a star in spiral galaxy	Student explains correctly and in detail the age, location, and appearance of a star in a spiral galaxy.	Student explains correctly the age and appearance of a star in a spiral galaxy.	Student incorrectly describes a star in a spiral galaxy.	Student does not describe a star in a spiral galaxy.

 How do scientists learn about distant objects in the universe?

SCORING RUBRIC	SCORE 4	SCORE 3	SCORE 2	SCORE 1
Describe types of tools and tell what information they can provide	Student describes types of tools correctly and in detail and explains the information each type can provide.	Student describes types of tools correctly and partially explains the information each type can provide.	Student makes mistakes when describing the types of tools and explaining the information they can provide.	Student does not describe any tools and does not explain the information they can provide.

Standardized Test Prep

Multiple Choice

Circle the letter of the best answer.

1. The table below gives an estimate of star distribution in the Milky Way galaxy. According to the table, what is the most common type of star in the Milky Way?

Type of Star	Percentage of Total
Main sequence	90.75 %
Red giant	0.50 %
Supergiant	< 0.0001 %
White dwarf	8.75 %

Ⓐ main-sequence star
B red giant
C supergiant
D white dwarf

2. What is the main factor that affects the evolution of a star?

A color   B brightness
Ⓒ mass   D parallax

3. What does a light-year measure?

A time   B volume
C brightness   Ⓓ distance

4. Which of the following best describes a reflecting telescope?

Ⓐ Isaac Newton invention
B has an objective lens
C is the smallest telescope
D has a mirror lens

5. Which statement explains the big bang theory?

A The universe formed from a series of explosions over billions of years.
B The universe will explode in 10 million years and destroy our solar system.
Ⓒ The universe formed very quickly from an enormous explosion.
D The universe gradually heated up until it exploded.

Constructed Response

Use the diagram below and your knowledge of science to help you answer Question 6. Write your answer on a separate sheet of paper.

Milky Way Side View
Sun   Center   Bulge

6. Describe the appearance of the Milky Way as you would see it both from Earth and from a point directly above the galaxy. Why does the galaxy look different from different places?
See TE note.

Standardized Test Prep

Test-Taking Skills

INTERPRETING TABLES Tell students that when they interpret tables, they should be sure to look at the entire table before choosing an answer. In this case, the table is not arranged in either increasing or decreasing order of occurrence. If they do not look at the whole table, they are likely to miss the correct answer.

Constructed Response

6. From Earth, the Milky Way looks like a thick ribbon of stars across the night sky. This is because we are looking at it from one of its arms, so it is like looking at it from the edge of a dinner plate. From above and below, the Milky Way would look like a disc or a spiral because you would be outside it and able to see the entire galaxy.

Additional Assessment Resources

Chapter Test
EXAMVIEW® Assessment Suite
Performance Assessment
Progress Monitoring Assessments
SuccessTracker™

CHAPTER 4

ELL Support

5 Assess Understanding

Have ELLs complete the Alternate Assessment. Provide guidelines on the information it must cover, and a rubric for assessment. You may wish to have them complete the activity in small groups of varying language proficiencies.

Beginning

LOW/HIGH Allow students to work on designing the game board and game pieces.

Intermediate

LOW/HIGH Allow students to write the questions and answers.

Advanced

LOW/HIGH Allow students to write the instructions for playing and scoring the game.

Remediate If students have trouble with...

QUESTION	SEE LESSON	STANDARDS
1	4	
2	4	
3	2	
4	1	
5	6	
6	5	

Science Matters

Hot Science

Have students read *Black Holes*. Explained that a black hole is created when an object cannot withstand its own gravity. Stellar-sized black holes are formed when stars run out of fuel. The star explodes in a supernova and leaves behind a black hole. Astronomers are not certain what causes supermassive black holes to form.

There are more black holes in the universe than astronomers can count. Fortunately, none are close enough to pose any danger to Earth. The closest stellar-sized black hole scientists have discovered is 1,600 light-years from Earth. The closest supermassive black hole is at the center of the Milky Way, 28,000 light-years away. The gravity of a black hole pulls everything in its gravitational field into it, but objects outside of a certain distance are not affected. An object within that radius would have to travel at the speed of light to escape the pull of the black hole.

Because black holes absorb light rays, they are invisible. Scientists are able to tell where they are when they pass through a cloud of interstellar matter or when they are close enough to a star to pull matter away from it. As matter is pulled into the black hole, it heats up. The heat ionizes the atoms, which emit X-rays, so scientists know to look for this kind of X-ray emission when searching for black holes.

Ask: **How does a stellar-sized black hole compare to a supermassive black hole?** *(A stellar-sized black hole is smaller than a supermassive black hole.)* **What do scientists use to find black holes?** *(Telescopes, X-ray emissions, radio waves.)*

SCIENCE MATTERS

Hot Science

BLACK HOLES

Scientists can't see them, but they keep studying them. For years, astronomers have known that black holes exist. The extreme gravity of a black hole allows nothing to escape, not even light. So astronomers need to use some pretty high-powered tools to study them.

Astronomers use data from space telescopes to measure the visible light, X-rays, and radio waves emitted from objects near a black hole. Astronomers have used this data to learn a lot about black holes. They know that black holes come in two main sizes— stellar-sized, formed when massive stars collapse inward, and supermassive.

Supermassive black holes are found in the center of galaxies. The gravity from the black hole helps bind the stars, star systems, star clusters, dust, and gas into a galaxy.

Evaluate It Black holes are often described in movies and science fiction novels. Find one example of a black hole in a novel, graphic novel, TV show, or movie. Write an essay that explains how the black hole is described in your sources. Evaluate the source's scientific accuracy, and correct any inaccurate information.

◀ This image of two galaxies colliding was taken by the Hubble Space Telescope in 2008. Astronomers believe that supermassive black holes are at the center of galaxies.

162   Stars, Galaxies, and the Universe

Quick Facts

In April 1990, NASA launched a telescope into space named for Edwin P. Hubble, who confirmed that the universe is expanding. The Hubble telescope orbits Earth once every 97 minutes, sending information back to astronomers on Earth. The Hubble has helped scientists learn about many cosmic phenomena, including galaxies in all evolutionary stages and protoplanetary disks where new planets are likely formed. Any astronomer in the world can request time to use the telescope and the information they collect is eventually released to the entire scientific community. The Hubble is the size of a large school bus and has two large mirrors it uses to focus light. The telescope is powered by solar energy, which is collected using two large solar panels. Have students present a proposal of what they would like to study by using the Hubble telescope.

APPRENTICE ASTRONOMERS

Kids in the Boston area have their heads in the stars. At least the lucky ones do. They're part of the Youth Astronomy Apprenticeship (YAA) program run by four astronomical and educational institutions in the area.

The goal of YAA is to give urban kids more exposure to astronomers and astronomy. In after-school programs, apprentices learn many things, including how to understand and interpret images from a network of telescopes students control online, and how to prepare the images to illustrate their own research. In Stage 2 of the program, apprentices can go on to a summer apprentice program. In the summer program, participants are paid to help make museum exhibits and perform science and astronomy plays. Participants also help teach other people about the universe. Some students go on to become youth assistants, teaching the next group of young stargazers.

Are the apprentices "star-struck"? The YAA program hopes they are.

Design It Choose a topic in astronomy that interests you. Working with a partner, prepare an exhibit about that topic. Present your exhibit to members of your school community.

163

Kids Doing Science

Have students read *Apprentice Astronomers*. Explain that astronomy is the study of objects beyond Earth, including stars, planets, comets and meteors, as well as other cosmic phenomenon. Tell them that astronomers use telescopes and cameras to study objects in space. Telescopes range in size from the kind that stand on a tripod, such as the one pictured, to one so large that an entire building is needed to house it. Buildings that hold telescopes are called observatories and they are often found at universities.

Explain that humans have shown an interest in the stars from a very early time. Early people drew pictures of shapes they saw in the sky. Ancient societies believed gods lived in the sky and made up stories about them. They named groups of stars, called constellations, after the gods. When people began sailing across the sea, they used the position of the stars to navigate.

Point out that a clear sky is required to look at the stars, but there are other ways to study objects in space. Scientists study radio waves that come from space and analyze them to learn about what object(s) transmitted the radio waves. Astronomers also study data and materials brought back from space by astronauts. A telescope has even been launched into space to send images from space back to astronomers on Earth.

Ask: **Why do you think the YAA program focuses on students in urban areas?** *(Sample: Stars are harder to see in urban areas and this program allows them to see things they might not see otherwise.)* **Why do you think many observatories are built at universities?** *(Sample: Universities that offer astronomy programs have observatories for their students and often for research done by professors teaching at the schools.)*

Star Charts

Use these star charts to locate bright stars and major constellations in the night sky at different times of year. Choose the appropriate star chart for the current season.

Autumn Sky This chart works best at the following dates and times: September 1 at 10:00 P.M., October 1 at 8:00 P.M., or November 1 at 6:00 P.M. Look for the constellations Ursa Minor (the Little Dipper) and Cassiopeia in the northern sky, and for the star Deneb, which is nearly overhead in autumn.

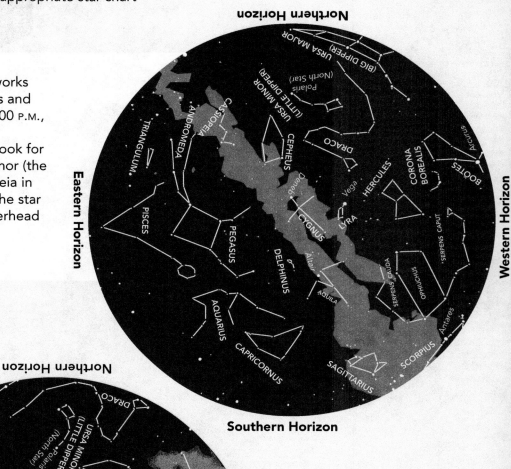

Winter Sky This chart works best at the following dates and times: December 1 at 10:00 P.M., January 1 at 8:00 P.M., or February 1 at 6:00 P.M. Look for the constellations Orion and Gemini; the bright star Sirius; and the Pleiades, a star cluster, in the winter sky.

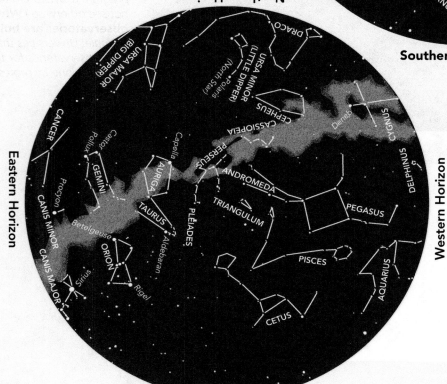

How to Use the Star Charts

Using a flashlight and a compass, hold the appropriate chart and turn it so that the direction you are facing is at the bottom of the chart. These star charts work best at 34° north latitude, but can be used at other central latitudes.

Spring Sky This chart works best at the following dates and times: March 1 at 10:00 P.M., March 15 at 9:00 P.M., or April 1 at 8:00 P.M. Look for the constellations Ursa Major (which contains the Big Dipper), Boötes, and Leo in the spring sky. The bright stars Arcturus and Spica can be seen in the east.

Northern Horizon

Eastern Horizon

DRACO

URSA MINOR (LITTLE DIPPER)

Polaris (North Star)

CEPHEUS

CASSIOPEIA

ANDROMEDA

TRIANGULUM

PERSEUS

ARIES

BOÖTES

Arcturus

URSA MAJOR (BIG DIPPER)

Capella

AURIGA

Pleiades

TAURUS

Western Horizon

VIRGO

LEO

CANCER

Castor

Pollux

GEMINI

Aldebaran

Regulus

Spica

Procyon

Betelgeuse

ORION

ERIDANUS

CORVUS

CANIS MINOR

Sirius

Rigel

HYDRA

CANIS MAJOR

LEPUS

COLUMBA

VELA

Southern Horizon

Northern Horizon

Eastern Horizon

DELPHINUS

CYGNUS

Deneb

LYRA

Vega

DRACO

HERCULES

CORONA BOREALIS

SERPENS CAPUT

CEPHEUS

Polaris (North Star)

URSA MINOR (LITTLE DIPPER)

URSA MAJOR (BIG DIPPER)

GEMINI

Castor

Pollux

CANCER

Altair

AQUILA

SERPENS CAUDA

OPHIUCHUS

SAGITTARIUS

SCORPIUS

Antares

LIBRA

BOÖTES

Arcturus

VIRGO

Spica

LEO

Regulus

HYDRA

Western Horizon

CORVUS

CENTAURUS

Southern Horizon

Summer Sky This chart works best at the following dates and times: May 15 at 11:00 P.M., June 1 at 10:00 P.M., or June 15 at 9:00 P.M. Look for the bright star Arcturus in the constellation Boötes overhead in early summer. Toward the east, look for the bright stars Vega, Altair, and Deneb, which form a triangle.

165

GLOSSARY

A

absolute brightness The brightness a star would have if it were at a standard distance from Earth. (139)
magnitud absoluta Brillo que tendría una estrella si estuviera a una distancia estándar de la Tierra.

apparent brightness The brightness of a star as seen from Earth. (139)
magnitud aparente Brillo de una estrella vista desde la Tierra.

asteroid belt The region of the solar system between the orbits of Mars and Jupiter, where many asteroids are found. (111)
cinturón de asteroides Región del sistema solar entre las órbitas de Marte y Júpiter, donde se encuentran muchos asteroides.

asteroid One of the rocky objects revolving around the sun that are too small and numerous to be considered planets. (114)
asteroide Uno de los cuerpos rocosos que se mueven alrededor del Sol y que son demasiado pequeños y numerosos como para ser considerados planetas.

astronomical unit A unit of distance equal to the average distance between Earth and the sun, about 150 million kilometers. (83)
unidad astronómica Unidad de medida equivalente a la distancia media entre la Tierra y el Sol, aproximadamente 150 millones de kilómetros.

axis An imaginary line that passes through a planet's center and its north and south poles, about which the planet rotates. (11)
eje Línea imaginaria alrededor de la cual gira un planeta, y que atraviesa su centro y sus dos polos, norte y sur.

B

big bang The initial explosion that resulted in the formation and expansion of the universe. (154)
Big bang Explosión inicial que resultó en la formación y expansión del universo.

binary star A star system with two stars. (149)
estrella binaria Sistema estelar de dos estrellas.

black hole An object whose gravity is so strong that nothing, not even light, can escape. (147)
agujero negro Cuerpo cuya gravedad es tan fuerte que nada, ni siquiera la luz, puede escapar.

C

calendar A system of organizing time that defines the beginning, length, and divisions of a year. (12)
calendario Sistema de organización del tiempo que define el principio, la duración y las divisiones de un año.

chromosphere The middle layer of the sun's atmosphere. (90)
cromósfera Capa central de la atmósfera solar.

coma The fuzzy outer layer of a comet. (113)
coma Capa exterior y difusa de un cometa.

comet A loose collection of ice and dust that orbits the sun, typically in a long, narrow orbit. (5, 113)
cometa Cuerpo poco denso de hielo y polvo cuya órbita alrededor del Sol es típicamente excéntrica.

constellation A pattern or grouping of stars that people imagine to represent a figure or object. (6)
constelación Patrón de estrellas que se dice se asemeja a una figura u objeto.

convection zone The outermost layer of the sun's interior. (89)
zona de convección Capa más superficial del interior del Sol.

convex lens A lens that is thicker in the center than at the edges. (128)
lente convexa Lente que es más gruesa en el centro que en los extremos.

core The central region of the sun, where nuclear fusion takes place. (89)
núcleo Región central del Sol, donde ocurre la fusión nuclear.

corona The outer layer of the sun's atmosphere. (91)
corona Capa externa de la atmósfera solar.

cosmic background radiation The electromagnetic radiation left over from the big bang. (155)
radiación cósmica de fondo Radiación electromagnética que quedó del *Big bang*.

crater 1. A large round pit caused by the impact of a meteoroid. (33) 2. A bowl-shaped area that forms around a volcano's central opening.
cráter 1. Hoyo grande causado por el impacto de un meteoroide. 2. Depresión de forma más o menos circular que se forma alrededor de la parte central de un volcán.

D

dark energy A mysterious force that appears to be causing the expansion of the universe to accelerate. (156)
energía negra Misteriosa fuerza que parece acelerar la expansión del universo.

dark matter Matter that does not give off electromagnetic radiation but is quite abundant in the universe. (156)
materia negra Materia que es muy abundante en el universo y no despide radiación electromagnética.

dwarf planet An object that orbits the sun and is spherical, but has not cleared the area of its orbit. (84)
planeta enano Un cuerpo esférico que orbita alrededor del Sol, pero que no ha despejado las proximidades de su órbita.

E

eclipse The partial or total blocking of one object in space by another. (25)
eclipse Bloqueo parcial o total de un cuerpo en el espacio por otro.

eclipsing binary A binary star system in which one star periodically blocks the light from the other. (149)
eclipse binario Sistema estelar binario en el que una estrella bloquea periódicamente la luz de la otra.

electromagnetic radiation The energy transferred through space by electromagnetic waves. (126)
radiación electromagnética Energía transferida a través del espacio por ondas electromagnéticas.

ellipse An oval shape, which may be elongated or nearly circular; the shape of the planets' orbits. (81)
elipse Forma ovalada que puede ser alargada o casi circular; la forma de la órbita de los planetas.

elliptical galaxy A galaxy shaped like a round or flattened ball, generally containing only old stars. (152)
galaxia elíptica Galaxia de forma redonda o semejante a una pelota desinflada, que generalmente sólo contiene estrellas viejas.

equinox Either of the two days of the year on which neither hemisphere is tilted toward or away from the sun. (16)
equinoccio Cualquiera de los de dos días del año en el que ningún hemisferio se retrae o inclina hacia el Sol.

escape velocity The velocity an object must reach to fly beyond a planet's or moon's gravitational pull. (49)
velocidad de escape Velocidad que debe alcanzar un cohete para salir del empuje gravitacional de un planeta o luna.

G

galaxy A huge group of single stars, star systems, star clusters, dust, and gas bound together by gravity. (152)
galaxia Enorme grupo de estrellas individuales, sistemas estelares, cúmulos de estrellas, polvo y gases unidos por la gravedad.

gas giant The name often given to the outer planets: Jupiter, Saturn, Uranus, and Neptune. (102)
gigantes gaseosos Nombre que normalmente se da a los cuatro planetas exteriores: Júpiter, Saturno, Urano y Neptuno.

geocentric Term describing a model of the universe in which Earth is at the center of the revolving planets and stars. (79)
geocéntrico Término que describe un modelo del universo en el cual la Tierra se encuentra al centro de los planetas y estrellas que circulan a su alrededor.

geostationary orbit An orbit in which a satellite orbits Earth at the same rate as Earth rotates and thus stays over the same place all the time. (66)
órbita geoestacionaria Órbita en la que un satélite orbita alrededor de la Tierra a la misma velocidad que rota la Tierra y que, por lo tanto, permanece en el mismo lugar todo el tiempo.

globular cluster A large, round, densely-packed grouping of older stars. (150)
cúmulo globular Conjunto grande y redondo de estrellas viejas densamente agrupadas.

greenhouse effect The trapping of heat near a planet's surface by certain gases in the planet's atmosphere. (98)
efecto invernadero Retención del calor irradiado por un planeta en su atmósfera ocasionada por ciertos gases atmosféricos.

gravity The attractive force between objects; the force that moves objects downhill. (19)
gravedad Propiedad de atracción entre los cuerpos; la fuerza que mueve un cuerpo hacia abajo.

H

heliocentric Term describing a model of the solar system in which Earth and the other planets revolve around the sun. (80)
heliocéntrico Término que describe un modelo del universo en el cual la Tierra y los otros planetas giran alrededor del Sol.

Hertzsprung-Russell diagram A graph relating the surface temperatures and absolute brightnesses of stars. (140)
diagrama Hertzsprung-Russell Gráfica que muestra la relación entre la temperatura de la superficie de una estrella y su magnitud absoluta.

Hubble's law The observation that the farther away a galaxy is, the faster it is moving away. (155)
ley de Hubble Observación que enuncia que mientras más lejos se encuentre una galaxia, se aleja con mayor rapidez.

I

inertia The tendency of an object to resist a change in motion. (20)
inercia Tendencia de un cuerpo de resistirse a cambios de movimiento.

irregular galaxy A galaxy that does not have a regular shape. (152)
galaxia irregular Galaxia que no tiene una forma regular.

K

Kuiper belt A region where many small objects orbit the sun and that stretches from beyond the orbit of Neptune to about 100 times Earth's distance from the sun. (111)
cinturón de Kuiper Región en la cual muchos cuerpos pequeños giran alrededor del Sol y que se extiende desde más allá de la órbita de Neptuno hasta aproximadamente cien veces la distancia entre la Tierra y el Sol.

L

law of universal gravitation The scientific law that states that every object in the universe attracts every other object. (19)

ley de gravitación universal Ley científica que establece que todos los cuerpos del universo se atraen entre sí.

light-year The distance that light travels in one year, about 9.5 million million kilometers. (134)
año luz Distancia a la que viaja la luz en un año; aproximadamente 9.5 millones de millones de kilómetros.

lunar eclipse The blocking of sunlight to the moon that occurs when Earth is directly between the sun and the moon. (26)
eclipse lunar Bloqueo de la luz solar que ilumina la Luna que ocurre cuando la Tierra se interpone entre el Sol y la Luna.

M

main sequence A diagonal area on an Hertzsprung-Russell diagram that includes more than 90 percent of all stars. (141)
secuencia principal Área diagonal en un diagrama de Hertzsprung-Russell que incluye más del 90 por ciento de todas las estrellas.

maria Dark, flat areas on the moon's surface formed from huge ancient lava flows. (33)
maria Áreas oscuras y llanas de la superficie lunar formadas por enormes flujos de lava antiguos.

mass The amount of matter in an object. (19)
masa Cantidad de materia que hay en un cuerpo.

meteor A streak of light in the sky produced by the burning of a meteoroid in Earth's atmosphere. (5,115)
meteoro Rayo de luz en el cielo producido por el incendio de un meteoroide en la atmósfera terrestre.

meteorite A meteoroid that passes through the atmosphere and hits Earth's surface. (115)
meteorito Meteoroide que pasa por la atmósfera y toca la superficie terrestre.

meteoroid A chunk of rock or dust in space, generally smaller than an asteroid. (33, 115)
meteoroide Un trozo de roca o polvo, generalmente más pequeño que un asteroide, que existe en el espacio.

microgravity The condition of experiencing weightlessness in orbit. (63)
microgravedad Manifestación de la falta de pesadez al estar en órbita.

neap tide The tide with the least difference between consecutive low and high tides. (30)
marea muerta Marea con la mínima diferencia entre las mareas altas y bajas consecutivas.

nebula A large cloud of gas and dust in space. (143)
nebulosa Gran nube de gas y polvo en el espacio.

neutron star The small, dense remains of a high-mass star after a supernova. (146)
estrella de neutrones Restos pequeños y densos de una estrella de gran masa tras ocurrir una supernova.

Newton's first law of motion The scientific law that states that an object at rest will stay at rest and an object in motion will stay in motion with a constant speed and direction unless acted on by a force. (20)
Primera ley de movimiento de Newton Ley científica que establece que un cuerpo en reposo se mantendrá en reposo y un cuerpo en movimiento se mantendrá en movimiento con una velocidad y dirección constantes a menos que se ejerza una fuerza sobre él.

nuclear fusion The process in which two atomic nuclei combine to form a larger nucleus, forming a heavier element and releasing huge amounts of energy; the process by which energy is produced in stars. (89)
fusión nuclear Unión de dos núcleos atómicos que produce un elemento con una mayor masa atómica y que libera una gran cantidad de energía; el proceso mediante el cual las estrellas producen energía.

nucleus 1. In cells, a large oval organelle that contains the cell's genetic material in the form of DNA and controls many of the cell's activities. **2.** The central core of an atom which contains protons and neutrons. **3.** The solid inner core of a comet. (113)
núcleo 1. Orgánulo ovalado de una célula que contiene el material genético en forma de ADN y controla las distintas funciones celulares. **2.** Parte central de un átomo que contiene los protones y los neutrones. **3.** Centro denso e interior de un cometa.

observatory A building that contains one or more telescopes. (130)
observatorio Edificio que contiene uno o más telescopios.

Oort cloud A spherical region of comets that surrounds the solar system. (111)
nube de Oort Región esférica de cometas que rodea al sistema solar.

open cluster A star cluster that has a loose, disorganized appearance and contains no more than a few thousand stars. (150)
cúmulo abierto Cúmulo de estrellas que tiene una apariencia no compacta y desorganizada, y que no contiene más de unas pocos miles de estrellas.

optical telescope A telescope that uses lenses or mirrors to collect and focus visible light. (128)
telescopio óptico Telescopio que usa lentes o espejos para captar y enfocar la luz visible.

orbit The path of an object as it revolves around another object in space. (12)
órbita Trayectoria de un cuerpo a medida que gira alrededor de otro en el espacio.

orbital velocity The velocity a rocket must achieve to establish an orbit around a body in space. (49)
velocidad orbital Velocidad que un cohete debe alcanzar para establecer una órbita alrededor de un cuerpo en el espacio.

parallax The apparent change in position of an object when seen from different places. (132)
paralaje Cambio aparente en la posición de un cuerpo cuando es visto desde distintos lugares.

penumbra The part of a shadow surrounding the darkest part. (25)
penumbra Parte de la sombra que rodea su parte más oscura.

phase One of the different apparent shapes of the moon as seen from Earth. (22)
fase Una de las distintas formas aparentes de la Luna vistas desde la Tierra.

photosphere The inner layer of the sun's atmosphere that gives off its visible light; the sun's surface. (90)
fotósfera Capa más interna de la atmósfera solar que provoca la luz que vemos; superficie del Sol.

planet An object that orbits a star, is large enough to have become rounded by its own gravity, and has cleared the area of its orbit. (5, 84)
planeta Cuerpo que orbita alrededor de una estrella, que tiene suficiente masa como para permitir que su propia gravedad le dé una forma casi redonda, y que además ha despejado las proximidades de su órbita.

planetesimal One of the small asteroid-like bodies that formed the building blocks of the planets. (86)
planetesimal Uno de los cuerpos pequeños parecidos a asteroides que dieron origen a los planetas.

prominence A huge, reddish loop of gas that protrudes from the sun's surface, linking parts of sunspot regions. (92)
prominencia Enorme burbuja de gas rojiza que sobresale de la superfice solar, y conecta partes de las manchas solares.

protostar A contracting cloud of gas and dust with enough mass to form a star. (143)
protoestrella Nube de gas y polvo que se contrae, con suficiente masa como para formar una estrella.

pulsar A rapidly spinning neutron star that produces radio waves. (146)
pulsar Estrella de neutrones que gira rápidamente y produce ondas de radio.

Q

quasar An enormously bright, distant galaxy with a giant black hole at its center. (152)
quásar Galaxia extraordinariamente luminosa y distante con un agujero negro gigante en el centro.

R

radiation zone A region of very tightly packed gas in the sun's interior where energy is transferred mainly in the form of electromagnetic radiation. (89)
zona radioactiva Región al interior del Sol de gases densamente acumulados y donde se transmite energía principalmente en la forma de radiación electromagnética.

radio telescope A device used to detect radio waves from objects in space. (130)
radiotelescopio Aparato usado para detectar ondas de radio de los cuerpos en el espacio.

reflecting telescope A telescope that uses a curved mirror to collect and focus light. (128)
telescopio de reflexión Telescopio que usa un espejo curvado para captar y enfocar la luz.

refracting telescope A telescope that uses convex lenses to gather and focus light. (128)
telescopio de refracción Telescopio que usa lentes convexas para captar y enfocar la luz.

remote sensing The collection of information about Earth and other objects in space using satellites or probes. (66)
percepción remota Recolección de información sobre la Tierra y otros cuerpos del espacio usando satélites o sondas.

revolution The movement of an object around another object. (12)
revolución Movimiento de un cuerpo alrededor de otro.

ring A thin disk of small ice and rock particles surrounding a planet. (103)
anillo Disco fino de pequeñas partículas de hielo y roca que rodea un planeta.

rocket A device that expels gas in one direction to move in the opposite direction. (46)
cohete Aparato que expulsa gases en una dirección para moverse en la dirección opuesta.

rotation The spinning motion of a planet on its axis. (11)
rotación Movimiento giratorio de un planeta sobre su eje.

rover A small robotic space probe that can move about the surface of a planet or moon. (59)
rover Pequeña sonda espacial robótica que puede desplazarse sobre la superficie de un planeta o sobre la Luna.

S

satellite An object that orbits a planet. (5, 53)
satélite Cuerpo que orbita alrededor de un planeta.

scientific notation A mathematical method of writing numbers using powers of ten. (134)
notación científica Método matemático de escritura de números que usa la potencia de diez.

solar eclipse The blocking of sunlight to Earth that occurs when the moon is directly between the sun and Earth. (25)
eclipse solar Bloqueo de la luz solar que ilumina la Tierra que ocurre cuando la Luna se interpone entre el Sol y la Tierra.

solar flare An eruption of gas from the sun's surface that occurs when the loops in sunspot regions suddenly connect. (92)
destello solar Erupción de los gases de la superficie solar que ocurre cuando las burbujas de las manchas solares se conectan repentinamente.

solar system The system consisting of the sun and the planets and other objects that revolve around it. (83)
sistema solar Sistema formado por el Sol, los planetas y otros cuerpos que giran alrededor de él.

solar wind A stream of electrically charged particles that emanate from the sun's corona. (91)
viento solar Flujo de partículas cargadas que emanan de la corona del Sol.

solstice Either of the two days of the year on which the sun reaches its greatest distance north or south of the equator. (16)
solsticio Uno de los dos días del año en el que el Sol alcanza la mayor distancia al norte o al sur del ecuador.

space probe A spacecraft that has various scientific instruments that can collect data, including visual images, but has no human crew. (59)
sonda espacial Nave espacial que tiene varios instrumentos científicos que pueden reunir datos e imágenes, pero que no tiene una tripulación.

space shuttle A spacecraft that can carry a crew into space, return to Earth, and then be reused for the same purpose. (57)
transbordador espacial Nave espacial que puede llevar a una tripulación al espacio, volver a la Tierra, y luego volver a ser usada para el mismo propósito.

space spinoff An item that has uses on Earth but was originally developed for use in space. (64)
derivación espacial Objeto que se puede usar en la Tierra, pero que originalmente se construyó para ser usado en el espacio.

space station A large artificial satellite on which people can live and work for long periods. (58)
estación espacial Enorme satélite artificial en el que la gente puede vivir y trabajar durante largos períodos.

spectrograph An instrument that separates light into colors and makes an image of the resulting spectrum. (138)
espectrógrafo Instrumento que separa la luz en colores y crea una imagen del espectro resultante.

spectrum The range of wavelengths of electromagnetic waves. (127)
espectro Gama de las longitudes de ondas electromagnéticas.

spiral galaxy A galaxy with a bulge in the middle and arms that spiral outward in a pinwheel pattern. (152)
galaxia espiral Galaxia con una protuberancia en el centro y brazos que giran en espiral hacia el exterior, como un remolino.

spring tide The tide with the greatest difference between consecutive low and high tides. (30)
marea viva Marea con la mayor diferencia entre las mareas altas y bajas consecutivas.

star A ball of hot gas, primarily hydrogen and helium, that undergoes nuclear fusion. (5)
estrella Bola de gases calientes, principalmente hidrógeno y helio, en cuyo interior se produce una fusión nuclear.

sunspot A dark area of gas on the sun's surface that is cooler than surrounding gases. (92)
mancha solar Área gaseosa oscura de la superficie solar, que es más fría que los gases que la rodean.

supernova The brilliant explosion of a dying supergiant star. (145)
supernova Explosión brillante de una estrella supergigante en extinción.

T

telescope An optical instrument that forms enlarged images of distant objects. (128)
telescopio Instrumento óptico que provee ampliaciones de los cuerpos lejanos.

terrestrial planets The name often given to the four inner planets: Mercury, Venus, Earth, and Mars. (95)
planetas telúricos Nombre dado normalmente a los cuatro planetas interiores: Mercurio, Venus, Tierra y Marte.

thrust The reaction force that propels a rocket forward. (48)
empuje Fuerza de reacción que propulsa un cohete hacia delante.

tide The periodic rise and fall of the level of water in the ocean. (29)
marea La subida y bajada periódica del nivel de agua del océano.

GLOSSARY

U

umbra The darkest part of a shadow. (25)
umbra La parte más oscura de una sombra.

universe All of space and everything in it. (134)
universo Todo el espacio y todo lo que hay en él.

V

vacuum A place that is empty of all matter. (63)
vacío Lugar en donde no existe materia.

velocity Speed in a given direction. (48)
velocidad Rapidez en una dirección dada.

visible light Electromagnetic radiation that can be seen with the unaided eye. (126)
luz visible Radiación electromagnética que se puede ver a simple vista.

W

wavelength The distance between the crest of one wave and the crest of the next wave. (127)
longitud de onda Distancia entre la cresta de una onda y la cresta de la siguiente onda.

weight A measure of the force of gravity on an object. (19)
peso Medida de la fuerza de gravedad sobre un cuerpo.

white dwarf The blue-white hot core of a star that is left behind after its outer layers have expanded and drifted out into space. (145)
enana blanca Núcleo caliente y azul blanquecino de una estrella que queda después de que sus capas externas se han expandido y esparcido por el espacio.

INDEX

ACKNOWLEDGMENTS

Staff Credits

The people who made up the *Interactive Science* team—representing composition services, core design digital and multimedia production services, digital product development, editorial, editorial services, manufacturing, and production—are listed below.

Jan Van Aarsen, Samah Abadir, Ernie Albanese, Zareh MacPherson Artinian, Bridget Binstock, Suzanne Biron, MJ Black, Nancy Bolsover, Stacy Boyd, Jim Brady, Katherine Bryant, Michael Burstein, Pradeep Byram, Jessica Chase, Jonathan Cheney, Arthur Ciccone, Allison Cook-Bellistri, Rebecca Cottingham, AnnMarie Coyne, Bob Craton, Chris Deliee, Paul Delsignore, Michael Di Maria, Diane Dougherty, Kristen Ellis, Theresa Eugenio, Amanda Ferguson, Jorgensen Fernandez, Kathryn Fobert, Julia Gecha, Mark Geyer, Steve Gobbell, Paula Gogan-Porter, Jeffrey Gong, Sandra Graff, Adam Groffman, Lynette Haggard, Christian Henry, Karen Holtzman, Susan Hutchinson, Sharon Inglis, Marian Jones, Sumy Joy, Sheila Kanitsch, Courtenay Kelley, Chris Kennedy, Toby Klang, Greg Lam, Russ Lappa, Margaret LaRaia, Ben Leveille, Thea Limpus, Dotti Marshall, Kathy Martin, Robyn Matzke, John McClure, Mary Beth McDaniel, Krista McDonald, Tim McDonald, Rich McMahon, Cara McNally, Melinda Medina, Angelina Mendez, Maria Milczarek, Claudi Mimo, Mike Napieralski, Deborah Nicholls, Dave Nichols, William Oppenheimer, Jodi O'Rourke, Ameer Padshah, Lorie Park, Celio Pedrosa, Jonathan Penyack, Linda Zust Reddy, Jennifer Reichlin, Stephen Rider, Charlene Rimsa, Stephanie Rogers, Marcy Rose, Rashid Ross, Anne Rowsey, Logan Schmidt, Amanda Seldera, Laurel Smith, Nancy Smith, Ted Smykal, Emily Soltanoff, Cindy Strowman, Dee Sunday, Barry Tomack, Patricia Valencia, Ana Sofia Villaveces, Stephanie Wallace, Christine Whitney, Brad Wiatr, Heidi Wilson, Heather Wright, Rachel Youdelman

Photography

All uncredited photos copyright © 2011 Pearson Education.

Cover, Front and Back
NASA

Front Matter
Page vi, Tom Fox/Dallas Morning News/Corbis; **vii,** Corbis; **viii,** ESA/J. Clarke (Boston University)/Z. Levay (STScI)/NASA; **ix,** ESA/HEIC/Hubble Heritage Team (STScI/AURA)/NASA; **xi laptop,** iStockphoto.com; **xiii br,** JupiterImages/Getty Images; **xvi laptop,** iStockphoto.com; **xx bkgrnd,** NASA; **xx earth,** Apollo 17 Crew/NASA; **xxi l,** NASA Marshall Space Flight Center Collection; **xxi r,** ESA/CXC/JPL-CalTech/NASA.

Chapter 1
Page 1 spread, Tom Fox/Dallas Morning News/Corbis; **3 b,** Space Frontiers/Getty; **3 full moon,** John W. Bova/Photo Researchers, Inc.; **3 quarter moon,** John W. Bova/Photo Researchers, Inc.; **3 crescent moon,** John W. Bova/Photo Researchers, Inc.; **4** Sheila Terry/Science Source; **5 bkgrnd,** UVimages/Amana Images/Corbis; **5 l inset,** NASA; **5 m inset,** NASA; **5 r,** T. Rector (University of Alaska Anchorage), Z. Levay and L. Frattare (Space Telescope Science Institute) and National Optical Astronomy Observatory/Association of Universities for Research in Astronomy/National Science Foundation/Solar System Exploration/NASA; **8 bkgrnd,** Ted Spiegel/Corbis; **9,** Frank Zullo/Photo Researchers, Inc.; **10 t,** Robert Harding Picture Library Ltd/Alamy; **10 b,** John White Photos/Alamy; **13 tl,** Werner Forman/UIG/Getty Images; **13 tr,** Dea/A. Dagli Orti/Getty Images; **13 mr,** SSPL/Getty Images; **17,** Gavin Hellier/Photolibrary Group; **18–19 spread,** Blend Images/Alamy; **22 moon series,** Jeff Vanuga/Corbis; **22,** UV Images/Amana Images/Corbis; **24 l,** Eckhard Slawik/Photo Researchers, Inc.; **24 ml,** John W. Bova/Photo Researchers, Inc.; **24 m** John W. Bova/Photo Researchers, Inc.; **24 mr;** John W. Bova/Photo Researchers, Inc.; **24 r,** John W. Bova/Photo Researchers, Inc.; **25,** Space Frontiers/Getty; **26 lunar eclipse;** Fred Espenak/Photo Researchers, Inc.; **28 l and r,** Michael P. Gadomski/Science Source; **31,** Klaus Lang/All Canada Photos/Alamy; **32 m,** Omikron/Photo Researchers, Inc.; **32–33 spread,** JPL/USGS/NASA; **34 earth in chart,** NASA Langley Research Center; **34 moon in chart,** JPL/USGS/NASA; **34–35 spread,** Apollo 11 Image Library/NASA; **36 br,** Omikron/Photo Researchers, Inc.

Interchapter Feature
Page 40 ml, Andy Crawford/University Museum of Archaeology and Anthropology, Cambridge/Dorling Kindersley; **40 tl,** iStockphoto.com; **40 bl,** iStockphoto.com; **41 bl,** NASA; **41 bkgrnd,** NASA.

Chapter 2
Pages 42–43 spread, Donald Miralle/Getty Images; **45 c1,** NASA/AP Images; **45 c2,** NASA; **45 b,** StockLite/Shutterstock; **46,** Yesikka Vivancos/epa/Corbis; **47,** U.S. Civil Air Patrol/NASA; **49,** Mark Scheuern/Alamy; **52,** David Seal/NASA; **53 t,** NASA/Science Photo Library, **53 cr,** NASA, **53 cl,** Ria Novosti/Science Photo Library; **53 br,** Detlev van Ravenswaay/Science Photo Library; **53 bl,** Sovfoto/Eastfoto; **54 bl,** Hulton Archive/Getty Images; **54 tl,** RGB Ventures LLC dba SuperStock/Alamy; **54–55 footprints,** NASA; **55 b,** Corbis; **54–55 bkgrnd,** NASA; **55 tl,** Science Source; **56,** John Frassanito & Associates; **60 t,** NASA/Johns Hopkins University Applied Physics Laboratory/Southwest Research Institute/Photo Researchers, Inc.; **60 b,** Roger Arno/NASA; **61 b,** JPL/NASA; **61 tr,** David Ducros/Science Photo Library/Photo Researchers, Inc.; **62,** NASA/Science Photo Library; **63,** UPI Photo/NASA; **64 tl,** William King/Getty Images; **64 girl with cell phone,** Mark Andersen/Rubberball; **64 satellite,** Mark Evans/iStockphoto.com; **64 astronaut,** AP Photo/NASA; **64 shoes,** iStockphoto.com; **65 tr,** Terry Vine/Getty Images; **65 headphones,** StockLite/Shutterstock; **65 m,** Mehau Kulyk/Photo Researchers, Inc.; **65 shoes,** NASA Human Spaceflight Collection; **66 inset,** Joe Raedle/Getty Images; **66 b,** Kodiak Greenwood/The Image Bank/Getty Images; **67 inset b,** Steven Puetzer/Getty Images; **67 b,** Robert Nickelsberg/Getty Images; **67 2nd from top,** Colin Anderson/Blend Images/Corbis; **67 t,** John Tomaselli/Alamy; **68 t,** Mark Scheuern/Alamy; **68 m,** Roger Arno/NASA; **68 b,** Robert Nickelsberg/Getty Images.

ACKNOWLEDGMENTS

Interchapter Feature
Pages 72–73 all, NASA.

Chapter 3
Pages 74–75 spread, ESA/J. Clarke (Boston University)/
Z. Levay (STScI)/NASA; **77 b,** JPL/Caltech/T. Pyle (SSC)/NASA;
77 t, NASA Lunar and Planetary Laboratory; **78 r,** Walter
Myers; **78 l,** Walter Myers; **80 r,** Detlev van Ravenswaay/Photo
Researchers, Inc.; **80 l,** Crawford Library/Royal Observatory,
Edinburgh/Photo Researchers, Inc.; **81 r,** Pictorial Press Ltd/
Alamy; **81 l,** SPL/Photo Researchers, Inc.; **82,** Johns Hopkins
University Applied Physics Laboratory/NASA; **84 b,** Friedrich
Saurer/Alamy; **84–85 middle row,** NASA Lunar and Planetary
Laboratory; **85,** NASA Lunar and Planetary Laboratory;
87, NASA Lunar and Planetary Laboratory; **88,** LOOK Die
Bildagentur der Fotografen GmbH/Alamy; **90 bkgrnd,**
Space Frontiers/Hulton Archive/Getty Images; **90–91 sun,**
NASA Solar and Heliospheric Observatory Collection; **92 r,**
SOHO/ESA/NASA; **92 l,** SOHO-EIT Consortium/ESA/NASA;
94 Frida Kahlo, Bettmann/Corbis; **94 Venus,** Magellan
Project/JPL/NASA; **94 Helen Keller,** Bettmann/Corbis;
94 Sojourner Truth, Library of Congress Department of
Prints and Photographs [LC-USZ62-119343]; **95 Mercury,**
Messenger Teams/Johns Hopkins University Applied
Physics Laboratory/NASA; **95 Venus,** Magellan Project/JPL/
NASA; **95 Earth,** Apollo 17 Crew/NASA; **95 Mars,** NASA;
96 Mercury, Messenger Teams/Johns Hopkins University
Applied Physics Laboratory/NASA; **96 Earth,** Apollo 17 Crew/
NASA; **97 Venus,** NASA; **97 Earth,** Apollo 17 Crew/NASA;
97 Venus surface, JPL/USGS/NASA; **97 tl,** NASA; **100 b,**
Mars Exploration Rover Mission/JPL/NASA; **100 lander,** JPL/
CalTech/NASA; **100 Mars,** NASA; **100 Earth,** Apollo 17 Crew/
NASA; **100 Mars,** NASA; **101,** Goddard Space Flight Center
Scientific Visualization Studio, and Virginia Butcher (SSAI)/
NASA; **102,** Judy Dole/The Image Bank/Getty Images; **103
Jupiter,** JPL/NIX/NASA **103 Saturn,** JPL/NASA; **103 Uranus,**
ESA/L. Sromovsky (University of Wisconsin–Madison)/ H.
Hammel (Space Science Institute)/K. Rages (SETI)/NASA; **103
Neptune,** NASA; **104 r,** JPL/NASA; **104 tr,** Apollo 17 Crew/
NASA; **104 tl,** JPL/NIX/NASA; **105 bkgrnd,** NASA; **106
Saturn,** JPL/NASA; **106 Titan,** JPL/University of Arizona/
NASA; **106 Iapetus,** JPL/Space Science Institute/NASA; **106
Mimas,** JPL/NASA; **107 br,** JPL/Space Science Institute/
NASA; **107 bl,** Science Source/Photo Researchers Inc.; **107
tl,** Apollo 17 Crew/NASA; **107 t,** JPL/NASA; **108 b,** Lawrence
Sromovsky, University of Wisconsin–Madison/W. M. Keck
Observatory; **108 tr,** Apollo 17 Crew/NASA; **108 tl,** ESA/L.
Sromovsky (University of Wisconsin–Madison)/H. Hammel
(Space Science Institute)/K. Rages (SETI)/NASA; **109 b,** L.
Sromovsky/P. Fry (University of Wisconsin–Madison)/NASA;
109 tl, Apollo 17 Crew/NASA; **109 tr,** NASA; **110 bkgrnd,**
Alan Sirulnikoff/Getty Images; **110 inset,** Courtesy Haley West;
112, Detlev van Ravenswaay/Photo Researchers, Inc.; **113,**
Jerry Lodriguss/Photo Researchers, Inc.; **114 inset,** JPL/NASA;
114 bkgrnd, JPL/ Caltech/T. Pyle (SSC)/NASA; **115,** Paolo
Koch/Photo Researchers, Inc.; **116 t,** SOHO-EIT Consortium/
ESA/NASA; **116 br,** Jerry Lodriguss/Photo Researchers, Inc.;
116 bl, JPL/NIX/NASA.

Interchapter Feature
Page 120 bkgrnd, JPL/Cornell University/NASA; **121 tr,**
Science Source; **121 br,** NASA.

Chapter 4
Page 122 spread, JPL-CalTech/STScI/Vassar/NASA/
Photo Researchers, Inc.; **125 b, bkgrnd** Bojan Pavlukovic/
Shutterstock; **125 c1,** CXC/MIT/UMass Amherst/M.D. Stage/
NASA Chandra Space Telescope Collection; **125 t,** David
Parker/Photo Researchers, Inc.; **125 c2,** B.A.E. Inc./Alamy;
126, Chip Simons/Getty Images; **127 t,** Bjorn Rorslett/
Science Photo Library/Photo Researchers; **127 br,** Bjorn
Rorslett/Science Photo Library/Photo Researchers; **127 bl,**
Don Farrall/Getty; **128 bkgrnd,** Gerard Lodriguss/Photo
Researchers; **129 sombrero galaxy,** The Hubble Heritage
Team (STScI/AURA)/NASA; **129 Hubble telescope,** NASA
Hubble Space Telescope Collection; **129 supernova remnant,**
CXC/Rutgers/J. Warren et al.; Optical: NASA/STScI/U. Ill./Y.
Chu; Radio: ATCA/U. Ill./J. Dickel/NASA; **129 Cone Nebula,**
H. Ford (JHU)/G. Illingworth (UCSC/LO)/M. Clampin (STScI)/
G. Hartig (STScI)/ACS Science Team/ESA/NASA; **129 large
magellanic cloud,** ESA, HEIC, and The Hubble Heritage Team
(STScI/AURA)/NASA; **130 b,** David Parker/Photo Researchers,
Inc.; **130 t,** Matt York/AP Images; **132,** Science Source/Photo
Researchers, Inc.; **135 Earth,** NASA; **135 sun,** SOHO/ESA/
NASA; **135 Andromeda Galaxy,** Chris Cook/Science Source;
135 Alpha Centauri, Eckhard Slawik/Photo Researchers, Inc.;
136, NASA/CXC/M. Weiss; Spectra: NASA/CXC/SAO/J. Miller,
et al./NASA Chandra Space Telescope Collection; **138–139
spread,** Data Copyrights ESA/ESO/NASA FITS Liberator/
NASA Digitized Sky Survey; **141,** Larry Landolfi/Photo
Researchers, Inc.; **142,** ESA/CXC/JPL-CalTech/J. Hester and
A. Loll (Arizona State Univ.)/R. Gehrz (Univ. Minn.)/STScI/
NASA; **143,** ESA/The Hubble Heritage Team/NASA;
145 bkgrnd, European Space Agency and Justyn R. Maund
(University of Cambridge)/NASA; **145 inset,** CXC/MIT/
UMass Amherst/M.D. Stage/NASA Chandra Space Telescope
Collection; **148 bkgrnd,** Kuiper Airborne Observatory/NASA;
150 b, Mpia-hd, Birkle, Slawik/Photo Researchers, Inc.;
150 t, JPL/NASA; **151 r,** Ken Biggs/Photo Researchers, Inc.;
151 l, ESA/C. Carreau/NASA; **152 b,** B.A.E. Inc./Alamy;
153 tl, Robert Gendler/Science Source; **153 tr,** Science
Source/Photo Researchers, Inc.; **153 b,** JPL-CalTech/T. Pyle
(SSC)/NASA; **154,** ESA/The Hubble Heritage Team/NASA;
154, Eliot J. Schechter/Getty Images; **155 bl,** NASA;
156–157 bkgrnd, Bojan Pavlukovic/Shutterstock;
158 tr, NASA.

Interchapter Feature
Page 162, NASA; **163,** Mike Brinson/The Image Bank/
Getty Images.

take note

use this space for lesson planning ideas and notes

take note

use this space for lesson planning ideas and notes

Place the outside corner, the corner away from the dotted line, in the corner of your copy machine to copy onto letter-size paper.

The Expanding Universe

How do astronomers learn about distant objects in the universe?

Blended Path
Active learning using Student Edition, Inquiry Path, and Digital Path

Lesson Pacing: 1–2 periods or $\frac{1}{2}$–1 block

🕐 **SHORT ON TIME?** To do this lesson in approximately half the time, do the Activate Prior Knowledge activity on page 154. A discussion of the Key Concept on page 155 will familiarize students with the lesson content. Have students do the Quick Lab. The rest of the lesson can be completed by students independently.

Preference Navigator, in the online Planning tools, allows you to customize *Interactive Science* to your own teaching style. You can also edit lesson plans by selecting the Lesson Planner option.

Digital Teacher's Edition allows you to access your Teacher's Edition and Resource materials online.

Lesson Vocabulary

- big bang
- Hubble's Law
- cosmic background radiation
- dark matter
- dark energy

Content Refresher

Professional Development Note

Dark Matter Observations of the movement of stars and galaxies and theories about how the universe formed indicate that much more mass exists in the universe than can be seen with modern technology. The missing mass is called dark matter. Although little is known about this mysterious missing mass, it is possible that dark matter consists of some combination of normal matter and as-yet-unknown types of subatomic particles. The normal matter might include nonluminous objects such as brown dwarfs (failed stars that are not massive enough to produce nuclear fusion, which causes stars to shine), neutron stars, black holes, and cooled white dwarfs.

It is theorized that most dark matter may consist of exotic, unknown particles. These particles could be types of neutrinos or a group of particles called weakly interacting massive particles (WIMPS). Neutrinos are generated by our sun during nuclear processes. They are transmitted by the solar wind and light. Since these teensy particles have no electric charge and a smaller mass than electrons, humans are not even aware that neutrinos constantly flow through their bodies.

LESSON OBJECTIVE

🔑 State what the big bang theory says about the universe.

ENGAGE AND EXPLORE

Teach this lesson using a variety of resources. Begin by reading **My Planet Diary** as a class. Have students share ideas about what they know about previous space shuttle missions. Then have students do the **Inquiry Warm-Up activity.** Students will explore how the universe expands. Discuss what the students observed about the dots as the balloon expanded. The **After the Inquiry Warm-Up worksheet** sets up a discussion about the direction in which a universe expands. Have volunteers share the questions they posed about the universe in question 4.

EXPLAIN AND ELABORATE

Teach Key Concepts by explaining how the universe formed and why some scientists believe that it will expand forever. Then have students practice the inquiry skill in the **Apply It activity.** Use **Figure 2** to illustrate how the universe is likely to continue to expand in the future. To **Support the Big Q,** discuss what scientists think is most likely to happen to the universe in the future and what supporting evidence they have for this theory. Hand out the **Key Concept Summaries** as a review of each part of the lesson. Students can also use the online **Vocab Flash Cards** to review key terms.

EVALUATE

Have students take the **Lesson Quiz.** For an alternate assessment, see the **EXAM**VIEW® Assessment Suite, Progress Monitoring Assessments, or SuccessTracker™.

 **Support**

1 Content and Language
The word *cosmic* originates from the Greek word *kosmikós* meaning "universe."

Place the outside corner, the corner away from the dotted line, in the corner of your copy machine to copy onto letter-size paper.

5 How do Earth, the moon, and the sun interact?

Blended Path Active learning using Student Edition, Inquiry Path, and Digital Path

Lesson Pacing: 1–2 periods or $\frac{1}{2}$–1 block

⏱ **SHORT ON TIME?** To do this lesson in approximately half the time, do the Activate Prior Knowledge activity on page 28. A discussion of the Key Concepts on pages 29 and 30 will familiarize students with the lesson content. Have students do the Quick Lab. The rest of the lesson can be completed by students independently.

Preference Navigator, in the online Planning tools, allows you to customize *Interactive Science* to your own teaching style. You can also edit lesson plans by selecting the Lesson Planner option.

Digital Teacher's Edition allows you to access your Teacher's Edition and Resource materials online.

my science online.com

Lesson Vocabulary

- tide
- spring tide
- neap tide

 Content Refresher

Frequency of Tides One lunar day is 24 hours and 50 minutes, the time it takes for a specific spot on the surface of Earth to rotate once relative to a specific position under the moon.

One lunar day is 50 minutes longer than one solar day. There are two reasons why: Earth and the moon rotate and revolve in the same direction, and one complete moon revolution occurs 50 minutes faster than one complete rotation of Earth.

Because Earth rotates through two tidal bulges each lunar day, most coastal areas experience two high tides and two low tides every 24 hours and 50 minutes. Each high tide and low tide occurs in half that time, every 12 hours and 25 minutes. Water at the shore goes from high to low or low to high in 6 hours and 12.5 minutes, and there is relatively little difference between successive high and low water. These tides are called semi-diurnal. However, tides along some coasts do not follow this exact pattern. For instance, on the north shore of the Gulf of Mexico, the tide is diurnal, meaning that it moves in and out again only once in a 24-hour period. Likewise, the Pacific Northwest experiences mixed tides. While the area experiences two high and two low tides a day, those tides are characterized by a significant disparity between successive tides.

LESSON OBJECTIVE

🔑 Explain what causes tides.

ENGAGE AND EXPLORE

Teach this lesson using a variety of resources. Begin by reading **My Planet Diary** as a class. Have students share what they already know about tides. Then have students do the **Inquiry Warm-Up activity.** Students will predict tide times for coastal cities. The **After the Inquiry Warm-Up worksheet** sets up a discussion about the high tide times at different cities on the same coast. Have volunteers share their answers to question 4 naming a city in Maine that would have about the same high tide time as Nantucket.

EXPLAIN AND ELABORATE

Teach Key Concepts by explaining that tides are caused by interactions between the moon and different parts of Earth. **Support the Big Q** by discussing the relationship between Earth's motion and tides. Continue to **Teach Key Concepts** by explaining that the position of the sun can also affect the heights of tides. Have students practice the inquiry skill in the **Apply It activity.**

Hand out the **Key Concept Summaries** as a review of each part of the lesson. Students can also use the online **Vocab Flash Cards** to review key terms.

EVALUATE

Have students take the **Lesson Quiz.** For an alternate assessment, see the **EXAM**VIEW® Assessment Suite, Progress Monitoring Assessments, or SuccessTracker™.

Ⓔ Ⓛ Ⓛ Support

1 Content and Language
Write Cloze sentences for students to complete with the vocabulary terms for the lesson.